The Radio Amateur's
V H F Manual

A Manual of Amateur Radio Communication on the
Frequencies Above 50 Megahertz

BY

EDWARD P. TILTON, W1HDQ
Vhf Editor, *QST*.

FM Chapters By

Douglas A. Blakeslee, W1KLK
Asst. Technical Editor, *QST*.

Published by

THE AMERICAN RADIO RELAY LEAGUE,Inc.

Newington, Connecticut 06111

Foreword

Probably no segment of amateur radio has moved so rapidly in recent years as "The World Above 50 Mc" which is this book's concern. Though *The Radio Amateur's VHF Manual* was introduced in 1965, and completely reworked in 1968, developments in the vhf realm have come so fast, and in such bewildering variety, that this third edition is already overdue.

Frequencies above 50 MHz have always been prime experimenter territory, but in the Seventies they are increasingly a communicator's world, as well. As such they are attracting an ever-higher percentage of the world's users of the radio-frequency spectrum — military, governmental, and commercial, as well as amateur. Just since this book was first produced, we have seen amateur communication via the moon become a worldwide reality on all amateur frequencies from 144 to 2450 MHz. Amateur satellites have shown ever more clearly that the days of "DX" (if the term means "distance" of the conventional variety) are numbered. Who could listen to Apollo conversations (frequently using channels close to our 2300-MHz band) and not realize that we are in the midst of nothing less than a communications revolution?

The more conventional aspects of vhf and uhf hamming have been moving with equal speed. All-solid-state equipment of remarkable utility has made the vest-pocket ham station a reality. Coming soon, the "wrist radio"? Vhf and uhf repeaters make commonplace a degree of 'round-the-clock reliability undreamed of even a few years ago. Extensive use of ssb techniques has extended the range of voice communication far beyond the best we could manage heretofore. More occupancy, more effective equipment, bigger antennas, and growing propagation knowledge are showing new potentials of all our bands, up through at least 10,000 MHz.

Obviously, it's time for a new *VHF Manual*. Edition Three is full of new material, but it retains the down-to-earth readability of its widely acclaimed predecessors. Like them, it is mainly the work of *QST*'s long-time VHF Editor, Edward P. Tilton, W1HDQ. Ed's experience span has seen the bands above 50 MHz all the way, from their early status as get-lost room for a special breed of ham, to their now-recognized stature as a major asset for all amateurs.

Assisting Ed with much interesting and practical information on fm and repeaters is Douglas A. Blakeslee, W1KLK, for some years now a fixture on the *QST* masthead, as Assistant Technical Editor. We trust that you'll find them a good team.

JOHN HUNTOON, W1RW
General Manager, ARRL

Newington, Conn.

Ross A. Hull, vhf pioneer, and QST Associate Editor, 1931-1938.

Ross saw the potential of the then-uncharted world above 50 MHz perhaps more clearly than any other man of his time. The technical excellence of his equipment designs and his enthusiasm in print and in person fired the imagination of a whole new generation of radio amateurs, among them the author of this book. Hull's discovery and eventual explanation of tropospheric bending of vhf waves has been called "one of the truly outstanding examples of scientific achievement by an amateur in any field of human endeavor."

CONTENTS

Abbreviations used in Text and Drawings

(Older form shown in parentheses)

A – ampere (amp.)
ac – alternating current
af – audio frequency
afc – automatic frequency control
afsk – audio frequency-shift keying
agc – automatic gain control
a-m – amplitude modulation
ATV – amateur television
avc – automatic volume control
bc – broadcast
bci – broadcast interference
BFO – Beat-frequency oscillator
ccw – counterclockwise
CFM – cubic feet per minute
coax – coaxial cable
COR – carrier-operated relay
CRT – cathode-ray tube
ct – center tap
cw – continuous wave
dB – decibel
dc – direct current
dpdt – double-pole double-throw
dpst – double-pole single-throw
dsb – double sideband
DX – long distance
EME – earth-moon-earth, moonbounce
FCC – Federal Communications Commission
FET – field-effect transistor
ft^3/min – cubic feet per minute (CFM)
fm – frequency modulation
GDO – grid-dip oscillator
GMT – Greenwich Mean Time
H – Henry (hy.)
hf – high frequency
Hz – hertz (cycle)
IC – integrated circuit
ID – inside diameter
i-f – intermediate frequency
JFET – junction field-effect transistor
k – kilo
kHz – kilohertz (kc. – kilocycle)
kW – kilowatt
lf – low frequency
LO – local oscillator
lsb – lower sideband
luf – lowest usable frequency
mA – milliampere
MARS – Millitary Affiliate Radio System
mH – millihenry
MHz – megahertz (Mc. – megacycle)
mic – microphone
mix – mixer
MOSFET – metal-oxide semiconductor field-effect transistor
ms – millisecond
m.s. – meteor scatter

muf – maximum usable frequency
mV – millivolt
mW – milliwatt
nbfm, nfm – narrow-band frequency modulation
NC – normally closed
NO – normally open
npn – negative-positive-negative
OD – outside diameter
osc – oscillator
oz – ounce
PA – power amplifier
PEP – peak-envelope power
pF – picofarad ($\mu\mu$F – micromicrofarad)
PIV – peak-inverse voltage
pm – phase modulation
pnp – positive-negative-positive
pot – potentiometer
PRV – peak-reverse voltage
PTT – push-to-talk
rcvr – receiver
rf – radio frequency
rfc – radio-frequency choke
RFI – radio-frequency interference
rms – root-mean-square
s.a.s.e. – stamped self-addressed envelope
SNR – signal-to-noise ratio
spdt – single-pole double-throw
spst – single-pole single-throw
ssb – single sideband
SSTV – slow-scan TV
SWR – standing-wave ratio
TE – transequatorial (propagation)
tpi – turns per inch
T-R – transmit-receive
TV – television
TVI – television interference
usb – upper sideband
uhf – ultra-high frequency
V – volt
VCO – voltage-controlled oscillator
VCXO – voltage-controlled crystal oscillator
VFO – Variable-frequency oscillator
vhf – very-high frequency
VOM – volt-ohmmeter
VOX – voice-operated break-in
W – watt
WAC – Worked All Continents
WAS – Worked All States
ww – wire wound
wv – working voltage
xtal – crystal
μ – micro (10^{-6})
μF – microfarad (uf.)
μH – microhenry (uh.)

Chapter 1

How It All Started

Those of us who make the frequencies above 50 Mc. our principal stamping ground tend to think of v.h.f. as the "new frontier" of amateur radio. Actually it is as old as the art of radio communication itself. While universal use of the upper reaches of the radio spectrum is a fairly modern phenomenon, some of the earliest work with electromagnetic radiation, and perhaps the first actual communication by radio, were on wavelengths near our present 2-meter band.

The resonator of Heinrich Hertz, and the practical applications of it by Marconi, operated around 150 Mc. And if you think that the beam you are using is a recent development, consider the fact that Hertz used a rudimentary form of Yagi in 1888, and Marconi employed a parabolic reflector to extend the range of his first equipment before the turn of the century. But Marconi and a generation of radio pioneers to follow him moved to the longer waves to achieve greater coverage. The ultra-high frequencies lay dormant for 20 years thereafter.

The Drive for DX

ARRL and *QST* had been in existence for nearly ten years before frequencies higher than 15 Mc. were discussed in any detail. Transmitters using vacuum tubes had replaced spark rigs in the early '20s, and the unfolding possibilities of DX on wavelengths below 200 meters caused adventurous amateurs to probe ever higher in frequency. Each move upward produced new miracles of DX, culminating in worldwide communication with low power – in *daylight* – when gear was finally made to work in the 14-Mc. region. The next band then open to amateurs was at 56 Mc. It was widely assumed that if workable 5-meter gear could be built, this band would be even better for DX than 80, 40, and 20 meters had progressively turned out to be.

Just getting there was thought to be the principal problem. Technical Editor R. S. Kruse pointed the way in the October, 1924, issue of *QST*, with "Working At 5 Meters," perhaps the first v.h.f. constructional article ever published.[1] In the next few years much *QST* space would be devoted to 5-meter gear, but trying to use it was a frustrating business. Transmitters were simple oscillators; stabilization of any kind was all but unknown, and not even considered for 5-meter rigs. Receivers were regenerative detectors – hard to get going at all, and then incredibly cranky to tune. Oscillators using de-based tubes, mounted bottom-up to reduce lead inductance, and receivers with foot-long insulated tuning shafts to hold down hand capacity

The footnotes refer to the bibliography at the end of the chapter.

were the order of the day. The wonder was that hams of the middle Twenties made gear work on 7 or 14 Mc., let alone 56![2,3,4]

This was c.w., remember. You had to chase a wandering signal with a receiver that was touchy beyond belief, even with stable signals. But 5-meter gear was made, and it worked after a fashion. When the first pioneers heard one another across town they were ready for a shot at Australia, or Europe. This technique had brought results before on lower frequencies, why not on 56 Mc.?[3] Then came several years of largely fruitless effort. There were scattered "heard" reports, some rather dubious in the light of present knowledge of v.h.f. propagation, but rarely was there two-way communication over more than a few miles.

By 1928, interest lagged. There were rumblings of DX on our new band at 28 Mc. The DX drive tended to move lower in frequency, and for about two years the world above 50 Mc. was inhabited mainly by experimenters, rather than communicators.

Working at 5 Meters
By S. Kruse, Technical Editor

LAST month I said that ordinary methods worked perfectly well down to 20 meters but special care was needed below that. Since that time hundreds of stations have been working at 40 and 80 meters, not very many at 20 meters—and very few indeed at 5 meters. Most of the 20 and 5 meter work has failed because of an unsteady wave which could not be read, altho very strong at the receiver. The moral is to make a 5-watt tube work steadily rather than to make a 250-watt tube work unsteadily.

Getting Down

I also advised the use of one tube only. This was correct at 40 meters, is still more

cuit is shown because it is simple. Series feed is used because this is to be a loose-coupled set and therefore no harm will come from series feeding. Shunt feed can be used but there will be more trouble in making the chokes work well.

Now we are down to a very small helix, and no capacity except that of the tube—can we make this thing oscillate?

The Circuit

The complete circuit is shown in Fig. 2. A little study will show this to be the same circuit as in Fig. 1, with the addition of the radio frequency chokes needed to make the tube oscillate.

To tell when the set is oscillating the

A 5 METER OSCILLATOR SET COMPLETE
At the left is the 3" helix and next to it the baseless C-302 tube with its chokes and condensers. Beyond that is the Acme filament transformer, then a Weston 100-mil. D.C. instrument used to measure the plate current. The plate power is supplied by the home-made transformer at the right. The filament voltage is controlled by the E210 Bradleystat at the right end of he board. This rheostat is connected in the primary circuit of the filament transformer. The circuit is shown in Fig. 2.

important at 20 meters, and it is almost out of the question to make several American tubes work in parallel at 5 meters. The reason for this is the insistence of our tube makers in bringing all terminals out in a bunch at one end of the tube. If they would only bring the plate out somewhere else we would have little trouble. The

simplest test is to touch the plate coil with a wood handled screwdriver. Be careful— the burns from even a 5-watt oscillator are pretty painful.

If the screwdriver does not spark try raising the plate and filament voltage a bit, then try putting the plate and grid turns a bit closer together. If the screwdriver

In probably the first v.h.f. constructional article ever published, Technical Editor Kruse described a 5-meter oscillator in *QST* for October, 1924. The oscillator tube, barely visible just to the right of the tank coil, was a debased C-302 resting bottom-up on its glass envelope.

Short-Range Phone Does It

Up to this time, most amateurs were code men. Phone was coming in, but it was frowned on as wasteful of frequency and was often treated as an unwanted stepchild. Then a few u.h.f. experimenters began modulating their rigs,

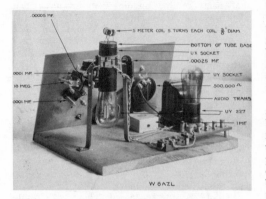

Autodyne receiver used by W8AZL in pioneering 5-meter work with W8PK and W8ABX. V.h.f. adaptation of the superregenerative detector, which was to popularize v.h.f. operation in a big way, was still a year away. From September, 1930, *QST*.

and unwittingly triggered off a boom that was to establish the 5-meter band as desirable communications territory in the minds of a whole new generation.

The experience of early 5-meter phone experimenters John Long, W8ABX, and E. O. Seiler, W8PK, was typical. They were working on 80 one night in the summer of 1930, when a thunderstorm not far away made communication difficult. W8ABX was running his 5-meter rig simultaneously, and when W8PK listened on 5 he found, to his amazement, that signals were far clearer than on 80. Here, for the first time, the 5-meter band was seen to have real worth: it would work over short paths with voice, when noise levels, high activity, or other adverse factors were present on lower frequencies.[5]

Receivers were still a bottleneck, however. The regenerative receiver, critical enough on any frequency, was an operator's nightmare at 56 Mc. Enter here the superregenerative detector. Invented years before, the superregen had not found much favor with amateurs.[6] It was useless for c.w., and its broad frequency response and raucous audio quality gave it a bad name in voice work. But on 56 Mc., where there was band width to burn, broad tuning was almost a blessing.

In retrospect we can see several factors combining to accelerate 5-meter interest as ham radio moved into the Thirties. The wedding of the modulated oscillator and the superregenerative detector would start things rolling again. The modulated oscillator sounded awful on selective receivers now in use on lower frequencies,

and it used up more than its share of high-priority kilocycles. But there was plenty of room on 5, and the unstable signal didn't sound bad at all when received on the broad-tuning "rush-box."

Soon it was found that these two castoffs had something else in their favor: If stations were not too close together in frequency, their transmitters and receivers could be operated simultaneously. This was "duplex phone," a wholly new concept. Two hams could converse as easily by radio as over the telephone, or face to face. Duplex was an overnight sensation, with obvious advantages over c.w., and the monologue voice technique then used on lower bands.

The ill wind of economic depression blowing across the land had made thousands of hams idle. With much time and little money, they were ripe for a kind of hamming that could be carried on with makeshift gear, largely made by hand or with parts robbed from discarded radio receivers. Not only from junk sets, either; as 5-meter interest boomed, more than one family's radio listening time was rationed, while the ham of the house reddened the plates of Type 45 or 71A tubes, lifted from the broadcast set for service in a 5-meter oscillator. Simple low-cost gear; duplex phone; the thrill of something new, yet within the reach of nearly everyone — these were magnets that drew countless newcomers, including the author of these lines, into amateur radio in the early Thirties.

As all through the history of the hobby, *QST* struck the spark. The July, 1931, issue was fat with v.h.f. lures. Technical Editor Lamb had 11 pages on u.h.f. oscillators,[7] some working as high as 400 Mc., where some farsighted administrator had set aside a narrow band for amateur experimenters. Associate Editor Ross A. Hull, who would become one of the v.h.f. man's legendary heroes, fanned the flame with down-to-earth 5-meter receivers,[8] adding reports on *mobile* receiving tests, for good measure. Hull's "Duplex Phone on 56 Mc." in August[9] described more simple gear, and set forth

Cover picture from August, 1931, *QST* shows the modulated-oscillator transmitter that helped trigger the 5-meter boom of that eventful summer. Two 71As in a push-pull oscillator were modulated by parallel 47s.

the operating concept that was to build the fire to conflagration proportions.

The urge to work around the world was forgotten; the aim now was to work across town, reliably, on voice. If 5-meter waves traveled only in straight lines, then we would get up on the hills to extend our horizons. "Working portable" became a great weekend outdoor sport wherever there were hams and mountains. Duplex suggested voice relaying, and hilltop stations worked up haywire patching systems, to hook valley dwellers up with stations they could not hear direct. Message relaying also boomed, and on weekends, points as far apart as New York and Boston were connected by snappy relay circuits, thanks to three or four hilltop portables along the way.[10]

Another *QST* cover shot shows Managing Editor W1SZ hauling up the 8-element beam that was to make 5-meter history at Selden Hill in the fall of 1934.

DX Again

Almost from the first widespread 5-meter activity in the summer of 1931, it was seen that signals did not always travel strictly in straight lines. Stations not within pure line-of-sight range could communicate at times, and the degree to which this was possible was seen to vary. But most of us were too busy trying to improve our equipment to pay much attention to propagation. Then, in the summer of 1934, Ross Hull began experimenting with beam antennas.[11] Hanging a stick-and-wire system of 4 half waves in phase, with reflectors, over the porch roof at Selden Hill, West Hartford, Ross fired up a 200-watt oscillator and blazed away in the direction of Boston. Selden Hill was a fine location, with a clear sweep across the Connecticut Valley, but it was less than 300 feet above sea level. The horizon, 12 to 20 miles distant, was solid with hills 1000 feet and more in elevation, for 50 miles or so, before the countryside sloped down to the coastal plain of Eastern Massachusetts and Rhode Island.

This sort of path had never been bridged on 5 meters. The best DX previously worked by Ross and his associate, W1ANA, and members of the Headquarters Staff who worked with them at Selden Hill, had been a portable on a hilltop 35 miles away. All hands were justifiably excited, therefore, when use of the new directive array produced two-way contacts with many stations in Eastern New England, 75 to 125 miles distant.

Operating on a 24-hour basis, the gang soon found that although signals of some sort were nearly always receivable over at least 100 miles, there was a tremendous variation in level. A signal would all but block the receiver at times, and then a day, an hour, or even minutes later it would drop almost into the noise.

Why? At this juncture what had been little more than a lark to the enthusiastic Hull took on the aspects of a long-term challenge. He set up schedules around the clock, and kept them religiously. He scanned reams of data on all kinds of natural phenomena. Eventually he developed a photographic recording technique, especially to compile a running record of the signal variations of experimental station W1XW, at the Blue Hill Observatory, near Boston. Records were plotted against lunar cycles, weather data, temperature and barometric pressure curves — anything that might affect 5-meter propagation.[12]

We won't attempt to retell the story here, for you can find it all in Ross's own words in *QST*. (See bibliography at the end of this chapter.) Read Hull's account for yourself, and see why his discovery of air-mass boundary bending of v.h.f. waves, and eventual development of a theory to explain it,[13] has been called "one of the outstanding achievements by an amateur in any field of scientific endeavor."

DX of a more remarkable variety was noted in the spring of 1935.[14] One day in May, 5-meter men in eastern cities were amazed to hear strangers in their midst; fellows signing W8 and W9 calls. Michigan, Ohio, Illinois — on 5 meters? Impossible — must be bootleggers trying to pull a fast one! But contacts were made and QSLs exchanged; the signals were genuine. It happened more often in 1936, and soon everyone was looking for 5-meter DX, as word spread like wildfire whenever the band opened up. Most contacts were between 500 and 900 miles, with some out to 1200. A pattern for the propagation was evolved by Harvard University's J. A. Pierce, W1JFO, in a scholarly analysis of 5-meter DX in September, 1938, *QST*.[15]

In the same issue was the biggest DX news yet: details of a transcontinental QSO between W1EYM, Fairfield, Conn., and W6DNS, San Diego, Cal., a record that would stand as long as we had the 5-meter band.[16] Dr. Pierce charged this all up to sporadic ionization in the *E* region of the ionosphere, and pointed out some possible causes. His writings and those of Ross Hull are real milestones in the amateur's contribution to radio propagation knowledge. We can be proud that they came years in advance of similar work by scientific and governmental agencies.

Nathaniel Bishop, W1EYM, Fairfield, Conn., and Harold Hasenbeck, W6DNS, San Diego, Cal., made the first transcontinental 56-Mc. QSO, July 22, 1938.

Meanwhile, v.h.f. was growing up. Power was increasing; receivers were getting better; beam antennas were becoming common. QRM was getting worse steadily, and it became obvious that something must be done. That "something" was the elimination of the broad signals radiated by unstable transmitters, so that selective receivers could be used effectively. The day of the simple rig was drawing to a close, and effective December, 1938, FCC required amateurs on the 56-Mc. band to meet the transmitter stability requirements imposed on lower frequencies. This brought a wonderful era to an end, but it started another.

Simple Gear Moves to 112 and 224 Mc

Some 5-meter men saw in the stabilization regulations the death knell of their favorite band.

Two of the famous "Gil" cartoons in *QST* for December, 1938, summed up the v.h.f. aspects of new FCC regulations then becoming effective.

A few gave up ham radio, rather than convert to the more complex stabilized transmitters. Others dropped to lower bands. But a sizeable number moved higher, and picked up on 112 Mc. where they had left off on 56. Using largely the same techniques that had served so well on 5, these fellows and many newcomers went through a cycle of activity and development reminiscent of early 5-meter days. Almost anything that had been done on 5 was repeated on 2 1/2, except for the working of long distances via ionospheric propagation. There was even considerable experimentation on 1 1/4, and interest in both bands was still rising at the time of the World War II close-down, December, 1941. Freed of their severe QRM problem after 1938, 5-meter workers concentrated on improving receivers, transmitters, antennas, and operating techniques. Reliable operating ranges stretched out to 200 miles and more, for the better stations.

One more DX propagation mode would be brought to light before the wartime close-down. Who did it first, where, or when, is not precisely known, but the first rumblings were heard in 1937. "Rumblings" is the right word, for these weird signals were characterized by terrific distortion, rendering modulation of any kind almost unreadable. Often the signal was little more than a rumble or roar. At first nobody knew what was up, but before long it was found that distortion and signal strength peaked when antennas were aimed north. Eventually this happened on a clear night, and all across the northern sky was seen the eerie glow of aurora borealis! Not much was known about the nature of the aurora then, but amateur 5-meter observations were put to good use in studying it. Until the wartime cessation of activity, and again after 1945, amateur reports gathered by ARRL contributed in a significant way to increased understanding of auroral phenomena.[17]

The Modern Era

Except for limited use of the 112-Mc. band in the War Emergency Radio Service, all amateur activity came to an abrupt end on December 7, 1941. Military communications and radar, meanwhile, expanded all through the spectrum, employing frequencies and techniques hardly dreamed of by most hams. Especially in v.h.f. and microwaves great strides were made during the war period, and many among us doubted that amateur radio could ever catch up. But hams were in the thick of it, in laboratories and in the field, and they learned their lessons well enough to be off and running when the war was over in the fall of 1945. A complete reshuffling of our allocations had been made, and after a temporary start on the old bands at 56 and 112 Mc., we moved to new assignments at 50, 144, and 220 Mc. We also now had bands at 420 Mc. and at intervals all through the assigned portion of the microwave spectrum. There was work to do!

The change from 56 to 50 Mc. was especially intriguing, in view of the rising solar activity curve. Would the new band "open up" when we reached the top of the sunspot cycle a year or two hence? By now, scientists were making predictions as to the maximum usable frequency for F_2-layer propagation, but they were not overly optimistic. The best guess was that 50 Mc. was a bit too high.

Worldwide V.H.F. DX at Last!

Fortunately, most v.h.f. men did not know about these predictions. Noting that British TV signals on 45 Mc. could be heard now and then, and hearing from keen observers across the Atlantic that American signals and harmonics were filtering through in Europe on frequencies as high as 47 Mc. on occasion, amateurs set up test schedules in the fall of 1946. On mornings when conditions appeared favorable, American 50-Mc. men transmitted toward Europe, listening for replies on 28 Mc., there being no 50-Mc. band in Europe.

Just before noon on November 24, 1946, a test transmission by W1HDQ, West Hartford, Conn., brought a frantic *"I'm hearing you on 50 megacycles!"* from G6DH, Clacton-On-Sea, Essex, England, and the first v.h.f. communication across the Atlantic was on. G5BY, near Plymouth, heard the test at the same time, joining G6DH in the transatlantic cross-band QSO a few minutes later. Shortly after noon the same day, W4GJO, Orlando, Fla., worked W6QG, Santa ANA, Cal., for the first transcontinental 50-Mc. F_2-layer QSO. Pacific DX came in January, 1947, when KH6DD worked J9AAK, Okinawa, extending the 50-Mc. DX record to 4600 miles.

In March, 1947, W4IUJ, West Palm Beach, Fla., worked OA4AE, Lima, Peru, thereby winning the Milwaukee Radio Club trophy for the first two-way intercontinental v.h.f. QSO, the cup having been resting at ARRL Headquarters for nearly ten years. Crossband DX of phenomenal proportions came at about this same time, resulting from checks made by PAØUN and PAØUM with ZS1P and ZS1T, 6000 miles to the south. August, 1947, brought a new two-way record, 5300 miles, between W7ACS/KH6 and VK5KL.

Though not credited as such at the time, this probably was the first DX QSO via a propagation medium that was to be exploited later on the Mexico-to-Argentina path. Around the end of August, 1947, XE1KE, Mexico City, began work-

ing LU6DO, Temperly, Argentina, and other LUs on 50 Mc. These contacts were made later in the day than F_2-layer predictions called for. Sometimes propagation lasted well into the evening hours, an unheard-of thing on frequencies this high. Eventually labeled *transequatorial scatter*, this mode of propagation rates as one of the outstanding discoveries in amateur v.h.f. history.[18]

The New Bands Prove Their Worth

Progress on 144 Mc. and higher frequencies was also notable in the early postwar years. Aided by the availability of the SCR-522 and other military communications units on the surplus market, 2-meter men converted largely to stabilized equipment and selective receivers, and operating ranges expanded rapidly. Tropospheric propagation was found to be more favorable on 144 than on 50 Mc., and the record for two-way work was extended gradually, reaching 1400 miles by 1951. Auroral communication was found to be possible on 144, and this mode provided much exciting 144-Mc. DX. Exploitation of the reflecting properties of ionized trails of meteors opened the way to more 2-meter DX. Two leaders in this field were W4HHK, Collierville, Tenn., and W2UK, New

Eileen and Denis Heightman of G6DH, British end of the first transatlantic v.h.f. QSO, November 24, 1946. Receiving W1HDQ on 50 Mc., Denis replied on 28 Mc. The following year, operating with special temporary authorization, G6DH was the first British station to work two-way across the Atlantic on 50 Mc.

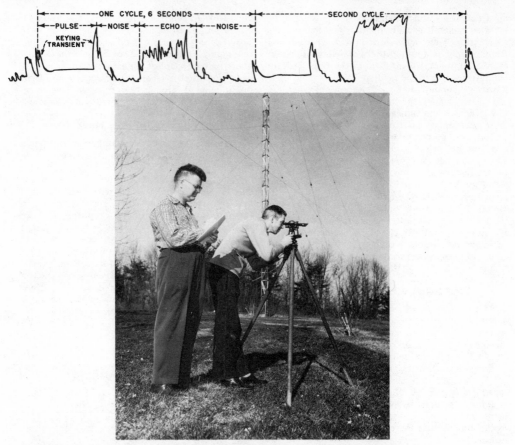

Visual record of an historic achievement — the first amateur signals sent to the moon and back. After three years of work, Ross Bateman, W4AO, and William L. Smith,W3GKP, shown here checking alignment of the huge stacked-rhombic array at W4AO, finally received echoes of their 144-Mc. signal reflected from the moon. The date: January 27, 1953.

Brunswick, N.J., who received the ARRL Merit Award of 1955, for their outstanding meteor-scatter work of 1953 and later.

The 220-Mc. and 420-Mc. bands had appeal for the experimentally inclined, and were soon shown to have great value for practical communications purposes as well. Development of efficient equipment and high-gain antennas showed that these bands were capable of reliable coverage nearly approximating that of 50 and 144 Mc.

Making use of tubes and components largely salvaged from war-surplus radar and navigational equipment, amateurs developed workable communications gear for all our microwave bands before the end of 1946, and in later years were able to extend communications distances out to several hundred miles on nearly all our u.h.f. and s.h.f. bands. Development along these lines continues to this day.

Intrigued by the possibilities of weak-signal work, amateurs made notable strides in utilizing various marginal modes of propagation such as moon reflection, ionospheric and tropospheric scatter, and even satellite communication. The first successful use of the moon for the reflection of amateur signals was accomplished by W4AO and W3GKP in January, 1953.[19] These two used advanced techniques on 144 Mc. to demonstrate that lunar communication was at least a possibility for amateurs. Two-way communication via the moon was a long time coming, and was finally achieved first on 1296 Mc. The work of W1BU and W6HB in communicating over 2500 miles by way of the moon in July, 1960, is a notable milestone.[20]

Propagation know-how paid off markedly for W6NLZ, Palos Verdes Estates, Cal., and KH6UK (also W2UK, mentioned above), Kahuku, Hawaii, when they were able to work across 2500 miles of the Pacific on 144 Mc. in July, 1957.[21] This was the longest path ever covered by tropospheric means by any communications service, and as such it achieved worldwide acclaim. Not satisfied, Chambers and Thomas went on in subsequent years to bridge the path on 220 and 432 Mc. Their superb work won for them the Edison Award for 1960, the only instance in which this award was given for scientific accomplishment.

Thus we have touched lightly on some highlights of amateur radio's long history of pioneering the use of frequencies once thought to be useless for any practical purpose. It is well for all of us, hams of the present and future, that we have this record of achievement behind us. In the years to come, the pressure on all frequencies above 50 Mc. is certain to rise, as if it were not already high enough. Every kilocycle, even to frequencies only dreamed of a few years ago, is eyed eagerly by many users of the radio spectrum. We have shown, from the earliest times, that it is good for everyone that amateurs have access to samplings of the radio-frequency spectrum, from bottom to top, whatever that may be. To continue to merit the confidence and support of the people and agencies who will decide future allocation of frequencies should forever remain one of our highest aims.

Historical QST References

[1] *Working at 5 Meters* . . . Kruse, October, 1924.

[2] *Pioneer Short Wave Work* . . . Jones, 6AJF, May, 1925.

[3] *Experimenter's Section* . . . 1925 to 1928.

[4] *Gear for wavelengths down to 3/4 meter* . . . January, 1926; August, 1927.

[5] *Making Practical Use of the 56-Mc. Band* . . . Long, W8ABX, September, 1930.

[6] *Superregeneration* . . ,. July through October, 1922.

[7] *Developments in U.H.F. Oscillators* . . . Lamb and Hull, July, 1931.

[8] *Five-Meter Receiving Progress* . . . Hull, July, 1931.

[9] *Duplex Phone on 56 Mc.* . . . Hull, August, 1931.

[10] *Progress reports and tests* . . . January, May, July, September, October, November, 1931.

Fundamental Crystal Control . . . April 1932.

Fun on 5 Meters . . . June 1932.

The first amateur microwave station. A. E. Harrison, W6BMS/2, and Reuben Merchant, W2LGF, built two of these stations and had them ready for communication on November 15, 1945, the day that our microwave bands were opened to amateur use. Frequency: 5600 Mc.

An All-Purpose 56-Mc. Station . . . December 1932. Summaries of activity appear throughout 1932 issues.

Behavior of U.H.F. Waves . . . Jones, March, 1933.

Graduating to Oscillator-Amplifier Transmitters for 56 Mc. . . . Griffin, W2AOE, May, 1933.

Firing Up on the Newly-Opened Ultra-High Frequencies . . . Hull, September and November, 1934.

[11] *Extending the Range of U.H.F. Stations* . . . Hull, October and December, 1934.

[12] *Air-Mass Conditions and the Bending of U.H.F. Waves* . . . Hull, June, 1935.

[13] *Air-Wave Bending of U.H.F. Waves* . . Hull, May 1937.

[14] *Five-Meter Signals Do the Impossible* . . . August, 1935, was first published report of authenticated 5-meter skip. July issues of 1936 and 1937 contain summaries of reported DX.

[15] *Interpreting 56-Mc. DX* . . . Pierce, September, 1938 (E-layer theory)

[16] *Further Reports of 50-Mc. DX* . . . September, 1938.

[17] Moore, "Aurora and Magnetic Storms," June, 1951.

[18] Cracknell, "Transequatorial Propagation of V.H.F. Signals," December, 1959.

[19] Tilton, "Lunar DX on 144 Mc.," March, 1953.

[20] September, 1960.

[21] September, 1957, p. 62.

Regular coverage of the v.h.f. and higher bands, *On the Ultra-Highs* , began in December, 1939. Later called *The World Above 50 Mc.*, it has told the month-by-month story of amateur v.h.f. progress ever since.

John T. Chambers, W6NLZ, center, and Ralph Thomas, KH6UK, right, receive Edison Award trophies from General Electric vice-president L. Berkley Davis, in Washington ceremony, February 23, 1961. Award was in recognition of the transpacific communication by these outstanding amateurs on 144, 220, and 432 Mc.

Chapter 2

A Vast Resource

AMATEUR BANDS ABOVE 50 MHz

The true extent and worth of the frequencies above 50 MHz that are available to amateurs are rarely appreciated, even by those who spend most of their operating time there. The various vhf, uhf, and microwave bands are listed below, with the emissions that may be used in each. It will be seen that there is considerable subdivision of the bands

50 to 54 MHz

50.0 to 50.1 MHz – A1 (cw telegraphy) only. Advanced and Extra Class licensees only.

50.1 to 54 MHz – A1, A2 (tone-modulated telegraphy), A3 (amplitude modulation and narrow-band fm), A4 (facsimile). All classes except Novice.

51.0 to 54 MHz – A0 (unmodulated carrier; duplex operation), plus above.

52.5 to 54 MHz – Wide-band fm, plus above.

144 to 148 MHz

144.0 to 144.1 MHz – A1 only. All classes except Novice and Technician.

144.1 to 148 MHz – A0, A1, A2, A3, A4. Wide-band or narrow-band fm. All classes except Novice and Technician.

145.0 to 147.0 – All license classes. Novice must use code only, no more than 75 watts input, and crystal control. No frequency above 147 MHz may be used by Novices.

220 to 225 MHz*

All above modes. All classes except Novice.

* All amateur frequencies above 220 MHz are shared with Government Radio-Location Service, which has priority. Operation in the 220-MHz band is restricted in parts of Texas and New Mexico. Final-stage input in the 420-MHz band is limited to 50 watts in Florida, Arizona, and parts of Alabama, Texas, New Mexico, Nevada, and California, as set forth in Part 97.61 of the *US Regulations*. Permission to use 1000 watts may be obtained by amateurs in restricted areas by individual application to FCC.

by modulation methods. There are also restrictions as to who may use some frequencies, depending on the class of license held by the operator. This information is subject to change. Though the table is accurate for the publication date, early 1972, readers should consult the latest edition of the *Radio Amateur's License Manual* for current restrictions.

420 to 450 MHz*

All above modes, plus A5 (television, slow or fast scan).

1215 to 1300 MHz

All above modes.

2300 to 2450 MHz

All above modes, plus pulse.

3300 to 3500 MHz

All modes.

5650 to 5925 MHz

All modes.

10,000 to 10,500 MHz

All modes except pulse.

21,000 to 22,000 MHz**

All modes.

40,000 MHz and all higher

All modes.

** Subject to change. World Conference on Space Communication, Summer, 1971, assigned 24,000 to 24,250 MHz in place of 21,000 to 22,000 MHz. Frequencies were also assigned for amateur transmitting satellites, as follows: 7.0 to 7.1, 14.0 to 14.25, 21.0 to 21.45, 28.0 to 29.7, 144 to 146, 24,000 to 24,050, and (on shared basis) 435 to 438 MHz. Effective date of these assignments not known at publication date. Watch *QST* for announcement.

WHAT CAN WE DO HERE?

In terms of band widths and potential occupancy by amateurs, this is a world almost beyond comprehension. As seen in Fig. 2-1, amateur bands from 80 through 10 meters, which carry most of the occupancy load, total 3300 kilohertz – less than the width of any vhf band. Vhf assignments include 13 MHz, or almost four times the frequency spread of all lower amateur bands combined. The 420-MHz band is wider than the *entire spectrum* from dc to the top of the 10-meter band. Each band above 1000 MHz is wider still. Our inability to show these figures in scale is worth remembering when we worry over congestion in the amateur bands between 3.5 and 30 MHz!

Our historical review, Chapter 1, emphasized the amateur's role in uncovering the true worth of the vhf bands. Our potential in this field is far from exhausted. Though great scientific strides have been made, by no means all is known of the ways by which signals in the vhf and higher frequency ranges are propagated to distant points. Nature still surprises even the best-informed amateur, and admittedly this is a factor in the appeal of the world above 50 MHz. Knowing something of propagation media we can, however, take advantage of the opportunities nature affords us, and we will enjoy our work more and do it better than if we merely take what comes our way, without question or observation. Here are some propagation tips, band by band.

50 MHz

Perhaps no band is more interestingly placed in the radio spectrum than this, from the standpoint of propagation vagaries. Working in borderline territory between the "DX bands" and those normally considered useful mainly for local communication, the 50-MHz enthusiast samples both worlds. Though DX is not his daily lot, he will see, at one time or another, nearly every known form of long-distance propagation. His reliable range with moderate power and relatively simple equipment is likely to equal anyone's, for the 50-MHz region is less susceptible than lower frequencies to adverse effects that tend to break up or impair communication. Consistent coverage over a radius of 100 miles or more is not unusual, and this can be extended considerably by use of optimum equipment and communications techniques.

Variety is frequently afforded by *tropospheric bending*, which extends local coverage by two to three times the normal. *Sporadic-E skip* offers DX in the range of 400 to 1200 miles or so, and multiple-hop effects may extend this up to 2500 miles or more on occasion. *Auroral propagation* to all distances up to 1000 miles is fairly common in the high latitudes. DX *via the F_2 Layer* may be possible during the peak years of the sunspot cycle, providing contacts at distances of 2000 miles and more. *F_2-layer backscatter* fills in the shorter distances at these times. *Ionospheric scatter* and

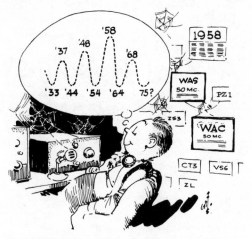

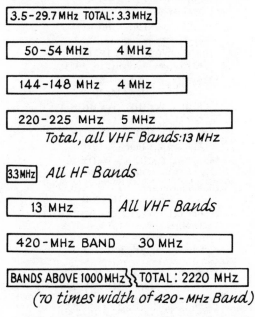

3.5–29.7 MHz TOTAL: 3.3 MHz

50–54 MHz   4 MHz

144–148 MHz   4 MHz

220–225 MHz   5 MHz

Total, all VHF Bands: 13 MHz

3.3 MHz *All HF Bands*

13 MHz   *All VHF Bands*

420-MHz BAND   30 MHz

BANDS ABOVE 1000 MHz ⟩ TOTAL: 2220 MHz

(70 times width of 420-MHz Band)

reflections from meteor trails afford the proficient operator chances for work over 600 to 1200 miles on a regular basis on 50 MHz. *Transequatorial propagation* is good for several thousand miles, in low latitudes and in periods of high solar activity. More about each of these modes later.

144 MHz

Except that it lacks some of the long-distance ionospheric possibilities, the 144-MHz band is not unlike 50 MHz. Tropospheric propagation tends to improve with frequency, so 144 MHz is superior to 50 in this respect. Whereas tropospherically propagated 50-MHz signals are seldom heard beyond 300 miles, 144-MHz work out to 500 miles or more by this mode is fairly common. Up to 1400 miles over land and 2500 miles over water have been covered by tropospheric bending on 144 MHz.

Sporadic-*E* skip is rare on 144 MHz, though lack of alert observers in the more favorable areas may have caused us to miss some 144-MHz DX opportunities of this kind in the past. Auroral propagation is quite similar to 50 MHz, except that borderline conditions may show on the lower frequency and not on 144 MHz. Distances up to 1300 miles have been covered, but 200 to 700 miles is most common. Use of cw is almost a necessity because of the high degree of distortion produced by the auroral reflection.

Of the rare modes, meteor scatter and tropospheric scatter have been most exploited by 144-MHz operators. Each requires fairly high transmitter power, skill in the use of cw, and the best possible receivers and antennas. Communication by way of the moon is just possible on 144 MHz, and considerable progress has been made in EME work in the last decade by W6DNG, K6MYC, VK3ATN, KØMQS, W2NFA, ZL1AZR, F8DO, SM7BAE, and others.

Fig. 2-1 — Amateur bands at the upper end of the rf spectrum defy portrayal in scale. At the top are our hf bands, which total 3300 kHz (3.3 MHz) in width. Next below, on the same scale, are the three amateur vhf bands, each wider than all hf bands combined.

A new scale is needed to show these bands in relation to our 420-MHz band, and this in turn fails to indicate the scope of amateur assignments above 1000 MHz. These would require 70 strips the size of the one shown for the 420-MHz band, which is itself wider than the whole rf spectrum from dc through 30 MHz!

220 MHz

This band is similar to 144 MHz in its tropospheric propagation possibilities. The overland record is about 900 miles, and the 2500-mile path from the West Coast to Hawaii has been bridged with good signals. No ionospheric propagation has been observed. Auroral conditions are less favorable than on 144, but some DX of this kind has been worked, mostly under 700 miles. Communication by way of the moon was not accomplished until 1970, but 220-MHz possibilities appear at least equal to those on 144 MHz. More universal activity is needed on this and all higher amateur bands to assess their real worth for long distances.

420 MHz

Exploitation of this band suffered because of the power restrictions imposed until a few years ago, but it is now known that tropospheric possibilities are excellent. The terrestrial two-way record, 1210 miles from Kansas to Connecticut, is an example. The West-Coast-to-Hawaii path has been covered one way on 432 MHz with strong signals. Lunar and satellite possibilities appear better than on lower frequencies, and distances as great as New England to Hawaii and California to Europe have been covered, by way of the moon.

1215 MHz and Higher

Though not fully exploited by amateurs thus far, the frequencies above 1000 MHz offer vast opportunities for interesting work. Here is the true "frontier" – a world we must explore if the traditions of amateur pioneering are to be maintained. Distances up to 400 miles have been worked on 1215 MHz with low power under conditions of tropospheric bending, and much greater distances certainly are possible. Reflection from the moon shows great promise. No two points on the earth's surface where the moon can be seen simultaneously are beyond the possible range of this mode of communication on these frequencies.

Amateur experience in our microwave bands is too meager to permit us to assess their true potential. Distances beyond line of sight have been covered on all amateur frequencies up through 10,000 MHz, indicating the presence of tropospheric bending. Necessity for use of high antenna gains with resultant sharp beam patterns, almost rules out the random operation that characterizes

amateur radio on lower frequencies. Our microwave assignments have tremendous potential for point-to-point communication, and they might well supplement lower frequencies for scheduled work.

Pulse modulation is one means by which the microwaves can be put to practical use by amateurs, this being usable on all our frequencies above 2300 MHz except in the 10,000-MHz band.

The existing DX records for each of our bands above 50 MHz are listed below:

Terrestrial Two-Way Records

50MHz: LU3EX – JA6FR
   12,000 Miles – March 24, 1956
144 MHz: W6NLZ –KH6UK
   2540 Miles – July 8, 1957
220 MHz: W6NLZ –KH6UK
   2540 Miles – June 22, 1959
420 MHz: W0DRL – K1PXE
   1210 Miles – August 16, 1971
1215 MHz: W6DQJ/6 – K6AXN/6
   400 Miles – June 14, 1959
2300 MHz: W4HHK –WA4HGN/4
   249 Miles – July 11, 1970
3300 MHz: W6IFE/6 – K6HIJ/6
   214 Miles – June 18, 1970
5650 MHz: K6HIJ/6 – W6OYJ/6
   214 Miles – June 18, 1970
10,000 MHz: W7JIP/7 – W7LHL/7
   265 Miles – July 31, 1960
21,000 MHz: W2UKL/2 – WA2VWI/2
   27 Miles – Oct. 24, 1964

EME Two-Way Records

144 MHz: SM7BAE – ZL1AZR
   11,055 Miles – March 4, 1969
220 MHz: WB6NMT – K2CBA
   2650 Miles – March 16, 1970
420 MHz: WA6LET – G3LTF
   5730 Miles – Sept. 25, 1965
1215 MHz: WB6IOM – G3LTF
   5492 Miles – April 27, 1969
2300 MHz: W3GKP – W4HHK
   840 Miles – Oct. 19, 1970

MORE ACTIVITY NEEDED

PROPAGATION BEYOND THE HORIZON

Radio waves travel in straight lines unless forced to do otherwise. In some respects, vhf waves are less easily reflected than waves of lower frequency, so consistent vhf communication with low power tends to be essentially local in character, covering only slightly more than line-of-sight distances. There are many ways by which the wave energy may be reflected, refracted, or scattered, however, and the vhf man will do well to become familiar with the principal ones at least. Some are shown in Fig. 2-2.

Tropospheric Bending is the most common form of vhf DX.[1] Though observable on all radio frequencies, it is most pronounced in the vhf range and higher. It is the result of change in refractive index of the atmosphere at the boundary between air masses of differing temperature and humidity characteristics. These boundaries occur in the first few thousand feet above the earth, so their effect is most prevalent at distances under about 150 miles, though it may extend much farther.

Air masses often move on a very large scale, retaining their original character over considerable periods of time. A large mass of cold air of polar origin may be overrun by warm air from the south. When this happens, an *inversion* is said to exist, the normal state of affairs being a 3-degree drop in temperature for each 1000 feet of altitude. Such a boundary may prevail for 1000 miles or more along a more-or-less stationary weather front, producing amazing DX in the vhf and uhf ranges. There is an easily observed tie-in between visible weather conditions and vhf coverage.[2] Daily weather maps published in many newspapers and often shown in rudimentary form in television weather broadcasts may help the vhf enthusiast to anticipate favorable propagation.[3] Detailed weather maps may be obtained from the U. S. Weather Bureau on a subscription basis.

Tropospheric bending is most common in fair, calm weather of the warmer months, though it can occur at any season. Atmospheric convection in coastal areas, over the Great Laeks Basin, or in the valleys of major rivers, produces the required stratification of air, making these regions somewhat more desirable vhf territory than irregular

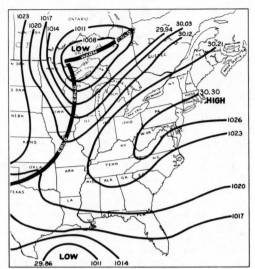

Fig. 2-3 — A readily available guide to tropospheric propagation conditions is a weather map, showing pressure distribution and frontal lines. On the October day that this map appeared in eastern newspapers, the 2-meter band was open from Nova Scotia to at least North Carolina for several hours.

mountainous terrain, far inland. Though the experienced meteorologist would call the following advice an over-simplification of a complex picture, the vhf man should watch for slow-moving areas of high barometric pressure and concentrate on the trailing edges of such areas. See Fig. 2-3. Such favorable conditions are most often observed in the early fall months.

What is known as the *U. S. Standard Atmosphere* curve[4] is shown in Fig. 2-4, left. The solid line is the normal decrease in temperature with height. The broken line shows a relative humidity of 70 percent, from ground to 12,000 feet. Figures in parentheses are the ratio of grams of water vapor to kilograms of air, called the *mixing ratio.* No tropospheric bending would be observed under these conditions. At the right are upper-air readings

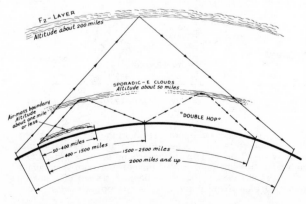

Fig. 2-2 — The principal means by which vhf signals may be returned to earth, showing the approximate distances over which they are effective. The F_2 layer, highest of the reflecting layers, may provide 50-MHz DX at the peak of the 11-year sunspot cycle. Such communication may be world wide in scope. Sporadic ionization of the E region produces the familiar "short skip" on 28 and 50 MHz. It is most common in early summer and late December, but may occur at any time, and regardless of the sunspot cycle. Refraction of vhf waves also takes place at air-mass boundaries, making possible communication over distances of several hundred miles on all vhf bands. Normally it exhibits no skip zone.

of an inversion over Toledo, Ohio, on a September evening some years ago. On this occasion 2-meter signals were traversing the 750-mile path from Northern New Jersey to the Chicago area.

Particularly over water in the lower latitudes, and less often over land areas, something approximating a duct may form, in which vhf waves are propagated over very long distances, following the curvature of the earth in the manner of uhf energy within a waveguide. This *ducting* has accounted for much of our extreme vhf and uhf DX. Notable examples are the spanning of the Pacific from Southern California to Hawaii on 144, 220, and 420 MHz by W6NLZ and KH6UK,[5] achievements which must always rank among the most significant in amateur vhf annals.

Tropospheric communication on 144 MHz along the Atlantic Seaboard over distances as great as New England to Florida, and overland contacts up to 1400 miles, are also products of tropospheric ducting. Scientific investigations over the South Atlantic have shown ducts capable of propagating signals on frequencies even below 50 MHz, but true ducting is rare in amateur experience below 144 MHz. It occurs most often in the uhf region, and extensive occupancy of the amateur bands above 400 MHz should enable us to exploit its possibilities more fully in years to come.

Sporadic-*E* Skip results from reflection of vhf waves by dense patches of ionization in the *E* region of the ionosphere, roughly 50 miles above the earth. Causes are still not completely understood and its occurrence is predictable only in a general way, but its effects are well known to generations of vhf enthusiasts.[6] Layer height and electron density determine the skip distance, but 50-MHz propagation is most common over distances of 400 to 1200 miles. Often signals are very strong, though they may vary rapidly over quite wide ranges. Ionization may develop simultaneously in several areas, making multiple-hop propagation possible and extending the working range to as much as 2500 miles. Signals are usually heard from intermediate distances at such times.

E-layer vhf propagation is most common in the months of May, June, and July. There is a shorter season in December and January, and the effect may occur at random times throughout the year. The long and short seasons are reversed in the southern hemisphere. Duration and extent of E_s openings tend to be greater in the long season. June is the peak month ordinarily, with country-wide openings lasting for many hours at a time at this season. The early evening and before-noon hours are most productive.

The upper-frequency limit for sporadic *E* is not known. It is observed fairly often up to about 100 MHz, and scattered instances occur in the 144-MHz band. Increased activity on 144 MHz has enabled amateurs to observe the effect in this band more often in recent years. Ionization develops rapidly, with effects showing first on lower frequencies. Observation of the 28-MHz band, or commercial frequencies between 30 and 50 MHz[7] will usually give the 50-MHz enthusiast some advance notice of an impending opening. Similarly, the condition of the 50-MHz band or the vhf fm or television frequencies may give clues as to the possibility of 144-MHz propagation.[8]

As ionization density increases and the maximum usable frequency rises, the skip distance on a given frequency shortens. Thus, very short skip on 50 MHz may portend a 144-MHz opening. The alert observer should watch for short 50-MHz skip near the midpoint of a potential 1200-to-1400-mile path, as the best indication of a 144-MHz DX chance. Hearing a 50-MHz station in Cincinnati working another in St. Louis, for example, would be a good omen for a 144-MHz operator in Washington, D.C., indicating the possibility of 2-meter propagation to Oklahoma City or Wichita. Plotting observed skip on a map of the United States will help one to grasp the significance of what he hears.[9]

Like most other vhf DX modes, sporadic-*E* skip was discovered by amateurs (see Chapter 1) and it quickly became a popular sport among 5-meter men of the 1930s. To commercial users of the vhf

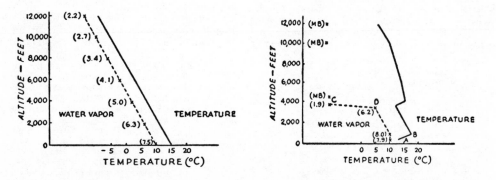

Fig. 2-4 — Upper-air conditions that produce extended-range communication on the vhf bands. At the left is shown the U.S. Standard Atmosphere temperature curve. The humidity curve (dotted) is that which would result if the relative humidity were 70 percent from the ground level to 12,000 feet elevation. There is only slight refraction under this standard condition. At the right is shown a sounding that is typical of marked refraction of vhf waves. Figures in parentheses are the "mixing ratio" — grams of water vapor per kilogram of dry air. Note the sharp break in both curves at about 4000 feet.

spectrum it is known mainly for its nuisance value, but to 50-MHz men it is the DX mode supreme. Though the number and quality of openings vary somewhat from year to year, E_s propagation does not appear to be closely related to sunspot activity.

Auroral Propagation involves reflection of vhf waves from the auroral curtain in the northern skies,[10] usually at acute angles. It is most common at 50 and 144 MHz, the number and duration of openings decreasing markedly at higher frequencies. Some auroral work has been done on 220 and 420 MHz. It may eventually become feasible above 1000 MHz, if very large arrays are used. Scientific investigations with very high power and large antenna arrays have shown auroral returns at frequencies of several thousand Megahertz.

The reflecting properties of the aurora vary rapidly, with the result that the returned vhf signal is badly distorted by multipath effects. Voice modulation is often unintelligible on 50-MHz signals, and nearly always so at 144 MHz. Keyed cw is, therefore, the most effective mode of operation for auroral work. Suppressed-carrier ssb is a poor second, followed by a-m, nfm, and wide-band fm, in that order.

The number of auroras seen each year, and the opportunities for vhf communication via the aurora, vary with *geomagnetic* latitude. Since the geomagnetic pole is quite near Thule, Greenland, geomagnetic latitude lines slope upward with respect to geographical latitude as we look to the west. Bangor, Maine, sees many more auroras than does Seattle, though the latter city is farther north. New York, Philadelphia, and Washington far outdo Reno and Northern California, which lie along the same geographical latitude. Aurora DX has been worked on 144 MHz as far south as 30 degrees in Southeastern U.S.A., but seldom or never in El Paso, Phoenix, or Los Angeles, all of which are well north of latitude 30.

Auroras follow seasonal patterns, being most common around the equinoxes (March and September). They may occur at any time, however, and summer and midwinter auroras are not uncommon in the more northerly states. Aurora effects are observed most often in the late afternoon or early evening, lasting for a few minutes to many hours. The southerly extent also varies greatly. Strong and widespread disturbances may peak in the early evening, drop off for about two hours before midnight, and then return, lasting until dawn or after.

The optimum heading for a vhf antenna array varies with the position of the aurora and may change rapidly, just as the visible display does. Usually an eastern station will work the greatest distance to the west by aiming as far west of north as possible, but this does not always follow. Constant probing with the antenna is recommended, especially if an array with a really sharp pattern is being used.

Developing auroral conditions may be observed by monitoring signals in the region from the broadcast band up to about 5 MHz or so. If signals in the 75-meter amateur band, for example, begin to waver suddenly in the afternoon or early evening hours, taking on a dribbling sound, an

auroral disturbance may be getting under way. Its effects will not be long in showing on the bands higher in frequency, if the disturbance is pronounced. Distortion of voice on 28 or 50 MHz, when the array is aimed north, is evidence that the effect has reached these bands, and it is time for the vhf man to go to work on cw.

On 50 or 144 MHz the buzzing sound characteristic of an auroral return may be heard even on local signals, when both antennas are aimed north. The great-circle distance workable via the aurora

WHEN IN DOUBT— AIM NORTH

extends from local out to more than 1000 miles, but hops of a few hundred miles are most common. Range depends to some extent on transmitter power, antenna gain, and receiver sensitivity, but patience and operating skill are important.

There is much to be learned about auroral propagation. On 50 MHz, for example, an occasional aurora will produce clear voice signals from distances out to 1200 miles or more, not unlike those encountered in sporadic-E skip propagation. These may be accompanied by the distorted signals from shorter distances, the degree of distortion decreasing with frequency. On rare occasions, a long-haul east-west skip may be observed, permitting work over distances up to 2000 miles or more, such as between the first and seventh call areas.

A somewhat similar type of propagation is observed more often by the few vhf operators of the far north. They have found 50-MHz communication possible occasionally with stations in the northern tier of states and adjacent Canadian areas, apparently by something approximating an ionospheric skip, using the auroral zone as a reflecting medium.[11] The number and geographical distribution of auroras and auroral propagation on the vhf bands vary with the solar activity cycle, the maximum auroral incidence apparently lagging the sunspot peak by approximately two years. The arctic effects described immediately above have been observed on 50 MHz at the bottom of the solar cycle, so their relation to solar conditions is by no means clear.

F_2-Layer DX may be possible in the peak years of the 11-year sunspot cycle. This ionospheric mode, responsible for most DX on lower frequencies, opened the 50-MHz band for world-wide communication during solar peaks of 1947 to 1950, 1956 to 1960, and 1968 to 1969. Particularly in the late 1950s, the 50-MHz band was excellent for distances of 2000 miles or more, for many hours at a time, almost daily during the winter months. The first scattered F_2 DX of solar cycle 20 came in 1967, but the peak was far below those of the two previous cycles.

Frequencies near the maximum usable (*muf*) produce the strongest F_2-layer signals, and multiple-hop effects and combinations with other forms of propagation may provide 50-MHz communication over very long paths. Africa to California, U.S.A. to Japan, Hawaii to Australia, and even South America to Japan, were covered frequently in the late 1950s, with signal strengths rivaling the best ever experienced on lower frequencies. Only lack of 50-MHz privileges for amateurs of many countries prevented 50 MHz from becoming the prime amateur DX band during this memorable period.

Whether like conditions will prevail during future peaks of solar activity is a matter of some conjecture. Sunspot records dating back to about 1750, Fig. 2-5, show long-term trends indicating that we may be near the end of an era of generally high activity. Thus it is possible that peaks of the magnitude of recorded cycles 18 and 19 may not recur within the lifetimes of readers of these pages. Cycle 20, peaking in 1968-69, showed a lower trend.

The muf can be checked readily with a general-coverage receiver.[12] Since propagation near the muf is very good, signals will be heard from somewhere on any frequency that is alive. The 10-meter band provides good clues, for its skip distance shortens markedly as the muf rises toward 50 MHz. If 10 is open for long periods daily, and the skip shortens to 1200 miles or less during the peak hours, the muf is approaching 50 MHz. This is the time to watch the frequencies just below 50 MHz, making note of the highest frequency at which DX signals can be heard, and the time of day when they appear. A daily record of these observations will show if the muf is rising. Enough use of the vhf range is made, almost everywhere in the world, so that there will be plenty of evidence of an imminent 50-MHz opening. Usually there are many signals, both in the band and near it. European television made 50-MHz DX work dif-

ficult for amateurs in Eastern U.S.A. during peak hours of Cycle 19, and hundreds of other European signals and harmonics were audible whenever the band was open in that direction.

Ionospheric prediction maps are available from the U.S. Government Printing Office, Washington, DC 20402. *Ionospheric Predictions*, OT-TRER 13, is in four volumes: Vol. 1 explains the use of the maps, 30 cents. Vols. 2, 3, and 4, $3.00 each, contain maps for predicted Zurich smoothed relative sunspot numbers of 10, 110, and 160, respectively. Interpolation of data from two volumes must be made for solar-activity periods of intermediate levels. Information on predicted sunspot numbers in contained periodically in propagation forecast bulletins, transmitted by W1AW and many Official Bulletin Stations.

Since the muf is related to the position of the sun, it is highest at roughly noon at the midpoint of a given path. It tends to be highest in the low latitudes, and lowest along paths traversing the auroral zones. The highest recorded F_2 muf was in the vicinity of 75 MHz.

Back-Scatter signals from amateur stations inside the skip zone indicate high muf and also show the direction in which conditions are most favorable for long-distance work. The F_2 layer has almost mirror qualities near the muf. Signals reflected from it come down at a distant point on the earth's surface, from which they scatter in all directions. Some of the energy comes back to the ionosphere and is reflected back to earth. Thus a station in Virginia, for example, will be heard by a station in Ohio, when both have their antennas aimed at Europe and that path is open for both of them.

Signals scattered back to or near to their point of origin are weak and have a high degree of multipath distortion, somewhat like those reflected from the aurora. Voice may be only partly readable, and cw is highly effective under such conditions. Back-scatter is usually strongest for stations no more than a few hundred miles apart, but back-scatter QSOs have been made between points as widely separated as New England and Mexico City. When this occurred, both stations were aiming at a common "open" point in the South Atlantic. Alaska and California, with a common opening to Japan, have had similar experiences. Often the direct path between the two

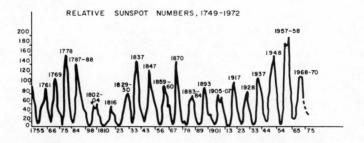

Fig. 2-5 — Relative sunspot number records dating back to before 1750 show that the last two solar peaks, known as cycles 18 and 19, were the highest in all of man's observation of the sun. Looking at the long-term curve indicates that we may be moving into an era of generally low solar activity.

stations will produce no signals, the circuit being open only via the longer back-scatter route.

A similar condition may be observed during periods of sporadic-E propagation (see page 18) though the shorter skip may make E-layer back-scatter hard to distinguish from other modes of propagation.

Transequatorial Propagation during the afternoon and evening hours is possible for 50-MHz stations situated at optimum distances from the geomagnetic equator, roughly 1500 to 2500 miles above and below. See Fig. 2-6. This mode is associated with high sunspot periods, but because it is effective at frequencies up to at least 1.5 times the observed daytime muf for the F_2 layer, it runs for a longer portion of the solar cycle than does the normal F-layer propagation described above. It has been observed over paths that cross the equator at angles as low as 45 degrees, and at greater distances than given above, but long paths and large deviations from the north-south route show lower muf and shorter openings.

Typical TE paths of high reliability are Puerto Rico to Argentina, Japan to Australia, and the Mediterranean area to Southern Rhodesia.[13] These circuits continue to show TE propagation in the 50-MHz band long after F_2-layer DX has expired. At the peak of Cycle 19 the TE mode was observed over most of the United States, and in Europe as far north as the British Isles on isolated occasions. The spring and fall months show this mode to the best advantage. Signals may have a high degree of flutter, but voice readability is seldom seriously impaired.

Ionospheric Scatter is usable for marginal 50-MHz communication over distances comparable to those encountered in single-hop E_s, mainly 600 to 1200 miles. Because only a very small part of the energy scattered in the E region of the ionosphere returns to earth, such signals are extremely weak. Large antennas, fairly high transmitter power, and good receivers are essential, and even with all these only cw emission can be expected to produce consistent results. Though ionospheric scatter is now widely used for military communication over long distances its adaptation to amateur use is limited.[14] Operation on carefully kept schedules, with the precise frequencies to be used known in advance, is almost a necessity, but amateur experience on many 50-MHz scatter circuits has shown that the bare essentials of communication can be exchanged, if good equipment and operating skill are available at both ends of the path.

When there are aiding factors, such as developing sporadic-E ionization, or more than the average number of meteors near the midpoint, ionospheric scatter circuits improve markedly, even though the path may not be considered "open" in the normal sense.

Tropospheric Scatter is similar to the ionospheric form, except that it occurs nearer to the earth's surface, and consequently shows mainly as an extension of the normal working range of vhf stations. It is effective at all frequencies, 50 MHz and higher, but has been used by amateurs mainly

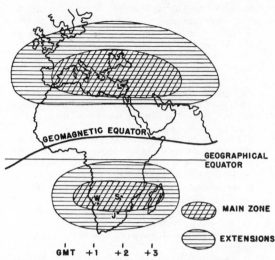

Fig. 2-6 — Main and occasional zones of transequatorial 50-MHz propagation, as described by ZE2JV, show Limassol, Cyprus, and Salisbury, Rhodesia, to be almost ideally positioned with respect to the curving geomagnetic equator. Windhoek, Southwest Africa, is also in a favorable spot. Johannesburg somewhat less so.

for 144-MHz work. Experience has shown that with optimum equipment, signals can be exchanged on 144 MHz consistently at distances out to 450 to 500 miles[15] regardless of propagation conditions. Such signals are very weak and difficult to copy, and as in all weak-signal work, cw is the only mode by which communication can be carried on effectively in tropospheric scatter over the extreme distances.

Meteor Scatter is one of the more esoteric forms of vhf DX currently worked by amateurs. Meteors entering the earth's atmosphere from outer space burn up rapidly in the E region of the ionosphere due to friction. In the process a cylinder of dense ionization is formed as a trail behind the meteor. A 50-MHz signal reflected from this trail may appear as a few words of readable voice, from a station up to 1200 miles away. If you make a habit of tuning the 50-MHz band carefully for considerable periods, you may have heard these bursts from time to time. On 144 MHz, the same meteor would provide a much shorter burst, perhaps no more than a "ping" heard when the receiver beat oscillator is on.

Meteors are constantly entering the earth's atmosphere, so if a vhf receiver is left tuned to a distant station its signal pings will be heard at random intervals at all times. The number and duration of bursts increase greatly during major showers listed in Table I, and they may come often enough to permit communication of sorts between cooperating stations.[16] Meteor bursts are heard frequently on any 50-MHz ionospheric-scatter circuit, rising suddenly far above the weak residual signal that is characteristic of such communication. On 144 MHz there is normally no residual signal beyond a few hundred miles, so only the meteor bursts are heard. Occasionally during major meteor showers, bursts of up to a minute or more of continuous 144-MHz signal may be received.

Such fortunate breaks are by no means necessary for communication between dedicated enthusiasts. Using high keying speeds and precisely timed transmissions on accurately known frequencies, they often achieve exchanges of information on a series of bursts of no more than a few seconds' duration each.

The usual arrangement is for one station to transmit for exactly one minute, 30 seconds, or even 15 seconds, following which the other takes over for a like period. Detailed procedure is agreed on in advance. Typically, a signal report (S1, S2, or S3, indicating duration of bursts, rather than signal strength) is sent immediately upon identification of the other station. When the signal report is received, an R is transmitted repeatedly, signifying receipt.

Daily schedules kept through a major shower peak will usually yield enough bursts on at least one day to complete a contact within an hour or less of such cooperative effort. A long loud burst is usually the signal to abandon timed transmissions abruptly and try for a complete exchange before signals disappear. Very short sequences, such as 15 seconds each way, have the advantage of making it likely that any appreciable burst will be usable in this way.

Information in the meteor shower table should be used as a guide, and not relied on completely. Showers may not peak at exactly the same time from year to year, and those having widely spaced periodic peaks may be deflected and not appear at all. The times given are local standard.

After putting on the biggest show in amateur radio history up to that time, October, 1946,[17] the Giacobinids were deflected, and were hardly discernible 13 years later. On the other hand, the surprising resurgence of the November Leonids in 1965 and 1966 provided 144-MHz meteor DX of unprecedented proportions.[18] The August Perseids and December Geminids are dependable year after year, and are highly favored for vhf scheduling on that account.

Minor showers listed in the table may offer little more opportunity for communication than do the random meteors always entering the earth's atmosphere. Scheduled work over the right distances, especially between 2200 and 0900 local time, should yield some results practically every day.

Voice contacts are made occasionally during meteor showers, and success in this has increased as voice-controlled ssb has become more widely used.

Lunar Communication has been the dream of vhf men for a generation, but successful use of the earth-moon-earth (EME) path is still very difficult. Pioneering 2-meter men received their own signals reflected from the moon in 1953,[19] and long distances have been covered two-way in recent years.[20] Marginal communication via the moon has been carried out over long distances on the 220-,

420-, 1215-, and 2300-MHz bands, but only with very sophisticated equipment. Communication by reflection from the moon remains a challenge to the more advanced amateur, and it is a fine project for clubs having the facilities, ability, and determination to achieve a measure of success.

The requirements are fairly well established. They include the maximum legal power, the ultimate in receiver performance, very large antennas capable of being aimed and controlled accurately,[21] and a willingness to work with very weak cw signals. Because very high receiver selectivity is often used, to realize the best possible signal-to-noise ratio, stability requirements in both transmitter and receiver are critical.

Antenna problems are similarly staggering. At 144 MHz, an antenna gain well in excess of 20 dB is required. Polarization rotation along the path, out and back, makes it appear that circular polarization offers the best chance of success. Because of the reflection of the signal, the polarization sense should be reversed between transmission and reception, in listening for one's own echoes.

The polarization rotation problem is largely eliminated above 1000 MHz, but the difficulties of generating sufficient power, and building a good enough receiver are multiplied. Detailed discussion of moonbounce problems is beyond the scope of this book. Study of the references at the end of this chapter is recommended to the serious would-be worker in this field.

Progress in amateur communication via the moon has been steady, though largely unspectacular, in recent years. Because the ultimate in equipment of every kind is required, it is probably unrealistic to expect that any great "breakthrough" in this field will suddenly make reliable communication by moon *reflection* practical within the framework of the amateur regulations. The prospect of a lunar repeater is, however, quite another matter. Man's progress in the mastery of space travel being what it is, repeaters on the moon could revolutionize our whole approach to amateur radio communication within a decade.

Passive and Active Satellites offer possibilities for worldwide communication in the vhf range and higher frequencies. The former consists of a reflector of some sort, as in the Echo series, presenting problems even more severe than those involved in lunar communication. Very good equipment is required, and antennas designed for tracking must be used, if this mode of communication is to be used by amateurs.

Active satellites pick up the transmitted signal and relay it, usually on another frequency. While such a device is relatively easy for the amateur to use, the design and operational problems are formidable. The number of signals it can accommodate at any one time is severely limited. The active satellite is expected to play a large role in amateur radio of the future, as are other communications ramifications of the space age. Problems, possibilities, and results with active satellites have been discussed extensively in *QST*.[22]

Table I—Meteor Shower Data for V.H.F. Use

Shower and Date	Time Visible Rise	Set	Optimum Paths and Times N-S	NW-SE	E-W	SW-NE	Hourly Rate Visual	Radio	Velocity km/sec	Period Years	Next Maximum
* January 3–5 Quadrantids	2300	1800	—	0300–0800 SW	0800–0900 S	0900–14C0 SE	35	45	45	7	Note 1
January 17 Cygnids	0230	2130	—	0600–1100 SW	1100–1300 S	1300–1800 SE	—	—	—	—	—
February 5–10 Aurigids	1200	0330	—	1400–1730 SW	—	2130–0100 SE	—	—	—	—	—
March 10–12 Boötids	2200	0830	2330–0030 W 0530–0630 E	0330–0530 NE	0230–0330 N	0030–0230 NW	—	—	—	—	—
March 20 Coma Berenices	1800	0630	2130–2300 W 0100–0300 E	2000–2130 SW	—	0300–0430 SE	—	—	—	—	—
* April 19–23 Lyrids	2100	1100	0230 W 0530 E	2330–0100 SW	—	0700–0830 SE	8	12	51	415	Note 1
* May 1–6 Aquarids	0300	1200	—	0830–1000 NE	0630–0830 N	0500–0630 NW	12	12	66	76	Note 1
May 11–24 Herculids	1800	0630	2130–2300 W 0100–0300 E	2000–2130 SW	—	0300–0430 SE	—	—	—	—	—
May 30 Pegasids	2300	1200	0300–0430 W 0630–0800 E	0130–0300 SW	—	0800–0930 SE	—	—	—	—	—
June 2–17 Scorpiids	2000	0300	—	0100 NE	2300–2400 N	2200 NW	—	—	—	—	—
June 27–30 Pons Winnecke	Does not set; min. at 0900		—	1500–1830 SW	1830–2330 S	2330–0300 SE	—	—	—	—	—
July 14 Cygnids	1800	1000	—	2100–2330 SW	0130 S	0330–06C0 SE	—	—	—	—	—
July 18–30 Capricornids	2030	0400	—	0100–0200 NE	2300–0100 N	2200–2300 NW	—	—	—	—	—
* July 26–31 Aquarids	2200	0600	—	0300–0500 NE	0100–0300 N	0000–0100 NW	10	22	50	3.6	Note 1
* July 27–August 14 Perseids	Does not set; min. at 1730		—	2330–0300 SW	0300–0800 S	0800–1130 SE	50	50	61	120	Note 1
August 10–20 Cygnids	1200	0700	—	1700–1930 SW	2130 S	2330–0200 SE	—	—	—	—	—
August 21–23 Draconids	Does not set; min. at 0900		—	1500–1830 SW	1830–2330 S	2330–0300 SE	—	—	—	—	—
August 21–31 Draconids	Does not set; min. at 0700		—	1300–1630 SW	1630–2130 S	2130–0100 SE	—	—	—	—	—
September 7–15 Perseids	2130	1200	—	0030–0200 SW	—	0700–0830 SE	—	—	—	—	—
September 22 Aurigids	2100	1230	—	0030–0200 SW	—	0700–0830 SE	—	—	—	—	—
October 2 Quadrantids	0500	0000	—	0900–1400 SW	1400–1500 S	1500–2000 SE	—	—	—	—	—
October 9 Giacobinids	0600	0300	—	1100–1600 SW	1600–1700 S	1700–2200 SE	Note 2		20	6.6	1972
October 12–23 Arietids	1900	0700	2130–2330 W 0230–0430 E	—	—	—	—	—	—	—	—
* October 18–23 Orionids	2230	0930	0000–0200 W 0600–0800 E	0430–0600 NE	0330–0430 N	0200–0330 NW	15	30	68	76	Note 1
* Oct. 26–Nov. 16 Taurids	1900	0630	2100–2300 W 0300–0500 E	0130–0300 NE	0030–0130 N	2300–0030 NW	10	16	27	3.3	Note 1
* November 14–18 Leonids	0000	1230	0300–0500 W 0800–1000 E	—	—	—	12	Note 3	72	33.2	1999
November 22–30 Andromedids	1300	0600	—	1600–2000 SW	—	2300–0300 SE	Note 4	—	22	6.7	1977
* December 10–14 Geminids	1900	0900	0030 W 0330 E	2130–2300 SW	—	0500–0630 SE	60	70	35	1.6	Note 1
* December 22 Ursids	Does not set; min. at 2030		—	—	0130–1530 S	—	13 Note 5	13	38	13.5	1972, 1985
* May 19–21 Cetids	0530	1430	—	1100–1230 NE	0900–1100 N	0730–0900 NW	—	—	20	37	—
* June 4–6 Perseids	0500	1730	0800–1000 W 1300–1500 E	—	—	—	—	—	40	29	—
* June 8 Arietids	0330	1530	0600–0800 W 1100–1300 E	—	—	—	Note 6	—	70	38	—
* June 30–July 2 Taurids	0500	1700	0700–0900 W 1300–1500 E	1130–1300 NE	1030–1130 N	0900–1030 NW	—	—	30	31	—

* Major showers—Last four are daylight showers.

Times given are local standard at path midpoint

NOTES

1. These streams are evenly distributed and little year to year variation is to be expected.
2. Very concentrated stream. Peak years give up to 400 meteors per minute, but with duration of only 6 hours. 1946 peak was most concentrated shower in amateur radio experience up to that time (see December, 1946, QST, page 43) but 1959 recurrence was deflected and was hardly observable.
3. Peak years give 60/hour visual. In the peak years of the 1800s, prior to being deflected by Jupiter and Saturn, this shower gave 1200 per minute. Spectacular results in 1965 and 1966 are reported in Jan. 1966 QST, page 80, and Jan. 1967, page 83.
4. Before being deflected by Jupiter this stream gave peak year rates of 100/minute. No notable rates have been observed since, though the stream could return.
5. Short duration shower. Peak years the radio rate is 165/hour.
6. This intense daylight shower begins June 2 and runs to June 14 with radio rates from 25 to 70/hour.

RELIABLE VHF COVERAGE

In preceding pages we discussed means by which our bands above 50 MHz may be used intermittently for communication far beyond the visual horizon. In emphasizing DX we should not neglect a prime asset of the vhf bands: reliable communication over relatively short distances. The vhf region is far less subject to disruption of local communication than are frequencies below about 30 MHz. Since much amateur communication is essentially local in nature, our vhf assignments could carry a much greater load then they presently do, and this would help solve interference problems on lower frequencies.

Possibly some amateur unwillingness to migrate to the vhf bands is due to misconceptions about the coverage obtainable. This reflects the age-old idea that vhf waves travel only in straight lines, except when the DX modes enumerated above happen to be present. Let us survey the picture in the light of modern wave-propagation knowledge and see what the bands above 50 MHz are good for on a day-to-day basis, ignoring the anomalies that may result in extensions of normal coverage.

It is possible to predict with fair accuracy how far you should be able to work consistently on any vhf or uhf band, provided a few simple facts are known. The factors affecting operating range can be reduced to graph form, as described by D. W. Bray, K2LMG.[23] To estimate your station's capa-

bilities, two basic numbers must be determined: *station gain*, and *path loss*. Station gain is made up of eight factors: receiver sensitivity, transmitted power, receiving antenna gain, receiving antenna height gain, transmitting antenna gain, transmitting antenna height gain, and required signal-to-noise ratio. This looks complicated but it really boils down to an easily made evaluation of receiver, transmitter, and antenna performance. The other number, path loss, is readily determined from the nomogram, Fig. 2-7. This gives path loss over smooth earth, for 99 percent reliability.

For 50 MHz, lay a straightedge from the distance between stations (left side) to the appropriate distance at the right side. For 1296 MHz, use the full scale, right center. For 144, 220, and 432, use the dot in the circle, square, or triangle, respectively. Example: at 300 miles the path loss for 144 MHz is 215 dB.

Station Gain

The largest of the eight factors involved in station gain is receiver sensitivity. This is obtainable from Fig. 2-8, if you know the approximate receiver noise figure and transmission-line loss. If you can't measure noise figure, assume 3 dB for 50 MHz, 5 for 144 or 220, 8 for 432, and 10 for 1296, if you know that your equipment is working

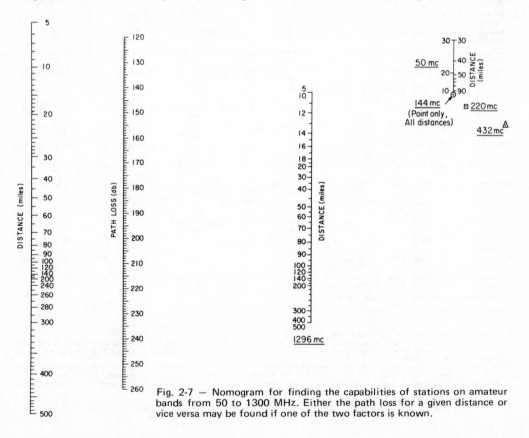

Fig. 2-7 — Nomogram for finding the capabilities of stations on amateur bands from 50 to 1300 MHz. Either the path loss for a given distance or vice versa may be found if one of the two factors is known.

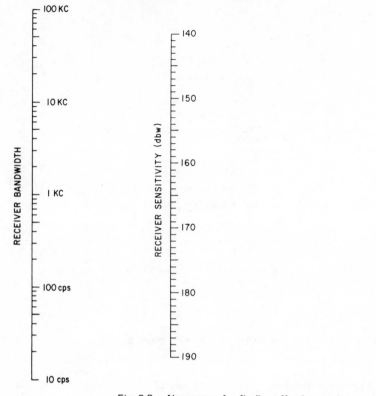

Fig. 2-8 — Nomogram for finding effective receiver sensitivity.

moderately well. Line loss can be taken from Table 8-III for the line in use, if the antenna system is fed properly. Lay a straightedge between the appropriate points on either side of Fig. 2-8, to find effective receiver sensitivity in dB below one watt (dbW). Use the narrowest bandwidth that is practical for the emission intended, with the receiver you will be using. For cw, an average value for effective work is about 500 cycles. Phone bandwidth can be taken from the receiver's instruction manual.

Antenna gain is next in importance. Gains of amateur antennas are often exaggerated. For well-designed Yagis they run close to 10 times the boom length in wavelengths. (Example: a 24-foot Yagi on 144 MHz is 3.6 wavelengths long. 3.6 X 10 = 36, or about 15 1/2 dB.) Add 3 dB for stacking, where used properly. Add 4 dB more for ground-reflection gain. This varies in amateur work, but averages out near this figure. We have one more plus factor: antenna height gain, obtainable from Fig. 2-9. Note that this is greatest for short distances. The left edge of the horizontal center scale is for 0 to 10 miles, the right edge for 100 to 500 miles. Height gain for 10 to 30 feet is assumed to be zero. It will be seen that for 50 feet the height gain is 4 dB at 10 miles, 3 dB at 50 miles, and 2 dB at 100 miles. At 80 feet the height gains are roughly 8, 6, and 4 dB for these distances. Beyond 100 miles the height gain is nearly uniform for a given height, regardless of distance.

Transmitter power output must be stated in dB above 1 watt. If you have 500 watts output, add 500/1, or 27 dB, to your station gain. The transmission line loss must be subtracted from the station gain. So must the required signal-to-noise ratio. The information is based on cw work, so the additional signal needed for other modes must be subtracted. Use 3 dB for ssb and 7 dB for a-m. Loss due to fading must be accounted for. It has been shown that for distances beyond 100 miles the signal will vary plus or minus about 7 dB from the average level, so 7 dB must be subtracted from the station gain for high reliability. For distances under 100 miles, fading diminishes almost linearly with distance. For 50 miles, use minus 3.5 dB for fading.

What It All Means

After adding all the plus-and-minus factors to get the station gain, use it to find the distance over which you can expect to work reliably, from the nomogram, Fig. 2-7. Or work it the other way around: find the path loss for the distance you want to cover from the nomogram and then figure out what station changes will be needed to overcome it.

The significance of all this becomes more obvious when we see path loss plotted against frequency for the various bands, as in Fig. 2-10. At the left this is done for 50 percent reliability. At the right is the same information for 99 percent

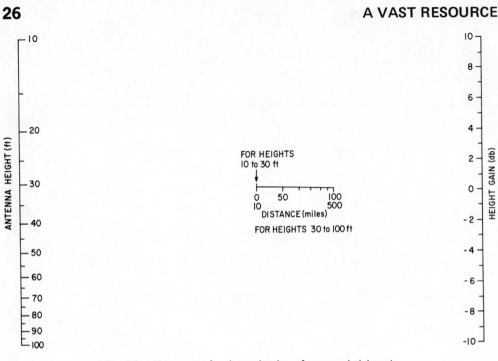

Fig. 2-9 — Nomogram for determination of antenna-height gain.

Working out a few typical amateur vhf station setups with these curves will show why an understanding of these factors is important to any user of the vhf spectrum. Note that path loss rises very steeply in the first 100 miles or so. This is no news to vhf men; locals are very strong, but stations 50 or 75 miles away are much weaker. But what happens beyond 100 miles is not so well known to some of us.

reliability. For near-perfect reliability, a path loss of 195 dB (easily countered at 50 or 144 MHz) is involved in 100-mile communication. But look at the 50 percent reliability curve: the same path loss takes us out to well over 250 miles. Few amateurs demand near-perfect reliability. By choosing our times, and accepting the necessity for some repeats or occasional loss of signal, we can maintain communication out to distances far beyond those usually worked by vhf men.

From the curves of Fig. 2-10, we see that path loss levels off markedly at what is the approximate limit of working range for average vhf stations using voice. Work out the station gain for a 50-watt station with an average receiver and moderate-sized antenna, and you'll find that it will come out around 180 dB. This means about a 100-mile working radius in average terrain, for good but not perfect reliability. Another 10 dB may extend the range to as much as 250 miles. Just changing from a-m phone to cw can thus do wonders for you. A bigger antenna, a higher one if your present beam is not at least 50 feet up, an increase in power to 500 watts from 50, an improvement in receiver noise figure if it is presently poor — any of these things can make a big improvement in reliable

coverage. Achieve all of them, and you will have very likely tripled your sphere of influence, thanks to that hump in the path-loss curves. This goes a long way toward explaining why using a 10-watt packaged station and a small antenna, fun though it may be, does not begin to show what the vhf bands are *really* good for.

About Terrain

The coverage figures derived from the above are for average terrain. What of stations in mountainous country? Though an open horizon is generally desirable for the vhf man, mountain country should not be given up as hopeless until it has been proven so. Help for the valley dweller often lies in the optical phenomenon known as *knife-edge refraction.*[24] A flashlight beam pointed

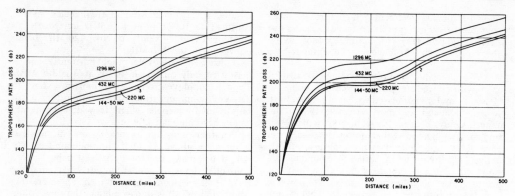

Fig. 2-10 — Path loss vs. distance for amateur frequenceis above 50 MHz. Curves at the left are for 50 percent of the time; those at the right for 99 percent. The former is the more representative of amateur radio requirements.

at the edge of a partition does not cut off sharply at the partition edge, but is refracted around it, partially illuminating the shadow area. A similar effect is observed with vhf waves passing over ridges; there is a shadow effect, but not a complete blackout. If the signal is strong where it strikes the mountain range, it will be heard well in the bottom of a valley on the far side.

This is familiar to all users of vhf communications equipment who operate in hilly terrain. Where only one ridge lies in the way, signals on the far side may be almost as good as on the near. Under ideal conditions (a very high and sharp-edged obstruction near the midpoint of a path long enough so that signals would be weak over average terrain), knife-edge refraction may yield signals even stronger than would be possible with an open path.

The obstruction must project into the radiation patterns of the antennas used. Often mountains that look formidable to the viewer are not high enough to have an appreciable effect, one way or the other. Since the normal radiation from a vhf array is several degrees above the horizontal, mountains that are less than three degrees above the horizon, as seen from the antenna, are missed

paths are common in high-mountain country. Mt. Rainier, Mt. Hood, and other majestic peaks of the Northwest are examples, and the mountains of California provide many others. Mt. McKinley in Alaska has demonstrated remarkable capabilities for both knife-edge and reflector service.

Rolling terrain, where obstructions are not sharp enough to produce knife-edge refraction, still does not exhibit complete shadow effect. There is no complete barrier to vhf propagation; only attenuation, which varies widely as the result of many factors. Thus, even valley locations are usable for vhf communication. Good antenna systems, preferably as high as possible, the best available equipment, and above all, the willingness and ability to work with weak signals may make possible outstanding vhf work, even in sites that show little promise by casual inspection.

by the radiation from the array. Bulldozing them out of the way would have substantially no effect on vhf signal strength in such cases.

Mountains that are really high but not situated or shaped so that they exhibit knife-edge effects may be useful in another way: as a reflector visually common to two stations that do not have a direct open path between them. Such reflection

OPERATING MODES

Almost every amateur has one mode of operation that he prefers over all others. Once this was a simple choice between phone and code, but today's picture is more complex. The voice operator on the vhf bands can use amplitude modulation, suppressed-carrier single-sideband or double-sideband, or frequency modulation, either wide or narrow-band. The code man can employ conventional cw, keyed tone modulation, or frequency-shift keying. Other modes include television (slow-scan or wide-band), radio teletype (with either audio- or radio-frequency shift), facsimile and pulse. Because some of these are wide-band modes, taking up more space than would be permissible in crowded lower bands, the choice open to the

inhabitant of the world above 50 MHz is wider than for any other amateur.

Though many of us tend to concentrate on one mode, there is much to be said for versatility. With foresight in planning his station, the vhf enthusiast can incorporate several modes of operation with little difficulty. Though a-m phone is heavily entrenched in vhf work, other modes have much to offer. The most effective system for long-distance vhf work is keyed cw, and it is also the simplest of all communications systems in its transmitter requirements. There is no valid reason why cw capability should not be built into every vhf station, yet a surprising number of vhf men make no use of it. This is lamentable, for as shown in

Fig. 2-10 the improvement gained through intelligent use of cw can double or triple the effective operating range of any vhf station. Probably by no other means can vhf coverage be extended so easily.

An appreciable improvement in consistent range with voice can be achieved by going to single-sideband, as compared with a-m phone. Both cw and sideband are more effective than other modes mainly because they occupy a narrower band of frequencies. Cw requires essentially no space at all, and thus it permits almost infinite receiver selectivity when suitable techniques are employed. Sideband requires less than half the spectrum space of other voice modes. No power is wasted in transmitting a carrier, this being supplied, in effect, by the receiver's beat oscillator. The bfo is also an important factor in the effectiveness of cw.

Frequency modulation, all but ignored by a generation of vhf men, has great potential worth. With suitable receiving techniques, fm provides almost totally noise-free communication within its service area. Either wide-band or narrow-band fm is easily incorporated in a vhf transmitter, and because it adds nothing to the power that must be dissipated by the tubes, or to the voltage that components must be capable of withstanding, the full cw ratings of all parts of the transmitter apply to fm as well. Perhaps most important of all, fm eliminates practically all chance of audio-type interference in TV receivers, broadcast sets, hearing aids, and other audio amplifiers, and so is invaluable in solving interference problems for the amateur in densely populated areas. Not widely appreciated is the fact that, with proper receiving techniques, fm is at least the equivalent of a-m in reliable vhf coverage. Only cw and ssb are superior.

Tone modulation (A2) is a simple means of sending code on the vhf bands with any voice transmitter. It is only slightly better than a-m phone for weak-signal work, but it is fine for code practice, and for use on frequencies where either the receiver or the transmitter may not be stable enough for cw, or where the receiver does not have a bfo.

Use of frequency-shift keying (fsk) is confined mainly to radio-teletype work, but it could be employed for cw. With today's voltage-variable capacitors, it is a simple matter to shift the frequency for fsk.

Slow-scan television has no special vhf connotation. Conventional high-quality TV (fast scan)

requires a very wide band of frequencies, so it is confined to bands from 420 MHz up. Nearly all amateur TV is currently on the 420-MHz band, between 436 and 450 MHz.

Pulse is a very wide mode inherently and is permitted only on certain bands above 2300 MHz. Though employed only to a limited extent in amateur communication, it has interesting possibilities on frequencies where its wide-band nature can be accommodated.[25]

Another emission is usable on all amateur frequencies above 51 MHz: unmodulated carrier, A∅. It has many uses, not the least being remote control systems for model aircraft, boats, and the like. Much neglected by vhf men, an interesting adaptation of A∅ is duplex phone. In using A∅ the operator need identify only once every ten minutes or less, and he is not *required* to have any intelligence on the signal in between identifications. This permits running the transmitter while tuning for other signals, either on the same band as the transmitter, or on another band. The 50- and 144-MHz bands tend to become congested at their low ends, so it is well to use duplex technique only in the less-occupied upper portions. The U.S. Regulations allow A∅ only above 51 MHz for this reason, and it is well to check the frequencies to be used for A∅ to see that they are unoccupied, before embarking on duplex work.

Use of low power, separate antennas for transmission and reception, and earphones in place of speakers are aids to effective duplex operation. Especially where signals are reasonably strong, as in local work, duplex provides a ready give-and-take exchange that can be far more pleasant and efficient than the one-way monologue that conventional methods entail.

QST VHF PROPAGATION BIBLIOGRAPHY

[1] Hull, "Air-Mass Conditions and the Bending of UHF Waves," June, 1935, and May, 1937.

[2] "On the Very Highs," July, 1944.

[3] Hoisington, "Painless Prediction of Two-Meter Openings," October, 1949.

[4] Collier, "Upper-Air Conditions for 2-Meter DX," September, 1955.

[5] "World Above 50 Mc.," September, 1957, P. 68, August, 1959, p. 68, and September, 1960, p. 78.

For a report on conditions during typical overland ducting, see Botts, "A Night to Remember," January, 1970, p. 88.

[6] Pierce, "Interpreting 56-Mc. DX," September, 1938.

[7] Helton, "Sporadic-E Warning Service for the 6-Meter Man," July, 1961.

[8] Ennis, "Working 2-Meter E-Layer DX," June, 1967.

[9] Wilson, "Midlatitude Intense Sporadic-E Propagation," December, 1970, and March, 1971.

[10] Moore, "Aurora and Magnetic Storms," June, 1951. Dyce, "More About Auroral Propagation," January, 1955.

[11] Mellen, Milner, and Williams, "Hams on Ice," January, 1960.

[12] Heightman, "Any DX Today?" January, 1948.

[13] Cracknell, "Transequatorial Propagation of

VHF Signals," December, 1959. "More on Trans-equatorial Propagation," August, 1960, p. 47. Whiting, "How TE Works," April, 1963.

[14] Moynihan, "VHF Scatter Propagation," March, 1956. Taylor, "Working Ionospheric Scatter on 50 Mc.," December, 1958.

[15] Moore, "Over the Hills and Far Away," February, 1951.

[16] Bain, "VHF Meteor Scatter Propagation," April, 1957.

[17] "World Above 50 Mc.," December, 1946, p. 43.

[18] Leonids summaries: January, 1966, p. 81, and January, 1967, p. 83.

[19] Tilton, "Lunar DX on 144 Mc.," March, 1953.

[20] A bibliography of moonbounce references is available from ARRL, no charge. Send stamped self-addressed envelope.

[21] Michaels, "Tracking the Moon," January, 1965.

[22] OSCAR-Amsat Bibliography available from ARRL, no charge. Send stamped self-addressed envelope.

[23] Bray, "A Method for Determining VHF Station Capabilities," November, 1961.

[24] Craig, "Obstacle Gain at 50 Mc. and Higher," March, 1958.

[25] Guba and Zimmer, "Pulse — A Practical Technique for Amateur Microwave work," February through May, 1963. Also see Chapter 13 of this manual.

Chapter 3

Reception Above 50 MHz

RECEIVER CHARACTERISTICS

Nowhere in amateur radio is optimum reception so important as on the frequencies above 50 MHz. Selectivity, stability, sensitivity, smooth tuning, ability to reject unwanted signals — important attributes in any amateur receiver — are even more desirable in vhf work. Receiver problems are similar on all amateur frequencies, but ideal solutions vary greatly for different parts of the spectrum and modes of operation. Whether your station is a transceiver or a receiver-transmitter combination, an understanding of basic receiver principles and consideration of your primary operating objectives are vital to your future as a vhf enthusiast. We will examine each of the above qualities as it affects vhf communication.

Selectivity

On lower frequencies selectivity is desirable mainly to prevent interference between stations in our crowded bands. It serves this end for vhf men, too, but it is also important in achieving the best possible signal-to-noise ratio. Receiver noise output, for a given input signal level, is related to bandwidth; the wider the bandwidth the greater the noise. This is not important in reception of strong signals, but for best readability of weak signals no more bandwidth should be used than is necessary to pass the intelligence on a signal. This kind of selectivity is mainly determined by the i-f system in a superheterodyne receiver, and the means for achieving it do not change much with signal frequency.

Stability

As selectivity is increased, the need for good stability rises, and as we go higher in frequency the difficulty of achieving satisfactory stability also rises. Thus it is almost standard procedure to use crystal-controlled frequency converters in vhf reception, doing the tuning at some lower or *intermediate frequency* where stability is more readily attained. Like selectivity, stability is then mainly a matter of the design of the lower-frequency components of the vhf receiving system.

Sensitivity and Noise Figure

Here we reach the parting of the ways with our hf brethren. Reception of weak vhf signals is limited by factors quite different from those affecting bands below 30 MHz. On frequencies up to the lower portion of the vhf spectrum, reception is limited almost entirely by noise picked up by the antenna. This may be man-made (ignition, power-line noise, electrical noise from motors, neon signs and the like) or natural, such as galactic or solar noise and atmospherics. With modern tubes, transistors, and circuits the noise contribution by the hf receiver itself is inconsequential. To prove this for yourself, tune an hf receiver to some spot below 30 MHz where no signals are heard. Turn off the agc and advance the gain controls until noise is heard. Now remove the antenna. If your receiver is stable and well shielded it should go dead quiet, or nearly so. The noise was practically all coming in on the antenna.

Now try the test with a vhf receiver, on 144 MHz or higher frequencies. Chances are that the noise will change hardly at all, antenna on or off, if

your location is a quiet one. This demonstrates where most vhf noise comes from: the receiver makes it. The amount of noise it makes, over that of a theoretically perfect receiver whose noise is entirely external, is called the *noise figure*. Reducing the noise generated within the hf receiver to the ultimate would avail you little or nothing in weak-signal reception on bands up through 30 MHz, but you can improve reception in the vhf range markedly if you can amplify incoming signals faster than you build up the noise generated internally. Hence the emphasis on low-noise amplifiers in vhf receiver design.

The noise output of a receiver, by itself, is of no importance at any frequency. How much a signal stands out above the receiver noise (called *signal-to-noise ratio*) is important on any frequency, and it is compounded of many factors, including selectivity as well as noise figure. Noise figure, on the other hand, is almost entirely a matter of the design and adjustment of the first stages of a vhf receiving system, and it is *independent of bandwidth*. We'll look into this complex business of low-noise reception in more detail later on, but it is important to keep the above facts in mind.

Mechanical Considerations

The best selectivity, stability, and sensitivity are of little use if you cannot tune the receiver effectively. Nothing is more disconcerting than a receiver that tunes too rapidly, or in sloppy fashion. Backlash in tuning mechanisms is very annoying, and the higher the selectivity the more troublesome it becomes. These are mechanical problems, but don't under-estimate their importance in building or choosing equipment for vhf work. Few receivers are entirely satisfactory in these respects, and many low-priced ones are all but useless. The would-be vhf enthusiast will do well to check the mechanical qualities of a receiving system with great care.

Rejection of Unwanted Signals

A vhf receiver could score high in all the above categories and still be unsatisfactory if it responds to signals of other services near our bands, or overloads readily when near neighbors come on the air in or near the band we're trying to use. No receiver is completely free of spurious responses, so we may have a difficult choice here. In areas of high population density, where there may be vhf men in every block, and TV, police, aircraft, fm, and other vhf services on almost every available

frequency, ability of a receiver to reject unwanted signals may have to take precedence over other desirable characteristics, particularly low-noise figure. We may have to give the receiver help in the form of a filter of some sort. See Chapter 15.

It should be obvious from what has been said thus far that there is no one "perfect receiver." Even with unlimited resources and design skill at our disposal, we still must examine our own particular set of operating circumstances and objectives, and select equipment or techniques that offer the best overall hope for success.

TYPES OF VHF RECEIVERS

From here on we use the term "vhf" loosely. Calling only those frequencies between 30 and 300 MHz by this name is a grouping more semantic than technical, and we will include the 420-MHz band and even higher frequencies more often than not. In the light of present techniques, the logical dividing line between vhf and uhf methods lies somewhat above our 420-MHz band, rather than at 300 MHz.

Reception on 50 through 450 MHz can be accomplished in many ways, but vhf receivers are of two principal types: the superregenerator and the superheterodyne. The first may be very simple – one tube or transistor and little else other than an antenna, a tuned circuit, and headphones. Common additions are one or more audio stages to operate a speaker, and an rf amplifier stage, to improve performance and reduce detector radiation. The superheterodyne may be complete in itself, usually with four or more tubes or transistors, or it may be a combination of a vhf converter and a communications receiver intended for use on lower frequencies.

The Superregenerative Detector

Today's newcomer may not be too familiar with this wonderful device (and probably it's just as well!) but it was almost standard equipment in early vhf work. To give the Devil his due, the "rushbox" was a potent factor in popularization of the vhf bands – and for good reason. Nothing of comparable simplicity has been found to equal its ability to detect weak signals, but like all simple devices the superregen has serious limitations. It provides little selectivity, has a high and rather unpleasant background noise level, and radiates a broad interfering signal around its receiving frequency. While various refinements may minimize

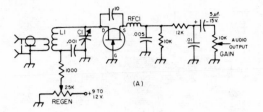
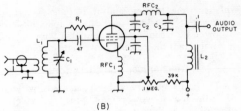

Fig. 3-1 — Circuits of typical superregenerative detectors using a field-effect transistor, A, and a tetrode tube, B. Regeneration is controlled by varying the drain voltage on the detector in the transistor circuit, and the screen voltage in the tetrode or pentode. Values of L1 and C1 should be adjusted for the frequency involved, as should the size of the rf choke, RFC1.

C2, C3 — 0.001-μF disk ceramic. Try different values up to 0.005 for desired audio quality.

L2 — Small audio or filter choke; not critical.

R1 — 2 to 10 megohms.

RFC1 — Single-layer rf choke, to suit frequency.

RFC2 — 85-mH rf choke.

these objectionable features, the superregenerative receiver is used today mainly where its small size, light weight, and low power drain are all important, as in short-range portable work.

Most tubes and transistors that do well in other vhf receiving applications make good superregenerative detectors. With tubes, tetrode or pentode types are favored at 50 or 144 MHz, as variation of their screen voltage offers smooth control of regeneration. Triodes are better for higher frequencies. Typical circuits are shown in Fig. 3-1. If no rf amplifier is used, operating conditions and the coupling to the antenna should be adjusted so as to permit superregeneration with the lowest satisfactory power input, to hold down detector radiation. An rf amplifier stage ahead of the detector will reduce or eliminate radiation, and by isolating the detector from the antenna will make control of regeneration less critical. It will also add some gain and selectivity.

Superheterodyne Receivers

Because amplification is more efficient at low frequencies than high, it is standard vhf practice to use only as much rf amplification as may be needed for good noise figure, and then convert the signal to a lower or intermediate frequency, to be amplified and detected. This is the basic superheterodyne principle, used in nearly all radio reception today.

The simplest superhet receiver for 50 MHz is shown in Fig. 3-2A. The antenna feeds a mixer stage operating at the signal frequency, in this case 50 to 54 MHz. A tunable oscillator, usually at some lower frequency (though it can be higher) supplies energy to beat with the signal and produce an intermediate frequency (i-f) which is then amplified and detected. In our example the oscillator is 5 MHz below the signal frequency, and the i-f is, of course, 5 MHz. You could build the simple receiver with as few as two dual-purpose tubes, but its gain would be low and its selectivity poor. You would not be happy with it for long.

Gain can be increased with more i-f amplifier stages, but a simple 5-MHz amplifier, as in 2A, is not sufficiently selective, so we go to what is known as double conversion, Fig. 3-2B. Here a second oscillator and mixer convert the 5-MHz

signal to 455 kHz, where gain and selectivity come much easier. Also added here is an rf amplifier stage, for improved noise figure and better sensitivity.

You could go right to 455 kHz in the first conversion, by suitable choice of frequency range for the tunable oscillator, but this gives rise to a serious image problem. Suppose we want to listen to someone on 51 MHz. With an i-f of 455 kHz, the oscillator would then be on 50.545 MHz, 455 kHz away from the signal frequency. The mixer responds to signals 455 kHz on *either* side of the oscillator frequency, so someone on 50.090 MHz would interfere with the desired signal on 51 MHz. All superhets have this problem, but when a high i-f is used (roughly 10 percent of the signal frequency is common) the selectivity of the first tuned circuits of the receiver is sufficient to reject the unwanted image signal. Thus, for good image rejection, most vhf receivers employ double- or triple-conversion circuits.

So far we have used a tunable oscillator and fixed intermediate-frequency amplifiers. In the vhf range, however, tunable oscillators may not be stable enough for narrow-band reception, so we more often use a crystal-controlled source for the first conversion, as in Fig. 3-2C. Here the first intermediate frequency is variable, so the i-f, detector and audio system (portion to the right of the vertical broken line) may take the form of a communications receiver that tunes the desired frequency range, in this example 14 to 18 MHz. Our rf amplifier, first mixer, and crystal oscillator are usually built in a single unit called a crystal-controlled converter. This converter-receiver combination is the most common approach to amateur vhf reception in use today.

There are uses for the single-conversion receiver, however, especially where simplicity, low cost, and small size are more important than high selectivity. Also, by use of advanced i-f design techniques, particularly involving the crystal-lattice filter, it is possible to develop excellent selectivity at high intermediate frequencies. Though fairly expensive, the high-frequency crystal filter has much to recommend it. Requiring only a single conversion for good selectivity, it reduces the possibility of unwanted signals being heard, and it makes possible optimum performance with fewer stages and circuits than multiple-conversion systems.

A promising overall receiving system for the vhf man is the use of such a single-conversion setup for the 50-MHz band as the basic receiving unit of the station. This would have a tunable oscillator; converters for 144 MHz and higher bands would be crystal-controlled, with 50 to 54 MHz as the tunable first intermediate frequency.

It should be emphasized that the frequencies given in the above discussion are examples only. Almost any combination of oscillator and intermediate frequencies can be used and many factors govern the choice. These will be taken up later.

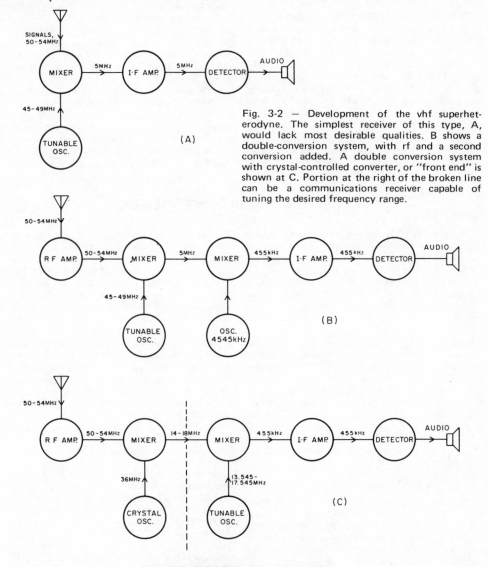

Fig. 3-2 — Development of the vhf superheterodyne. The simplest receiver of this type, A, would lack most desirable qualities. B shows a double-conversion system, with rf and a second conversion added. A double conversion system with crystal-controlled converter, or "front end" is shown at C. Portion at the right of the broken line can be a communications receiver capable of tuning the desired frequency range.

TRANSISTORS OR TUBES?

The proliferation of vhf and uhf transistors in recent years has tended to give the impression that anyone still using vacuum tubes in receiving equipment is hopelessly out of date. Is there any justification today for going other than the solid-state route? There may be, especially for the fellow who has been in the game long enough to have accumulated a considerable inventory of equipment designed around tubes. Many inexpensive and reliable tubes do an entirely adequate job in receivers for 50 and 144 MHz. Circuits for their use will be discussed in following pages.

Interest in portable or mobile work may tip the scales in favor of transistors. They have no competition where power consumption is a factor. Also, at 220 MHz, and even more so at 420 MHz, the receiving performance of the better transistors is unequalled by tubes, at any price.

The newcomer to the vhf scene probably will start with solid-state receiving gear, but choosing the right transistors for the various jobs may not by easy. Some helpful pointers can be given, and since the frequency of operation is important in making the choice, the merits and weaknesses of various transistor types are given by bands.

Transistor Selection

50 MHz Any small-signal vhf amplifier transistor should give more than adequate gain and noise figure at 50 MHz. Bipolar types are generally rather poor as to cross-modulation and other overloading problems, so the insulated-gate FET (IGFET OR MOSFET) is a logical choice for rf amplifier and mixer service. The junction FET (JFET) is nearly as good, and circuits for its use are somewhat simpler than for the MOSFET, though the latter is preferable for mixer use, at least.

144 MHz Similar to 50 MHz, in general, except that low-noise types rated for use up to at least 200 MHz should be used.

220 MHz Paying a bit more for transistors rated for use up to 400 MHz or so may be worthwhile in the rf amplifier, at least, though inexpensive FETS still work very well at this frequency. Expensive uhf bipolar types are capable of lower noise figure than FETs and may have a slight edge in rf amplifier stages.

420 MHz Most FETs presently available offer noise figures around 5 dB above about 250 MHz or so, while the better bipolars yield as low as 2 dB, up to 500 MHz. In a 2-stage rf amplifier, use the best transistor available for the first stage, which will then set the noise figure of the system. A lower-specification transistor will do well enough in the second stage.

Uhf mixers will be discussed in detail later. The oscillator in a vhf or uhf converter nearly always operates at a frequency in the lower vhf range, so transistor selection is of little importance in this stage. Any inexpensive vhf transistor will do.

Preferred tube types will be discussed stage by stage, in the section to follow.

RECEIVER "FRONT-END" DESIGN

Whether the receiving portion of the vhf station is a complete receiver, part of a transceiver or transverter, or a converter ahead of a communications receiver for lower frequencies, the part of it that we'll be concerned with here is described in connection with Fig. 3-2B or C. Only that portion on the left side of the broken line in Fig. 3-2C is important to us at this time, as this *front end* is a major factor in the effectiveness of the receiving system. The hf, i-f, detector, and audio portions are covered thoroughly in any modern edition of the *Radio Amateur's Handbook*. We concentrate here on the vhf front-end circuits: the rf amplifier, mixer, and oscillator. Combined in a single unit to be used as a communications-receiver accessory, these comprise a vhf or uhf converter. (The mixer stage of this unit may be called a "converter" in some literature. We will call it a *mixer* here, and use the term *converter* only in connection with complete front-end circuitry.)

RF Amplifiers

Each of the three stages of the converter plays an important role in achieving the objectives described in the first paragraphs of this chapter. The main job of the rf amplifier is to establish the noise figure of the system. To do this it must amplify incoming signals, while generating as little noise as possible on its own. A typical vhf amplifier using a good transistor may have a gain of 15 dB, while generating only 2 dB of noise. If the gain minus the amplifier noise (15 − 2 = 13, in this case) is more than the noise figure of the rest of the receiving system, the small noise level of the rf stage will mask the noise generated in all following stages.

The average good vhf mixer will have a noise figure of 7 to 10 dB, so the amplifier in the above example is adequate for the job. This answers a commonly asked question: "If one stage is that good, wouldn't two be better?" As far as ability to detect weak signals in concerned, nothing would be gained by adding another rf amplifier stage.

There *are* legitimate reasons for having more than one stage. Some types of amplifiers that are desirable in other ways may not have enough gain with one stage. And on frequencies above 200 MHz or so, adequate single-stage gain is increasingly difficult to obtain. If more than one stage is required, only the first one need have the very best low-noise performance. In the example above, if the first-stage gain were only 10 dB (as might well be the case in a 432-MHz converter) a second-stage noise figure of 4 to 5 dB would be satisfactory, if the total gain of the two stages is 15 to 20 dB. Typically this could mean a ten-dollar transistor in the first stage and a two-dollar one in the second. Much the same situation pertains in vacuum-tube amplifiers.

If more gain is required in the overall receiving system than that needed to establish the noise figure, with a little to spare, it can be made up in the i-f stages more readily and at less expense than in the front end. An i-f amplifier built into the converter is a useful accessory, since it permits the gain of the converter to be adjusted to the optimum for the receiver in use. Examples of converters with i-f amplifiers built in are given in the following chapter. A total rf-stage gain of more than 20 dB ahead of the first mixer is seldom required.

Low-Noise Transistors and Tubes

Transistor data sheets often list a confusing array of specifications, most of which need not concern us here. Usually the noise figure and gain that can be expected at various frequencies are given for transistors designed for rf amplifier service. It is well to select types that are rated to well above the frequency you're going to use. There is no point in using an expensive 500-MHz transistor on 50 MHz, but don't use a cheap one rated for up to 30 MHz, either.

The ultimate in low-noise figure is not vital in a 50-MHz stage, as external noise is still a limiting factor at this frequency. Noise from the antenna is amplified along with the 50-MHz signals. A system noise figure of 5 or 6 dB is plenty good enough, as it will permit reception of several dB of "antenna noise," even in the quietest location. Optimum 50-MHz reception is thus possible with dozens of inexpensive tubes or transistors, and a single amplifier stage is adequate in most 50-MHz front ends.

Good rf amplifier performance is still possible with a single stage at 144, though two may be needed in grounded-gate (grounded-grid) applications. Transistor selection becomes somewhat more critical, and low noise figure is more important. Still, the ultimate is not required, and a system noise figure of 3 dB is adequate. Transistors rated to 200 or 250 MHz should suffice.

At 220 MHz or higher, the better low-noise types rated to 500 MHz or so begin to pay off, though there are inexpensive transistors that work well at 220. The best obtainable may be worth their cost at 420, and two-stage amplifiers are more often used.

Tubes may not have noise-figure ratings given in their characteristics sheets. If not, look for the *transconductance*, which should be 5000 or more for a pentode, and 10,000 or more for a triode, for best results. Pentodes such as the 6AK5 and 6CB6 work well at 50 MHz. A pentode rf stage would be very similar to the mixer circuit, Fig. 3-6C. Triodes are preferred for 144 and higher frequencies. Several dual triodes (6BQ7, 6BZ7, 6BC8, 6BS8, and others) will do for 50 or 144 MHz. Currently the most-used single triode is the Nuvistor (6CW4, 6DS4). Small in size and well adapted to circuit-board use, it is probably the best low-cost triode available for vhf amplifier service.

Amplifier Circuits

Most transistor and triode rf amplifiers require neutralization. This is done inductively in the examples of Fig. 3-3, but capacitive methods are usable, and examples appear in the following chapter. The JFET (A) MOSFET (B) and the triode (C) will be seen to be quite similar, except

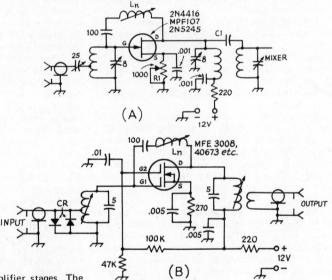

Fig. 3-3 — Neutralized vhf amplifier stages. The JFET amplifier, A, and the triode tube version, C, will be seen to be very similar. The MOSFET, B, requires a few more components, but has good resistance of overloading.

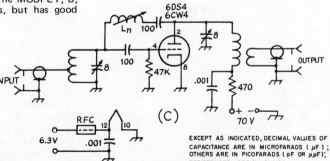

EXCEPT AS INDICATED, DECIMAL VALUES OF CAPACITANCE ARE IN MICROFARADS (μF); OTHERS ARE IN PICOFARADS (pF OR μμF); RESISTANCES ARE IN OHMS; k = 1000, M = 1000 000.

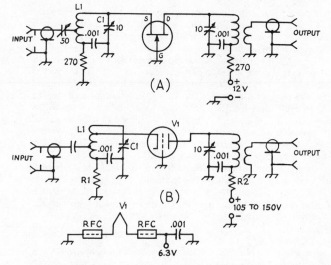

Fig. 3-4 — Grounded-gate FET preamplifier and its grounded-grid triode equivalent tend to have lower gain and broader frequency response than other amplifiers described. Use of ferrite-bead rf
chokes in the heater circuit is shown in
B. Select values of R1 and R2 to suit
tube type. The tuned input circuit,
L1C1, can be eliminated and the antenna
coupled directly to the input element,
for extreme simplicity, as in remote
amplifiers.

for the heater circuit in the tube version. All may
be used effectively from 50 through 225 MHz. Coil
and capacitor values depend on frequency. Operating conditions and adjustment of neutralization
should be set up for minimum noise figure, rather
than maximum gain.

Interstage coupling in 3-3A is intended for
band-pass effect. The value of C1 should be
adjusted for the desired bandwidth. Similar output-
coupling circuitry could be used with B and C. The
low-impedance coupling shown for these circuits is
for preamplifier service, where a coaxial line is run
between the amplifier and the receiver with which
it is to be used.

Protection of the amplifier, shown in B, can be
applied to any first-stage circuit. The diodes, CR,
are connected in opposite polarity between the
antenna line and ground, to conduct on either
cycle of rf charges built up on the antenna. In
circuit C, the rf choke shown in the 6.3-volt line is
a ferrite bead, placed over the heater lead, close to
the socket.

An alternative to neutralization lies in the
grounded-gate (grounded-base or grounded-grid)
circuit of Fig. 3-4. The "grounded" element may
be connected directly to the chassis, or bypassed
thereto, so long as it is maintained at ground
potential for rf. Bypassing may be critical, and
only the best rf bypass capacitors (button-mica or
ceramic feedthrough types) should be used. Ceramics of the disk variety are seldom effective above
about 100 MHz or so. Their use may encourage
oscillation, as the bypassed element must isolate
the input and output circuits.

When a vacuum tube is used, the heater circuit
should be kept above ground potential, along with
the cathode. This is achieved through use of
low-resistance heater chokes, which may be ferrite
beads, as in 3-4B.

The input impedance of this type of amplifier is
low, and it is broad-band and relatively low-gain,
by nature. Two stages may be needed to mask
mixer noise, on this account. Where only a small
amount of gain is needed, a simplified version may

be used wherein a tuned input circuit is eliminated,
and the low-impedance input is direct to the
cathode or corresponding transistor element. If
selectivity is needed in the input circuit, it is
customary to tap the input element down on the
tuned circuit, as in 3-4B. Both the cathode tap and
the point of connection of the antenna line should
be adjusted for minimum noise figure, though
neither will be particularly critical.

The virtues of both types of amplifiers are
combined in the popular cascode circuit, in which
a neutralized first stage works into a grounded-grid
second stage. The latter loads the former heavily,
resulting in a broad-band amplifier that may be
stable, even without neutralization, though the
noise figure of the system is better when the first
stage is neutralized. The cascode is most often used
with dual triodes, but separate triodes and transistors work equally well. Two versions are shown in
Fig. 3-5, the series-cascode, B, being somewhat the
simpler of the two, and most often used with dual
triodes. Optimum use of the cascode may require
heater chokes, as in 3-5A. These must carry the
heater current without voltage drop. Ferrite beads
are ideal, though handwound chokes also are
usable.

Instability may arise in a cascode circuit as a
result of ineffective bypassing of the grid, base, or
gate in the second stage. Such oscillation cannot be
corrected by adjustment of the neutralizing coil,
Ln. Series-resonant bypassing may be helpful when
this is encountered.

Adjusting RF Stages

The first step in adjusting an rf amplifier is to
set the tuned circuits at the approximate frequency. This can be done with the aid of a dip meter, or
by peaking the circuits for maximum response
while actually receiving. In circuit A, the only
additional step is to adjust the tap position on L1
for best noise figure or signal-to-noise ratio. Noise
figure adjustments are best made with a noise
generator, as detailed in the test equipment chap-

ter. The work can be done on a weak steady signal, if care is used to get the *greatest margin of signal over noise*, rather than merely maximum gain.

In adjusting antenna coupling, the best noise figure may be found as the coupling is increased a bit *beyond* the point where maximum signal is obtained. The gain and signal level may drop slightly, but the noise falls off faster at this point, so signal-to-noise ratio actually improves at the start of over-coupling. Gain can be made up anywhere in the receiver, but noise figure is set by the first stage, and predominantly in the first tuned circuit. This cardinal principle of vhf receiver design should be borne in mind at all times.

In neutralizing rf stages other than the series cascode, the operating voltages can be removed from the stage to be neutralized, and the coil Ln adjusted for *minimum* response on a strong signal. All other circuits are peaked for maximum response. There is interlocking of adjustments, so repeat these operations several times. Now put the neutralized stage back into normal operation, and recheck all adjustments for optimum signal-to-noise ratio, or lowest noise figure. Merely tuning for maximum gain can degrade the noise figure by several dB, even when the amplifier is not actually oscillating.

In any amplifier that is working properly, adjustments other than on the input circuit and neutralization of the first stage affect only gain. For this reason it is usually practical to stagger-tune any following circuits, if necessary, to obtain reasonably flat response across the desired bandwidth. Better bandpass characteristics are obtainable with the double-tuned circuit in amplifier A of Fig. 3-3. Its coupling capacitor, C1, can be varied to provide different degrees of coupling and selectivity. Usually values of 1 to 3 pF are used. These are readily obtained by twisting insulated leads of hookup wire together for a half inch or so.

Using Rf Preamplifiers

It is important to design the front-end stages of a vhf receiver for optimum performance, but we often want to improve reception with equipment already built. Thousands of fm receivers formerly in commercial service, now revamped for amateur work in the 50-, 144-, and 420-MHz bands, were built before modern low-noise tubes and transistors were available. Though otherwise useful, these receivers have excessively high noise figure. Many other commercial and home-built vhf converters and receivers are not as sensitive as they might be.

Though it would be better to replace the rf stages of such equipment with more modern devices, the simpler approach is usually to add an outboard rf amplifier using a low-noise tube or transistor. In the fm example, the quieting level of some receivers can be improved by as much as 10 dB by addition of a simple transistor amplifier. Similar improvement in noise figure of some receivers for other modes is also possible; particularly band-switching communications receivers that have vhf coverage.

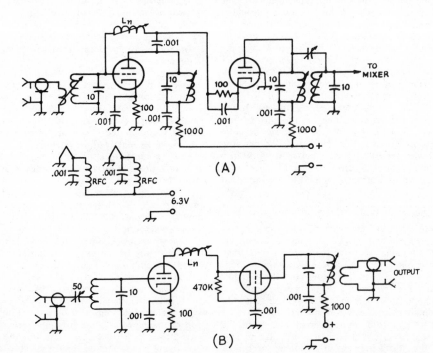

Fig. 3-5 — Cascode amplifier circuit combines grounded-cathode and grounded-grid stages, for high-gain and low-noise figure. Though tubes are shown, the cascode principle is usable with transistors as well. Examples are given in later constructional information. Rf chokes must be able to carry the tube heater current.

Any of the basic amplifier circuits of Fig. 3-3, 4, and 5 can be adapted to preamplifier service. Examples of amplifier construction are given in the following chapter. Circuits shown in the vhf converters described can also be used in preamplifiers.

Preamplifiers are useful mainly with older equipment which is deficient in front-end gain or noise figure. Most vhf gear built in recent years should be satisfactory in these respects, if it is operating properly. Checks with a preamplifier should be made to determine if an improvement in reception of very weak signals is possible. It is the margin of signal over noise, with and without the amplifier, that counts. Any amplifier added to any receiver will result in higher S-meter readings, but these are meaningless unless weak-signal reception actually improves.

When a preamplifier is tried with the receiving portion of a transceiver or transverter, be sure that it is connected in the line to the receiving portion *only*. An external amplifier connected in the main line to the antenna will be damaged or ruined if the transmitter portion of such equipment is accidentally turned on. This has happened to many transceiver owners who should have known better!

Front-End Protection

The first amplifier of a receiver is susceptible to damage or complete burnout through application of excessive voltage to its input element by way of the antenna. This can be the result of lightning discharges (not necessarily in the immediate vicinity), rf leakage from the station transmitter through a faulty send-receive relay or switch, or rf power from a nearby transmitter and antenna system. Bipolar transistors often used in low-noise uhf amplifiers are particularly sensitive to this trouble. The degradation may be gradual, going unnoticed until the receiving sensitivity has become very poor.

No equipment is likely to survive a direct hit from lightning, but casual damage can be prevented by connecting diodes across the input circuit as shown in Fig. 3-3B. Note that these are in opposite polarity, to protect against damage during either half of the cycle. Either germanium or silicon vhf diodes can be used. Both have thresholds of conduction well above any normal signal level, about 0.2 volt for germanium and 0.6 volt for silicon. A check on weak-signal reception should be made before and after their connection.

MIXERS

Conversion of the received energy to a lower frequency, where it can be amplified more efficiently than at the signal frequency, is a basic principle of the superheterodyne receiver. The stage in which this is done may be called a "converter," or "frequency converter," but we will use the more common term, *mixer*, to avoid confusion with *converter*, as applied to a complete vhf receiving accessory. Mixers perform similar functions in both transmitting and receiving circuits. Transmitting applications will be found in other portions of this book.

A receiver for 50 MHz or higher usually has at least two such stages; one in the vhf or uhf converter, and usually two or more in the communications receiver that follows it. We are concerned with the first mixer. Whether it works into a communications receiver or the i-f stages of a complete vhf or uhf receiving unit is not important here.

The Diode Mixer

There are many types of mixers, the simplest being merely a diode with the signal and energy on the heterodyning frequency fed into it, somewhat in the manner of the 1296-MHz example, Fig. 3-6A. The mixer output includes both the sum and the difference frequencies. Either can be used, but in this application it is the difference, since we are interested in going lower in frequency.

With a good uhf diode in a suitable circuit, a diode mixer can have a fairly low noise figure, and this is almost independent of frequency, well into the microwave region. The effectiveness of most rf amplifiers falls off rapidly above 400 MHz, so the diode mixer is almost standard practice in amateur microwave communication. All diode mixers have

some conversion *loss*. This must be added to the noise figure of the i-f amplifier following, to determine the overall system noise figure. Low-noise design in the first i-f stage is thus mandatory, for good weak-signal reception with a diode mixer having no rf amplifier preceding it. Purity of the heterodyning energy and the level of injection to the mixer are other factors in the performance of diode mixers.

Balanced mixers using hot-carrier diodes are capable of noise figures 1 to 2 dB lower than the best point-contact diodes. Hot-carrier diodes are normally quite uniform, so tedious selection of matched pairs (necessary with other types of diodes) is eliminated. They are also rugged, and superior in the matter of overloading.

The i-f impedance of a balanced hot-carrier diode mixer (Fig. 3-6B) is on the order of 90 ohms, when the oscillator injection is about one milliwatt. Thus the mixer and a transistorized i-f amplifier can be separated physically, and connected by means of 93-ohm coax, without an output transformer.

Conversion loss, around 7 dB, must be added to the noise figure of the i-f system to determine the overall system noise figure. Unless a low-noise preamplifier is used ahead of it, a communications receiver may have a noise figure of about 10 dB, resulting in an overall noise figure of 17 dB or worse for a vhf system with any diode mixer. A good i-f preamplifier could bring the receiver noise figure down to 2 dB or even less, but the system noise figure would still be about 9 dB; too high for good reception.

An amplifier at the signal frequency is thus seen to be required, regardless of mixer design, for optimum reception above 50 MHz. The rf gain, to

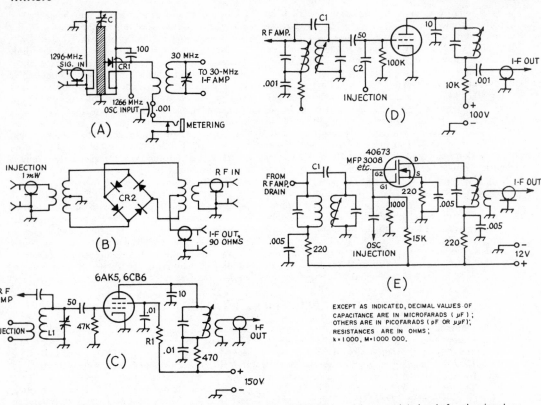

Fig. 3-6 — Vhf and uhf mixer circuits. A diode mixer for 1296 MHz, with a coaxial circuit for the signal frequency, is shown in A. CR1 is a uhf diode, such as the 1N21 series. A balanced mixer, as in B, gives improved rejection of the signal and injection frequencies. If hot-carrier diodes are used for CR2, sorting for matched characteristics is eliminated. The pentode mixer, C, requires low injection and works well below about 200 MHz. The triode mixer, D, has a simplified i-f output circuit, and bandpass coupling to the rf stage. C1 and C2 can be insulated wires twisted together for about 1/2 inch, as needed. Insulated-gate FET mixer, E, is ideal for transistor receivers.

override noise in the rest of the receiver, should be greater than the sum of noise figures of the mixer and the i-f system. Since the noise figure of the better rf amplifiers will be around 3 dB, the gain should be at least 20 dB for the first example in the previous paragraph, and 12 dB for the second.

These facts show clearly the worth of building a low-noise i-f amplifier into any uhf converter. It makes the job of the rf amplifier, a critical stage at best, considerably easier.

Transistor and Tube Mixers

Any mixer is prone to overloading and spurious responses, so a prime design objective should be to minimize these problems. Several factors enter into this. Choice of the transistor or tube to be used, the selectivity of the circuits preceding it, and the purity and level of the injection energy are important. Usually a mixer can be set up for good noise figure or good resistance to overloading, but not both. In a very simple receiver having no rf amplifier, the mixer would be set up for low noise figure. Where an effective rf amplifier is used ahead of it, the mixer can be tailored for best overloading and cross-modulation characteristics. A mixer that draws appreciable current tends to be noisy; the

more current, the more noise. But it resists overloading better than one whose current drain is held low, in the interest of good noise figure. Most vhf and uhf converters have rf amplifiers, so their mixers are normally adjusted to reduce overloading, whether the device used is a transistor or a vacuum tube.

In amateur vhf reception, overloading may come from near neighbors operating in the same band, or from strong commercial signals on the frequencies adjacent to the amateur band. In-band signals can be prevented from overloading the mixer only by adjustment of the mixer operating conditions, and by keeping the rf amplifier gain to the minimum needed for good noise figure. Out-of-band signals can be held down by use of selective circuits in the antenna and rf amplifier. Double-tuned coupling circuits for this purpose are shown in some of our rf amplifier and mixer examples, herewith.

The injection level from the oscillator affects mixer performance, though it is not critical when a good rf amplifier precedes the mixer. Until it affects the mixer adversely in other ways, raising the injection level raises the mixer conversion gain. A simple check is made by observing the effect on signal-to-noise ratio as the injection is varied. At preferred injection levels, the gain will vary but the signal-to-noise ratio will not change. The injection should then be set for conversion gain a few decibels above that at which lower injection causes a drop in signal-to-noise ratio.

Pentode tubes make simple and effective mixers for 50, 144, or even 220 MHz. Triodes work well on any frequency up to about 500 MHz or so, though diode mixers are commonly used in 420-MHz converters and for all higher frequencies.

The pentode mixer of Fig. 3-6C gives good conversion gain and is readily adjusted for low noise figure *or* resistance to overloading, by changing the value of R1. It may be as high as one megohm, for low current drain and resultant low-noise figure, or as low as a few thousand ohms, for best overload characteristics. Bias and supply voltage variations have similar effects on triode and transistor mixers.

The triode mixer, D, is similar to the pentode, except for the screen circuit in the latter. Various methods of feeding in the injection voltage, and of taking off the i-f output signal are shown in Fig. 3-6 mainly as examples, rather than because of any advantage of one method or the other.

Oscillation, most commonly found in triode mixers, may result from inadvertent resonances near the signal frequency in the output circuit. The 10-pF capacitor shown connected from the output element to ground in some of our circuits is connected close to the mixer plate, collector, or drain and to ground, with the shortest possible leads, to break up this tendency to resonance, and prevent oscillation. When such oscillation does occur it is often mistaken for rf-stage instability, and much time may be wasted trying to neutralize it out – in the wrong stage.

The insulated-gate FET (IGFET or MOSFET, 3-6E) is superior to other htransistors in resistance to overloading, though the JFET is also good. An objection to the former, the ease with which it can be damaged by inadvertent application of small voltages in handling, has been taken care of by building in small protective diodes. Such transistors work as well as their unprotected predecessors.

INJECTION STAGES

Oscillator and multiplier stages that supply heterodyning energy to the mixer should be as stable and free of unwanted frequencies as possible. They are similar to exciter stages of vhf transmitters, and their basic principles are discussed in more detail in Chapters 5 and 6. Stability is no great problem in crystal-controlled converters, if the oscillator is run at low input and its supply voltage is regulated. Simple Zener regulation, as in Fig. 3-7A is adequate for a transistor overtone oscillator. A higher order of regulation is desirable for tunable oscillators.

Unwanted frequencies generated in the injection stages can beat with signals outside the intended tuning range. In a typical example, Fig. 3-7B, an FET overtone oscillator on 43.333 MHz feeds a diode tripler to 130 MHz. This frequency beats with signals between 144 and 148 MHz, to give desired responses at 14 to 18 MHz. The multiplier stage also has some output at twice the crystal frequency, 86.666 MHz. If allowed to reach the mixer, this can beat with fm broadcast signals in the 100-MHz region that leak through the rf circuits of the converter. There are many such annoying possibilities, as any amateur living near high-powered fm and TV stations will know.

Spurious frequencies can be kept down by using the highest practical oscillator frequency, no multiplier in a 50-MHz converter, and as few as possible for higher bands. Some unwanted harmonics are unavoidable, so circuit precautions are often needed to prevent both these harmonics and the unwanted signals from reaching the mixer. Selective coaxial or trough-line circuits are practical aids in uhf receivers. Trap circuits of various kinds may be needed to "suck out" energy on troublesome frequencies.

The series trap in Fig. 3-7B reduces the level of the 86-MHz second harmonic of the crystal frequency. A 58-MHz parallel-tuned trap can be connected in the antenna line to absorb Channel-2 TV signals that could otherwise beat with the second harmonic of a 36-MHz oscillator in a 50-MHz converter that works into a 14-MHz i-f $(36 \times 2 - 14 = 58)$.

Unwanted frequencies also increase the noise output of the mixer. This degrades performance in a receiver having no rf amplifier, and makes the job of an amplifier, if used, more difficult.

Frequency multipliers in vhf receivers generally follow transmitting practice, except for their low power level. The simple diode multiplier of Fig. 3-7B will often suffice. Its parallel-tuned 130-MHz circuit emphasizes the desired third harmonic, while the series circuit suppresses the unwanted second harmonic. The trap is tuned by listening to a spurious fm broadcast signal and tuning the series capacitor for minimum interference. The 130-MHz tripler circuit should be peaked for maximum response to a 2-meter signal. Do not detune this circuit to lower injection level. This should be controlled by the voltage on the oscillator, the coupling between the oscillator and multiplier, or by the coupling to the mixer from the 130-MHz circuit.

Tunable Oscillators

Any tunable vhf receiver must have a variable oscillator somewhere along the line. (See Fig. 3-2.) At this point the intermediate frequency is fixed, and the oscillator tunes a range higher or lower than the signal frequency by the amount of the i-f. In the interest of stability, it is usually lower. In Fig. 3-7C a simple JFET oscillator tunes 36 to 40 MHz, for reception of the 50-MHz band with a fixed 14-MHz i-f. Its stability should be adequate for a-m or fm reception, but it is unlikely to meet the requirements for ssb or cw reception fully, even at 50 MHz, and certainly not higher bands.

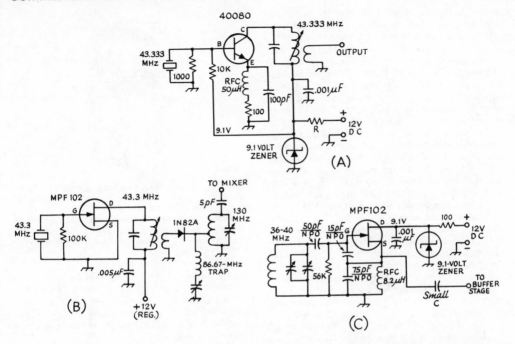

Fig. 3-7 — Typical oscillator and multiplier circuits for vhf converters. A bipolar transistor with Zener-diode regulation of the collector voltage is shown at A. The indicated frequency is for 144-MHz converters with 14-MHz output. The FET circuit, B, includes a diode tripler to 130 MHz, with a series trap to absorb unwanted second-harmonic energy at 86 MHz. A triode tube would require essentially the same basic circuit. The tunable oscillator, C, would be suitable for a 50-MHz converter with fixed 14-MHz i-f.

Using a tunable oscillator and a fixed intermediate frequency (Fig. 3-2A or B) does have merit. It can be used with a crystal-controlled hf receiver, or with any communications receiver that has inadequate tuning facilities. Covering entire vhf bands with communications receivers having limited tuning range is an example. With the i-f fixed, the precise frequency to be used can be selected carefully to prevent interference from signals riding through in the hf range. Better selectivity at the intended receiving frequency is also possible, if the rf and mixer-tuned circuits are gang-tuned with the oscillator. The front-end stages can then be designed for optimum selectivity across the band, and no broad-banding of these circuits is required.

Most vhf reception with high selectivity is with double-conversion setups, with the tunable oscillator serving the second conversion, as in Fig. 3-2C. Such hf oscillators are treated in detail in *The Radio Amateur's Handbook*, and in Chapter 6 of this book. The oscillator should run at the lowest practical input level, to minimize drift due to heating. The supply should be well-regulated pure dc. Mechanically rugged components and construction are mandatory. The circuits should be shielded from the rest of the receiver, and coupling to the mixer should be as light as practical. Drift cycling due to heating can be minimized if the oscillator is kept running during transmitting periods. Leaving the entire converter running is even better.

COMMUNICATIONS RECEIVER PROBLEMS

Most of the information in this chapter has to do with crystal-controlled converters, since this is a common approach to vhf reception. Unless the hf receiver with which the converter is to be used is satisfactory in the qualities discussed in the first paragraphs of this chapter, the best vhf converter design will be largely wasted. Let us consider the communications receiver from the point of view of the vhf converter user.

Selectivity: If a receiver is satisfactory for the hf amateur bands, it will be selective enough for vhf service. Most communications receivers will satisfy all but the most critical users in this respect.

Several degrees of selectivity are desirable: 500 Hz or less for cw, 2 to 3 kHz for ssb, and 6 to 8 kHz for a-m and fm phone are useful.

Stability: Tuning with converters imposes no special stability problems. Some receivers, particularly older or inexpensive ones, may have progressively poorer stability on each higher-frequency band, so this may be a factor in choosing the converter output frequency range for use with a given receiver.

Sensitivity: The ability of a vhf receiving setup to detect weak signals is determined almost entirely by the first stage of the vhf converter. Any communications receiver worthy of the name will have more gain and sensitivity than you'll ever need in using a converter with it.

Mechanical Qualities: These probably rate first in choosing a receiver for vhf converter use. In general-coverage receivers the tuning rate of the dial system is very important to the vhf man, whereas it may be only a minor consideration to other users. Such receivers ordinarily cover from the broadcast band through 30 MHz, usually in four to six ranges. On inexpensive receivers having four bandswitch positions, each range covers such a wide frequency spread that the number of kilohertz per rotation of the tuning knob is almost certain to be excessive. Receivers having five bands may be better, but usually the tuning rate will be too high on frequencies above about 10 MHz or so. This may be a factor in selecting the most desirable converter output frequency range. Some of the better general-coverage receivers have six or more bandswitch positions. Only these give adequate tuning smoothness for the vhf man, ordinarily.

There are ways around this problem. One is to mount a vernier mechanism in place of the knob on the general-coverage dial. Usually a mounting arrangement can be worked out that will not disfigure the receiver in any way. Two examples are shown in Fig.s 3-8 and 9. The first utilizes a 5-to-1 vernier drive, the other a two-speed drive.

An alternative approach with two-dial receivers is to do the tuning with the bandspread dial, resetting the general-coverage dial as each additional swing of the bandspread mechanism is made. This gives good tuning rate, but after the first swing the calibration is lost. Because the two are connected in parallel, changing the setting of the general-coverage capacitor changes the number of kilohertz a given number of revolutions of the other capacitor will cover. A better solution is to use separate crystals in the converter, for each desired frequency range.

Rejection of Unwanted Signals

Image rejection is the principal concern here. Single-conversion receivers with 455-kHz i-f systems have relatively poor image rejection, so there is a tendency for strong signals to be repeated 910 KHz away from the desired response. This trouble is worse at the high end of the receiver's coverage

Fig. 3-9 — Example of use of a two-speed planetary mechanism to slow down the tuning rate on the general-coverage dial of an inexpensive communications receiver.

Fig. 3-8 — Typical mounting for a vernier dial to be used on a general-coverage receiver. Mechanical arrangements can be worked out to fit most receivers without the necessity for drilling holes or otherwise permanently disfiguring the receiver. Adjacent control shafts and nuts provide convenient anchorages.

than at the low. Up through about 10 MHz, most receivers are selective enough in their rf circuits so that the image is not bothersome, so a converter output frequency range beginning at 7 MHz, for example, may be preferable to one starting at 14 MHz.

Most receivers made prior to the late 1940s were single-conversion models. Except for the image problem, many such older receivers are quite satisfactory for vhf converter service, so this is an important factor in selecting the converter output frequency. An old but good receiver may be a better value for the money than an inexpensive newer model, since the vhf man is primarily concerned with receiver qualities that have not changed greatly in many years of receiver development. Some receivers dating back even to before World War II still serve the vhf man's needs quite well, if the converter output frequency is kept low.

Some receivers may not be completely shielded, with the result that stations operating in the converter output frequency range may be heard along with the desired vhf signals. This is a converter design problem as well, but corrective measures may have to be applied at the receiver. The three-terminal antenna connection plate used on many communications receivers is shown in Fig. 3-10. Usually Terminal 1 is connected to the chassis inside the receiver. This connection may act as a coupling loop for i-f signals. Removing the internal connection and grounding terminal 1 on the outside of the chassis may correct this.

A better solution is to install a coaxial fitting on the rear wall of the chassis. When this is done, the lead normally connected to Terminal 2 inside the receiver should be permanently grounded, and the lead that went to Terminal 3 should be connected to the inner conductor of the coaxial fitting.

Receivers may pick up signals through the ac line to some extent. Bypassing the ac lead inside the chassis should take care of this source of i-f leak-through. Some receivers, such as early models of the HRO, have separate power supplies. Power cable leads may pick up signals, and also radiate harmonics of the receiver oscillator that may show up in the tuning range of the vhf converter. Filtering and bypassing power supply leads is required in these instances, much as would be done in TVI-prevention work on a transmitter. See Chapter 15 for examples.

To tell whether signals at the intermediate frequency are coming through because of receiver deficiencies or directly through the vhf converter, try running the receiver alone with its antenna terminals shorted. If no signals are heard in this condition it can be assumed that the trouble lies in the converter. The problem may be one of improper bonding between the receiver and converter chassis. The outer conductor of the coax interconnecting the units may not be enough. Place the converter close to the receiver, and then bond the two together with a heavy braid or strap of copper. Often this will eliminate the leak-through trouble. Effective bypassing of the converter power circuits is another step if the bonding fails. Use 0.01-μF disk capacitors for this purpose. Lower values may not provide complete bypassing at frequencies under about 10 MHz.

General-Coverage vs. Amateur-Band Receivers

Except for a few models that have a special tuning range for vhf converters, receivers designed for amateur-band service exclusively do not meet the vhf man's tuning needs fully. The obvious solution to this problem is to use more than one crystal in the vhf converter. Two crystals will give the required 4-megahertz spread with receivers that tune 28 to 30 MHz, for example. This may not be entirely satisfactory, however, as the performance of some receivers is poor in the 28-MHz range compared to lower frequencies.

Vhf men who want the best reception with a minimum of crystal changing may decide to forfeit coverage of some parts of the vhf bands in favor of

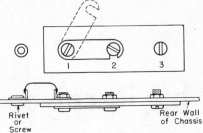

Fig. 3-10 — The 3-terminal antenna connection plate used on many communications receivers may be a source of interference from signals picked up at the converter output frequency. Remove the loop from Terminal 1 to ground (inside the receiver) and connect 1 to ground on the outside of the chassis. Ground the i-f coax to Terminals 1 and 2, and connect the inner conductor to Terminal 3. Better still, install a coaxial fitting on the rear wall of the chassis, to replace the terminal board entirely.

those that can be covered readily on ranges where their receivers work best. This might mean using a receiver's 400-kHz coverage at 14 MHz with two converter crystals, for example, to give 144.0 to 144.4 MHz and 145.0 to 145.4 MHz, or any other segments that may happen to fit a local activity picture.

Some communications receivers themselves use crystal-controlled oscillators with a tunable i-f system. Crystals are usually supplied to cover the amateur bands from 3.5 to 30 MHz with such receivers. In some instances (as for example the Collins S-Line), crystals can be obtained to extend the continuous coverage. Continuous coverage from 14 to 15.8 MHz is possible with a 75S-1 or S-3, for example, by substituting suitable crystals in the 21- and 28-MHz positions for those supplied with the receiver.

RECEIVING FREQUENCY MODULATION

Effective transmission and reception of fm require techniques very different from those used with other voice modes. Frequency modulating a transmitter is quite simple, but the i-f and detection circuits for fm are not readily incorporated into most communications receivers. The fm receiver is specifically designed to reject all forms of amplitude modulation, and the receiver bandwidth and the transmitter deviation must be matched closely. Unless both qualities are provided, fm will be markedly inferior to any other voice method. With well-coordinated design, vhf fm systems are unmatched in their ability to provide reliable noise-free communication over a local service area.

Techniques that resulted in the current boom in fm and repeaters are described in detail elsewhere in this book. We call attention here to a system that has gone all but unused in amateur work, but which has great potential for reliable high-quality voice communication on the higher bands. This is true wide-band fm, using equipment that is well within the capabilities of the relative newcomer to home-building of ham gear.

The bandwidth used in fm broadcast reception is ideal for bands where there is room for it, particularly 220 MHz and higher. Suitable fm tuners for use with 220- or 420-MHz converters are everywhere, in the form of home-entertainment units, from pocket portables to expensive hi-fi tuners. Several communications receivers still found on the used-equipment market are usable. The Hallicrafters SX-42, SX-62, and SX-43 are ideal, as they offer both wide-band fm and narrow-band a-m and cw in the 27-MHz range, at the flip of the mode switch. Converters described in Chapter 4 can be used with such receivers, for multipurpose work. The S-27 and S-36 cover similar frequency ranges, but do not have narrow-band cw or a-m capability. All these receivers are fine fm broadcast sets, as well. The S-240 is a modern fm a-m receiver that should work well if the amateur-band converter is modified for 88-MHz output.

Very simple transmitting equipment for true wide-band fm is discussed in Chapter 5.

Chapter 4

V h f Receivers, Converters and Preamplifiers

This chapter will present practical examples of principles discussed in detail in Chapter 3. To conserve space and show a wide variety of projects for the home-builder of vhf gear, we will lean heavily on the previous chapter for explanatory material. It should be stressed here that building equipment from this book, like working from nearly all material published by ARRL, bears little resemblance to building from kit-type instructions. Our purpose is not merely to provide "plans" for vhf equipment, but rather to give the builder an opportunity to learn something about design, adjustment, and operation of the equipment, beyond the usual kit-builder's skills in the use of a soldering iron and simple hand tools.

It is *possible* to build equipment described in this book without first acquiring some knowledge of how the circuits work and why they are designed the way they are, but the better method is go get your money's worth from the principles chapters. If you have not already done it, we strongly recommend reading Chapter 3 thoroughly, particularly those portions relevant to any project you are about to embark on in the vhf receiving field. This may well save you time and trouble, in the end. An understanding of principles is basic to success with projects to be described here.

Though this is termed a "vhf" chapter, some equipment for the 420-MHz band is included, where circuit features are not unlike those of equipment for lower bands. The 420-MHz band tends to be borderline in nature, so other items for this band will be found in the UHF and Microwaves chapter, where techniques employed are more characteristic of higher bands.

RECEIVING SYSTEMS

A means of listening is the first requirement of the vhf newcomer. If he already has an adequate receiver for the lower frequencies, a vhf converter is his logical first step into the world above 50 MHz. The stringent requirements for good vhf reception do not lend themselves to simple solutions otherwise, mainly because of the variety of modes open to the vhf communicator. Fairly simple receivers for a-m phone can be built, but they will not work well for fm reception, and probably not at all for ssb. The latter two modes account for a considerable portion of the activity currently heard in the 50- and 144-MHz bands, and they are not compatible to any great extent.

The superregenerative tuner covering 14 to 18 or perhaps 26 to 30 MHz, once an accepted simple-receiver approach for the beginner,[1] is ineffective for these modes. It will work reasonably well for a-m phone reception, but it is no more than an annoying makeshift for cw, ssb, or fm. The direct-conversion receiver, which has had quite a play in the simple-receiver field,[2] does pretty well on ssb or cw, but it is almost useless for fm, and not much better for a-m, especially if the frequency stability of the a-m signal is anything but the best. A complete solid-state receiving system for all

[1] For this and other numbered references, see bibliography at the end of this chapter.

TABLE 4-I

Crystal and injection frequencies for use with common intermediate frequencies in vhf converters.

Band, MHz	Crystal and multiplier frequencies for i-f beginning at:					
	7 MHz		14 MHz		28 MHz	
	Osc	Multi	Osc	Multi	Osc	Multi
50	43.0	—	36.0	—	22.0	—
144	45.667	137	43.333	86.67	38.667	136
220	53.25	213	51.5	206	48.0	192
432	Undesirable		46.444	418	44.889	404

TABLE 4-II

Nominal inductance of coils required for typical converter circuits of Chapters 3 and 4. Resonant frequency is varied by movement of coil slug, or (in air-wound coils) by changing capacitor value.

Freq, MHz	Nom. L, μH	Freq, MHz	Nom. L, μH
7 - 11	27	36 - 40	1
19	4.5	40 - 45	0.8
22 - 26	3	45 - 50	0.7
26 - 28	2.5	50 - 55	0.6
30.5	1.5	136 - 139	0.15

amateur bands up through 148 MHz is described in general terms in *QST* for January, 1971, and more completely in recent editions of the *Handbook*[3] — but it is far from being a beginner's project, and it makes no provision for fm. A tunable converter for 14 MHz, to work into car-radio or home receivers for the broadcast band[4] could be used as a limited-range tuner for vhf converters having 14-MHz output. It works well with ssb, a-m, and cw, and not too badly as a slope-detection method for fm. Probably the closest thing to a universal system is discussed briefly in a *QST* article on integrated circuits.[5] It does well on all four modes, and it is relatively simple to use, considering all the things it is capable of doing, but it hardly fits the "A Simple . . . ." mold, so popular in beginner articles of a bygone era.

Receiving systems and adaptations primarily for fm appear in our chapters devoted to that mode, later in this book. What follows in this chapter is presented in terms of a separate converter used ahead of a communications receiver, but the same basic circuits apply to the receiver front-end portions of transceivers and transverters.

Choosing the Intermediate Frequency

A portion of the preceding chapter goes into the problems encountered with various types of communications receivers, when they are used with vhf converters. There is no one tuning range that is ideal for all converters or for all receivers. The converters to follow have different intermediate frequencies, mainly to show how these can be

handled, rather than because of any marked advantage of one i-f with a particular converter. The choice is more likely to be dictated by the nature of the receiver the prospective converter-builder owns.

The 50-MHz converter immediately following this section shows use of 7 MHz as the low end of the tuning range. This might be fine with some receivers, but 14 MHz could be a better choice with others, or 28 MHz with still others. Our practical constructional examples show converters with various intermediate frequencies. Tables I and II present the basic information needed to build-in the injection and output circuits to fit your needs.

Receiving with Vacuum Tubes

It will be apparent to the reader that receiving equipment described in this book is almost entirely of solid-state design. This is not to imply that vhf converters using tubes are no longer worth considering. Rather, it was felt that with an excellent selection of vacuum-tube designs readily available from *QST*, the *Handbook*, and previous editions of this *Manual*, available space could be used to better advantage by concentrating on equipment built around transistors.

The bibliography at the end of this chapter lists several vacuum-tube receiver and converter articles that are still in demand.[6] Where the publication in question is not available to the reader, ARRL will supply photocopies of the original articles for 25 cents per page.

SIMPLE JFET CONVERTER FOR 50 MHz

Field-effect transistors provide freedom from overloading comparable to the better vacuum-tube rf amplifiers. Inexpensive junction FETs are now available that give excellent noise figure and gain in the vhf range. The FET is quite similar in characteristics to a tube amplifier, and it will be seen from a comparison of the schematic diagrams that the simple 50-MHz converter of Fig. 4-1 is not unlike the triode converters previously described. It should be equal to a tube version in performance, and it has a considerable edge in overall simplicity, since it can operate directly from a 9- or 12-volt battery.

Circuit Details

In the interest of bandpass response and rejection of out-of-band signals, double-tuned circuits are used for the input and interstage coupling. Protective diodes, CR1 and CR2, between the antenna connection and ground, prevent damage to the first stage from rf leakage from the transmitter, or transient voltages such as might result from nearby lightning discharges.

The rf and mixer transistors may be any of several vhf FETs. The inexpensive MPF-102 from

Motorola, and similar types available from other sources, rated for rf amplifier service to 100 MHz or higher should be more than adequate. The rf transistor is operated grounded-gate, which is the equivalent of grounded-grid use of a vacuum tube. Such a stage is relatively low-gain, but it is stable

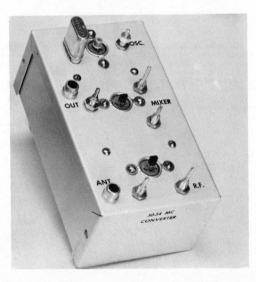

Fig. 4-1 — 50-MHz converter with field effect transistors in the rf and mixer stages.

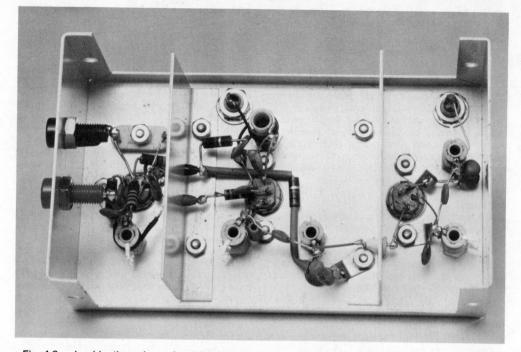

Fig. 4-2 — Looking into the under side of the 6-meter converter the mixer is in the center, with the rf stage at the right and the oscillator at the left.

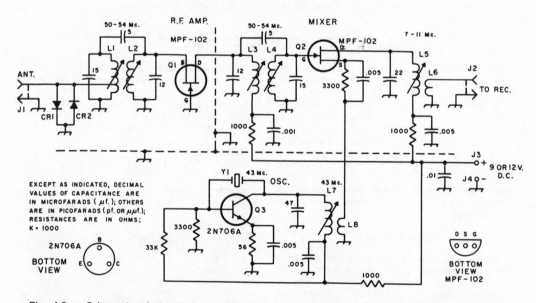

Fig. 4-3 — Schematic of the 6-meter FET converter. All resistors are 1/2-watt composition. All capacitors are disk or tubular ceramic.

CR1, CR2 — Germanium diode (1N34A suitable).
J1, J2 — Phono connector.
J3, J4 — Insulated banana jack one red, one black.
L1-L4, incl. — 0.68 μH, slug-tuned (Millen 69054-0.68*). L1 has tap added at 2nd turn from ground end.
L5 — 11 to 24 μH slug-tuned (Miller 4507).

L6 — 5 turns insulated wire over cold end of L5.
L7 — 0.33 μH slug-tuned (Millen 69054-0.33*).
L8 — 1 turn small-gauge insulated wire over cold end of L7.
Y1 — 43.0-MHz third-overtone crystal (International Crystal Co. Type F-605).

* Available directly from James Millen Mfg. Co., 150 Exchange Street, Malden, MA.

and does not require neutralization. At 50 MHz, at least, the gain is adequate for good reception, when the stage is used with a grounded-source mixer, as shown.

The oscillator uses a bipolar transistor with a 43-MHz crystal. Any vhf transistor will do here. The mixer output is 7 to 11 MHz for coverage of 50 to 54 MHz, but the 14-MHz range could be used equally well. In that case the coil and crystal information could be taken from Tables I and II.

Construction

The converter case is a 3 X 5-1/4 X 2-1/4-inch Minibox, with the parts mounted on the cover portion. Shields are mounted across the chassis to keep down unwanted interstage coupling. Parts layout is not particularly critical, though the approximate relative positions of the principal rf components should be followed, for best results. Phono connectors were used for the input and output fittings, J1 and J2. These work well enough, though you may prefer the better quality of BNC or other coaxial fittings.

Colored tip jacks J3 and J4 on the rear wall are used to bring in the operating voltage. Small feedthrough bushings (Johnson Rib-Loc) are mounted in the interstage shields, for leads between sections. In Fig. 4-2 the rf amplifier stage is at the right side of the picture, the mixer at the center, and the oscillator at the left.

Adjustment

Check the wiring, to be sure that it is correct and complete, then connect the converter to the communications receiver input, and apply dc voltage through J3 and J4. The receiver noise level will increase markedly, if the converter oscillator is working. Turning the slug in L7 should bring this about, if it does not start immediately. Set the slug at a point where oscillation will occur each time the voltage is applied.

It should now be possible to hear any reasonably strong signal, actually on-the-air or from a vhf signal generator. Peak all core studs in the rf and mixer circuits for maximum signal strength, and the adjustment should be nearly complete. It may be helpful to stagger-tune L3, L4, and L5 for uniform response across the desired frequency range. This results in somewhat lower than maximum gain, but does not affect the noise figure adversely, as this is determined mainly by the first tuned circuit. L1 and L2 should be adjusted carefully for best signal-to-noise ratio on a weak signal, rather than for maximum gain, if there is a difference discernible.

In adjusting the coil slugs, be sure that the circuits actually peak. Occasionally there will appear to be a peak which is actually the centering of the slug in the winding. If this happens, you need more turns in the coil or more capacitance across it.

ADVANCED JFET CONVERTERS FOR 144 AND 220 MHz

The converters of Figs 4-4 through 4-11 were designed to provide optimum performance and flexibility. They show examples of several techniques that can be used to advantage in vhf converter design generally, as well. Two junction FETs are used in a transistor version of the familiar cascode circuit. The JFET mixer has 28-MHz output, permitting coverage of at least 2 MHz of the vhf band on most receivers, with a single converter crystal.

The 28-MHz i-f amplifier, while not absolutely necessary with the better communications receivers, gives enough overall gain for use of the converter with receivers whose performance at 28 MHz may be questionable. More important, it permits setting the converter output level at the optimum point for any receiver. Using an integrated circuit simplifies this stage, as most of the parts are in the IC itself.

The oscillator and multiplier stages use inexpensive bipolar transistors, with collector-voltage regulation on the oscillator. These stages are isolated from the rf portion with copper shielding. The supply voltage is fed in through a "polarity

Fig. 4-4 — A look at the completed 2-meter etched circuit FET/IC converter and its 12-volt ac-operated power supply. Top appearance of the 220-MHz version is almost identical.

Fig. 4-5 — Top surface of the 2-meter converter. The i-f gain control knob is at the upper right. The input jack for the 12-volt supply is just to the left of the gain control. The i-f output jack is at the lower right, and the rf input jack is at the lower left on the board. The IC is located at the far right, just above the i-f output connector.

insurance" diode, CR1. You can't hurt the converter by getting supply polarity wrong. If you're sure you'll never do this, the diode can be omitted.

Options

Several JFETs will do for Q1, Q2, and Q3, some of them more expensive than the MPF-102s and 107s used. The 2N4416, a top-rated JFET, for example, showed no measurable advantage in either the 144- or the 220-MHz converter. A power supply is shown, for use where operation from ac power is a convenience, but all-battery power is attractive for portable work, particularly in connection with an all-transistor communications receiver. The i-f amplifier, the voltage regulation of the oscillator, and the polarity-insurance diode can all be considered optional. You can build a good converter without them, but optimum performance, versatility and safety are assured through their inclusion.

Construction

The converters described above are assembled on 4-1/2 X 6-1/2-inch etched circuit boards (Vector CU65/45-1). A layout drawing, Fig. 4-9, will help you to make your own layout, or a template can be obtained if you wish.* Ready-made boards can be purchased.* Shields of flashing copper isolate

* Full-size template similar to Fig. 4-9 sent upon receipt of 25 cents and stamped self-addressed envelope. Address ARRL Technical Dept., Newington, CT 06111, and mention figure number, publication, and edition number.
Readymade boards may be obtained from individual suppliers listed from time to time in QST.

the various sections of the converter. Where these are soldered or bolted to the circuit board it is necessary to trim away portions to prevent shorting out the circuits. The shields do not show clearly in Fig. 4-8, so their approximate location can be checked out by the dashed lines in Fig. 4-6. Locations of the key components can be determined from the layout drawing, Fig. 4-9, and from the top and bottom photographs.

The chassis is a matching Vector assembly made of two of their Fram-Loc rails 2 X 6-5/8 inches (Vector SR2-6.6.062), two 2 X 4-1/2 inches (SR2-4.6/062), and a bottom cover (PL4566). A standard chassis could be used, if the cover plate is cut out to fit the circuit board.

Power Supply

The converter requires about 12 volts dc at 45 mA. The ac-operated 12-volt dc supply for fixed-station use, Figs. 4-4 and 4-7, is built in a 4 X 5 X 2-inch aluminum box with bottom plate. For portable work the converter might be operated from the same source as a transistorized communications receiver with which it is to be used, or from a car battery. A bank of 8 D-cells will provide many hours of intermittent use.

If mobile operation is planned, it would be prudent to connect an 18-volt Zener diode across J3, to protect the transistors from transient peaks which occur in automotive electrical systems. Under normal conditions the Zener would not conduct.

Checkout

Before applying operating voltage, make a thorough check of the soldering operations on the circuit board, to be sure that the job is complete and correct, and that there are no incidental shorts.

With a test signal (generator, or on-the-air, starting with a high level) on about 145 MHz, adjust L1, L2, L3, L4, L6, and L8 for maximum output. If the test signal cannot be heard, it is likely that the oscillator, Q4, has not started. In this case, adjust L10 until an increase in noise occurs, indicating the start of oscillation. Detune the slug out of the coil slightly, until the oscillator will start whenever voltage is applied.

The inductance of L1 and L4, and the position of the tap on L1, should be adjusted for best (lowest) noise figure, if a noise generator is available. These adjustments can be made on a weak signal, if careful observation of the margin of the signal over noise is maintained. There is interaction between these adjustments, so several resettings of each may have to be made for optimum reception. Reasonably flat response across the desired tuning range can be achieved by stagger-tuning the rest of the circuits, both rf and i-f, as only the input and neutralizing coils will affect noise figure measurably.

The gain control, R1, should be set so that the noise level, with no signal, just shows on the

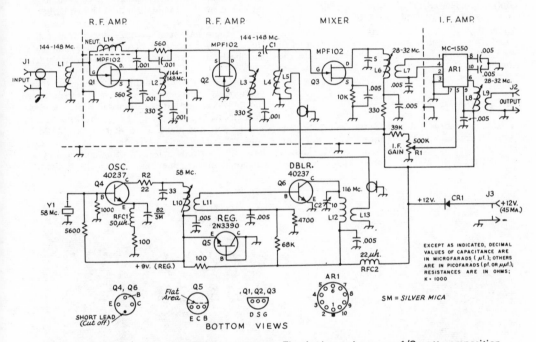

Fig. 4-6 — Schematic of the 144-MHz converter. Fixed-value resistors are 1/2-watt composition. Fixed-value capacitors are disk or tubular ceramic unless stated otherwise.

AR1 — Motorola MC-1550 integrated circuit. Take output from L7, if amplifier stage is not used.
C1 — Gimmick capacitor: two 1-inch lengths of insulated hookup wire, twisted 6 times. A 2-pF fixed-value ceramic capacitor can be substituted.
C2 — 10-pF piston-type trimmer (Centralab 829-10).
CR1 — Silicon diode, 50 PRV or greater, at 200 mA.
J1 — BNC-style chassis connector.
J2, J3 — Phono jack.
L1 — 6 turns No. 24 enam., wire to occupy 3/8 inch on slug-tuned form, 1/4 in. dia; (Miller 4500-4) tap 1-1/4 turns above ground end.
L2 — 4 turns No. 24 enam. wire to occupy 3/8 inch on same type form as L1.
L-3 — 5 turns No. 24 enam. to occupy 3/8 inch on same type form as L1.
L4 — 4 turns No. 24 enam. to occupy 3/8 inch on same style form as L1.

L5 — 2 turns insulated hookup wire over ground end of L4.
L6, L8 — Slug-tuned, 1.6 to 2.8 μH (Miller No. 4503).
L7, L9 — Three-turn link over cold ends of L6 and L8. Use small-diameter insulated hookup wire.
L10 — 5 turns No. 24 enam. wire to occupy 3/8 inch on Miller 4500-4 slug-tuned form.
L11 — 2-turn link of small-diameter wire over cold end of L10.
L12 — 5 turns No. 20 tinned copper wire (or enam.), 5/16-inch diameter, 3/8 inch long.
L13 — 2 turns small-dia insulated hookup wire inserted in cold end of L12, 1/4-inch dia.
L14 — 9 turns No. 24 enam. wire, close wound on same style form as L10.
Q1-Q6, incl. — For text reference purposes.
R1 — 500,000-ohm control, linear taper.
RFC1 — 50-μH rf choke (Millen J-300-50).
RFC2 — 22-μH rf choke (Millen J-300-22).
Y1 — 58-MHz third-overtone crystal (International Crystal type F-605).

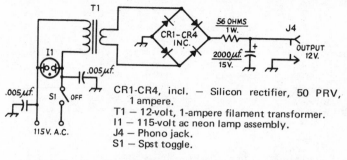

Fig. 4-7 — Schematic of the converter power supply. The 2000-μF capacitor is electrolytic, others are disk ceramic, 1000-volt units. The 56-ohm resistor was selected to give the proper power-supply voltage when used with the circuit of Fig. 4-6 (12 volts dc).

CR1-CR4, incl. — Silicon rectifier, 50 PRV, 1 ampere.
T1 — 12-volt, 1-ampere filament transformer.
I1 — 115-volt ac neon lamp assembly.
J4 — Phono jack.
S1 — Spst toggle.

receiver S-meter. In this way the signal readings will then be more useful than is often the case with converter-receiver combinations where no i-f gain control is included. The setting for various receivers may vary markedly, but it should be remembered that the position of this control has no bearing on the ability of the system to respond to weak signals, if it is set high enough so that the noise output of the converter can be heard, or seen on the meter.

THE 220-MHz MODEL

The superiority of transistors over tubes becomes more marked as the upper frequency limit of the tubes concerned is approached. Thus a well-designed 220-MHz converter using the better

transistors may outperform one using anything but the most expensive and hard-to-get vacuum tubes. The 220-MHz converter of Fig. 4-10 is almost a duplicate of the 144-MHz model shown earlier in this chapter. Its weak-signal sensitivity should be better than has been possible heretofore at this frequency, for anything of comparable simplicity and moderate cost. It was built by Tom McMullen, W1SL.

To save space and avoid duplication, only those portions of the converter that are different from the 144-MHz version are discussed here. An identical circuit board is used. The circuit, Fig. 4-11, is similar, but not identical to that of the 144-MHz converter. The same parts designations are used insofar as possible. Self-supporting coils and cylindrical ceramic trimmers are used in the rf circuits.

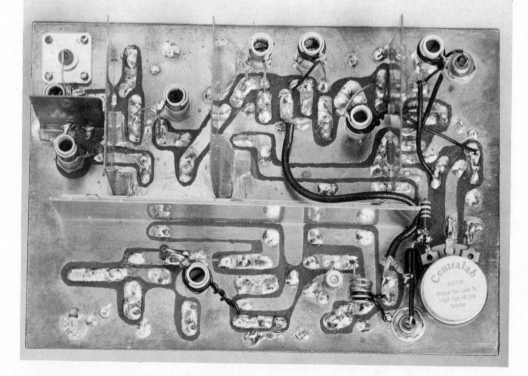

Fig. 4-8 —Bottom of the circuit board. The i-f gain control and 12-volt power jack are at the lower right. The input circuit and rf stages are at the upper left. The mixer is at the upper center, and the IC i-f amplifier is at the upper right. The oscillator chain extends along the lower portion of the board. The interstage shields are in place, but are difficult to see in this photo.

Fig. 4-9 — Layout of the etched circuit board. The lines show where the key components are mounted and indicate the way the semiconductor leads are indexed. This is a bottom view of the board (copper side). The white areas indicate the copper that remains after etching.

* Break and bridge with 100 ohms, 220 MHz only.

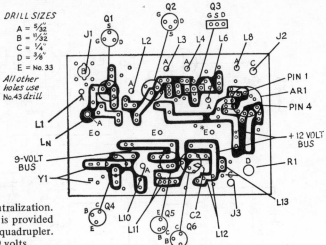

The first rf stage has capacitive neutralization. Injection at 192 MHz (for 28-MHz i-f) is provided by a 48-MHz crystal oscillator and a quadrupler. Oscillator voltage is Zener-regulated at 9 volts.

Almost any silicon vhf transistor will work in the oscillator and quadrupler stages. The rf and mixer are FETs. Judging from experience with the preamplifiers described elsewhere in this chapter, most vhf junction FETs should work well here. A noise figure of 3 dB or better should be obtainable with several different types, in addition to the Motorola MPF series shown here. Some MPF types are now available only with 2N numbers. The MPF-107 is now sold as the 2N5486. The 28-MHz i-f amplifier stage is not shown, as it is identical to that in the 144-MHz converter. It is definitely recommended, not only to assure adequate gain for some of the less-effective communications receivers, but also to permit setting the desired converter output level to match the particular receiver in use.

Fig. 4-10 — Interior of the 220-MHz FET converter. Minor differences from the 144-MHz model, Fig. 4-6 are discussed in the text. The rf mixer and i-f amplifier circuits, left to right, occupy the upper half of the circuit board. Board layout is similar to that of Fig. 4-9, except as described.

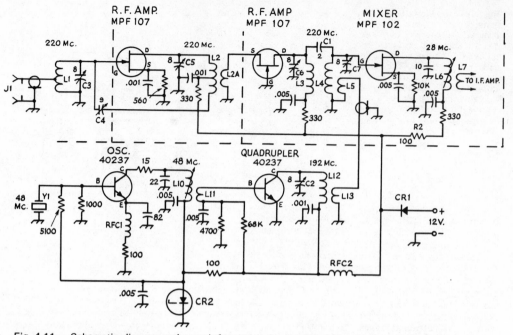

Fig. 4-11 — Schematic diagram and parts information for the 220-MHz converter. Only those portions wherein there are differences from the 144-MHz circuit, Fig. 4-6, are shown. Parts are labelled similar to those of the 144-MHz converter, wherever possible. The MPF-107 is now sold as 2N5486.

C1 — 2 pF or 2 1-inch lengths of insulated wire, twisted six times.
C2, C3, C6, C7 — 8-pF cylindrical ceramic trimmer (Centralab 829-7).
C4 — 9-pF subminiature trimmer (Johnson 189-503-4).
CR1 — Silicon diode, 50 PRV or greater, 200 mA or more.
CR2 — 9-volt Zener diode.
J1 — BNC coaxial fitting.
L1, L3, L4, L12 — 3 turns No. 22, 1/4-inch dia, 1/4 inch long. Tap L1 at one turn from ground end.

L2 — 6-1/2 turns No. 22, 1/4-inch dia, 1/2 inch long. Tap at 2 turns from top end.
L2A — 3 turns insulated wire between turns of L2.
L5 — 1 turn insulated wire between bottom turns of L4.
L6, L7 — Same as in 144-MHz model.
L10 — 7 turns No. 22 5/16 inch long, on 1/4-inch iron-slug form (Miller 4500-4 form).
L11 — 2 turns insulated wire over bottom turns of L10.
L13 — 1 turn insulated wire between first two turns of L12.
R2 — See text.
RFC1, RFC2 — 25-μH rf choke (Millen J-300-25).
Y1 — 48-MHz third-overtone crystal.

One difference between this converter and the one for 144 MHz might not be readily apparent, but it is important. Note the resistor, R2, in the line to the mixer drain circuit. This is not in the 2-meter version. It was put into the 220-MHz model when a signal-frequency resonance developed in the circuit board, causing an oscillation problem that took some chasing down! Looking at the layout drawing of the circuit board, Fig. 4-9, pick out the 12-volt bus running from near the middle of the board horizontally to the right, before dropping vertically into the lower half. This should be severed below the letter "A" on the sketch. The 100-ohm R2 is bridged across the gap.

Other minor mechanical differences resulting from the slightly modified circuitry in the rf portion are apparent from the photographs. The small shield between L1 and L14 in the 2-meter model is not needed here. The neutralizing capaci-

tor, C4, appears about where L14 was. The cylindrical trimmers, C3, C5, C6, and C7, are mounted where the slug coils are seen in the 144-MHz model. Note the mounting positions of the rf coils. L1, L3, and L4 are similar: their axes parallel to the chassis. L2 is perpendicular to it.

Adjustment

The first step should be to get the oscillator and multiplier running. It may be advisable to keep voltage off the stages other than the ones being checked, at this point. Make sure that the oscillator is on 48 MHz, and no other frequency. (In this type of circuit it is possible to get oscillation on the crystal fundamental, in this case 16 MHz, if the collector circuit does not resonate at 48 MHz.) Now fire up the quadrupler and peak C2 for maximum energy at 192 MHz.

With the converter connected to the receiver, there should be a marked increase in noise when voltage is applied to the rf, mixer, and i-f amplifier stages. The i-f can be peaked for maximum noise at 28 MHz. It is helpful at this point to have a signal on 220. A dipper signal will do. It is also desirable to have a properly matched antenna connected to J1, unless a good signal generator with 50-ohm termination is available for alignment purposes. If a random antenna must be used, put a 50-ohm resistor across J1 to simulate the eventual load, for neutralization purposes.

There may be no oscillation in the rf stages, regardless of tuning, if the converter is operated with a proper load. If this is the case it is merely necessary to adjust the neutralizing capacitor, C4, and the tuning of the input circuit, L1C3, for best signal-to-noise ratio on a weak signal. All other circuits affect only the gain and frequency response characteristics, so they can be adjusted for flat response across the desired frequency range, and there will be no sacrifice in the ability of the system to respond to weak signals.

Most realistic operation of the receiver's S-meter will be obtained if the meter adjustment is set so that there is an appreciable reading on noise only, with no signal. The converter i-f gain control is then set so that the meter reads S-0 or S-1, with the antenna on. In this way the relative strength of signals will be indicated on the meter, within the usual variations encountered with these none-too-reliable devices. The receiver's antenna trimmer, if there is one, can also be used as an auxilliary gain control, and it will have no effect whatever on the sensitivity of the system.

FET PREAMPLIFIERS FOR 50, 144, AND 220 MHz

Fig. 4-12 — Transistor preamplifiers for 50, 144, and 220 MHz, left to right. Appearance is similar, except for the type of tuned circuit used.

Where a vhf receiver lacks gain, or has a poor noise figure, an external preamplifier can improve its ability to detect weak signals. Some multiband receivers that include the 50-MHz band are not as good as they might be on 6. Converters for 144 MHz haing pentode rf stages, or using some of the earlier dual triodes, may also need some help. Some fm transceivers currently in use were built before low-noise amplifiers were readily available. Most 220-MHz converters are marginal performers, at best. The field-effect transistor preamplifiers of Fig. 4-12 should improve results with these, and with any other receivers for these bands that may not be in optimum working condition.

The circuits of the amplifiers are similar, though iron-core coils are used in the 50-MHz model, and air-wound coils in the other two. The grounded-source circuit requires neutralization. This is done with capacitive feedback, rather than with the inductive circuit commonly used. A tapped input circuit is used in the 50-MHz amplifier, and capacitive input is shown for the other two, though this was done mainly to show alternative circuits. The output circuit is matched to the receiver input by means of C2.

Many inexpensive transistors will work well in these amplifiers. Motorola MPF-102, 104, and 106,* all low-priced molded-plastic units and the more expensive metal-case 2N4416 were tried, and all were more than adequate. The MPF-102 is the least expensive, and surprisingly, it was as good as any, even on 220 MHz. Careful readjustment is required when changing transistors, so the builder should not jump to conclusions about the relative merit of different types.

Construction

The amplifiers were built in small handmade boxes, aluminum for the 50- and 144-MHz models, and flashing copper for the 220-MHz one, but any small metal box should do. Those shown are 1-1/2 X 2 X 3 inches in size. The transistor socket is in the middle of the top surface, and the BNC input and output fittings are centered on the ends. The tuned circuits are roughly 3/4 inch either side of the transistor socket, but this should be adjusted for good layout with the parts available. Flat

* Only the MPF-102 is still available. Others now have 2N numbers. The MPF-107 is now 2N5486.

ceramic trimmers are used for tuning the 144-MHz amplifier, and the cylindrical type in the 220-MHz one. Sockets were used mainly to permit trying various transistors; they could be wired directly in place equally well. Printed-circuit construction would be fine, if you like this method.

Adjustment

The preamplifier should be connected to the receiver or converter with which it is to be used, with any length of coaxial cable, or by hooking J2 directly to the converter input jack with a suitable adapter. If you have a noise generator or signal generator, connect it to J1. If not, use a test signal from a grid-dip oscillator, or some other signal source known to be in the band for which the amplifier was designed. Preferably a matched antenna for the band in question should be hooked to J1, if a signal generator is not used. A 50-ohm resistor across J1 may be helpful if a random antenna is used for the adjustment work.

Set the neutralizing capacitor near half capacitance; then, with no voltage yet applied, tune the input and output circuits roughly for maximum signal. (The level may be only slightly lower than it would be with the converter or receiver alone.) Now apply voltage, and check current drain. It should be 4 to 7 mA, depending on the voltage. Probably there will be an increase in noise and signal when voltage is turned on. If not, the stage may be oscillating. This will be evident from erratic tuning and bursts of noise when adjustments are attempted.

If there is oscillation (and it is likely) move C1 in small increments, retuning the input and output circuits each time, until a setting of C1 is found where oscillation ceases, and the signal is amplified. All adjustments interlock, so this is a see-saw procedure at first. Increasing the capacitance of C2 tends to stabilize the amplifier through increased loading, but if carried too far will have an adverse effect on gain. The best setting is one where the input and output circuits do not tune too critically, but the gain is adequate.

The input circuit is first peaked for maximum signal, but final adjustment should be for best signal-to-noise ratio. This process is very similar to that with tube amplifiers, and the best point will probably be found with the input circuit detuned on the low-frequency side of the gain peak. In listening to a weak modulated signal, the fact that the noise drops off faster than the signal with a slight detuning is quite obvious. Typically the meter reading may drop about one full S-unit, while the noise level drops two S-units. The exact setting depends on the neutralization, and on the loading, both input and output, and can only be determined by experiment, with a noise generator or a weak signal.

Results

Because external noise is more of a limiting factor in 50-MHz reception than on the higher bands, tuning for best reception is not critical on this band. Very likely you can set the neutralization to prevent oscillation, peak the input and output circuits roughly, and you'll be all set. On 144 the job is fussier if the amplifier is to effect a real improvement, particularly if your receiver is a fairly good one. This preamplifier should get you down to the point where external noise limits your reception, for sure, if you were not there before. On 220 the preamp is almost certain to help, unless you already have an exceptional receiving setup, and optimum performance is worth the trouble you take to get it. With all three, you should be certain that, if a given signal can be heard in your location, on your antenna, you will now be able to hear it.

Warning: if the preamp is to be used with a transceiver, be sure to connect it in the line to the receiver only, not in the main line from the transceiver to the antenna. It is best to do this before any work is done on the amplifier; otherwise you're sure to throw the send-receive switch inadvertently and finish off the transistor.

If you're in doubt about the possibility of rf coming down the antenna line, connect protective diodes across the input, as shown with CR1 and CR2 in one of the circuits. Install these after the preamplifier tuneup, and check weak-signal reception with and without them, to be sure that they are not causing signal loss. Junction-type field-effect transistors are capable of withstanding much more rf voltage than bipolar transistors, so this kind of protection may not be needed in situations where it would have been mandatory with earlier types of transistor front ends.

Fig. 4-13 — Interiors of the FET preamplifiers, in the same order as in Fig. 4-12. The input end is toward the right in each unit.

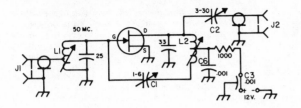

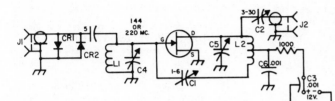

Fig. 4-14 — Circuit diagrams and parts information for the FET preamplifiers. Values of capacitors not described are in pico-farads (pF or μμF).

C1 — 1.3- to 6.7-pF subminiature variable (Johnson 189-502-5).
C2 — 3- to 30-pF miniature mica trimmer.
C3 — 0.001-μF feedthrough (Centralab MFT-1000; FT-1000 in 220-MHz amplifier).
C4, C5 — 3- to 12-pF ceramic trimmer in 144-MHz amplifier; 1- to 6-pF cylindrical ceramic in 220.
C6 — 0.001-μF 50-volt mylar. Omitted in 220-MHz model.
CR1, CR2 — 1N34A or similar germanium diode.

J1, J2 — Coaxial fitting. BNC type shown.
L1 — 50 MHz; 7 turns No. 24 enamel on 1/4-inch iron-slug ceramic form, tapped at 3 turns from ground end (Form is Miller 4500). 144 MHz: 3 turns No. 22, 1/4-inch dia, 3/8 inch long. 220 MHz: same, but with 2 turns 1/8 inch long.
L2 — 50 MHz: 10 turns like L1, but center-tapped. 144 MHz: 5 turns No. 22, 1/4-inch dia, 1/2 inch long, center-tapped. 220 MHz: Same but 4 turns.

432-MHz Version

Results with these preamplifiers were so gratifying that a 432-MHz model was tried. This was quite similar in layout, except that the metal case 2N4416 was used, and it was wired directly in place instead of using a socket. The transistor was suspended in a small notch in the bottom edge of a shield, which was mounted across the middle of the assembly. The case and source leads were soldered to the shield, with the gate lead projecting into the front compartment and the drain lead into the rear. The trimmers, C4 and C5, were 0.5 to 3 pF and the input and output loading capacitors were 6-pF miniature variables like C1 in the other units. The coils were No. 20 tinned 3/16-inch diameter, 1-3/4 turns in L1 and 3 turns, center-tapped for L2.

After some considerable juggling of adjustments, this stage was stabilized, and then tested with a poor crystal-mixer converter that serves as a trial horse in such work. The preamplifier gave about 10 dB gain, and this was all improvement in the converter noise figure. But it was not enough; this test setup requires about 18 dB gain for optimum performance and complete over-riding of the mixer and i-f noise. For setups needing only a few dB gain, such a preamp should do very well.

ALL–FET CONVERTERS FOR 50 AND 144 MHz

The converters of Figs. 4-15 through 4-19 were designed to be part of a complete receiving setup for all amateur bands from 1.8 to 148 MHz.[3] They are included here to show matching converters for 50 and 144 MHz, of relatively simple design and construction. Because the drawings are those used in the complete *Handbook* project,[3] the component numbering does not start at 1 for each type of part, in this condensed version. The sensitivity resulting when these converters are used with any 28-MHz receiver of good performance should be more than adequate, and the overall noise figure should be around 2.5 dB. Their MOSFET mixers provide high conversion gain, and resistance to overloading and cross-modulation effects. Rejection of out-of-band signals is improved by the use of double-tuned coupling circuits in several places in each converter.

All essential circuit features and adjustment procedure have been discussed at length in con-

Fig. 4-15 — The twin vhf converters are housed in a homemade aluminum box which has removable top and bottom covers for easy access to the circuit boards. Each converter has its own input and output jacks so that simultaneous operation is possible.

Fig. 4-16 — The darker of the two circuit boards is the 6-meter converter, shown at the bottom of the photo in this inside view. Since the circuit boards are identical in pattern, some of the holes are left blank on the 6-meter model, as there is one less stage in its oscillator section. The protective diodes at the antenna jacks were not installed when these photos were taken.

The converters are built on identical circuit boards, though different board materials were used here to make the separate units stand out photographically. Full-scale templates for laying out the boards are available from ARRL.*

The input circuits have protective diodes. Coupling into the first tuned circuit is inductive, in the 50-MHz converter, as adjustment of coupling for lowest noise figure is not required at this frequen-

nection with earlier projects in this book, and in the preceeding chapter, so they will not be given in full here. Probably the only "different" circuit in these two converters is the capacitive divider used to couple the i-f output (at 28 to 30 MHz) into the associated communications receiver.

* Converters originally described in October, 1969, *QST*, p. 37. Mention in ordering templates, and send 25 cents and stamped self-addressed envelope. Circuit boards made for ARRL construction projects are available from individual suppliers, listed from time to time in *QST*.

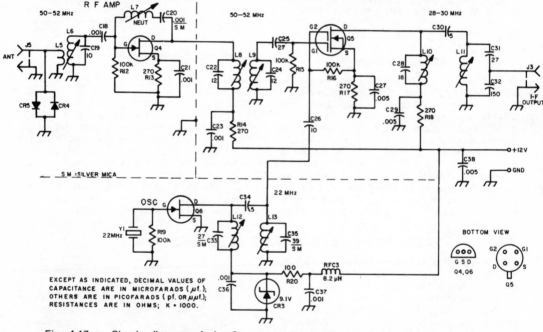

Fig. 4-17 — Circuit diagram of the 6-meter converter. Resistors are 1/2-watt composition. Capacitors are disk ceramic unless specified differently. Numbered components not appearing in the parts list were so identified for circuit-board layout purposes.

CR3 — 9.1-volt, 1-watt Zener diode (Motorola HEP-104 or equiv.).
CR4, CR5 — Small signal silicon switching diodes (1N914).
J2 — BNC or SO-239-type chassis connector.
J3 — Phono connector.
L5 — 3 turns of small insulated wire wound over the ground end of L6.
L6, L8, L9 — 10 turns No. 24 enam. wire, close-wound, on J. W. Miller 4500-4 iron-slug form.
L7 — 25 turns No. 30 enam. on 4500-2 form.
L10-L13, incl. — 12 turns No. 24 enam.,

close-wound, on J. W. Miller 4500-2 iron-slug form.
Q4, Q6 — Junction FET, Motorola MPF-102 (HEP-802 or 2N4416 suitable).
Q5 — Dual-gate MOSFET, Motorola MFE3008 (RCA 3N141 also suitable. Gate-protected version: RCA 40673).
RFC3 — 8.2-μH miniature rf choke (James Millen 34300-8.2).
Y1 — 3rd-overtone crystal (International Crystal Co. type EX).

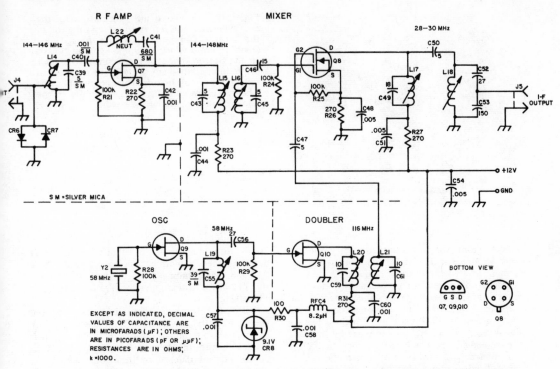

Fig. 4-18 — Circuit of the 2-meter converter. Resistors are 1/2-watt composition. Capacitors, unless otherwise noted, are disk ceramic. See Fig. 4-17 and text for explanation of component numbering.

CR6, CR7 — 1N914 or equivalent.
CR8 — 9.1-volt, 1-watt Zener diode (Motorola HEP-104 or equiv.).
J4 — BNC or SO-239-type chassis connector.
J5 — Phono connector.
L14 — 4 turns No. 24 enam. to occupy 3/8 inch on J. W. Miller 4500-4 iron-slug form. Tap 1 turn from ground end.
L15, L16, L19 — 5 turns No. 24 enam. to occupy 3/8 inch on same-type Miller form as L14.
L17, L18 — 15 turns No. 24 enam. wire, close--wound, on J. W. Miller 4500-2 iron-slug form.
L20, L21 — Same as L14, but no tap.

L22 — 9 turns No. 30 enam., close-wound, on J. W. Miller 4500-2 iron-slug form (J. W. Miller Co., 19070 Reyes Ave., Compton, CA 90221; write for catalog and prices).
Q7, Q9, Q10 — Junction FET, Motorola MPF-102 (2N4416 suitable).
Q8 — Dual-gate MOSFET, Motorola MFE3008 (RCA 3N141 also suitable. Gate-protected version: RCA 40673).
RFC4 — 8.2-μH miniature rf choke (James Millen 34300-8.2).
Y2 — 58-MHz 3rd-overtone crystal (International Crystal Co. type EX).

cy. The point at which the antenna line is tapped on the input coil in the 144-MHz converter can be adjusted for lowest noise figure, with the aid of a noise generator or by listening to a weak test signal and making comparisons of the margin of signal over noise.

The injection stages are similar, except for the addition of a doubler in the 144-MHz model. If any difficulty arises from unwanted harmonics of the oscillator or injection frequencies, a suitable trap can be connected in the lead to Gate 2 of the mixer. This can be a parallel or a series circuit. Examples of each will be found in Chapter 3. The double-tuned circuits in the injection stages should be tuned carefully for maximum desired-frequency output, in the process of adjusting any trap circuit for rejection of spurious signals.

Only the first-stage tuning and the neutralization are important in obtaining best noise figure. Other circuits in the rf and mixer stages can be

stagger-tuned for uniform response across the desired frequency range. This may drop the overall gain somewhat, but it should have no effect on the noise figure, if the first stage is working properly.

Construction

Scale templates for the etched-circuit board are available from ARRL.* The semiconductors are available from most of the larger mail-order houses, or from any Motorola distributor. See October, 1970, *QST*, p. 14, for ordering restrictions. The slug-tuned coil forms are made by J. W. Miller and should be only those numbers specified. It will be noted that some coil-form numbers have a numeral 2 at the end (4500-2) while others have a 4 at the end of the number (4500-4). These numbers relate to the core material used, which is designed for a particular frequency of operation. The core material has a significant effect on the tuning range of the inductors, and can seriously affect the coil Q if

Fig. 4-19 — Looking into the bottom of the converter box, the 6-meter unit is at the top of the photo. Each converter has four 1-inch standoff posts which secure the circuit boards to the bottom plate of the cabinet. Rf shields of flashing copper are soldered to the ground foil on the circuit boards. They are notched out wherever they come in close proximity to the non-ground elements of the circuit.

of the wrong type. If substitute coil forms are used, be sure that they're designed for the frequency range over which they will be used.

These converters can be packaged in any style of box the builder prefers. In this instance, both units are housed in a single homemade enclosure which measures 6-3/4 X 5 X 2-1/2 inches. The top and bottom covers are held in place by means of No. 6 spade bolts which are attached to the side walls of the box. This style of construction can be handled with ordinary hand tools, and only four 90-degree bends are required. This box was made from a large aluminum cookie sheet purchased at a hardware store. The dull finish results from a lye-bath treatment given the aluminum after it was formed.

The converters are mounted on the bottom plate of the box by means of 1-inch metal standoff posts. Self-adhesive rubber feet are attached to the bottom of the box. Black decals are used to identify the terminals on the outside of the box.

A 4-terminal transistor socket is used for the 6-meter mixer MOSFET. At the time the 2-meter converter was built a socket was not on hand, but both converters should use sockets for the MFE-

3008s to minimize the possibility of transistor damage when soldering. The sockets are Elco 05-3308. The binding posts used for connecting the +12 volts to the converters are E. F. Johnson 111-102s.

HEP-56 (Motorola) rectifier diodes are connected from the 12-volt input terminals on the box to the 12-volt terminals on the circuit boards, their anodes toward the Johnson binding posts. These diodes prevent damage to transistors should the operator mistakenly connect the power supply leads for the wrong polarity. Positive voltage will pass through the diodes, but negative voltage will be opposed.

It is strongly recommended that the converters be housed in some type of metal enclosure, as was done here, to prevent oscillator radiation, and to insure against random pickup of interfering commercial signals by the mixer circuit. This precaution is especially important in areas where commercial fm and TV transmitters are nearby.

Adjustment procedure for these converters is essentially the same as for units described earlier in this chapter, and given in general terms in Chapter 3.

A LOW-NOISE 432-MHz CONVERTER

There is usually great emphasis on the need for a good low-noise uhf transistor in at least the first stage of a 432-MHz converter, but the rf stage or stages cannot do the whole job. Good front-end design is often hampered by deficiencies elsewhere in the converter. These can include inadequate injection to the mixer, and poor noise figure in the stage immediately following the mixer. The converter of Figs. 4-20 through 27 does well with a single

Fig. 4-20 — The 432-MHz converter is built on the cover plate of a standard aluminum chassis. The "cigar-box effect" results from application of contact paper with simulated wood-grain finish to all exposed surfaces.

A Low–Noise 432–MHz Converter

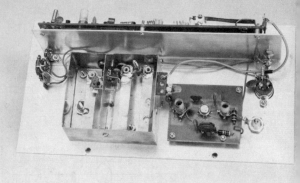

Fig. 4-21 — Interior of the 432-MHz low-noise converter, showing the rf and i-f amplifier assemblies. Strip-lines in the rf assembly are, left to right, L1, L3, and L4. The wire loop coupled to L3 is the neutralizing device, L2, with a capacitor tab coupling to L1. The small mixer diode is just visible, close to the right side of the rf assembly. The 28-MHz i-f amplifier is the square circuit board at the lower right.

rf amplifier stage, because the mixer has plenty of injection, and it is followed by a low-noise i-f amplifier. The latter is especially important when the intermediate frequency is in the 28-MHz range, as some communications receivers have rather poor noise figure and gain in this region.

Circuit

The rf amplifier (see Fig. 4-23) uses a 2N5032 uhf bipolar transistor, with grounded emitter and neutralization. This gives more gain than the commonly used grounded-base circuit, so only one rf stage is needed to override mixer noise and establish the noise figure of the system. Tuned lines are used in the input, collector, and mixer-input circuits, for some selectivity and rejection of unwanted frequencies. The segment of the band near 432 MHz used for weak-signal work is so narrow that rf selectivity presents no problems. The amplifier collector current is adjusted for optimum signal-to-noise ratio by varying the base bias, by means of R1. The bias source is Zener regulated by CR1.

The mixer is a Schottky-barrier diode, CR2. It works into a 28-MHz i-f amplifier stage using an integrated circuit. The amplifier may not be needed with communications receivers that work well in the 10-meter range, but it adds little to the cost and complexity of the converter, and its gain control, R2, is handy for setting the converter gain to the optimum level for any receiver.

The injection system (Fig. 4-24) uses more transistors and components than most converters have for this purpose, but the string of doublers is easy and inexpensive to build, and it produces injection voltage to spare. Use of a starting frequency of 50.5 MHz makes checking the oscillator a simple matter if the builder has a 50-MHz receiver. A tuned-line filter, loosely coupled to the last doubler, helps to suppress unwanted products of the multiplier system.

Construction

The converter is built in three principal sub-assemblies, mounted on an aluminum plate that fits the top of a 5 X 9-1/2 X 2-inch chassis, thereby providing complete shielding. An L-shaped bracket

1-7/8 inches high and 8-1/2 inches long, supports the oscillator-multiplier assembly. The injection circuit board is mounted with 3-48 screws and short metal spacers, to provide lead clearance. Output from the tuned-line filter, C14L17, is taken off through L18 and small coax to the mixer.

Small screws and spacers are also used to mount the i-f amplifier to the cover plate. A small pc-type control, R2, reached through a hole in the side of the chassis, is used for gain adjustment. If the converter is to be used with several receivers, a shaft-type control could be substituted, and mounted on the cover or chassis to facilitate readjustment as needed. Lead lengths to R2 are not critical.

The rf amplifier enclosure and tuned lines are made of flashing copper. Dimensions are shown in Fig. 4-25. All holes should be drilled before cutting the metal and bending it to shape. Corners are soldered for rigidity and rf shielding. The lines, L1, L3, and L4, should be laid out and drilled before cutting the strips apart, as it is difficult to drill a clean hole in a narrow strip of flashing copper. The ends of the strips are bent up and soldered to the inside of the box.

A shield partition isolates the input line from the collector line, and also supports the transistor, Q1, which is mounted in a small hole near one end of the shield. The emitter lead is connected to the input side of the shield and the case lead to the collector side. Both leads are grounded by a 2-56 screw and nut, with no soldering needed. The entire assembly (the shield, Q1, R1, C2, and L2) can be completed before it is fastened in place with small sheetmetal screws. Note the "sense" of the neutralizing loop, L2. The grounded end is toward the transistor, and the hot end goes through a hole in the shield, toward the grounded end of the tuned lines. Cover the wire with insulating sleeving where it passes through the hole.

Fig. 4-22 — The oscillator-multiplier assembly is on a circuit board mounted on a full-length aluminum bracket that provides both support and shielding. The crystal oscillator is at the right end. The strip-line at the left end is L17, the tuned circuit of a 404-MHz filter in the output of the last doubler stage.

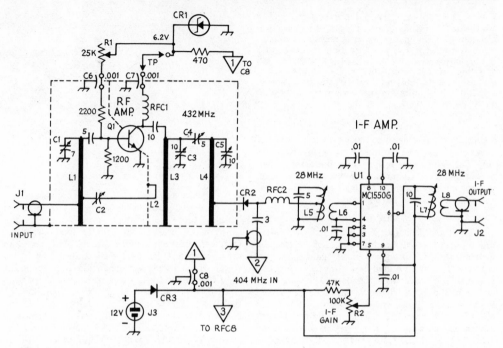

Fig. 4-23 — Schematic diagram and parts information for the rf and i-f portions of the 432-MHz converter.

C1 — 7-pF cylindrical trimmer (Centralab 829-7).

C2 — Copper tab 1/4 inch square, about 1/8 inch over L1, 1-5/8 inches from ground end. Adjust spacing for neutralization.

C3, C5 — 10-pF cylindrical trimmer (Centralab 829-10).

C4 — 5-pF piston trimmer.

C6, C7, C8 — .001-μF feedthrough (Erie 662-003-102K). C7 and a lug on the tie-strip serve as test points, and should be joined by a jumper when no meter is connected.

CR1 — 6.2-volt Zener diode.

CR2 — Hot-carrier diode (Hewlett-Packard 2811).

CR3 — 1-A, 100-PRV diode (Int. Rect. 5A1).

J1, J2 — BNC coaxial jack.

J3 — 2-pin polarized power connector.

L1 — Copper strip 3/8 X 2-1/4 inches after bending. Tap at 7/8 and 1-3/4 inches from ground end.

L2 — No. 24 enamel 1-11/16 inches long, bent as shown in Figs. 4-21 and 25.

L3, L4 — Copper strip 3/8 X 2-9/16 inches long after bending. Tap L4 3/4 inch from ground end.

L5, L7 — 20 turns No. 30 enamel on .162-inch slug-tuned form (Miller 27A013-7). Tap L5 10 turns from ground end.

L6, L8 — 3 turns small enameled wire over cold ends of L5 and L7.

Q1 — Low-noise uhf npn transistor, Motorola 2N5032.

R1 — 25K control, pc-type mounting (CTS R253B — Allied).

R2 — 100K control, pc-type mounting (CTS R104B — Allied).

RFC1 — .22-μH rf choke (Miller 4584).

RFC2 — 6 turns No. 26 enamel 1/8-inch dia, 3/8 inch long.

U1 — Motorola MC1550G integrated circuit.

The coupling capacitor, C4, is supported by its own leads, between L3 and L4. The mixer diode, CR2, is tapped on L4, through a hole in the side of the enclosure, and is supported on a small tie-strip, outside the assembly. The 3-pF injection-coupling capacitor, one end of RFC2, and the end of the small coax from the injection board are also supported by this strip.

Adjustment

Alignment of the oscillator-multiplier chain requires a dip meter or calibrated absorption wavemeter. To protect the amplifier transistor, Q1, do not apply voltage to it, or the bias-adjusting network, until all other stages are checked out. The oscillator should be checked to be sure that it is working only on the marked frequency. Improper adjustment of the coil L9 may allow oscillation on the crystal fundamental, about 16.83 MHz, and output at 50.5 MHz will be much too low to drive the following stage properly. There should be no evidence of rf in the 16-MHz region, or on twice the fundamental frequency. Be sure that the core tunes L9 *through* the crystal frequency.

Peak each doubler stage for maximum output at the desired frequency. If no indicator for 404 MHz is available, a simple Lecher-Wire setup (see Chapter 14) can be used, with a diode and milliammeter, to be sure that this circuit peaks properly. Injection on the proper frequency should

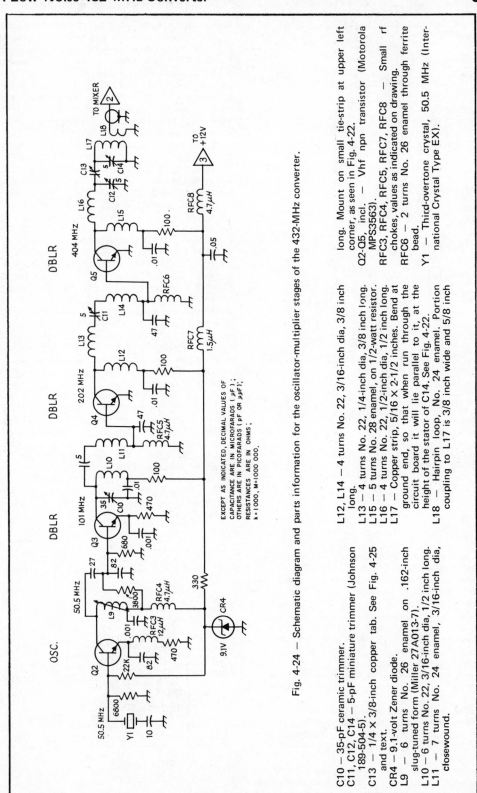

Fig. 4-24 — Schematic diagram and parts information for the oscillator-multiplier stages of the 432-MHz converter.

C10 — 35-pF ceramic trimmer.
C11, C12, C14 — 5-pF miniature trimmer (Johnson 189-504-5).
C13 — 1/4 × 3/8-inch copper tab. See Fig. 4-25 and text.
CR4 — 9.1-volt Zener diode.
L9 — 6 turns No. 26 enamel on .162-inch slug-tuned form (Miller 27A013-7).
L10 — 6 turns No. 22, 3/16-inch dia, 1/2 inch long.
L11 — 7 turns No. 24 enamel, 3/16-inch dia, closewound.

L12, L14 — 4 turns No. 22, 3/16-inch dia, 3/8 inch long.
L13 — 4 turns No. 22, 1/4-inch dia, 3/8 inch long.
L15 — 5 turns No. 28 enamel, on 1/2-watt resistor.
L16 — 4 turns No. 22, 1/2-inch dia, 1/2 inch long.
L17 — Copper strip, 5/16 × 2-1/2 inches. Bend at ground end, so that when run through the circuit board it will lie parallel to it, at the height of the stator of C14. See Fig. 4-22.
L18 — Hairpin loop, No. 24 enamel. Portion coupling to L17 is 3/8 inch wide and 5/8 inch

long. Mount on small tie-strip at upper left corner, as seen in Fig. 4-22.
Q2-Q5, incl. — Vhf npn transistor (Motorola MPS3563).
RFC3, RFC4, RFC5, RFC7, RFC8 — Small rf chokes, values as indicated on drawing.
RFC6 — 2 turns No. 26 enamel through ferrite bead.
Y1 — Third-overtone crystal, 50.5 MHz (International Crystal Type EX).

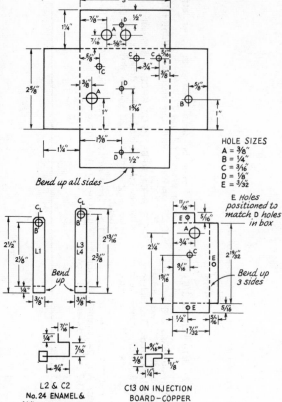

HOLE SIZES
A = 3/8"
B = 1/4"
C = 3/16"
D = 1/8"
E = 3/32"

E Holes positioned to match D holes in box

Bend up all sides

Bend up 3 sides

L2 & C2
No. 24 ENAMEL &
1/4" SQ. COPPER TAB

C13 ON INJECTION
BOARD—COPPER

Fig. 4-25 — Details of the copper parts of the rf amplifier and mixer assembly. It is suggested that layout work and drilling be done before the sheet of flashing copper is cut, as drilling of small pieces of thin metal is difficult.

bias-adjusting control, R1, should be set at maximum resistance, and a 10-mA meter connected in place of the jumper across the test points in the lead to RFC1. Be sure that solid connections are made, as accidental application of base bias, with no collector voltage, can ruin the transistor. A safer arrangement might be to use a lower range meter, with a suitable permanent shunt connected between the test points. The meter can then be removed from the circuit safely.

The collector current should be set to around 2 mA by adjustment of R1. Tune C1, C3, C4, and C5 for maximum response to the test signal, watching the collector current for any sign of change. Such fluctuation, or bursts of noise or rough-sounding notes in the receiver, indicates oscillation in the rf stage. The positions of the coupling loop, L2, and the capacitor tab, C2, should be adjusted to stop oscillation, if any is encountered.

After the converter has been stabilized, adjust the collector current for best signal-to-noise ratio, using a weak test signal. The data sheet for the 2N5032 indicates that best noise figure should be obtained with about 1 mA. Other good uhf transistors may require different values of collector current. Usually it will be found that highest gain will occur with somewhat more collector current than that giving the best signal-to-noise ratio, so it is important to make all tuning adjustments and current setting for the latter quality. Gain can be made up in the i-f stage.

An additional check can be made to be sure that the oscillator-multiplier string is giving the mixer adequate injection voltage. If it is, and if the rf stage is working properly, the injection can be reduced enough to cause the converter gain to drop several dB, before the signal-to-noise ratio is adversely affected. If adequate gain is available elsewhere in the converter, the best overall performance will generally be obtained with the injection level toward the lowest that will give good signal-to-noise ratio.

also cause a noise increase in the communications receiver, at 28 MHz. The copper tab, C13, provides loose coupling to the stator of C12. Adjustment is not critical, and a spacing of 1/8 inch should be about right. There is some coupling between the tuned line and the chassis, causing detuning and loss of injection, when the converter is assembled in its case. The circuit can be repeaked through a small hole drilled in the bottom of the chassis.

Moving the i-f gain control through its range should cause a smooth change in noise level at 28 MHz. L5 and L7 can be peaked roughly on noise, or on a 28-MHz signal.

The mixer tuning should result in a small noise increase as C5 is peaked. This adjustment can be made by using a harmonic of the dip oscillator, or the third harmonic of a 2-meter transmitter, for a test signal.

The rf amplifier can now be adjusted. Before voltage is applied to this stage, a 50-ohm resistor should be connected across J1, or a signal generator with a built-in termination should be used. The

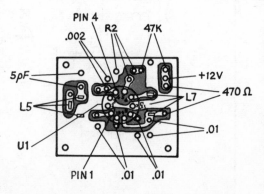

Fig. 4-26 — Half-scale drawing of the injection board, foil side.

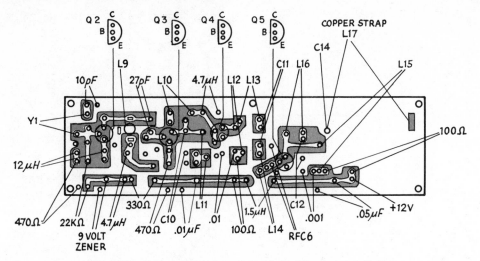

Fig. 4-27 — Half-scale drawing of the i-f amplifier board, foil side.

A BLANKER FOR PULSE–TYPE INTERFERENCE

Our frequencies from 220 MHz up are blessed with a minimum of static, but cursed with a maximum of pulse-type noise, thanks to the shared nature of our assignments above 200 MHz. The "Government Radio Positioning Service" is in there, too. This means radar interference, and radar looks like about the worst interference you can have. The situation could be worse, however, for elimination of static has yet to be accomplished while short pulses of the radar variety can be blanked out very effectively with suitable equipment.

Radar pulses, ignition, and most other noise encountered in the world above 200 MHz have fast rise time and thus can be dealt with if eliminated from the receiver before they get to circuits that are selective enough to lengthen the pulse. Ideally a noise blanker should be applied at the antenna terminals of the receiver. This is not necessarily impossible, but it is difficult, so customary practice is to employ a noise blanker in the circuits after the first mixer, before the selectivity-determining stages. This type of circuit as described in all modern editions of the ARRL *Handbook* for use at 455 kHz is adequate for eliminating auto ignition and the like, but radar interference is several orders of magnitude more severe. A noise blanker used in this manner is too late in the circuit of a vhf converter-receiver combination to prevent overloading of earlier stages.

The blanker of Fig. 4-28 is installed between the vhf or uhf converter and the receiver used as the i-f system, allowing the noise pulses to be eliminated before they reach the high-gain stages. One advantage of this approach is that no modification of existing equipment is required. The noise blanker is connected in the cable between the converter and receiver, and requires no other connections to either.

Circuit Description

The blanker uses two 6AG5s as amplifiers at the converter output frequency, in this instance 28 to 30 MHz or 14 to 18 MHz. It could be any other converter i-f, with suitable modification of the tuned circuits. The 6AG5s were used mainly because of their ready availability; other pentodes such as the 6BH6, 6BA6, 6AK5, and the like should work equally well. The input circuit of the

Fig. 4-28 — A noise blanker for insertion between a vhf or uhf converter and the following communications receiver. Model shown is set up for 28 to 30 MHz, but other converter output frequencies can be used by altering circuit constants.

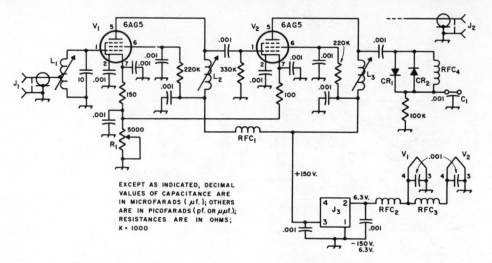

Fig. 4-29 — Schematic diagram and parts information for the noise blanker.

C1 — 1000-pF feedthrough capacitor.
CR1 — 1N64, 1N60, or similar diode.
CR2 — 1N920 or 1N3730 switching diode.
J1, J2 — BNC connector. J2 has extension wire to be trimmed in length and adjusted in position with respect to L3. See text.
J3 — 4-pin male power fitting.
L1 — 28 MHz: 10 turns No. 30 enamel, close-wound on 3/8-inch slug-tuned form, tapped at

3 turns. 14 MHz: 30 turns No. 30 enamel, tapped at 10.
L2 — Like L1, but no tap.
L3 — 13 turns like L2.
R1 — 5000-ohm miniature control.
RFC1-RFC3 — 27-μH rf choke.
RFC4 — 500-μH rf choke.

first stage is tapped to match the low-impedance line from the converter. Single-tuned circuits are used. A gain control is connected in the cathode leads of both tubes, and maximum gain is limited by 150- and 100-ohm series resistors.

The output of the second stage is coupled into a pair of back-to-back diodes, CR1 and CR2. The first is an ordinary second-detector diode such as the 1N64 or 1N60, the other a selected computer diode such as the 1N920 or 1N3730. Output brought out through C1 can be used to monitor visually the noise pulses which are being blanked. With a high-gain audio system connected to C1 all the signals in the bandwidth of the converter can be monitored. This is not practical for hearing weak signals, but it does provide continuous monitoring on a lightly occupied band.

The i-f output coupling for the following receiver is merely the very small capacitance of a wire connected to the center conductor of J2, and placed near the output coil, L3. No direct connection is made at this point. The stray capacitive coupling should be adjusted so that the gain through the noise blanker is the same as it was before the blanker was connected.

A word of warning: this is a high-gain lightly loaded amplifier. The rf chokes decoupling the heaters and plate leads are essential if stable operation is to be obtained. Physical layout like the original is also necessary, unless the builder is experienced in such matters.

Layout

The noise blanker is built in a standard 2 X 3 X 5-inch Minibox, with all rf components in a line down one side. The three coils are 2 inches apart, and the sockets are centered between them. The sockets are mounted so that the grid and plate pins, 1 and 5 respectively, are in a straight line, and nearest to their respective coil terminals.

A grounding lug is placed under each socket mounting nut. A wire is run from the one adjacent to Pin 7 across the socket to the center shield ring and then to Pin 3. Disk ceramic capacitors are connected with the shortest possible leads in the following manner: Pin 2 to Pin 3, Pin 7 to ground, Pin 4 to adjacent ground lug, and Pin 6 to this same lug. The bypasses at the bottom of the coils L2 and L3 are also returned to these lugs, which are adjacent to the side of the unit. Spare lugs on the coil form for L3 are used for tiepoints, for the junction of the three diodes and for the common point of CR3 and RFC4.

Adjustment and Use

After the wiring has been completed and checked for errors the tubes should be installed and the coils L1, L2, and L3 adjusted to the desired intermediate frequency with a grid-dip meter.

The unit should now be connected between an operating converter and its i-f receiver. The noise

Fig. 4-30 — Interior of the noise blanker. The input and power connector fittings are at the left end in this view.

level in the receiver should be adjusted by means of the stray coupling between L3 and J2, to be the same as before the blanker was installed.

The gain control in the blanker is *not* for purposes of adjusting output level. Its function is to adjust the input to the blanking diodes for optimum efficiency. Normally it will be at or near full gain. While listening to the noise it should be possible to remove the input cable from the blanker and observe that the noise drops to approximately the same level that it would if the blanker was not turned on.

It should be possible with a converter connected and the blanker gain control turned full on, to peak up L1, L2, and L3 for maximum noise without any evidence of regeneration. The 3-dB bandwidth of the blanking amplifier with the coils all peaked to the same frequency is approximately 500 kHz. Operation over 1500 kHz or more can be obtained with the coils adjusted in this manner.

In order to make the final adjustments on the blanker it is necessary to have a source of noise and a method of switching a blanker in and out of the circuit. First, tune in a strong pulse-type signal such as radar or very strong automobile-ignition noise. With the blanker in the circuit, the power to the blanker should be turned off and the rf gain on the receiver opened wide. At this time there should be no noise coming from the converter. Turning the converter power on and off should make no change in the output noise of the receiver.

Now the blanker should be turned back on and after warm-up the amount of noise reduction should be observed. When the blanker is properly operating there should be no noise *pulses*, regard-

less of their amplitude when the blanker is out. If the blanker provides a substantial reduction in noise pulses, but does not completely eliminate them, it is not working properly. There are only three reasons for this. The first is feedthrough around the blanker. The test for this was performed in a previous step and it is assumed that there was no feedthrough. There may be insufficient gain in the two amplifying stages. If you are using a normal vhf or uhf converter having 25 to 30 dB or more of gain, and tubes similar in characteristics to a 6AG5, the likelihood of low gain is quite small. The third and most likely reason for poor operation lies in the selection of the proper diodes for CR1 and CR2. Some experimentation with the polarity of the diodes and the size of the diode load is usually required to obtain optimum performance. The particular constants given in the circuit were successful in three different models tested and no difficulty should be encountered in obtaining optimum operation.

Results

The performance of the noise blanker in on-the-air operation leaves little to be desired from the standpoint of external noise elimination in uhf work. With or without noise, the insertion of the noise blanker in the circuit has no discernible effect on the readability of a weak signal. In the presence of pulse-type noise the signal continues to

Fig. 4-31 — Schematic diagram of the blanker power supply. Filter capacitors are electrolytic.

J1 — 3-pin female power connector.
T1 — Small replacement transformer, 125 volts at 30 mA, 6.3 volts at 1 A.
CR1 — 400-volt PRV silicon diode, 500 mA.

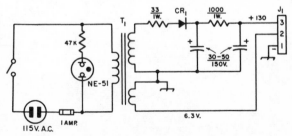

Fig. 4-32 — Power supply for use with the blanker or other equipment items requiring similar current and voltage.

be perfectly readable and the noise is not evident at all in the output of the receiver.

Like all good things there are some drawbacks to the use of a noise blanker. The worst of these is that a very strong local signal will overload the noise blanker and cross-modulate other signals on the band. This is an inherent trait of noise-blanker circuits for which no solution has been found. In order to obtain sufficiently strong blanking pulses, high-gain amplifiers are required and high-gain amplifiers necessarily overload. This disadvantage is far outweighed by the ability to copy weak signals in the presence of strong pulse-type interference. Even when the blanker is overloaded, signals which could not be heard through radar interference without it are readable.

Power Supply

Details of a simple power supply for the blanker are given in Figs. 4-31 and 4-32. This type of supply is useful for many purposes around a station where the owner likes to build small units such as preamplifiers, test equipment, and other items requiring only a small amount of current.

Bibliography

[1] Tilton, "Two-Band Station for the VHF Beginner," *QST*, July through October, 1961. Complete reprint of this widely used 4-part series is available for 50 cents, from ARRL, Newington, CT 06111. All components of this station were described in previous editions of this Manual: 14-MHz tuner, 50- and 144-MHz transmitters, modulator and power supply, SWR bridge, and converters for 50 and 144 MHz.

[2] DeMaw, "The D.C. 80-10 Receiver," *QST*, May, 1969, and 48th and 49th Editions, *The Radio Amateur's Handbook.*

[3] DeMaw, "More Thoughts on Solid-State Receiver Design," *QST*, January, 1971. Also 1972 *Handbook*, "A Receiving Package for 1.8 to 144 MHz."

[4] Hall and Wilson, "A Single-Band Converter," *QST*, May, 1971.

[5] Blakeslee, "A Second Look at Linear Integrated Circuits," *QST*, July, 1971.

[6] Constructional information on vhf receiving equipment using vacuum tubes:

Nuvistor Converters for 50 and 144 MHz Part 4 of a 4-part series, see Reference 1. Matching converters for 220 and 432 were added later in the *Handbook*, and in previous editions of this Manual. Photocopies of information not appearing in the *QST* series: add $1.00 to the reprint price of 50 cents.

W2AZL Two-Meter Converter Excellent converter design, originally in December, 1959, *QST*. (Photocopies $1.25) Also in Edition 1 of this Manual.

50- and 144-MHz Reception at Low Cost Simple converters and modification of BC-455. Photocopies from Edition 1 of this Manual, $1.25.

Bandswitching converter, 50 through 220 MHz, from *Standard Coil TV tuner*. Photocopies from previous editions, $1.00.

Superregenerative Receivers for 50 and 144 Mhz Photocopies from previous editions, $1.50.

50-MHz mobile converter with 12-volt Nuvistors Photocopy from Edition 1, 50 cents.

Copies of *QST* still in stock are available for the current cover price. Photocopies of out-of-print items will be made for 25 cents per page, on request. Glossy 8 by 10 prints of ARRL construction project photographs are available for $2.00 per print.

V H F Transmitter Design

Before we discuss transmitting techniques for the amateur bands above 50 MHz in detail it will be well for us to see what standards are set for us in the U.S. Regulations. The two numbered paragraphs below are not exact quotes, but they summarize pertinent regulations.

97.71 – Amateur stations operating below 144 MHz must employ adequately filtered dc plate power for transmitting equipment, to minimize modulation from this source.

97.73 – Spurious radiations from an amateur station below 144 MHz shall be reduced or eliminated in accordance with good engineering practice . . . . In case of A3 emission, the transmitter shall not be modulated to the extent that spurious radiation occurs, and in no case shall the carrier wave be modulated in excess of 100 percent. . . . Simultaneous amplitude and frequency modulation is not permitted. . . . The frequency of the emitted carrier wave shall be as constant as the state of the art permits.

It will be seen that stability and quality requirements imposed on all lower amateur frequencies apply equally on the 50-MHz band, but not to 144 MHz and higher. This is not to say that we should not strive for excellence on the higher bands, as well as on 50 MHz, but it is important to remember that we may be cited by FCC for failing to meet the required standards in 50-MHz work.

A sideband signal having excessive bandwidth, an a-m signal whose frequency jumps when modulation is applied, an fm signal that is also amplitude-modulated, a cw signal with excessive keying chirp or objectionable key clicks – any of these is undesirable on any band, but they are all *illegal* on 50 MHz. Any of them could earn the operator an FCC citation in 50-MHz work. And misinterpretation of these points in an FCC examination could cost the would-be amateur his first ticket.

From the stand-point of the law, there is a vast relaxation in the technical standards we must meet above the 50-MHz band. Looking at the question from the amateur point of view, however, there is little or none. The desirability of radiating the best signal that is technically feasible is the same throughout the vhf region, if the user is interested in worthwhile results, and in causing a minimum of trouble for his fellow users of the vhf bands.

It should be remembered that the use of unstable equipment is *legal* above 144 MHz, so long as the radiation from the transmitter remains entirely within the assigned frequency band. There are some circumstances where very simple and therefore unstable gear may serve useful ends, and these will be touched on later in this book, but our main emphasis will be on transmitters that employ crystal control or its equivalent in stability and freedom from spurious emissions. That such concern for clean signals is required by law only on the 50-MHz band will be largely ignored.

The frequencies above 50 MHz were once a world apart from the rest of amateur radio, in equipment required, in modes of operation and in results obtained. Today these worlds blend increasingly. Thus, if the reader does not find what he needs in these pages to solve a transmitter problem, it may be covered in the hf transmitting portions of the ARRL *Handbook*. This chapter deals mainly with aspects of transmitter design and operation that call for different techniques in equipment for 50 MHz and up.

DESIGNING FOR VHF SSB AND CW

Almost universal use of ssb for voice work in the hf range has had a major impact on equipment design for the vhf and even uhf bands. Many amateurs have a considerable investment in hf sideband gear. This equipment provides accurate frequency calibration and good mechanical and electrical stability. It is effective in cw as well as ssb communication. These qualities being attractive to the vhf man, it is natural for him to look for ways to use his hf gear on frequencies above 50 MHz.

Thus increasing use is being made of vhf accessory devices, both ready-made and homebuilt. This started years ago with the vhf converter, for receiving. Rather similar conversion equipment for transmitting has been widely used since ssb began taking over the hf bands. Today the hf trend is to one-package stations, called transceivers. The obvious move for many vhf men is a companion box to perform both transmitting and receiving conversion functions. Known as **transverters**, these are offered by several manufacturers. They are relatively simple to build, and are thus likely projects for the home-builder of vhf gear.

Transverter vs. Separate Units

It does not necessarily follow that what is popular in hf work is ideal for vhf use. Our bands are wide, and piling-up in a narrow segment of a band, which the transceiver encourages, is less than ideal use of a major asset of the vhf bands – spectrum space. Separate ssb exciters and receivers, with separate vhf conversion units for transmitting and receiving, tend to suit our purposes better than the transceiver-transverter combination, at least in home-station service.

Future of Other Modes

It should not be assumed that ssb will monopolize voice work in the world above 50 MHz in the way that it has the amateur voice frequencies below 29 MHz. Sideband is unquestionably far superior to other voice modes for weak-signal DX work, but where there is plenty of room, as there is in all vhf and higher bands, both amplitude and frequency modulation have merit. A low-powered a-m transmitter is a fine construction project for a vhf beginner, and fm has been gaining in popularity rapidly in recent years. A reprint of a very popular 4-part *QST* series describing a complete two-band a-m and cw station for the vhf beginner is available from ARRL for 50 cents.[1]

The decline in use of amplitude modulation has been mainly in high-powered stations. The heavy-iron modulator seems destined to become a thing of the past, but this should not rule out use of a-m. Many ssb transceivers are capable of producing high-quality a-m, and one linear amplifier stage can build as little as 2 watts a-m output up to 200 watts or so, with excellent voice quality, if the equipment is adjusted with care. It should be remembered that the transmitting converter (or heterodyne unit as it is often called) is not a sideband device only. It will serve equally well with a-m, fm, or cw drive.

THE OSCILLATOR-MULTIPLIER APPROACH

A basic difference between ssb transmitters and those for other modes is that the ssb signal, once generated, cannot be run through frequency multiplier stages to get to a higher frequency or band. Where modes other than ssb are used, generation of the signal usually involves an oscillator in the hf range, followed by one or more frequency multiplier stages, and at least one amplifier stage working at the final frequency. A signal of any kind at any frequency *can* be heterodyned to another frequency. but only amplitude-modulated and sideband signals *must* be.

The starting frequency of the oscillator-multiplier transmitter is usually in the 8-MHz range, though 6, 12, 18 MHz and other frequencies are also used. Typically, a 50-MHz transmitter is controlled at 8.334 to 9 MHz, the frequency then being tripled to 25 to 27 MHz, and doubled to 50 to 54 MHz, before amplifier stages build up the

[1] For this and other numbered references, see bibliography at the end of this chapter.

power level. A 144-MHz transmitter may start at 8 to 8.222 MHz, which is then tripled, doubled and tripled to 144 to 148 MHz. A 220-MHz lineup would use 8.149 to 8.333 MHz, tripled three times to 220 to 225 MHz. The portions of the 420- and 1215-MHz bands where stabilized equipment is usually employed are in third and ninth harmonic relation to the low end of the 144-MHz band. From these figures and from the chart, Fig. 5-1, it may be seen that coverage of 8 to 9 MHz in the oscillator stage could take care of most of our requirements through 1300 MHz.

Many other starting frequencies and orders of multiplication are usable. The oscillator-multiplier approach is convenient in multiband designs, and it is widely used in equipment other than the single-sideband variety. One weak point is that any instability in the controlling oscillator is multiplied: 6 times in the 50-MHz example of the previous paragraph, 18 times for 144-MHz operation, 27 times for the 220 MHz band, and so on. An oscillator that seems quite stable at 8 MHz may suffer from drift, hum modulation, mechanical instability or frequency modulation to the extent that the signal at the 54th harmonic, 432 MHz, may be unacceptable to the critical worker. This is particularly true of the conventional vfo. The crystal oscillator is much superior for frequency control on 144 MHz and higher bands.

The possibility that harmonics other than the desired ones will appear in the output should be considered in designing a vhf exciter. Such unwanted frequencies may be a source of interference to TV, fm, and other vhf reception in the vicinity of the amateur station. They can be reduced by taking suitable circuit precautions, but their interference potential should not be ignored.

The number of frequencies that could cause trouble can be reduced by using a high starting frequency in the vhf exciter. A 24-MHz oscillator instead of one at 6 or 8 MHz eliminates most of the harmonics that are potential sources of TVI in the low TV channels. Starting at 48 or 50 MHz is still better. There are good reasons for using 6 or 8 MHz, however, if precautions are taken to prevent radiation of unwanted harmonics. A stable oscillator is more readily built in this frequency range than for 24 MHz or higher. Crystals for 6 to 9 MHz are inexpensive, reliable and easy to use, while those for 12 MHz and higher cost more initially and require more care in application. Vhf crystals are used mainly where economy in number of stages and over-all current drain is an important consideration.

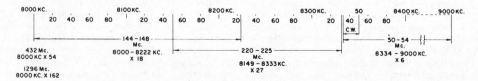

Fig. 5-1 — Our bands above 50 MHz are nearly harmonically related. The possibility of using a single frequency-control system for all bands from 50 through 1300 MHz is illustrated in this chart. The example is for oscillators in the 8-MHz region, but other frequency ranges such as 6 or 12 MHz may be used.

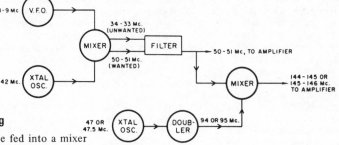

Fig. 5-2 — Block diagram of a typical heterodyning process for producing stable VFO-controlled signals at 50 and 144 MHz.

Heterodyning

Any two frequencies may be fed into a mixer stage to produce resultant frequencies equal to the sum and difference of the two. This process is inherent in the superheterodyne receiver, but it was not widely used in transmitters until the advent of single sideband. If a keyed or modulated signal is heterodyned properly, the product is an exact replica of the original signal, with no more frequency instability or bandwidth than was present in the two components mixed. Heterodyning is thus a good way of obtaining variable frequency control, since it is relatively easy to build a variable oscillator for the hf range that is adequately stable at its fundamental frequency.

The process is shown in block diagram form in Fig. 5-2. The control signal is generated at some frequency below about 10 MHz, 8 to 9 MHz in this example. A 42-MHz signal from a stable source beats with the control signal in the mixer. Two main products, one at 34 to 33 MHz, and the other at 50 to 51 MHz, result. The unwanted difference product is rejected by the filter, while the desired sum at 50 to 51 MHz is passed on to succeeding amplifier stages.

The vhf man who works 50 MHz and higher bands may employ heterodyning again to reproduce the 50-MHz signal on another band. In the example the 50-MHz signal is mixed with energy at 94 or 95 MHz, to give coverage of the lower half of the 144-MHz band. Other crystals can be used in either crystal oscillator to extend the coverage to any one-megahertz segment desired.

The chief problem in heterodyning is to prevent unwanted products from being radiated. In our example we use the sum of 42 and 8 to 9 MHz and 50 and 94 MHz but the differences are also produced. The selectivity of the tuned circuits may be sufficient to reject the unwanted products but this should not be assumed. The output of any transmitter employing heterodyning should be checked carefully to be sure that frequencies other than the intended one are not being radiated. A mixer stage requires only a very small amount of energy on the mixing frequencies to produce output, so harmonics and other components of the signals being mixed may beat with each other and produce all manner of unwanted frequencies. Mixing at low level, careful examination of the spectrum for spurious products, and use of highly selective circuits for passing on the desired product and rejecting others are musts for the builder of a heterodyne exciter.

Crystal Oscillators

Quartz crystals of many kinds and cuts are used for frequency control but all have one characteristic in common: when a voltage is applied across it, the crystal is distorted mechanically. The converse is also true: mechanical distortion of the crystal develops a voltage across it. This is the basic piezoelectric effect, discovered many years ago and applied to crystal control of oscillators as far back as the 1920s.

The greatly magnified edge views of crystal plates in Fig. 5-3 show, in simplified form, what happens to an oscillating crystal. The quiescent

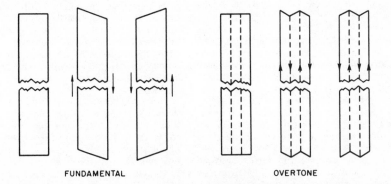

FUNDAMENTAL   OVERTONE

Fig. 5-3 — Greatly magnified edge views of quartz crystals, showing the mechanical distortion effect when voltage is applied across the crystal. At the left is a fundamental crystal, and at the right is one oscillating on its third overtone. Frequency of oscillation depends on crystal thickness — the thinner the crystal the higher the frequency.

state is at the far left. The next two sketches show the distortion at the positive and negative peaks of the oscillation cycle. The crystal is a very high-Q device. It will oscillate on one frequency only, determined principally by the thickness of the crystal. (The thinner the plate, the higher the frequency.) Connected properly in an oscillatory circuit, the crystal will control the frequency of oscillation within very narrow limits.

Crystals and circuits for their use in vhf transmitters are of two principal types: fundamental and overtone. It is important for the vhf worker to understand the basic difference between them. The fundamental crystal, whose mode of operation has just been described, is usually supplied for frequencies up to about 18 MHz. Though fundamental crystals can be made for frequencies up to about 30 MHz, they are very thin and difficult to handle and process above the normal commercial limit of 18 MHz. (Overtone crystals can be supplied for lower frequencies, and 12 MHz was the dividing line for many years.)

At frequencies above 12 to 18 MHz it is customary to go to overtone oscillators. Almost any crystal can be made to oscillate on its third overtone, which is roughly three times the frequency for which the crystal was ground. In overtone operation the crystal in effect breaks up into an *odd* number of layers, as shown in the right half of Fig. 5-3. The oscillation cycle is given in the two sketches at the right. Because of mechanical considerations, the overtone may not be an exact multiple of the fundamental frequency, though it is always close to it. Only the odd multiples are available as overtones; there is no such thing as a second, fourth, or sixth overtone. The fifth, seventh, and ninth overtones can be obtained quite readily with suitably processed crystals.

Overtone operation with crystals processed for fundamental service depends on several factors, principally the flatness of the crystal and the method of mounting in the holder. Because the layers for third-overtone oscillation in an 8-MHz crystal are less than 0.004 inch thick, and for higher-order overtones progressively thinner, it can be seen that minor variations in flatness or surface imperfections quickly inhibit overtone oscillation. Crystals clamped between metal plates, as in the common FT-243 holder, seldom work well above the third overtone.

Crystals processed for overtone operation usually can be made to oscillate on higher-order overtones than the intended frequency.[2] A crystal marked for 24 MHz, normally an 8-MHz fundamental, will often work well on 40 MHz, 56 MHz, or even 72 MHz in suitable circuits. Unless the purchaser specifies otherwise, crystal companies customarily supply third-overtone crystals for frequencies from about 18 to 54 MHz, fifth-overtone for 54 to 70 MHz, and seventh-overtone for frequencies up to around 100 MHz. Overtone crystals for frequencies as high as 150 MHz can be made, but in amateur service frequencies above about 72 MHz are seldom used for direct control.

For best stability any crystal oscillator should be run at low power input, and this is increasingly important as one goes to higher frequencies. The crystal oscillator should always be regarded as a device for controlling frequency, not as a source of rf power. Control of feedback is also important. However control is achieved, feedback should be at a level that will allow the oscillator to start readily, but not enough to cause heating or frequency jumping.

Crystal Oscillator Circuits

An almost infinite variety of crystal oscillator circuits may be employed in vhf transmitters. Only a few will be described here, to demonstrate basic principles. These will satisfy most requirements, and though the literature contains special claims for innumerable variations, proper adjustment and operating conditions are the principal factors in achieving the desired results.

A simple circuit useful for both fundamental and overtone oscillators is shown in Fig. 5-4A. It is essentially the same, whether the device used is a field-effect transistor, as shown, or a triode tube. An overtone circuit for bipolar transistors is shown at B. Feedback to sustain oscillation is mainly through the device capacitance in 5-4A, and the feedback frequency is determined by the tuned circuit, L1C1. With a fundamental crystal in place, the circuit may oscillate on the crystal frequency, regardless of the setting of L1C1, but output will rise sharply as the circuit is tuned through the crystal frequency.

An overtone crystal is merely one that has been processed and mounted in such a way as to encourage overtone oscillation. With an overtone crystal in place, if feedback is not concentrated on the desired overtone frequency by proper design and adjustment of L1C1, the circuit may oscillate only on the fundamental frequency, or perhaps not oscillate at all. The tuned circuit should have fairly high Q, and it should be adjusted with care, to be sure that oscillation is on the desired overtone frequency, and that there is no energy at the fundamental or second-harmonic frequencies. With a 24-MHz crystal, for example, there should be energy only on the marked frequency of the crystal, and none on 8 MHz (the fundamental) or 16 MHz (the second harmonic). If a signal is heard at 8 or 16 MHz, the oscillator may be loaded too heavily, or possibly the tuned circuit does not quite reach the overtone frequency. The latter is often the case with slug-tuned coils that may *appear* to tune, but which are actually only approaching resonance as the core centers in the winding.

If overtone oscillation is attempted with crystals made for fundamental use, more feedback is usually needed at the overtone frequency than is provided by the circuit just described. Two methods of supplying this feedback are shown in Fig. 5-4C and D. In D the crystal is effectively tapped up the output circuit by the capacitive divider, of which C3 is the adjustable component. The *lower* the capacitance the greater the feedback. Usually a fixed 50-pF capacitor will do for C3, though lack of an adjustment for feedback may allow this

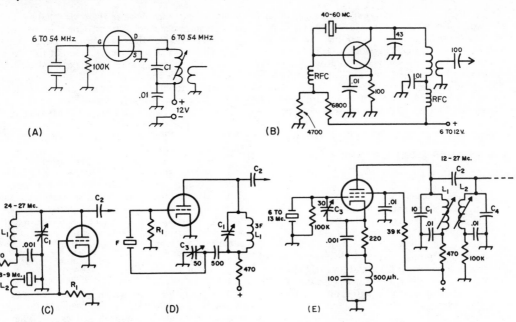

Fig. 5-4 — Typical crystal oscillator circuits. The FET circuit, A, works with either fundamental or overtone crystals, up to at least 54 MHz, though circuit Q is more critical for overtone operation. A comparable bipolar transistor circuit is shown at B. Circuits C and D can be used to make fundamental crystals oscillate on their third overtone, through control of feedback. Value of R1 depends on the tube type; 47,000 ohms to 100,000 ohms is common. Values of C1 and L1, L2 depend on frequency. A pentode oscillator-multiplier with double-tuned inductive coupling is shown in E. C2 should be the lowest usable value; about 2 pF in E, 10 pF in others.

circuit to oscillate on the fundamental frequency of the crystal. In C the crystal is part of an inductive feedback loop, L2, coupled to the tuned circuit, L1C1. Though adjustment of the feedback is not convenient this way, the circuit has the advantage of oscillating only on the overtone frequency. In all such circuits it is possible to have too much feedback, which can result in overheating of the crystal, multiple oscillation frequencies, or even free-running oscillation. The use of fundamental crystals for overtone service is an economy and a convenience that exacts its price in careful adjustment for the desired results.

Multiples of the crystal frequency (*not* overtones) can be obtained with the oscillator of Fig. 5-4E. Here the screen of the tetrode or pentode tube simulates the plate of a triode oscillator. The plate of the tube serves as a take-off element for harmonics of the crystal frequency, usually the second or third, though higher-order harmonics are present and can be used. The values of L1 and C1 determine which harmonic will be emphasized. Double-tuned inductive coupling, through the circuit L2C4, helps to reject unwanted harmonics. For best selectivity the capacitor C2 should be the lowest usable value, and the coupling between L1 and L2 should be the least that will pass the desired amount of energy at the intended harmonic frequency. Tighter coupling serves no useful purpose, and may raise the level of unwanted-harmonic energy passed on to succeeding stages.

In the tetrode oscillator the tube cathode is above rf ground by virtue of the rf choke and capacitor combination. Feedback is controlled by the variable grid-cathode capacitor, C3, which can be replaced with a fixed type once the approximate value needed is found. In its most common application in vhf transmitters, the oscillator plate circuit tunes roughly 24 to 27 MHz, permitting frequencies in this range to be taken off while using fundamental crystals at 6 to 6.75, 8 to 9, or 12 to 13.5 MHz. The stage is then an oscillator-quadrupler, tripler or doubler, respectively. With a wide-range variable capacitor for C1, adjacent harmonics can be tuned if this serves useful design ends.

This type of oscillator always works on the crystal fundamental frequency. The tuned plate circuit merely emphasizes the desired harmonic; it does not completely eliminate the other harmonics. The circuit is useful with pentode-triode tubes, with the triode portion doubling to 48 to 54 MHz.

The bipolar transistor oscillator, Fig. 5-4B, should have a high value of capacitance across the collector circuit, compared with other oscillators. Circuits for bipolar transistors must cope with the low impedances characteristic of this type of transistor. It may be necessary to tap the collector down on its tuned circuit, in order to develop sufficient Q for the circuit to work properly.

For best stability with any oscillator, crystal or other, the designer must follow certain rules:

1. Operating voltages must be constant, and except for tube heater voltage, pure dc. 2. The oscillator load should be unvarying, and the stage should not have to deliver power. 3. The oscillator should run at very low input, to avoid drift, both long-term and cyclical, due to heating and cooling. The ideal arrangement is to build the best oscillator that is practicable, and follow it with a class-A amplifier. This is called a *buffer,* implying effective isolation from load variations resulting from adjustment, keying or modulation of succeeding stages.

VARIABLE OSCILLATORS — VXO AND VFO

A variable capacitance or inductance, usually the former as a matter of convenience, can be made to vary the frequency of oscillation in a crystal oscillator circuit to some extent. In free-running oscillators a variable capacitor is usually the principal tuning device. Both types of oscillators will be discussed here, and practical examples are given in Chapter 6. The potential user should have a clear idea of the strengths and weaknesses of both these means of variable frequency control.

The VXO

If the inherent capacitance (crystal holder plus circuit strays) is kept low, a crystal oscillator can be "pulled" over a small frequency range by means of a variable capacitor across the crystal. A crystal oscillator in which this is done intentionally is called a VXO. A simple form merely varies the pressure (and thus the capacitance) on the metal clamping plates in the pressure-mounted type of crystal holder. See Chapter 16 for an example.

A better method employs a variable capacitor across the crystal circuit, which may include a variable inductor in series with the crystal, as shown in Fig. 5-5. The coil L1 "rubberizes" the crystal to a degree depending on the inductance value. Flexibility is obtained at the expense of stability, and the crystal oscillator is no better than the free-running type, if the series-coil idea is carried too far. With the variable capacitor alone the frequency pulling is slight, but the oscillator stability can be excellent if the numbered rules a few paragraphs back are followed.

With or without the series coil, most of the frequency change occurs with the first few pF of capacitance variation, so keeping stray capacitance to a minimum pays off in increased variable-frequency coverage. Usable frequency change also depends on the quality of the crystal and on the

mounting methods, both in the crystal holder and the crystal socket. A rule-of-thumb for crystal pulling allows a 750-Hz change, maximum, for each megahertz of crystal frequency, without the series coil . Thus, the 4.5 kHz to be expected with a 6-MHz crystal, and 6 kHz with an 8-MHz one translate to roughly 35 kHz per crystal at 50 MHz and 110 kHz at 144 MHz, without the series coil. This can be increased to 100 kHz at 50 MHz and 300 at 144 MHz with the coil in the circuit, before the stability of the oscillator is degraded to that of the average good VFO.

The VXO principle is widely used in fm transmitters, where precise "netting" of transmitter frequencies is required in repeater work. Obviously it also offers a simple approach to frequency modulation of the transmitter, by connecting a varactor diode in place of or in parallel with C1. The bias on the varactor is varied at an audio rate, with simple speech circuitry.

The VFO

Variable-frequency oscillators of the free-running type (VFO) are in great demand for vhf transmitter frequency control, but except where heterodyning to a higher frequency is used, as opposed to frequency multiplication, the VFO is generally unsatisfactory. Small instabilities, hardly noticeable in hf work, are multiplied to unacceptable proportions in the oscillator-multiplier type of transmitter. The fact that many such unstable VFO rigs are on the air, particularly on 6 meters, does not make them desirable, or even *legal*. Only careful attention to all the fine points of VFO design and use can result in satisfactory stability in vhf transmitters of the oscillator-multiplier type.

FREQUENCY MULTIPLIERS

Circuits for frequency multipliers are quite similar to those in straight-through smplifiers discussed in the following section, except that higher driving power and bias are usually needed in multiplier stages. It is important to keep in mind that in multipliers for the vhf bands the probability is that frequencies other than the desired harmonics will be present in the output. These can be sources of TVI in vhf transmitters. Examples are the 9th harmonic of 6 MHz and the 7th harmonic of 8 MHz, both falling in TV Channel 2. The 10th harmonic of 8-MHz oscillators falling in Channel 6 is a similar problem. These unwanted multiples can be held down by the use of the highest practical

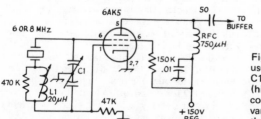

Fig. 5-5 — Typical variable crystal oscillator (VXO) uses the basic Pierce circuit. The variable capacitor, C1, may be connected directly across the crystal (high stability, small tuning range) or the series coil, L1, may be added for more frequency variation. Stability of the oscillator is degraded as the value of L1 is increased.

degree of selectivity in interstage coupling circuits in the vhf transmitter, and by proper shielding and interstage impedance matching. This last is particularly important in transistor frequency multipliers and amplifiers. More on avoiding TVI will be found later in this chapter, and in the chapter on interference problems.

The varactor multiplier (see UHF and Microwaves) is much used for developing power in the 420-MHz band. Requiring no power supply, it uses only driving power from a previous stage, yet quite high orders of efficiency are possible. A varactor tripler to 220 MHz is shown in Chapter 6. A 220-MHz exciter tuned down to 216 MHz makes a good driver for a 432-MHz varactor doubler. More commonly used is a tripler with 144-MHz drive. The output of a varactor multiplier tends to have appreciable amounts of power at other frequencies than the desired, so use of a strip-line or coaxial filter is recommended, whether the multiplier drives an amplifier or works into the antenna directly.

Frequency multipliers are usually single-ended though other combinations are possible. The "push-push doubler" (input push-pull, output parallel) gives good efficiency and rejection of odd multiples of the driving frequency. A push-pull tripler, often used with dual tubes, both tetrodes and triodes, is fairly efficient and tends to cancel even multiples of the driving frequency. There is little tendency to oscillation in frequency multipliers, and neutralization, screen-circuit bypassing and other stabilization devices of amplifier circuitry are seldom needed. Some points discussed in more detail in connection with transistor amplifiers may also apply to solid-state frequency multipliers to some extent, but instability problems are not common in multiplier stages.

POWER AMPLIFIERS

Principles of transmitter design and operation tend to be similar regardless of frequency. Basic amplifier theory is covered thoroughly in the ARRL *Handbook,* so modes of operation and circuit design of power amplifiers are discussed here only insofar as the special aspects of the vhf field are concerned. We look at the principal problems the vhf operator faces in thinking about increasing transmitter power.

Transistors or Tubes?

In receiving, this question has been answered on a strongly solid-state note. The problem is not quite the same in transmitting, except where low-power mobile and portable operation is the main concern. For more than a few watts of power, transmitting with transistors may have little to recommend it. The portable exciter using transistors, that can serve as a complete rig for portable work and as a driver for the home station, has some appeal, but tubes of some sort are almost inevitable in running appreciable power at the home base. Special transistor problems in amplifiers will be discussed as they arise in individual units, leaving tube techniques in amplifiers as our principal subject here.

Linear or Class C?

Amplifiers in vhf transmitters all once ran Class C, or as near thereto as available drive levels would permit. This was mainly for high-efficiency cw, and quality high-level amplitude modulation. Class C is now used mostly for cw or fm, and in either of these modes the drive level is uncritical, except as it affects the operating efficiency. The influence of ssb techniques is seen clearly in current amplifier trends. Today Class AB_1 is popular and most amplifiers are set up for linear amplification, for ssb and − to a lesser extent − a-m. The latter is often used in connection with small amplitude-modulated vhf transmitters, having their own built-in audio equipment. Where a-m output is available from the ssb exciter, it is also useful with the Class AB_1 linear amplifier, for only a watt or two of driver output is required. When used with an a-m phone transmitter, the linear amplifier is inherently a low-efficiency device, but it has its virtues, particularly when other modes of operation are planned.

Various routes to increased power are shown in Fig. 5-6. Our basic a-m and cw transmitter, A, requires only the linear amplifier, B, to run up to full legal power of 1 kilowatt. This can be a high-efficiency system on cw, delivering up to 750 watts output. As an a-m phone linear, its maximum power output is 350 watts, and it is likely to be much less. If the original transmitter includes provision for ssb, as well as cw and a-m, the linear becomes more attractive. Setup C can give full power on cw and ssb, and medium power on a-m, without auxiliary audio equipment.

Maximum power output on a-m phone requires a high-level modulator, as in D. A 500-watt audio system, needed to modulate a kilowatt amplifier, is an expensive and bulky proposition, and with the current trend to ssb in amateur voice communication, more and more vhf men are thinking twice before making the considerable investment in terms of money, space and weight that a kilowatt a-m phone station entails. There will undoubtedly be considerable use of a-m in vhf work for many years to come, despite the inroads of ssb, so the relative merits of linear and high-level modulated amplifiers deserve careful thought.

If one is to concentrate on a-m, to the exclusion of other modes, a plate-modulated power amplifier of no more than 200 to 500 watts input may be desirable. The cost of both rf and audio components rises very rapidly above the 500-watt level, and it may well be that the extra cost could be better spent in other ways.

For the all-mode operator, the linear approach is very attractive, since minor modification of the operating conditions will permit high-efficiency operation on cw and ssb, while retaining a-m

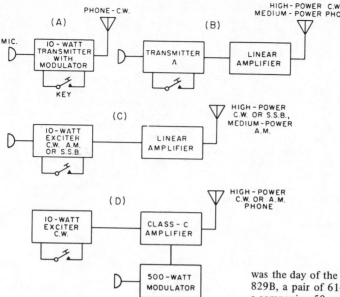

Fig. 5-6 — Some ways to increase power in a vhf station. Transmitter A is a typical packaged unit, complete with modulator and power supply. Adding a linear amplifier, B, can give up to 300-watts output on a-m phone, or 750-watts output on cw. The side-band exciter, C, usually also makes provision for cw and a-m, so it combines well with a linear amplifier for high power on ssb or cw, and medium power on a-m phone. A small rf unit, D, is used to drive a Class-C amplifier for high-efficiency cw. Addition of a modulator is required for high-efficiency a-m phone.

capability at a somewhat lower power level — all with a station that can be built compactly and at a moderate cost for the high-power portions.

A distinct advantage of the linear approach is the matter of driving power. With a Class AB₁ linear (most commonly used with vhf tetrodes), no driving power is required; only voltage. Kilowatt amplifiers of the grounded-cathode type can deliver over 300 watts output with nothing more than a 3-watt a-m rig as a driver. A little more drive will push the cw output to as much as 600 watts. With a driver output of 7 to 10 watts, the amplifiers will give up to 750 watts Class C output on cw, ssb or fm.

Operating conditions for linear service are critical. The amplifier must be heavily loaded. If it uses tetrodes, the screen voltage, and preferably the bias as well, should be regulated. The drive level must be watched closely, to be certain that the amplifier is never driven into the grid-current region, if it is operated Class AB₁. An oscilloscope is practically a necessity, if true linear conditions are to be achieved and maintained. In all these respects the linear is more demanding than Class-C cw or plate-modulated a-m service would be.

Grounded-Cathode or Grounded-Grid?

Nearly all vhf power amplifiers in amateur service have been of the grounded-cathode type, mainly because of the high drive requirements of the grounded-grid amplifier. In the heyday of a-m communication the typical rig was a transmitter or transceiver of no more than a few watts output. It had its own modulator, and the owner was not ordinarily interested in building additional high-powered audio equipment. His choices were then either a high-powered linear amplifier, or a medium-powered Class-C stage, the latter requiring a modulator of modest power to go with it. This

was the day of the 100-watt transmitter, usually an 829B, a pair of 6146s, or some similar setup, with a companion 50-watt modulator.

When vhf sideband became popular the usual ssb exciter was also a low-powered device, usually a low-level mixer and a Class-A amplifier, with no more than a few watts output on the vhf band in question. The logical amplifier for getting into the medium- or high-power brackets with this type of exciter is the grounded-cathode type, using tetrodes. This puts the station capability up to several hundred watts, with a single stage having very low driving power requirements.

Meanwhile, hf sideband was growing up around the 100-watt exciter and the grounded-grid kilowatt amplifier. It was only a question of time before vhf stations would follow the same route. Today there is an increasing trend to 100-watt transmitters and transceivers in vhf work, especially on the 50-MHz band. Thus, in the following chapter we show 50-MHz examples of both the low-drive grounded-cathode amplifier and the grounded-grid type requiring an exciter capable of delivering 25 watts output or more.

There is merit in both methods. The grounded-cathode amplifier using external-anode tetrodes is capable of very high efficiency, even with only a few watts of driving power. It can be shifted readily from one operating mode to another, to suit the type of drive to be used, and it lends itself nicely table-top style, requiring only a very small exciter. In return, it exacts a price in the form of rather critical adjustment for optimum results, and the need for neutralization. Its power-supply and metering requirements are fairly complex.

The grounded-grid amplifier can be quite simple in regard to circuit, construction and operation. Triodes work well, simplifying power-supply problems through elimination of the screen supply needed with tetrodes. Efficiency tends to be lower, but some of the driver power appears in the amplifier output. Neutralization is not ordinarily required. If the driving power is available, the grounded-grid amplifier is logical for increasing

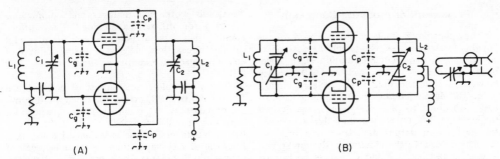

Fig. 5-7 — Loading effect of input and output capacitances in single-ended circuits limits their use at higher frequencies in the vhf range. In the push-pull circuit, right, these strays and also the tuning capacitances are in series across the tuned circuits, permitting use of a given tube type at much higher frequencies.

power, at least on 50 MHz. At 144 MHz and higher, drive is likely to be more of a problem, and tubes designed for grounded-grid service are mostly types that do not perform well much above 100 MHz.

The tetrode grounded-cathode amplifier is currently almost standard procedure for 144, 220, and 420 MHz. Above 1000 MHz, the trend reverts to grounded-grid, mainly because tubes available are coaxial uhf types designed especially for this application. The 2C39A, and its later version, the 3CX100A5, are widely used in medium-power grounded-grid service in the 1215-MHz band.

Single-ended, Parallel or Push-Pull?

On lower bands use of two or more tubes in parallel is almost standard practice. Often it is less expensive to use several small tubes in parallel than one larger one of the same total power capability. Parallel is preferred to push-pull in hf transmitters mainly because of its simpler circuitry and ready adaptability to bandswitching. Where tube and stray circuit capacitances do not represent a large percentage of the total, parallel connection of tubes is entirely satisfactory.

Looking at Fig. 5-7A, we can see readily why parallel operation is not practical for the higher vhf bands, using conventional tubes and circuits. The tube input and output capacitances, C_g and C_p, shown in broken lines, are in parallel with the tuning capacitors, C1 and C2, across the tuned circuits. Suppose we select a pair of good vhf tubes like the 4CX250B. This tube's input capacitance is 16 pF. Thus, in circuit A we have 32 pF, plus the minimum of C1, plus unavoidable circuit capacitances, all in parallel across L1. Output capacitance is 4.4 pF, so the plate circuit has 8.8 pF in C_p, plus

the minimum of C2 and circuit stray capacitance, across L2. Obviously it will not be possible to resonate conventional tuned grid and plate circuits at 144 MHz and higher, with tubes connected in parallel, even when they are types designed for vhf service.

In the push-pull circuit B, the input capacitances are in series across the tuned circuit. So are the two halves of the split-stator tuning capacitor, C1. The effective total capacitance across the tuned circuit will be about one fourth that of the parallel connection. The same is true in the plate circuit. It can be seen that our chances for reasonably good vhf circuit efficiency are vastly better with push-pull than with parallel.

With single-tube amplifiers the parallel effect of the tube and circuit capacitance still prevails, but it is not nearly so bad as with two or more tubes in parallel. Most single-ended amplifiers for the higher bands employ tank circuits which permit direct connection to the tube element or socket tab, with no leads in the usual sense. Coaxial lines or flat-strip tank circuits are preferred, especially for higher-power amplifiers. Even with the lowest possible capacitance, rf circulating current will run very high in a vhf amplifier, so low dc and rf resistance is of utmost importancee. Large conductors have the added advantage of helping to dissipate heat developed in the tube elements.

Because of their compact construction and short leads, power transistors work well in parallel up through 150 MHz, at least. It is also possible to use certain vhf and uhf tubes in parallel, with properly-designed strip-line circuits. This requires a complete break with conventional coil-and-capacitor concepts, as practical examples seen in later chapters will demonstrate.

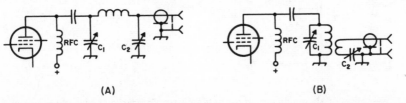

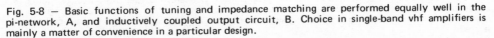

Fig. 5-8 — Basic functions of tuning and impedance matching are performed equally well in the pi-network, A, and inductively coupled output circuit, B. Choice in single-band vhf amplifiers is mainly a matter of convenience in a particular design.

Pi-Network or Inductive Coupling?

The pi-network tank circuit, Fig. 5-8A, is popular for transmitter use, largely because of its adaptability to band-switching amplifiers. In single-band vhf designs there may be little choice between it and the inductively coupled circuit, 5-8B. The output circuit of an amplifier has two basic functions: to tune the stage to the desired frequency, and to act as a matching device between the stage's high output impedance and the low-impedance load. In the pi-network the tuning and loading capacitors, C1 and C2, serve these purposes. With inductively coupled circuits, either the single-ended, 5-8B, or push-pull, 5-7B, the coil and the output coupling loop comprise the matching transformer. The two circuits work equally well, and choice between them can be dictated by adaptability to the particular amplifier being built.

Coils or Lines?

On lower frequencies the fact that any capacitor has some inductance and any coil some capacitance can be neglected in most circuit-design work, for these "strays" are too small to have any significant effect. At frequencies in the upper vhf range they become all-important. Connecting leads, which at lower frequencies merely join coils and capacitors, may, in a vhf circuit, have more inductance than the "coil" itself. Similarly, leads within tubes and sockets may become appreciable portions of a wavelength. Unavoidable capacitance in rf circuits also severely restricts the upper limit of frequency for satisfactory vhf amplifier performance.

At 50 MHz these factors are not insurmountable, if care is used in laying out amplifier stages. Single-ended or push-pull circuits such as Fig.

5-9A still work well if tubes and components designed for vhf service are used. Conventional circuitry may serve at 144 and even 220 MHz with suitable tubes, but in general the usefulness of coil-and-capacitor circuits is limited above 100 MHz.

Transmission-line adaptations of conventional tuned circuits, 5-9B, extend the range and improve performance as we reach frequencies where we "run out of coil" with the circuits at the left. In the push-pull version, the inductance L1 may take the form of a U-shaped loop, or it can be a pair of copper pipes, 1/8 to 1 inch or more in diameter, with an adjustable shorting device at the end away from the tubes to adjust the total inductance in the circuit. The single-ended version below it can be grounded at the left end, if a blocking capacitor is used at the grid, and the resistor R1 is connected from grid to ground. The effective electrical length of L1 can be made variable by use of a sliding contact.

With either circuit of B the upper limit of frequency is reached when C1 is removed and the ground point is moved up to the grid terminal. In practice, the limit is reached when there is no longer enough exposed circuit to permit effective coupling. We then can go to the circuits of C. The rf grid voltage E_g, is shown by the curve above each set of circuits. In A and B the zero-voltage point is at the center tap or bypassed end of L1, or at the left end of the line. If minimum rf voltage occurs close to the tube, the line can be extended a quarter wavelength to the left, and the tuning capacitance connected across the left end. The whole circuit, including tube and tuning capacitance, now becomes an electrical *half* wavelength of line, loaded capacitively by the tube at one end and C1 at the other.

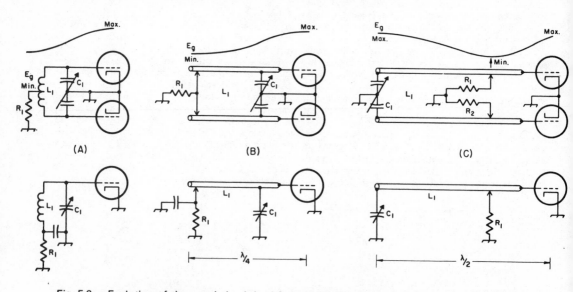

Fig. 5-9 — Evolution of the tuned circuit in vhf amplifiers. Conventional coil-and-capacitor tuning, A, becomes a quarter-wave line circuit in B. A half-wave circuit is shown at C. Each has a progressively higher upper useful frequency limit for a given type of tube, whether single-ended or push-pull design, is used.

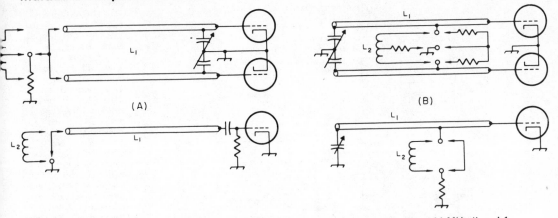

Fig. 5-10 — Simple tricks for achieving multiband capability in vhf circuits. The 144-MHz line, L1, becomes merely a lead or pair of leads when the 50-MHz circuit, L2, is plugged in at the point of lowest rf voltage.

The bias resistors R1 and R2 should be connected at the point of lowest rf voltage in C. This can be determined by feeding rf power into the circuit and touching L1 with a lead pencil or insulated metal object, until the point is found where there is no reaction on the circuit.

The half-wave line circuit will extend the useful frequency range well above the maximum obtainable with quarter-wave or coil-and-capacitor circuits. Though a grid circuit is shown in the examples of Fig. 5-9, the principle is equally applicable to plate circuits. The next steps after this, coaxial and cavity circuits, will be discussed in our uhf chapter.

Multiband Amplifier Circuits

Though conventional bandswitching and plug-in coil arrangements are ineffective at 144 Mhz and higher frequencies, it is possible to build multiband tank circuits for vhf transmitters. Simple adaptations of the plug-in coil idea are shown in Fig. 5-10A. Here a 144-MHz circuit, L1, is completed by plugging in a shorting bar at the end of the line. To use the circuit on 50 MHz or even lower frequencies, we plug in a suitable coil, L2. This general idea was used effectively in the plate circuit of a 4-65A amplifier for 28, 50, and 144 MHz described some years ago in *QST*[3] and the *Handbook*.[4]

A similar principle is applied to half-wave lines in B. Again the 144-MHz half-wave line, L1, becomes merely the "leads" between the 50-MHz coil, L2, and the tuning capacitor. Remembering

that the connection on a half-wave line is made at the point of lowest rf voltage, where it has no effect on the operation of the line, we realize that the 50-MHz circuit of B can even be permanently connected. This has been done many tines in both

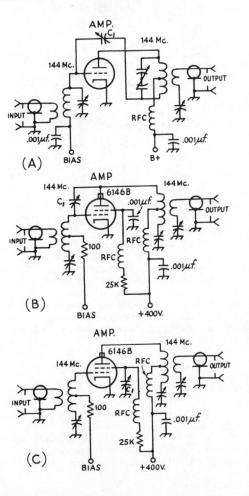

Fig. 5-11 — Typical neutralization circuits for vhf amplifiers. The circuit at A is used with triodes and most other amplifiers, with C1 coupling energy from the plate circuit back to the grid in the proper phase to cancel feedback through the tube. Circuits B and C may be needed with tetrodes, when the frequency is above that at which the tube is inherently neutralized. The variable capacitor C1 in circuit C is adjusted to provide a low-impedance path from screen to ground at the operating frequency.

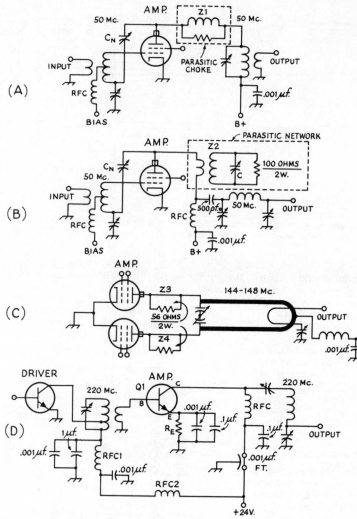

Fig. 5-12 — Parasitic suppression methods for vhf amplifiers. In circuit A, for 6-meter operation, Z1 is 3 or 4 turns of No. 14 wire, wound on a 100-ohm 2-watt noninductive resistor. Z1 tends to overheat in other than low-power circuits, so circuit B is more practical for high power. The windings of Z2 are determined by experiment, usually 2 turns of No. 14, side by side on a resistor like that in A, tuned to the parasitic frequency by capacitor C. Parasitics in circuit C are damped out with 56-ohm resistors bridged across portions of the plate leads, to give loading at the parasitic frequency. The transistor amplifier, D, is bypassed for both lf and vhf, to discourage feedback in both parts of the spectrum.

manufactured and home-built gear for 50 and 144 MHz, and it can be adapted to line tank circuits for still higher frequencies.

Some critical problems are involved in turning this trick for 50 and 144 MHz, especially when both the grid and plate circuits of an amplifier are operated in this way. Because of the nearly third-harmonic relationship, considerable care must be exercised in proportioning the tank circuits to prevent radiation of energy on unwanted frequencies, or oscillation troubles due to unwanted resonances in the grid and plate circuits. An example of a design in which these potential troubles were avoided by WØIC in *QST*.[5]

By thinking in terms of the job to be done, rather than of the way such tasks have been handled in the past, it is often possible to come up with solutions that are unique to the vhf field. A grid circuit tuning both 144 and 220 MHz made possible an efficient transmitter for these bands, in which only the plate circuit was changed. A

completely removable plate circuit also brought 432 MHz into the picture, permitting use of the stage as a doubler or tripler. This design by W1VLH appears in Edition 1 of this Manual.[6]

Stabilization

Most vhf amplifiers, other than the grounded-grid variety, require neutralization if they are to be satisfactorily stable. This is particularly true of AB1 amplifiers, which are characterized by very high power sensitivity. An example of conventional neutralization is shown in Fig. 5-11A.

A tetrode tube has some frequency where it is inherently neutralized. This is likely to be in the lower part of the vhf region, for tubes designed for hf service. Neutralization of the opposite sense may be required in such amplifiers, as in the example shown in Fig. 5-11B.

Conventional screen bypassing methods may be ineffective in the vhf range. Series-tuning the screen to ground, as in 5-11C, may be useful in this situation. A critical combination of fixed capacitance and lead length may accomplish the same result. Neutralization of transistorized amplifiers is not generally practical, at least where bipolar transistors are used.

Parasitic oscillation can occur in vhf amplifiers, and, as with hf circuits, the oscillation is usually at a frequency considerably higher than the operating frequency, and it cannot be neutralized out. Usually it is damped out by methods illustrated in Fig. 5-12. Circuits A and B are commonly used in 6-meter transmitters. Circuit A may absorb sufficient fundamental energy to burn up in all but low-power transmitters. A better approach is to use the selective circuit illustrated at B. The circuit is coupled to the plate tank circuit and tuned to the parasitic frequency. Since a minimum amount of the fundamental energy will be absorbed by the trap, heating should no longer be a problem.

At 144 MHz and higher, it is difficult to construct a parasitic choke that will not be resonant at or near the operating frequency. Should uhf parasitics occur, an effective cure can often be realized by shunting a 56-ohm 1-watt resistor across a small section of the plate end of the tuned circuit as shown in Fig. 5-12, at C. The resistor should be attached as near the plate connector as practical. Such a trap can often be constructed by bridging the resistor across a portion of the flexible strap-connector that is used in some transmitters to join the anode fitting to the plate-tank inductor.

Instability in solid-state vhf and uhf amplifiers can often be traced to oscillations in the lf and hf regions. Because the gain of the transistors is very high at the lower frequencies, instability is almost certain to occur unless proper bypassing and decoupling of stages is carried out. Low-frequency oscillation can usually be cured by selecting a bypass-capacitor value that is effective at the frequency of oscillation and connecting it in parallel with the vhf bypass capacitor in the same part of the circuit. It is not unusual, for example, to employ a 0.1-μF disk ceramic in parallel with a .001-μF disk capacitor in such circuits as the emitter, base, or collector return. The actual values used will depend upon the frequencies involved. This technique is shown in Fig. 5-12D.

Wide-Band FM with Simple Gear

Wide-band fm is very easily achieved with any transmitter that is VFO-controlled, using methods described in Chapter 6, Fig. 6-13 and associated text. Bandwidth comparable to that employed in entertainment-type fm broadcasting relaxes transmitter stability problems. Even a simple modulated-oscillator transmitter can be made to deliver good-quality fm, if the power supply is well-filtered and some provision is made to keep the deviation within the limits a 100-MHz fm broadcast receiver will accept. The stability of the modulated oscillator is not sufficient for use in heavily-occupied bands, but the simple approach is logical for the 420-MHz experimenter.

Equipment of elementary simplicity for use in the 220-MHz band described and demonstrated by W1CTW years ago[7] is still potentially useful.

The author of this book demonstrated an even simpler arrangement for 420-MHz work at many radio clubs and conventions. A little 6J6 oscillator was modulated by a 6AQ5 audio stage.[8] With speech input held so low that the modulation percentage was only about 5 per cent, the signal could be received with quite satisfactory quality with a simple tunable converter and an fm broadcast receiver. The signals sound more like a buzz-saw than speech, when picked up on a selective communications receiver, but with wide-band fm detection they can be above reproach. We have plenty of room for them above 220.5 MHz, and in the low part of our 420-MHz band.

Bibliography

[1] Tilton, "A Two-Band Station for the VHF Beginner," July through October, 1961, *QST*. Includes simple 14-to-18-MHz tuner; 10-watt transmitters for 50 and 144 MHz; receiving converters for 50 and 144 MHz; power supply, modulator and control unit; and vhf SWR bridge. Complete reprint of *QST* series, with templates for drilling principal surfaces, 50 cents per copy, from ARRL, Newington, Ct. 06111.

[2] Tilton, "Overtone Crystals — How and Where to Use Them," March, 1955, *QST*.

[3] Chambers, "450 Watts on VHF," September, 1949, *QST*.

[4] ARRL *Handbook*, 27th, 28th, and 29th Editions, Chapter 17.

[5] Maer, "The Perseids Powerhouse," October, 1959, *QST*.

[6] Southworth, "Using the 4X250B on 144, 220, and 432 Mc.," February, 1957, *QST*.

[7] Hadlock, "Wide-Band F. M. Gear for 220Mc.," March, 1961, *QST*.

[8] Tilton, "Simple Gear for the 420-Mc. Beginner," May, 1949, *QST*.

Chapter 6

Vhf Exciters and Amplifiers

As was done with the subject of receiving in two previous chapters, we are covering transmitter design, adjustment and operation in detail in one chapter, and practical examples in another. In the descriptive items to follow, explanatory material and adjustment procedure will be held to the minimum necessary for adequate coverage of each unit described. The reader is urged to examine Chapter 5 thoroughly before embarking on the construction of equipment to be described here.

This section will deal mainly with the rf portions of transmitters of the oscillator-multiplier type. Where items are coordinated in design with units that appear elsewhere in the book, the companion items will be pointed out. Power supplies and modulation equipment are seldom included, as these usually follow practice that changes only slightly over periods of many years. The reader is referred to appropriate sections of the ARRL *Handbook* for details of accessories that are needed in these fields.

Some mention of the 420-MHz band will be found herein, despite the designation of 30 to 300 MHz semantically as "vhf." Where the design techniques involved are truly uhf in nature, items for the 420-MHz band will be found in the chapter dealing with uhf and microwaves, later in the book.

FREQUENCY CONTROL

Most transmitters of the oscillator-multiplier type in this book are shown with crystal control. Though being able to move around at will is becoming almost as important in vhf work as on lower bands, the fact remains that many variable frequency-control systems presently in use above 50 MHz are far from satisfactory, except when heterodyning methods replace frequency multiplication. In the case of 50 MHz operation, some are downright illegal. From 144 MHz up we are not required by law to transmit stable signals, but self respect and consideration for others dictate that we keep our signals above reproach, regardless of frequency.

This is not easy when continously-variable frequency control is used, especially at 144 MHz and higher. A VFO that sounds good enough in the 8-MHz region may be only fair at its 6th harmonic in the 50-MHz band. At the 18th harmonic, 144 MHz, it very likely will be unacceptable to the critical ear. By the time we multiply 54 times, to 432 MHz, even average crystal control is not good enough for narrow-band work.

There are two solutions: heterodyning, which duplicates the fundamental-frequency stability on a higher frequency, and very special attention to the stability problem in oscillators that are to be followed by one or more frequency multipliers. An example of the latter approach is detailed below.

A VXO FOR 50 THROUGH 450 MHz

Crystal control has many advantages. By the very nature of the quartz crystal, the frequency of a crystal oscillator is maintained very close to the desired spot. The effects of heating (expansion and contraction of the oscillating device and its circuit elements), mechanical vibration and variations in supply voltages are greatly reduced, in comparison with these effects in any self-controlled oscillator.

Fig. 6-1 — A VXO especially for vhf use. Calibration on the front panel is for a favorite crystal used for cw work on 144 and 432 MHz. Crystal sockets at the lower left are mounted on insulating material, to reduce circuit capacitance to the lowest possible value. Frequency variation per crystal depends on which socket is used. Pointer knobs are for the output plate circuit and the spotting and power switches.

The vernier dial is a National type AM.

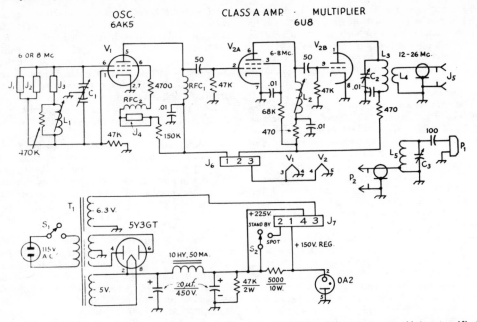

Fig. 6-2 — Schematic diagram and parts information for the VXO and power supply. Unless specified, resistors are 1/2 watt. Decimal values of capacitance are in μF; others in pF. Capacitors with polarity marked are electrolytic. Terminal strips J6 and J7 may be omitted and connections made directly where the power supply is built in. Pin 4 of J7 permits use of the supply for other purposes.

C1 — 100-pF per-section split-stator variable (Hammarlund HFD100). 50 pF per section also usable.

C2, C3 — 50-pF miniature variable (Hammarlund HF-50). Higher maximum capacitance (HF-100) may be used. Grounded-rotor type preferred.

J1 — Crystal socket for 0.05-inch pins, spaced 0.487 inch.

J2, J3 — Crystal socket for 0.095-inch pins, spaced 0.487 inch.

J4 — 2-terminal barrier strip. Omit if fm is not to be used. Remove jumper when fm is connected.

J5 — Coaxial receptacle.

J6 — 3-terminal barrier strip.

J7 — 4-terminal barrier strip.

L1 — 16-24-μH, iron slug, ceramic form (Miller 4507).

L2 — 24-35-μH, iron slug, ceramic form (Miller 4508).

L3 — 3.5-μH, 21 turns No. 24 tinned, 1/2-inch dia, 32 t.p.e.

L4 — 3 turns like L3, spaced 1 turn from it. Make both from single piece of B&W Miniductor No. 3004.

L5 — Same as L3, but tapped at 3 turns. Coax from L5 to P2 may be any convenient length.

P1 — 300-ohm line plug.

P2 — Coaxial cable fitting.

RFC1 — 750-μH rf choke.

RFC2 — 1.0 mH rf choke.

S1 — Spst switch.

S2 — Spst switch. (See text).

T1 — Power transformer capable of delivering 200 to 250 volts dc at 50 mA through filter, 6.3 volts ac at 1 A, and 5 volts ac at 3 A.

But even with crystal control, the fundamental requirements must be met if we are to have highly stable control of frequency. These become more stringent as the order of frequency multiplication is increased.

It is possible to "pull" the frequency of a crystal oscillator a small amount in several ways. A mechanical method is described in a later chapter, but it is adapted to use only with pressure-mounted crystals. Controlled voltage variation causes some shift, but is usually associated with large changes in output. Adding capacitance across the crystal works well with some crystals, and the swing with a given amount of capacity change can be increased by adding inductance in series with the crystal. (See previous chapter.) The frequency change with these methods (as with any other) is

limited by the amount of instability you are willing to accept.

The variable crystal oscillator (VXO) shown in Figs. 6-1 through 6-4 allows the operator a choice of variable capacitance alone, or in conjunction with a series coil. Furthermore, the amount of inductance in series with the crystal, and consequently the frequency shift obtained by rotating the variable capacitor, can be adjusted to suit the builder's desires. Since temperature variation is the principal cause of drift in crystal oscillators, this one is run at low input, and drift is held to a very small amount, even from a cold start. The oscillator runs continuously, so there is no heating and cooling cycle effect in transmitting.

With just variable capacitance (no series coil) the maximum usable swing is roughly 4.5 kHz at 6

MHz, or 6 kHz at 8 MHz, for crystals in the small metal hermetically-sealed holders. FT-243s and other pressure-mounted crystals having high holder capacitance may swing quite a bit less. There is a certain *total* capacitance at which each crystal goes out of oscillation, and it varies markedly from one to another, depending on crystal activity and mounting methods.

The 6000-kHz crystal shown plugged into the VXO in Fig. 6-1 covers 432.24 to 432.0 MHz and 144.08 to 144.0, without use of the series coil. This gives all the coverage usually needed for weak-signal cw work in these two bands, but the oscillation frequency goes lower than 6000 kHz, and if the crystal had been a shade higher frequency it would have been more useful for 144-MHz service. About 6001 or 6002 would have been ideal. Available swing is mainly on the low side of the marked frequency.

With the series coil, L1 in Fig. 6-2, about three times as much variation is possible without serious degrading of the stability. A range of 100 kHz at 50 MHz and 300 kHz at 144 is average for 6- or 8-MHz crystals. Rubberiness varies considerably from one crystal to the next, with the series coil and without it. One ordinary FT-243 surplus crystal at 8.38 MHz was adjustable over an operating-frequency range of 50.34 to nearly 50.0 MHz, but this is exceptional. The need for variable control is confined mainly to narrow high-activity segments of the vhf bands, so a few selected crystals will do the job for most vhf operators. Random crystals for other parts of the bands need not be swingers, ordinarily.

Operation on 220 or 420 is almost always channeled to one narrow segment per band, and this is handled easily with one crystal per band. Usually one crystal will serve for both 144 and 432, for use in the parts of these bands where high stability is most desirable. Use of the series coil is not recommended above the 144-MHz band.

Circuit Details

The oscillator, V1, is a 6AK5, but almost any small receiving rf pentode will do. The basic VXO idea can also be used with transistor oscillators.

The frequency is pulled by the split-stator capacitor, C1, connected between plate and screen. The oscillator plate voltage is regulated 150. Input is held to about 3 mA, combined plate and screen, so this oscillator is not going to move much unless you move it with C1. An rf choke is used in the plate circuit, instead of a resonant coil, as tuning here would pull the frequency.

To build up the low oscillator output to a usable level, and to provide isolation, a buffer amplifier follows, using the pentode section of a 6U8, V2A. This tube was selected because it has the lowest grid-plate capacitance of any dual tube of the pentode-triode class. The triode portion V2B, is a multiplier, the output frequency depending on the crystals used. Provision is made for covering 12 to 26 MHz with C2L3. The plate circuit of the pentode amplifier is broadly tuned, and an intermediate setting of the slug in L2 can be found that will permit use of either 6- or 8-MHz crystals in the oscillator. The plate circuit of the multiplier may then be tuned to the second, third, or fourth harmonic of 6 MHz or to the second or third of 8 MHz. Which output frequency you use may depend on the type of circuit into which the VXO works. More on this later.

Construction

Mechanical layout of the oscillator portion was dictated by the need to keep circuit capacitance to a minimum. The lower the total capacitance in the circuit, the higher the frequency will go with C1 at minimum, and the wider swing you'll achieve per crystal. This rules out crystal switching, though if convenience outranks crystal economy in your objectives, switching can be used. Crystal sockets are mounted on a Plexiglas insert in the front panel, instead of directly on the metal. The tuning capacitor is shimmed up an extra quarter inch above the chassis, to hold down its minimum capacitance, and rf leads through the chassis have half-inch clearance holes. Any one of these steps yields little, but combined they net quite a bit more coverage at 432 MHz. This dividend is at the low-C end of the range of C1, where oscillator stability is at its best.

Fig. 6-3 — Interior view of the VXO. The oscillator tube is at the right. The power supply, shown here as a separate assembly, could be built on the same chassis with the rf circuits, if the constructor wishes.

Fig. 6-4 —
Bottom of
the VXO.
The oscillator
components
are at the
right, the am-
plifier and
multiplier
stages near
the center,
and the pow-
er supply at
the left.

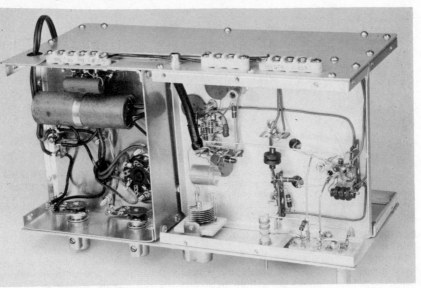

Three crystal sockets, J1, J2, and J3, are wired so that a crystal may be plugged into the circuit either with or without the series coil. Two different types of sockets in parallel, J1 and J2, permit small-pin or large-pin crystals to be plugged into the high-stability low-swing portion of the circuit. Use a wider variety of sockets if your crystal stock requires it, though each one adds a little capacitance.

Any crystal you plug into this circuit will oscillate on its fundamental, including those intended for overtone operation. Most crystals above 12 MHz are overtone types, the third overtone being used up to about 54 MHz. A crystal marked for 24 MHz will oscillate near 8 MHz, but not necessarily at exactly one-third the marked frequency. If you're ordering crystals especially for this purpose, we recommend 6 to 6.5 MHz, which will cover 50 to 52 MHz, 144 to 148, 220 to 225, and 432 to 450 MHz. The output frequency would then be, preferably, 12 to 13 MHz, as this will allow the crystal oscillator stage of most vhf transmitters to work as a frequency multiplier when driven by the VXO. Use of 8-MHz crystals and 24-MHz VXO output is usually satisfactory where the first stage in the transmitter proper is a pentode, but triodes may self-oscillate, unless operated as multipliers.

Coupling to the Transmitter

The coupling system shown in Figs. 6-5 and 6-6 is not the simplest way of hooking the VXO to a transmitter, but it has certain advantages. Low-impedance coupling terminated in the tuned cir-

cuit, L5C3, permits use of any convenient separation between the VXO and the transmitter. Rf from the plug, P1, can be fed into the transmitter in several ways. Some experimenting may be needed with your setup, but typical circuits are shown in Fig. 6-6.

Triode Overtone Oscillators. Don't try to plug directly into the crystal socket without modifying the circuit. Mounting an extra socket, J2 in Fig. 6-6A, allows you to return to direct crystal control at will, yet gives optimum transfer of power from the VXO. Remove the regular crystal from J1 when the VXO is used, of course. With the capacitive feedback circuit, Fig. 6-6B, the 50-pF capacitor should be shorted out, and the VXO output fed to J1.

Pentode Oscillators. The pentode crystal oscillator circuit used in many vhf transmitters should have its cathode rf choke shorted by means of a switch. Plugging into the crystal socket may work with such circuits, unmodified, but more reliable

Fig. 6-5 — Coupling assembly to be used for plugging into the exciter driven by the VXO. Components are L5, C3, and P1, of Fig. 6-2. The tuned circuit covers 12 to 26 MHz. A larger variable capacitor may be used to make the value of L5 less critical, if desired.

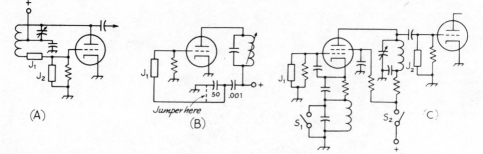

(A)   *Jumper here*
                  (B)   (C)

Fig. 6-6 — Modifications of various crystal oscillator circuits for VXO drive. J1 is the original crystal socket. J2, where required, is an additional socket, for VXO input. A and B are typical triode overtone oscillators. C is a popular pentode oscillator. Two options are shown for C. To convert the oscillator to a multiplier stage, close S1 and S2 and feed drive into J1. The oscillator may be disabled by opening S2, in which case drive is fed to J2.

operation is likely when the cathode is grounded for rf, as with S1 in Fig. 6-6C.

Another possibility in working into an existing transmitter is to disable the transmitter crystal oscillator, and couple into the grid of the second stage from the VXO. Opening the screen or B-plus lead of the first stage, as is done with S2 in Fig. 6-6C, is handy for this, and a crystal socket may be connected to the grid of the second stage, as shown by J2 in Fig. 6-6C. Here again, reversion to standard crystal control is easy.

Simplification is possible when the VXO is built directly into a transmitter designed for it. Here, the output of the isolation amplifier will be sufficient to drive a frequency multiplier to 24 MHz, so one stage is saved compared with the system wherein the VXO is used to work into the crystal oscillator stage of a transmitter designed for 6-, 8-, or 24-MHz crystals. But don't skip the buffer amplifier; its functions are vital.

Operation

For maximum stability, particularly in 432-MHz cw work, it is well to leave the VXO on continously during an operation period, and preferably warm it up a few minutes before going on the air. This way there is almost no frequency change, except those deliberately made by moving C1.

Refinements in the spotting technique can be made to suit the operator's preference, though the circuit is useful as shown. With power applied to the amplifier and multiplier through S2, the signal is just plainly audible on 432 MHz, when the heaters are on in the rest of the transmitter. It is stronger progressively on each lower band, but the signal from the oscillator alone is inaudible, even on 50 MHz. If you make a practice of zeroing the other fellow's frequency most of the time you may want to install a small relay, actuated by your main transmitter control, in parallel with S2. Then leave the switch in the open position normally, closing it only for spotting purposes. A spring-return substitute for S2 may be desirable in this case.

The series coil, L1, is adjusted by the core stud seen on the front panel, just to the right of the crystal sockets. Moving the core into the coil raises its inductance and increases the swing per crystal. Some practice with various crystals will be needed before you know just what to expect from each one. The coil comes into play only when the crystal is plugged into J3. Instability increases with inductance, and also with *increasing* capacitance in C1. Listen to the note critically, and check for mechanical effects when the unit is jarred. Don't push your luck, or expect to swish all over the band with one crystal, even though you'll find one now and then that will make this possible.

Generating FM

Frequency modulation of the VXO is easily done. A small audio voltage applied to the screen at J4 will give good-quality narrow-band fm on 220 MHz and higher, even with the high-stability oscillator arrangement. For 50- and 144-MHz work it may be necessary to use the series-coil circuit to get enough deviation for good audio recovery at the receiving end. All that is needed in the way of audio equipment is a microphone transformer, a flashlight cell and a carbon microphone. Remove the jumper shown across J1 in Fig. 6-2, of course.

A topnotch nfm signal can be generated with a very simple audio amplifier having a limiter, and a

Fig. 6-7 — Transistor VFO for vhf use. Tuning range is about 8 to 8.42 MHz as described.

Fig. 6-8 — Interior of the transistor VFO. The oscillator portion is built on a circuit board. The amplifier stage is close to the rear wall.

good microphone. Swinging the frequency with a varactor diode across C1 offers interesting possibilities, and somewhat more deviation than is possible with the screen-modulation method. Varactor-diode modulation is shown in the 220-MHz transmitter later in this chapter. For more on fm, see Chapters 10-12.

TRANSISTOR VFO FOR THE VHF BANDS

Sources of hum in variable-frequency oscillators using tubes (ac used on tube heater circuits, and inadequate filtering of the plate supply) can be eliminated with a transistor oscillator. Some other instability problems are more readily solved with transistors than with tubes. With a battery supply, frequency changes due to voltage fluctuation are nil. Drift cycles resulting from heating and cooling of the oscillator and its circuit components are greatly reduced in good transistor VFO design.

This is not to say that the transistor is a cure-all for VFO problems, but with proper attention to basic principles of oscillator design a reasonably good VFO using transistors can be made at moderate cost. An etched circuit board takes care of most vibration problems. The transistor should run far below its rated dissipation, to hold down heat cycling, and preferably run continuously during an operating period. The VFO should be in a position as free of external heat changes as possible. The oscillator should be isolated from the rest of the transmitter with suitable buffer and multiplier stages.

These points were considered in the design of the VFO unit shown in Fig. 6-7. Its transistor oscillator tunes 8.0 to about 8.42 MHz, or enough to cover the entire 144- and 220-MHz bands, and the 50-MHz band from the low end to about 50.5 MHz. More coverage can be included with a larger capacitor for C6. The oscillator input is less than 40 milliwatts, so there is little heating and warmup

drift, and this can be corrected by adjusting the temperature-compensating padder across the tuned circuit. A buffer-amplifier provides some isolation, and builds up the output up to permit operation with most vhf transmitters having crystal-controlled oscillators that multiply into the 24-25-MHz range.

Construction

The VFO is built in a box 3 inches square and 5 1/4 inches long. This was made to fit the job, and is not difficult to duplicate, but standard cases of something like this shape and size could be substituted, as there is nothing sacred about the layout. Tuning is by means of a small imported vernier dial, the knob of which was replaced with a larger one, in the interest of smooth control. The front panel is 3 1/2 by 3 1/4 inches in size, fastened to the case with bolts passing through 11/16-inch metal sleeves. These were filed down from their original 3/4-inch length.

Fig. 6-9 — Schematic diagram and parts information for the 8-MHz VFO unit. Parts not described below are numbered for identification in text. Where not otherwise indicated, capacitor values are in picofarads (pF or $\mu\mu$F). Those across tuned circuits are dipped-mica.

C6 — 15-pF variable (Millen 22015). For more tuning range use larger value.
C7 — 8- to 50-pF neg. temp. coef. ceramic trimmer (Centralab N-650).
J1, J2 — phono jack.
L1 — 3-μH slug-tuned coil: 13 turns No. 22 on 3/8-inch iron-slug form (Miller 42A336CBI, with 2 turns removed).
L2 — 1.3-μH slug-tuned coil: 14 turns No. 26 on 1/4-inch iron-slug form (Miller 4502).
L3 — 2 turns No. 26, wound over low end of L2.
CR1 — 9-volt Zener diode.
P1 — Phono plug. Short out if no spotting switch is used.
S1 — Remote spotting switch, any type.

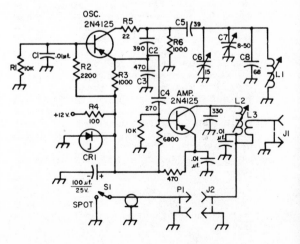

Fig. 6-10 — Bottom of the transistor VFO assembly. The oscillator circuit board assembly mounts over a 2-3/4-inch round hole. Power feedthrough bushings are in upper right corner.

Almost any hf or vhf transistors may be used. The circuit board is designed so that either p-n-p or n-p-n can be accommodated, and there is no advantage either way. Motorola 2N4125 plastic-case p-n-p types are shown. RCA 2N1177s were also tried. A zener diode, CR1, shown in the circuit diagram, does not appear in the photographs. This is used to regulate the supply voltage if other than a battery source is used. It would be important if the VFO were to be used for mobile work, on the car battery. In operation from a small separate battery the Zener can be omitted, and the positive voltage applied directly to the junction of R2, R3, and R4.

Adjustment and Use

Make certain that all circuits are wired correctly, then apply voltage. It would be well to check the current drawn, which will be about 10 mA at 12 volts and 7 to 8 mA with 9 volts. Of this, about two thirds is drawn by the amplifier. If the oscillator current is measured separately on a low-range meter, a slight flicker in current will be seen when the oscillator coil or tuning capacitor is touched, if the circuit is oscillating. The frequency can be checked roughly with a wavemeter, or the signal can be monitored on a receiver. A well-calibrated receiver tuning the 8-MHz range is handy, but not necessary. The signal can be heard in your 50- or 144-MHz receiver, if the VFO is connected to the transmitter with which it is to be used. Methods of connection to various types of crystal oscillator circuits are discussed in connection with the VXO. See Fig. 6-6 and associated text. A shielded 8-MHz coupling unit is shown in Fig. 6-12.

To calibrate the oscillator, turn capacitor C6 to all-in, and adjust the core slug in L1 so that the frequency is approximately 8000 kHz. This will be heard at the low end of the 144-MHz band, if you are listening there. It may be necessary to run a link from J1 to the 144-MHz receiver input, if you are not driving the transmitter at this time.

All oscillator components except the tuning capacitor, C6, are mounted on a multipurpose circuit board designed for service in ARRL projects where tunable oscillators are required. A layout is given in Fig. 6-11, if you want to make your own. If not, prepared boards can be purchased from suppliers mentioned in *QST* from time to time. The drawing and photographs should make clear where the various parts are mounted.

The amplifier stage is at the back of the chassis. The transistor is mounted on three small feedthrough bushings (Johnson Rib-Loc). These stay in place when pressed into a 0.136-inch hole. Two other Rib-Loc terminals provide for the connection of the power source. These and the output jack are on the back wall of the chassis. On a side wall, near the back, is another phono jack for external connection as a spotting switch or relay, to turn the amplifier stage on or off.

Small front and back plates have folded-over edges. The cover is a U-shaped piece, fastening to these, and to the sides of the chassis. The tuning capacitor mounts on the front panel with a nut on the rotor shaft. The type that grounds the rotor in this way is preferred to those having small mounting studs, as the electrical and mechanical grounding is much better. If more frequency coverage is desired, the tuning capacitor should be the next larger size than the 15-pF type shown. Plates can then be removed if the coverage is too great.

Fig. 6-11 — General purpose circuit board used for the transistor VFO is 2-7/8 inches square. Dark areas are etched. Board mounts over a 2-3/4-inch hole.

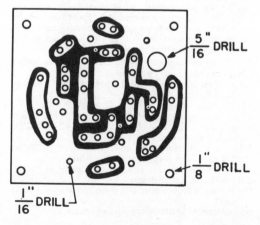

$\frac{5}{16}$" DRILL

$\frac{1}{8}$" DRILL

$\frac{1}{16}$" DRILL

Fig. 6-12 — Coupling assembly, for plugging into a transmitter crystal socket. Tuned circuit is similar to that shown in Fig. 6-2, except L5 has 24 turns. Interior appearance is similar to Fig. 6-5.

A drift check should next be made. Be sure that the receiver is not drifting, then turn the VFO on and note the drift for the next two minutes or so. If it is appreciable, it can be reduced by proper setting of the compensating trimmer, C7. Move the trimmer a few degrees either way, and reset the core slug so that the signal is again heard at 8 MHz. Check the drift cycle again. If there is less drift this time, from a cold start, you moved the trimmer in the right direction. If there is more, move the trimmer about as far in the opposite direction, reset the slug, and try again. A combination will be found eventually where the temperature-compensating qualities of the trimmer will almost exactly nullify the effect of the slight transistor warm-up drift. The temperature compensation, is really just a refinement. the stability of the oscillator is quite good without compensation, if you don't mind letting it run for 10 minutes or so before using it. It's not bad, even from a cold start.

A dummy load for the amplifier can be made with a 2-volt 60-mA pilot lamp, wired to a phono plug and inserted in J1. It will just glow when the amplifier output circuit is peaked, indicating an output of 30 to 40 milliwatts. This is enough to drive any of the common crystal oscillator circuits, if the coupling system of Fig. 6-2 is used. For an 8-MHz circuit, L5 in Fig. 6-2 should have 24 turns.

The simple bipolar transistor buffer stage does not afford a high degree of isolation. There will be an appreciable frequency change as the coupling circuit is adjusted, but the stability in actual use is fairly good. This is not a device for working close to the band edge, however. Play safe, and be sure that you know where you are.

This VFO was tested on 50 and 144 MHz with the "Two-Band Station" transmitters described in earlier editions of this Manual.[1] These were modified by installing a switch that shorts out the rf choke in the cathode circuit. See Fig. 6-6. The VFO works well with the 220-MHz transmitter described latter in this chapter, if the oscillator circuit of this unit is modified in a similar manner. It drove a Clegg 22-er nicely when the coupling

---

[1] "Two-Band Station for the VHF Beginner," QST, July through October, 1961. Complete reprint available from ARRL, Newington, CT 06111, price 50 cents. All components were described in previous editions of this Manual.

Fig. 6-12, was plugged into the crystal socket. In each instance the note quality was acceptable, and there is substantially no frequency modulation. Drift is no more than some crystal-controlled transmitters show at comparable frequencies. Stability does not approach that of the VXO just described, but it is better than many VFO units currently heard on the vhf bands.

Frequency Modulating the Transistor VFO

Noting that only about 12 pF of capacitance change is required to tune the VFO just described over an operating-frequency range of nearly 500 kHz at 8 MHz, it can be seen that frequency modulating it enough for present-day vhf fm communication would require only a tiny capacitance change across the tuned circuit. It was found by experiment that changing the capacitance across the *buffer* circuit, L2, with a varicap diode could pull the oscillator frequency adequately, and with reasonable stability and linearity.

A speech amplifier and limiter similar to that shown with the 220-MHz fm-cw transmitter of Fig. 6-26 was used, with the varicap diode connected through a small capacitor to the VFO amplifier collector circuit. An RCA Integrated Circuit Kit audio amplifier and tone oscillator, KC4003, was also used as an audio voltage source.

As a matter of convenience, the jack J2 in Fig. 6-9 was used for the audio voltage input. The diode

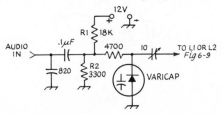

Fig. 6-13 — Basic circuit of a varactor diode modulator for generating fm with the VFO of Fig. 6-9. Values of R1 and R2 can be adjusted to give the bias required for the varicap diode in use.

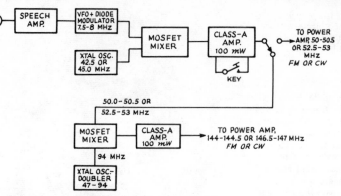

Fig. 6-14 — Typical example of a heterodyne-type exciter, giving 500-kHz tuning ranges in two bands. Stability and deviation in the fm signal are established in the VFO, tuning 7.5 to 8 MHz. The first amplifier can be keyed for cw.

and associated components were mounted under the chassis in the open area visible in Fig. 6-10. The added circuitry is shown in Fig. 6-13. R1 and R2 can be adjusted to give the bias value recommended for the varactor diode being used. This is not critical, and anything from 1 to 3 volts worked satisfactorily with several low-capacitance varicap diodes tried in this application. Only a fraction of a volt of audio is needed, when the VFO output frequency is being multiplied.

If operation is to be attempted in the parts of the 6- and 2-meter bands where fixed channels are in vogue, it is recommended that the oscillator be run continously, so that when the desired frequency is zeroed the VFO frequency will remain constant. The stability should be more than adequate to meet the fairly stringent requirements of this kind of communication, if this is done. (See Chapter 10.) The deviation should be adjusted so that the signal is of good quality when slope-detected on a communications receiver having average a-m selectivity. (Do not use a broad receiver such as is common in small a-m transceivers for this check.)

Heterodyne FM-CW Exciter

The upper portion of the system shown in Fig. 6-14 has been tried in mock-up form, working with both fm and a-m stations. The VFO circuit was tuned down by means of the core in L1 so that the coverage is roughly 7.5 to 8 MHz. The deviation can be adjusted by listening in this range, as there is no increase in deviation or instability when the signal is heterodyned to the operating frequency. The mixer is a MOSFET, with the variable oscilla-

tor fed into Gate 1 and a crystal oscillator of suitable frequency fed into Gate 2. The sum frequency is a 500-kHz tunable range, depending on the crystal selected, 50.0 to 50.5 or 52.5 to 53.0 MHz. A Class-A amplifier using any small-signal vhf amplifier transistor builds the mixer output up to usable level.

The 500-kHz ranges in the 50-MHz band thus produced can be heterodyned to similar ranges in the 144-MHz band, using another mixer and a crystal oscillator-multiplier with 94-MHz output. Additional crystals can be used in either crystal oscillator for more ranges. Adding crystals is preferable to increasing the VFO tuning range, for obvious mechanical and stability reasons.

The voltage applied to the first mixer, or to either Class-A amplifier, can be keyed for cw operation. Amplifier keying is probably the better, as the mixer has some small output, even with voltage removed, if both oscillators are left running. Keying of the oscillators results in inevitable chirp problems. Amplifier keying is excellent; there is no frequency pulling and no backwave.

The upper portion of the system has been used on the air, as shown, for local work, and as a driver for the tetrode amplifier of Fig. 6-38, which resulted in about 50 watts output. Results in both narrow- and wide-band fm work were very good, and the cw signal is excellent. The setup delivers up to 100 mW on 50 MHz, with about 100 mA drain at 12 volts. Many contacts have been made in the portion of the 50-MHz band where a-m phone is still widely used. Zeroing any frequency, for communication with a-m or fm stations, is easily done if a communications receiver is used. The key-up condition in the Class-A amplifier leaves

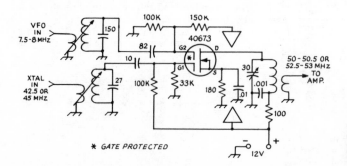

Fig. 6-15 — Circuit of the MOSFET mixer used in the heterodyne exciter shown in block-diagram form in Fig. 6-14. A Class-A amplifier is added to bring output up to usable level.

just about enough signal for spotting purposes, ordinarily.

The all-transistor 2-meter portion has not been tried, but the 50-MHz stages have been used with the heterodyne exciter described in Chapter 7, with equally good signal quality and zeroing ability in the 2-meter band. If we are to have tunable fm exciters that meet the stability requirements of channelized fm on the vhf bands, there is little doubt that the heterodyne approach is the logical way to do the job. It is good enough for ssb, which is much more critical as to stability than is fm. Though fixed-channel fm has many advantages,

and should be encouraged for mobile and repeater work, a tunable approach to fm communication is surely a "must," if we are to make the most of the home-station potential of this mode.

Further steps in the direction of versatility immediately suggest themselves to operators familiar with ssb transverters. The output of a sideband exciter in the 7-MHz range could be substituted for the fm input to the mixer, to develop vhf ssb with the mixer and crystal oscillators as shown. The VFO accessory could be eliminated entirely, if a varactor fm system were added to the tunable oscillator in the ssb rig.

VHF TRANSMITTER DESIGN AND PACKAGING

The amateur about to begin assembling a vhf station is frequently confused by the choice of transistors, tubes, circuits, operating modes and equipment packaging available to him. Having been exposed to the "station in a box" approach now so common on lower amateur frequencies, he may feel that he wants a similar one-package station for his vhf work. This is certainly convenient, especially if he plans to take ham radio with him on his travels, but it is by no means the most versatile way to set up a home station.

Many vhf operators do not build stations for the sole purpose of talking to people. We like to try different circuits, methods, and modes. We look forward to gradual building-up and refinement of our stations, as time, experience and financial resources permit. With some planning, today's low-powered transmitter becomes tomorrow's exciter. If it is a separate unit, it can still serve for portable work.

There is much to be said for subassembly design, even if the eventual objective is the containment of the whole station in one unit. Most equipment described in this book is worked out along these lines. Even the two complete medium-

powered rf units for 144 and 220 MHz are laid out so that the exciter and amplifier can be built and operated separately, if desired, though they go together in standard 17-inch-wide packages.

Use of circuit boards facilitates design by subassembly, permitting a compact end result without sacrificing easy modification. But metal-plate and chassis methods need not be considered obsolete, as the continuing popularity of many "old but good" designs demonstrates. A classic example of the long-life potential of sound subassembly design is seen in the still-extensive use of components of the "Two-Band Station for the VHF Beginner," featured in *QST* more than a decade ago, but still going strong in reprint form, despite its all-tube format,[1] Its transmitter units are still good for the man who wants an effective a-m and cw rig of simple design and moderate cost.

Another all-tube transmitter set for 50 and 144 MHz is available from *QST* and recent editions of the ARRL *Handbook.*[2] It provides somewhat more power than the 10-watters of Reference 1, and is complete with power and audio equipment.

2 **"50-Watt Transmitters for 6 and 2,"** *Radio Amateur's Handbook*, **Editions 44 through 48.**

A MEDIUM-POWERED 144-MHz TRANSMITTER

The transmitter of Figs. 6-16 through 6-23 was built in the ARRL Laboratory, specifically for the Headquarters Station, W1AW. Some aspects of its design may be slightly different from those the average vhf man would build into his station, but anyone wanting an efficient and reliable 144-MHz transmitter should find it of interest. The exciter and final amplifier are built on separate standard-sized chassis, and either may be used with other suitable equipment. The exciter makes a fine low-powered rf unit by itself, and the amplifier will

Fig. 6-16 — The 500-watt 144-MHz transmitter is built in separate assemblies using standard chassis sizes, yet it can be mounted on a standard 19-inch rack panel. The exciter, left, may also be used as a low-powered transmitter, capable of up to 10 watts output. Amplifier, right, has built-in bias supply. Its simple strip-line plate circuit is enclosed in a removable cover.

work well with any exciter capable of delivering over 5 watts output. Combined, the two units mount on a standard rack panel, making a compact rf section capable of delivering 300 watts output on cw and 200 watts a-m phone.

There is much to be said for a 500-watt level as the maximum power input for a vhf station. Overall cost and complexity are far lower than when the full legal power is used, and the difference in signal at a distant point is no more than barely noticeable. The economic advantage gained in staying below 500 watts input is particularly marked when a-m phone is the most-used mode of operation.

Exciter Design

The exciter is designed to permit shifting frequency over most of the band without extensive retuning. If the stages are peaked near the middle of a two-megahertz range normally used, very little readjustment of the exciter will be required. Even in moving from one end of the band to the other, only repeaking of the tripler and amplifier tuning capacitors will be needed. The tubes run at a conservative level, to assure trouble-free operation in the continuous nightly service encountered in bulletin and code-practice transmissions from the Headquarters station. Double-tuned inductively-coupled circuits throughout give the desired band-pass response, but with selectivity sufficient to attentuate unwanted multiples of the oscillator frequency that might go through to the amplifier and be radiated if simpler circuits were used.

There are three dual tubes in the exciter. The oscillator and multiplier stages are 6AR11 dual pentodes, and the output stage is a 6360 dual tetrode. A 6CX8 or similar pentode-triode could be substituted for the 6AR11 oscillator-tripler-doubler with only minor circuit changes. A 6360 is usable for the push-pull tripler, if the Compactrons are hard to come by. The oscillator, V1A, is set up

for 8-MHz crystals, though fundamental crystals at 6 or 12 MHz will also work. The switch S1 selects one of five crystals. One position may be used for VFO input of the switch S2 (not in the original unit) is incorporated to short out the cathode rf choke, RFC1.

The oscillator plate circuit multiplies to 24 MHz. Its plate coil, L1, is inductively coupled to the following grid circuit, L2, and the coupling is increased by the link, L3. The second pentode of V1 doubles to 48 MHz. Its plate circuit and the grid circuit of the push-pull tripler, V2, are also link-coupled. The tripler plate circuit and the grid circuit of the 144-MHz amplifier, V3, are inductively coupled. Amplifier output is taken off through a series-tuned link to a coaxial fitting on the rear wall of the exciter chassis.

Grid current in the tripler or amplifier stages can be measured by connecting a low-range milliammeter between the exposed terminal of C3 or C5 and the chassis. This is helpful in initial adjustment, and for trouble shooting, if needed.

The Final Amplifier

It is desirable that a transmitter be capable of running at moderate power, particularly in vhf work, where about 50 watts output is adequate for most communication. The external-anode type of vhf tetrode fits this need admirably, as it will run efficiently at inputs of 100 watts or less, yet it can be pushed up to 500 watts with complete safety.

The 4CX250R shown can be replaced with any tube of this family. Many builders will want to use the 4X150A, which can be found on the surplus market at attractive prices. It will work equally well, except for slightly reduced ratings. The socket specified takes the 4X150A, 4X250B, and 4CX250B and R. With a suitable socket, and possible modification of the grid circuit to take care of differing input capacitances, any of the many tubes of this general type can be used.

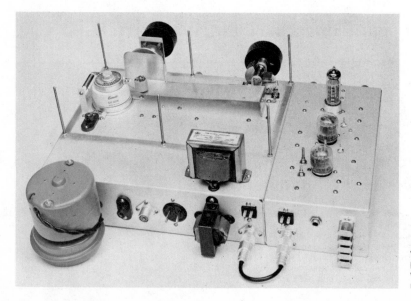

Fig. 6-17 — Rear view of the complete transmitter, with amplifier shield removed.

Fig. 6-18 — Interior view of the 144-MHz exciter. The oscillator portion is at the left. Note that all stages are inductively coupled, for maximum protection against spurious frequencies in the output.

The amplifier tank circuits are made from flashing copper, a readily-available material that can be cut and bent without special tools. Details of the grid inductance, L12, and the plate line, L13, are given in Fig. 6-23. Many plate circuits were made and tested to derive the shape of L13. These included copper pipes from 1/8 to 1 inch in diameter, and copper strips of several widths and configurations. The plate circuit was operated as a pi-network, as well as in the inductively coupled form shown here. When optimum L/C ratio was achieved (tuning to the desired frequency range with the lowest usable capacitance) there was no essential difference in results, so the convenient and safe grounded tank shown was adopted.

Power Circuits

Only two external power supplies are needed for the rf portion of the transmitter: one delivering 250 volts dc at about 150 mA, and a high-voltage supply giving anything up to 2000 volts at 300 mA. Control of the ac voltage input to the final-stage plate transformer by means of a Variac or Powerstat is an excellent way of adjusting the transmitter power level to the needs of the moment. A bias supply for the amplifier is built in. The single 250-volt source handles the exciter stages and final amplifier screen. It should have good regulation. The oscillator screen voltage should be regulated if the transmitter is to be used

for cw, or if the ultimate in oscillator stability is wanted. Otherwise Pins 1 and 3 of the power plug, P2, can be connected together.

The 4-pin fittings on the exciter and amplifier, J5 and J6, are wired so that meters for the final grid and screen current can be connected externally. The meters are not in the photographs, as they are mounted on a separate panel in the W1AW setup.

The filament transformers T1 and T2 connected back-to-back give isolation from the ac line for the bias supply, and take care of the heaters of the transmitter. The blower motor, B1, comes on whenever the primary of T1 is energized. The switch S4 is connected externally and does not appear in the photographs.

The exciter heaters should be operated at 6.3 volts, but the amplifier tube should run at 6.0, plus or minus 5 percent. With today's line voltages

Fig. 6-19 — The amplifier plate circuit is mainly a piece of flashing copper. It is grounded for dc, making for safety in operation and ease of construction. Tuning is by means of a disk capacitor on a brass lead-screw, right. Plate voltage is shunt-fed through the rf choke, upper right.

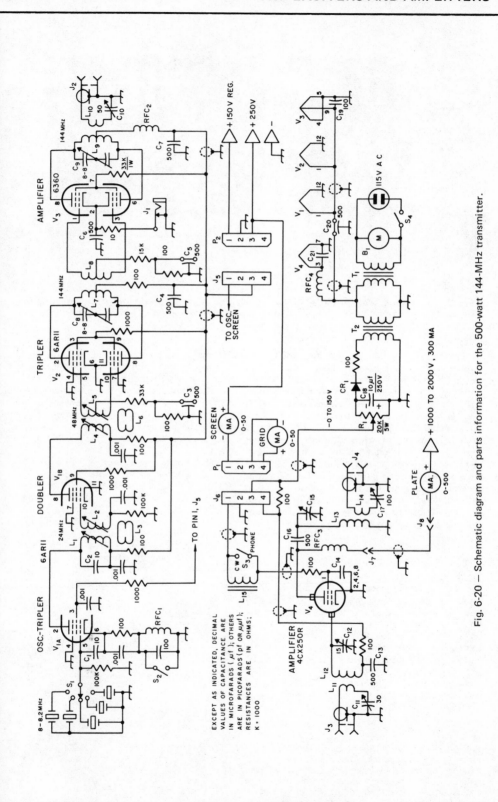

Fig. 6-20 — Schematic diagram and parts information for the 500-watt 144-MHz transmitter.

Fig. 6-21 — Interior of the amplifier compartment. The grid inductance, upper right, is a strip of copper supported at its left end by a button-mica capacitor and fastened to the grid terminal of the tube socket at the right end. The long piece of coax, left, brings the amplifier output to the rear of the chassis. The shorter section is used as a shielded high-voltage lead. Bias supply components are in the left center portion of the chassis.

B1 — Blower, 16 ft³/min or more.

C1, C2 — 10-pF dipped silver-mica capacitor

C3, C5, C20 — 500-pF feedthrough capacitor.

C4, C6, C7, C13 — 500-pF button-mica capacitor.

C8, C9 — Miniature split-stator variable, 8 pF per section (Bud LC-1659). Do not ground rotor.

C10 — 50-pF miniature variable (Hammarlund HF-50).

C11 — 30-pF mica trimmer.

C12 — 15-pF miniature variable (Hammarlund HF-15).

C14, C21 — Bypass built into air-system socket (Eimac SK-620).

C15 — Disk-type variable; see text and photos.

C16 — 500-pF 5000-volt transmitting capacitor (Centralab 858S-500).

C17 — 100-pF variable (Hammarlund MC-100).

C18 — 10-μF 250-volt electrolytic.

C19 — 100-pF ceramic, with 1/4-inch leads.

CR1 — 400-volt PRV diode, 100 mA or more.

J1 — Closed-circuit jack.

J2, J3, J4 — Coaxial connector, SO-239.

J5, J6 — 4-pin male power connector.

J7, J8 — High-voltage feedthrough connector (Millen 37501).

L1, L2 — 3.1-6.7 μH slug-tuned, ceramic form (Miller 4405). Remove 2 turns from L2.

L3 — Figure-8 loop of No. 24 enamelled wire around slug end of L1 and L2.

L4 — 1.5-3.2 μH slug-tuned, ceramic form (Miller 4404).

L5 — 11 turns No. 24 enamel on 3/8-inch iron-slug ceramic form (Miller 4400), center tapped.

L6 — Figure-8 loop No. 24 enamel around slug end of L4 and center of L5.

L7 — 4 turns No. 20 Nyclad, 1/2-inch dia, 3/8 inch long, center tapped. Leads are 1 and 1-1/2 inches long.

L8 — 4 turns No. 20 Nyclad, 1/2-inch dia, center tapped, with 1-1/4-inch leads. Bend outer turn on each end outward at 45-degree angle, and insert middle two turns about 1/4 inch into middle of L7. See text and photo.

L9 — 5 turns No. 18 tinned, 1/2-inch dia, 5/8-inch long, center-tapped, with 1-1/4-inch leads.

L10 — 3/4 turn insulated hookup wire, 1-inch dia, around center of L9.

L11 — Loop of No. 18 3 inches long. Adjust shape and position for maximum grid drive; see text.

L12 — Copper strip 4 X 3/4 inches; see Figs. 6-21 and 6-23

L13 — Copper strip 9-3/4 inches long with 1-3/4-inch tab bent up for fixed plate of C15. See Figs. 6-14 and 6-17.

L14 — Loop of copper 5/16 X 6 inches. Bend as per Fig. 6-23 and adjust position with respect to L13 for best output.

L15 — 10-H 50-mA filter choke.

P1, P2 — 4-pin female connector.

R1 — 20,000-ohm 5-watt control.

RFC1 — 500-μH rf choke.

RFC2 — Single-layer vhf choke, 1.3-2.7 μH (Millen 34300, 2.7 μH used).

RFC3 — No. 22 Nyclad closewound 1-3/16 inch on 1/4-inch Teflon rod; about 2.2 μH.

RFC4 — Approx. 5 feet No. 26 Nyclad closewound on 1/4-inch Teflon rod. Vary wire size and/or number of turns to drop heater voltage to 6.0 at tube socket. See text.

S1 — Single-pole 5-position wafer switch.

S2 — Toggle switch mounted close to RFC1. (Not in transmitter as shown.)

S3, S4 — Toggle switch. (S4 not in transmitter as shown.)

T1 — 6.3 volt 6-A filament transformer.

T2 — 6.3-volt 1.2-A filament transformer.

Fig. 6-22 — Hole layout for the exciter chassis. Hole sizes are A—1/8 inch, B—1/4 inch, C—3/4 inch, and D—1 inch. Because of variations in parts sizes, the builder should check with his components before drilling to these dimensions.

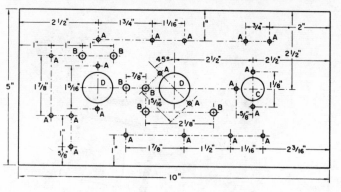

often running over 120, a filament transformer rated at 6,3 volts may give as much as 7. This is much too high for the 250 series tubes, so RFC4 was introduced to perform a dual role. Mainly, it drops the heater voltage to the desired level, but the rf isolation of the heater circuit it also provides certainly does no harm. Because the choke function is not critical, the wire size and/or number of turns can be varied to give 6.0 volts at the 4CX250 tube terminal, with your average   line voltage. It is well to measure this with an ac meter of known accuracy; vacuum-tube voltmeters are notoriously inaccurate on ac readings. The choke was not in place when the pictures were made. It is mounted alongside the tube socket, directly in the air stream from the cooling fan, so heating is no problem with wire sizes as small as No. 28.

Modulation of the transmitter for voice or tone (the latter is used in W1AW bulletin and code-practice transmissions) requires an external audio unit of at least 150 watts output. The audio choke, L15, connected in the screen lead, is shorted by S3 when cw of fm is used. Maximum plate voltage is 2000 for cw and 1500 for a-m, but the amplifier works well with voltages as low as 750. High voltage is brought in on a separate fitting, J8. A similar fitting, J7, inverted alongside the amplifier tube, is used to terminate the high-voltage feed to the shunt plate choke, RFC3.

Building the Exciter

Layout of parts in the exciter should be fairly clear from the photographs. The principal dimensions for drilling the top surface of the 5 by 10 by 3-inch chassis are given in Fig. 6-22. The builder will do well to check his components for minor variations before going ahead with the drilling.

Controls on the front wall of the chassis at the left are the crystal selector, S1, lower, and the 6360 plate capacitor, C9, above it. In the middle is the loading capacitor, C10, and at the right is the tripler plate capacitor, C8. On the rear wall, Fig. 6-17, we see the crystal sockets at the right, the cathode jack, J1, in the center, the power connector, J5, at the left, and below it the coaxial output connector, J2.

The tubes, V1, V2, and V3, are lined up back to front in that order. The oscillator plate and doubler grid coils, L1 and L2, are beside V1. The

doubler plate and tripler grid coils, L4 and L5, are between V1 and V2. All are slug-tuned. The 144-MHz coils are supported mainly on their own leads. The tripler and amplifier plate-tuning capacitors, C8 and C9, are alongside their respective tubes. They and the crystal switch are driven by extension shafts and couplings.

Liberal use is made of tie-point strips for mounting small parts, where they are not connected directly to other components that will support them. Disk-ceramic capacitors are used for bypassing in circuits up through 48 MHz. The 144-MHz circuits (except the heater circuit of V3) use button-mica or ceramic feedthrough capacitors, as disk ceramics are unreliable at this and higher frequencies. During initial testing of the exciter instability in the output stage was traced to the presence of rf in the heater circuits. The heater bypass on Pins 4 and 5 of V3, a 100-pF ceramic of the "dogbone" variety, with 1/4-inch leads, is series-resonant in the 144-MHz region. This turned out to be a simple and effective way of getting the heater down to ground potential for rf, and thus stabilizing the 6360 stage.

Heater leads are made with shielded wire. All power leads can be made this way, though it is not mandatory. Heater voltage for the exciter is brought through the side wall from the transformer, T1, in the amplifier compartment on a feed-through capacitor, C20. Plate power comes in via the 4-pin connectors J5 and P2, which have separate terminals for the oscillator screen, so that this element can be supplied with regulated voltage if desired.

Adjustment

The exciter should be tested with no more than 250 volts from the supply. Less can be used, and the builder can play safe by inserting a 5000-ohm 10-watt resistor in series with the voltage source temporarily. This will prevent tube damage in case of malfunction, and it will protect the supply in case of a dc short.

Start with voltage only on the oscillator plate and screen, leaving other power leads disconnected temporarily. Listen for the oscillator on 8 MHz, or on 24, 48, or 144 MHz, whichever of these frequencies is available for receiving. The note should be a pure crystal tone, and the frequency should vary little or none as L1 is tuned. The value of C1 may require change for some inactive crystals, though ordinarily the 10 pF specified will be satisfactory.

An rf indicator is now needed. This can take many forms. A 2-volt 60-mA pilot lamp with a 1/2-inch diameter loop soldered across it can be hung over the end of L1, and the core position adjusted for maximum lamp brilliance. A grid-dip meter in the output-indicating position may be coupled to L1 for this test. The latter is preferred, since it provides a check on the frequency of the output, which should be in the 24-MHz region, three times the crystal frequency.

A high-resistance voltmeter or vtvm can be used to measure relative grid voltage at the cold end of L2. A simple wavemeter (see Fig. 14-3) may be used to check the approximate frequency, as the grid voltage will dip sharply as the wavemeter is tuned through the oscillator output frequency. Tune the cores in L1 and L2 for maximum drive to V1B.

Now apply plate and screen voltage to V1B, and check similarly for 48-MHz output. Any of the above methods may be used, and in addition we have provision for measuring tripler grid current built into the exciter. Connect a low-range milliammeter from the exposed terminal of C3 to ground, and tune all core studs for maximum grid current. This should be about 1 mA, though more is fine if you can get it. Check with a wavemeter to be sure that the energy in L4 and L5 is on the 6th harmonic of the 8-MHz crystal, and on no other frequency.

Next connect the meter from the exposed terminal of C5 and ground, and apply plate and screen voltage to V2. Tune C8 for maximum amplifier grid current, which should be around 2 mA. Check with a wavemeter to be sure that the drive is on the 18th harmonic of the 8-MHz crystal frequency. A check on the need for neutralization, if any, should now be made. Tune the plate circuit of V3 slowly through resonance while watching the amplifier grid current. There should be no drop in grid current as this is done. A downward flicker would indicate feedback, which would require neutralization. This is easily done with a 6360 by soldering 1/2-inch pieces of insulated wire to the grid terminals, Pins 1 and 3. Bend the ends until

they are adjacent to the plate terminals, 6 and 8, respectively, adjusting their position until the change in grid current as the plate circuit is tuned is eliminated. Normally the 6360 does not require neutralization, and the exciter shown here was completely stable without it, after the heater bypass capacitor, C19, was installed.

Now apply plate and screen voltage to the 6360, and connect a dummy load to J2, preferably through a power-indicating SWR bridge. Adjust C9 and C10 for maximum power output, which should be 6 to 8 watts, with a 250-volt supply. Now, using a crystal frequency near the middle of the range over which you will normally operate, tune all adjustments through C8 for maximum amplifier grid current, and C9 and C10 for best output.

It will be seen that input to the 6AR11 pentodes runs only about the rated plate dissipation for the tubes. This makes for long tube life and trouble-free operation. The 6360 also operates conservatively, yet its output is adequate to drive the final amplifier. The exciter may also be used as a low-powered transmitter, and it is well-adapted to portable work, since its total drain is only a little over 100 mA at 250 volts. The output stage can be modulated with 6 to 10 watts of audio, or keyed in J1 for cw work.

Amplifier Construction

The final stage is built on a 10 by 12 by 3-inch aluminum chassis, which when fastened to the 5 by 10-inch exciter makes a complete 10 by 17-inch assembly that can be rack mounted. Our photographs were made before the panel was added, in the interest of clarity. The construction is extremely simple, and with the drawings of the grid and plate inductances, Fig. 6-23, the builder should have little trouble in duplicating the original. Arrangement of parts, other than in the rf circuits, is not important.

The Eimac SK-620A socket has a shield ring enclosing the screen contacts, a feature that may contribute to the exceptional stability of this amplifier. Other air-system sockets leave the screen ring of the tube exposed, and this has been a factor in neutralizing problems encountered with various external-anode tubes of the 150-250 series in the

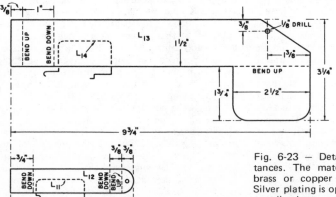

Fig. 6-23 — Details of the grid and plate inductances. The material is flashing copper, though brass or copper of heavier gauge may be used. Silver plating is optional. Approximate positions of coupling loops are shown in broken lines.

past. The push-pull amplifier for 144 MHz described elsewhere in this chapter required shield plates alongside the tube sockets, in order to achieve complete stability. Neutralization of this amplifier, if needed, is described at the end of this section.

The grid circuit is a short strap of copper, with its main portion about one inch away from the chassis. One end is supported on a button-mica capacitor, C13, and the other on the grid terminal of the tube socket. The input coupling loop, L11, is supported on a tie-point strip adjacent to the grid line, the loop extending underneath the copper strip.

The main portion of the plate line and the stationary plate of C15 are a single piece of flashing copper. This is fastened directly to the chassis at the left end, as viewed in Fig. 6-19. Plate voltage is shunt-fed through RFC3 to the tube anode. A copper strap wrapped around the anode supports the blocking capacitor, C16, which is bolted to both the plate strap and the plate inductance, L13. At the grounded end of L13 may be seen the series capacitor, C17, and the output coupling loop, L14. The nature of C16 is important. It must be a transmitting-type capacitor, capable of withstanding heat, high rf current, and high voltage. The TV-type "doorknob" capacitor often used for this purpose on lower frequencies is definitely not recommended for 144-MHz service.

When the amplifier was placed in service at W1AW it was found that vibration of the plate line caused by the blower motor was a source of operational difficulties, so a ceramic standoff was mounted near the middle of L13, to support it more rigidly on the chassis. We silver-plated all the plate line components, but measurements made carefully before and after show only a perceptible improvement from the plating.

The movable plate of C15 is a 2 1/4-inch aluminum disk mounted on a 1/4-20 brass lead screw. A matching nut soldered to a copper plate is bolted to an aluminum bracket to provide a bearing and electrical ground. When the panel is in place a tension spring can be added externally, by slipping it over the brass screw.

The shunt-feed rf choke, RFC3, may be seen in a horizontal position beside the tube, level with the top of the anode. Its back end is connected to a high-voltage feedthrough, J7. Under the chassis the matching portion of J7 is connected to a similar fitting, J8, on the back wall of the chassis, by means of coax used in lieu of high-voltage shielded wire. Another run of coax connects the output fitting, J4, with the hot end of the output coupling loop, L14.

The shield cover for the amplifier is a standard 7 by 12-inch chassis, notched to pass the shafts of C15 and C17, and held in place by wing nuts atop six 3 1/2-inch 6-32 threaded brass rods. These are fastened at the corners, and at the midpoint of each long side, with hex nuts above and below the main chassis surface. If you do your own metalwork you may be able to make a better shielded plate line than this; the dimensions of ours were dictated by available chassis sizes. The main chassis was polished with emery paper and steel wool

along the surface that makes contact with the cover. Good electrical contact is important here, and also at the grounded end of the plate line. The folded-over end of L13 is clamped to the chassis with a metal strip and two screws and nuts.

For effective cooling with a small blower it is important that there be very low air leakage out of the main chassis, except up through the tube socket. To this end, the holes in the corners of the chassis, the overlaps at the corners, and all holes made in mounting the various parts were sealed with plastic cement. A screened hole in the top cover allows the warm air to flow out of the plate compartment directly over the tube. A tight-fitting bottom cover is important for good cooling, perhaps more than for shielding.

The built-in bias supply, the audio choke in the screen lead, and the various components other than those in the rf circuits can be placed almost anywhere that suits the builder's fancy.

Firing Up

The first step in placing the amplifier in service is to check the grid circuit. Input coupling is best adjusted with a standing-wave bridge connected in the line between J2 and J3. A milliammeter should be between terminals 3 and 4 of P1, to read amplifier grid current. The object now is to obtain optimum coupling into the amplifier.

Apply power to the exciter, which also activates the amplifier bias supply. Leave the screen meter disconnected for the present, so that there will be no voltage on the amplifier screen. Adjust the exciter tuning and loading for maximum amplifier grid current. Now adjust C11 and C12 for minimum reflected power on the SWR bridge. If this is not zero, try various positions of L11 with respect to L12, readjusting their capacitors each time for lowest reflected power. The best power transfer between exciter and amplifier will occur at this point.

Adjust the bias control so that the amplifier grid current is 10 mA or less, and apply plate and screen voltage to the amplifier. Be sure that the amplifier is loaded at all times, to prevent excessive screen current. Satisfactory operation should be possible with plate voltages as low as 700, with 250 volts on the screen. If lower plate voltage is used for initial testing, the screen voltage should be dropped also, to keep screen current below about 30 mA. Keep a 50-ohm dummy load connected to J4 at all times, and be sure that C15 and C17 are adjusted so that power is being delivered to the load. Tube damage is more likely to develop from excessive screen dissipation than from anything that can happen to the plate in normal service, so keep a close watch on the screen meter, and be sure that dissipation is kept below 10 watts.

Adjust the position of L14 with respect to L13 for maximum output, readjusting the tuning and loading capacitors, C15 and C17, with each change in coupling. The tuning and the position of the coupling loop will change with various plate voltages, so final adjustment should be made with the plate voltage at the point where maximum efficiency is desired. If an accurate bridge or wattmeter is available, it should indicate operating efficiency in excess of 65 percent. Power output well over 300 watts was measured at 2000 volts, and 200 watts at 1500 volts, with inputs of 500 and 300 watts, respectively.

The amplifier can be run under a wide range of plate and screen voltages, bias and driving power, so long as none of the maximum ratings for the various elements is exceeded. With fixed screen supply, best efficiency will be obtained by juggling the grid bias, checking output meanwhile. Keep the final plate current below 250 mA and the screen current under 30. Screen current will be progressively lower as the plate voltage is raised, and may even go negative at plate voltages above 1000 or so, particularly with low drive. If a separate variable screen supply is used, there may be some advantage in using voltages above 250, so long as the screen dissipation is kept low.

Neutralization can be added, if necessary, as follows: A feed-through bushing (National TPB) is mounted under L13, so that it projects through the chassis under L12. A loop of wire about 1/2 inch on a side is connected from the bushing rod to the chassis, under L12. A brass capacitor plate about $1/2 \times 1$ inch is soldered to the top, under L13. Vary the position of the loop with respect to L12, and the plate with respect to L13, to achieve minimum rf feedthrough, with the exciter running and the amplifier having only heater voltage applied. Check with a sensitive rf indicator coupled to J3.

A 500-WATT FM AND CW TRANSMITTER FOR 220 MHZ

The 220-MHz transmitter of Fig. 6-24 was designed and built by R. B. Stevens, W1QWJ, and was first described in May 1969 *QST*. It is capable of 300 watts output, cw or fm, or the exciter portion can be used alone to deliver approximately 8 watts output.

The RF Circuits

Looking at the schematic diagram, Fig. 6-26, it will be seen that the first three stages of the transmitter look very much like any vhf transmitter using vacuum tubes. A conventional 6CL6 crystal oscillator, V1, uses 6-, 8-, or 12-MHz crystals, multiplying in its plate circuit to 24 MHz (12-MHz crystals should be the fundamental type.) A 6BQ5, V2, triples to 73 MHz, and drives a 2E26 amplifier, V3, straight-through on this frequency. A variable capacitor, C6, across the crystal, permits a small adjustment of the frequency.

A varactor tripler, driven by the 2E26, is used to get up to 220. Requiring no power supply of its own, it is capable of more than enough power output at 220 to drive the 500-watt amplifier.

The output of a varactor multiplier contains harmonics other than the desired one, so a strip-line filter is connected between the varactor output and the final amplifier grid circuit. The filter is a separate assembly mounted on the end of the chassis, visible in two of the photographs. Full details of the filter may be found in any edition of this Manual.

The final amplifier is a 4CX250 series external-anode tube, with a coaxial tank circuit. The B version is used here, but the R and F types have the same mechanical design.

The coaxial plate circuit follows a standard design. Such a tank has extremely high Q, and the heavy copper (or brass) construction offers considerable heat sinking. Probably its only disadvantage is the necessity for feeding the high voltage in

Fig. 6-24 — The 220-MHz transmitter is set up for rack mounting on 8-3/4-inch panel. Meters at the left can be switched to read driver plate, amplifier screen and amplifier plate currents, and amplifier plate voltage.

through some kind of rf bypassing device. This and the other mechanical features of a good coaxial tank are not readily made with the simpler tools. Details of the assembly are given in Fig. 6-30.

The final grid circuit, visible in Fig. 6-32 along with the varactor multiplier and the strip-line filter, is a half-wave strip-line. The fan blows cooling air into the grid compartment, up through the 4CX250 socket, and out through the end of the

Fig. 6-25 — Rear view of the 220-MHz transmitter. The exciter stages are on a circuit board in the foreground. Chassis at the right side houses the varactor tripler and the amplifier grid circuit. Air blows into this compartment and out through the center conductor of the coaxial plate-circuit assembly.

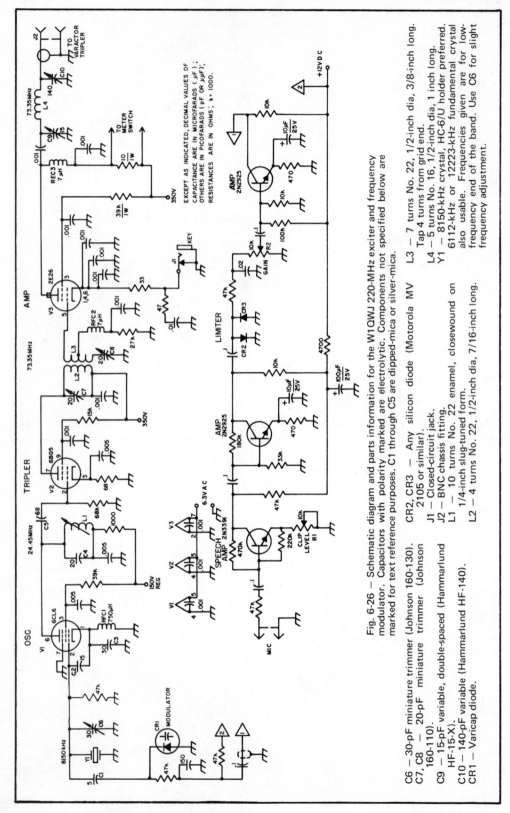

Fig. 6-26 — Schematic diagram and parts information for the W1QWJ 220-MHz exciter and frequency modulator. Capacitors with polarity marked are electrolytic. Components not specified below are marked for text reference purposes. C1 through C5 are dipped-mica or silver-mica.

C6 — 30-pF miniature trimmer (Johnson 160-130).

C7, C8 — 20-pF miniature trimmer (Johnson 160-110).

C9 — 15-pF variable, double-spaced (Hammarlund HF-15-X).

C10 — 140-pF variable (Hammarlund HF-140).

CR1 — Varicap diode.

CR2, CR3 — Any silicon diode (Motorola MV 2105 or similar).

J1 — Closed-circuit jack.

J2 — BNC chassis fitting.

L1 — 10 turns No. 22 enamel, closewound on 1/4-inch slug-tuned form.

L2 — 4 turns No. 22, 1/2-inch dia, 7/16-inch long.

L3 — 7 turns No. 22, 1/2-inch dia, 3/8-inch long. Tap 4 turns from grid end.

L4 — 5 turns No. 16, 1/2-inch dia, 1 inch long.

Y1 — 8150-kHz crystal, HC-6/U holder preferred. 6112-kHz or 12223-kHz fundamental crystal also usable. Frequencies given are for low-frequency end of the band. Use C6 for slight frequency adjustment.

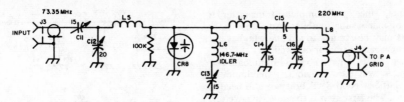

Fig. 6-27 — Circuit of the varactor multiplier, 73 to 220 MHz.

C11, C13, C14, C16 — 15-pF miniature variable (Johnson 160-107). Rotor of C11 must be insulated from chassis.
C12 — 20-pF miniature variable (Johnson 160-110).
C15 — 5-pF ceramic.
L5 — 8 turns No. 16, 1/2-inch dia, 7/8-inch long.

L6 — 4 turns No. 16, 1/2-inch dia, 1/2-inch long.
L7 — 3 turns No. 16, 3/8-inch dia, 3/8-inch long.
L8 — 3 turns No. 16, 3/8-inch dia, 3/8-inch long, tapped at 1 turn from grounded end.
CR8 — Varactor diode (Amperex H4A/1N4885).
J3, J4 — BNC fitting.

tank assembly, by way of the hollow inner conductor, L10. The coaxial output fitting, J6, the coupling loop, L11, and its series capacitor, C21, are mounted on a small detachable plate bent to fit the curvature of the coaxial assembly, and mounted near the outer end. The varactor tripler is built into the top of the amplifier grid assembly, as seen in Fig. 6-32, above the final grid circuit and the strip-line filter.

Generating the Frequency Modulation

Where only a small swing at the control frequency is needed, as in a vhf or uhf transmitter having a high order of frequency multiplication, the modulation can be applied very easily. A voltage-variable capacitor, CR1, changes capacitance in relation to the audio voltage applied across

it, and this changing capacitance is used to "pull" the frequency of the crystal oscillator slightly. A good 8-MHz crystal can be pulled up to 600 Hz in this way, depending on the values of C1 and C6 in Fig. 6-26. With 27 times frequency multiplication this gives a maximum deviation in excess of 16 kHz at the operating frequency, close to the optimum for some of the fm receivers currently in use in fixed-frequency service on 6 and 2. Lesser deviation, for work with communications receivers, most of them having about a 3-kHz bandwidth today, is merely a matter of applying less audio.

Adjustment and Operation

This is not intended to be a beginner's project, so detailed discussion of the mechanical layout will be omitted. The mechanical arrangement of the components could be altered to suit one's own

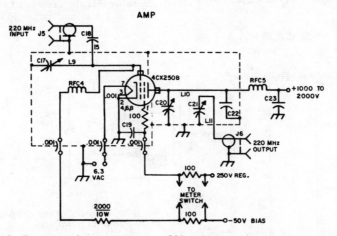

Fig. 6-28 — Schematic diagram and parts information for the 220-MHz final amplifier. Decimal values of capacitance are in microfarads (μF); others in pF.
C17 — 20-pF miniature variable (Johnson 160-110). Stator supports end of L9.
C18 — 15-pF silver-mica.
C19 — Capacitor built into socket assembly (Johnson 124-109-1 socket, with 124-113-1 bypass ring and 124-111-1 chimney).
C20 — Disk-type tuning capacitor; see Fig. 6-30.
C21 — 15-pF miniature variable (Johnson 160-107).

C22 — Built-in bypass capacitor; see Fig. 6-30.
C23 — 500-pF 5-kV or more.
J6 — N-type fitting.
L9 — Brass strip, 1/16 X 3/8 X 6-1/2 inches. Bolts to grid terminal on socket. Tap C18 7/8 inch from grid.
L10 — Coaxial line inner conductor; see Fig. 6-30.
L11 — Output coupling loop made from 3-1/4 inches No. 16. Cover with insulating sleeving and bend to 3/4 inch high and 1-3/4 inch long. See Fig. 6-30.
RFC4, RFC5 — 0.84-μH rf choke (Ohmite Z-235).
J5 — BNC fitting.

requirements, since the complete transmitter is made up of many subassemblies. Adjustment for best results may be strange to anyone who has not had experience with varactor multipliers.

The first step is to get a good 52-ohm load. For the present, it will have to handle a maximum of about 10 watts. A good SWR bridge is also needed for the tests. The first step is to adjust the exciter. Procedure here is like that for any similar lineup of tubes, but the 2E26 must be adjusted for optimum results when working into a 52-ohm load. Once an output of 10 to 12 watts is obtained in this way,

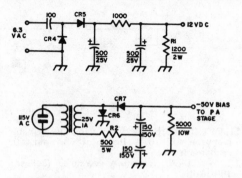

Fig. 6-29 — Circuit details of the built-in power supplies for amplifier bias (lower) and speech amplifier-modulator (upper) for the 220-MHz transmitter. Capacitors with polarity marked are electrolytic. All diodes are 200-volt PRV, 1 A. R1 and R2 are approximate values. Select for 12 and minus 50 volts output, respectively. Capacitance is in microfarads.

leave the tuning of the 2E26 and preceding stages alone thereafter.

Now connect the SWR bridge output to J3 of the varactor multiplier, and tune C11 and C12 for lowest SWR indication. Leave the 2E26 adjustments alone.

Now connect a coaxial cable from J2 to J3, and connect the bridge or wattmeter in a line from J4 to the dummy load. Adjust C13, C14, and C16 for maximum output at 220 MHz. Adjustments in the multiplier interlock, and several passes through all adjustments may be needed for best output. But remember that the 2E26 is set for a 52-ohm load. Leave it alone, and make the multiplier adjust-

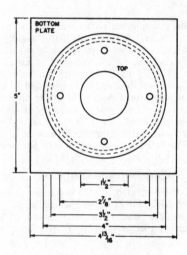

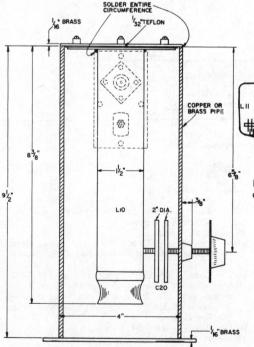

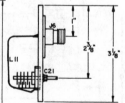

Fig. 6-30 — Details of the coaxial-line plate circuit of the 220-MHz transmitter.

Fig. 6-31 — Looking underneath the chassis of the 220-MHz transmitter, we see the speech amplifier clipper at the upper right, the exciter circuits across the bottom, power supply components at the lower right, and meter switching, upper left

ments do the job. An indication of some 8 watts or so of output should result in maximum grid current in the final amplifier.

It is likely that getting enough grid current for the 4CX250B will not be difficult, as the lineup described gives more than ample drive. Up to 20 mA grid current has been obtained, but not this much is needed. In fact, with fm or cw operation, only a slight increase in efficiency is noted after the drive is raised beyond the point where grid current begins to flow.

Adjustment of the coupling loop, L11, and the loading capacitor, C21, will be fairly critical when striving for the absolute maximum output. Following the manufacturer's recommendations as to maximum plate voltage and current, 2000 volts at 250 mA, resulted in about 320 watts output. Raising the plate current to 300 mA, by increasing the screen voltage, netted 400 watts output. Even at this input the tube seemed to be operating well and the tank circuit did not indicate excessive heating.

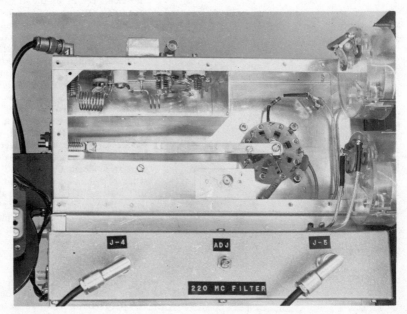

Fig. 6-32 — Looking into the amplifier grid compartment. The varactor tripler is in the upper left portion. Below the compartment is the 220-MHz strip-line filter.

AN 829B AMPLIFIER FOR 144 MHz

The dual tetrode known variously as the 829, 829B and 3E29 has been a fixture on the vhf scene for many years. Commonly available on the surplus market since the end of World War II, it is still one of the better vhf amplifier tubes in the 100-watt class. At surplus prices, it is also the cheapest. Inclusion of a rather old 2-meter amplifier in the first edition of this manual showed that there is still a considerable interest in this tube, so this modern version by W1CER, Figs. 6-33 to 6-37, is presented here. It features complete shielding, a recessed socket with shield ring, for isolation of the grid and plate circuits, and a metal strap plate circuit, for improved efficiency.

This amplifier was designed specifically for the 829-series tubes, but there are several other types that could be used, with minor modification of the design. The 5894 is a more efficient dual tetrode, capable of somewhat more power than the 829, and requiring less drive. Because of lower input and output capacitances, it will require more inductance in L2 and L3. The 832A, a smaller version of the 829 taking lower power and less drive, is also usable.

Construction

The amplifier is built on a 3 by 5 by 10-inch aluminum chassis, with an aluminum cage on top, 9 1/2 inches long, 4 inches wide and 4 1/2 inches high. Holes in the sides and rear of the top compartment, at the tube end, allow for air circulation. The cover is perforated aluminum, permitting the heat to rise from the tube, as cool air moves in from the side holes.

The 829B socket is an E. F. Johnson Type 122-101, designed for recessed mounting. Leads from the socket terminals 1, 4, and 7 to ground are

3/8-inch wide strips of copper or brass, to reduce lead inductance. The .001-μF. capacitors at Pins 3 and 5 are returned to Pin 4, using the shortest possible leads. The grid coil, L2, is mounted directly on the socket terminals, with the link, L1, inserted between turns at the center. A 3-lug terminal strip attached to the rear wall supports C1 and L1. A 5-terminal barrier strip on the outside rear wall is used for power supply connections.

Coaxial connectors for input and output are on opposite sides of the rear of the chassis. A UG-106/U shield hood covers the back of J2, to isolate it from J1 and prevent stray coupling between the input and output. The lead from J2 to the feed-through terminal and the high-voltage lead from the barrier strip to its terminal up front are made with coaxial cable.

Details of the plate circuit assembly and top enclosure are given in Fig. 6-37. The top edges of the plate line, L3, are soldered the full length of the stator posts of C2, for minimum stray inductance at this point. The tuning capacitor is supported on a plastic mounting block, which has narrow slots for L3. These can be cut in the plastic with a keyhole saw, after drilling starting holes at the top. See detail B. If Teflon of suitable thickness is available, it would be ideal for this support, as it is impervious to heat of the order encountered here. Plexiglas and other clear plastics are usable.

Teflon shafting would also be best for the rod that is to run from C2 out through the front panel. Wood dowelling is also suitable. Do not use metal stock, as it would be closely-coupled to L3. The rotor of C2 must be isolated from ground.

The low-impedance end of L3 is supported on a 1-inch ceramic pillar. Mount a No. 6 spade bolt at the exact center of the U bend in L3, thread the standoff onto this, and then bolt the bottom of the insulator in place. The coupling loop, L4, is supported on the stator post of C3 and the feed-through bushing to which the coax to J2 is connected, on the underside of the chassis. C3 is on the front wall of the shield enclosure, so L4 is soldered to it after the cover is in place.

The plate line was made of sheet brass, and then silver plated. Flashing copper will work equally well. If not plated, it should be polished thoroughly, and then coated with clear lacquer to reduce tarnishing. The lacquering should be done only after the assembly job is complete. It will be seen from detail C, Fig. 6-37, that there are two strips of thinner stock bolted to the ends of the stiff material of L3. Holes for these bolts should be larger than needed, so that the line, the straps, and the Fahnstock clips for the plate connections can be assembled loosely at first, then tightened in a

Fig. 6-33 — The 829-B amplifier, with its shield cover in place. Air circulation is provided by the screened holes and cover.

Fig. 6-34 — Top of the amplifier chassis, as seen from the rear with the shield cage removed. The output link with its black spaghetti tubing is just below the U-shaped plate tank inductor. The loading control, C3, is mounted on the shield cage and is not shown here.

Fig. 6-35 — Looking into the bottom of the chassis. The feedthrough bushings for plate power and rf output are at the left. Coax cable is used for the high voltage dc lead. Wide copper straps ground the filament and cathode pins of the tube socket. A hood over the back of J2, lower right, helps isolate the input from the output.

position such that no strain in placed on the tube plate pins. Be sure that the tube is seated properly in the socket before the final tightening of the line assembly.

Adjustment and Use

The amplifier may be driven in Class-C service with any exciter delivering 3 to 10 watts output. Operating conditions and maximum plate voltages for cw, a-m, and ssb service are given below. The 829B works well at lower plate voltages, and is often operated at about 400 to 450 volts in vhf applications. The maximum plate current at 450 volts is 200 mA, and this amplifier delivers about 55 watts output this way. A suitable supply for this voltage level can be made with a TV receiver power transformer.

Many amateurs look for a linear amplifier that can be used with the small a-m transmitters commonly used in vhf communication. This amplifier will operate as a linear, but unless the exciter is very low-powered the step-up may not be attractive. Output in a-m linear service is no more than half the maximum safe plate dissipation for the tube used. This means that an 829B linear is limited to about 15 watts output on a-m which may be good enough for use with a 1-watt transistor rig, but not very attractive at higher levels of exciter power. For more on linear amplifiers, their uses and limitations, see the preceding chapter, and "Tips on Linears" in this one.

Screen voltage should be regulated, in linear service, either a-m or ssb. For cw, fm, or high-level a-m, the screen can be supplied through a dropping resistor from the plate voltage source. The value will depend on many factors, but should be about 10,000 ohms at low plate voltages, rising to 35,000 at the high end of the range. Grid bias may also vary, and it may be obtained from a bias supply, or from a grid resistor (connected between RFC1 and Terminal 3 of the barrier strip) or both. In ssb or a-m linear service, it preferably should be regulated and adjustable.

Any tetrode amplifier can be run under widely varying conditions, so it can be adjusted to give optimum results with the power supplies you may have available, for modes of emission you are most interested in. The "typical operating conditions" listed in tube tables are guidelines, not laws, But when the tables say "Maximum Ratings," they mean it.

To adjust the 829B amplfier, apply heater voltage, and then connect the exciter to J1. Connect a milliammeter between Terminals 3 and 5, and turn on the exciter, noting the grid current. Adjust the position of L1 with respect to L2, and the turn spacing of L2, for maximum grid current. Now tune the plate circuit slowly through its range, watching the grid current. There may be a slight rise at resonance, but no downward dip. The latter would indicate need for neutralization, which was not required in this version. Grid current should run 7 to 12 mA for Class-C service.

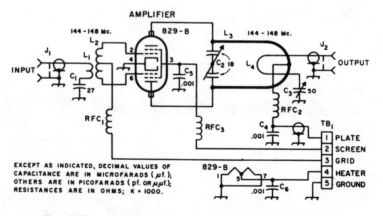

Fig. 6-36 — Schematic diagram of the 2-meter amplifier

C1 — 27-pF silver mica.
C2 — 18 pF per section, butterfly variable (E. F. Johnson 167-22 with 3 stator plates removed from each side. Also, two rotor plates are removed).
C3 — 50-pF variable (Millen 20050).
C4 — 0.001-μF transmitting ceramic (Centralab 858S).
C5, C6 — 0.001-μF 1000-volt disk.
J1, J2 — SO-239 connector.

L1 — 2 turns No. 22 insulated hookup wire in center of L2.
L2 — 5 turns No. 20 tinned wire, 5/16-inch diameter 1/2 inch long (see text).
L3 — Plate inductor. See Fig. 6-37 for dimensions.
L4 — 6-inch length of No. 12 enam. wire bent into a U with 1-1/4-inch spacing between sides (cover with spaghetti tubing).
RFC1, RFC2 — 2.7-μH choke (Millen 34300-2.7).
RFC3 — 0.8-μH rf choke (Millen 34300-.82).
TB1 — 5-terminal barrier strip (Millen 37305).

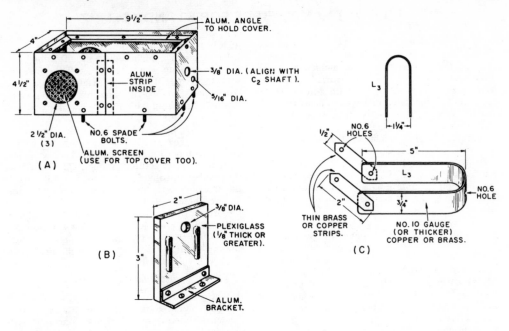

Fig. 6-37 — A — General layout of the shield box is shown at A. The box is made from No. 16 gauge aluminum stock. B — Details of the mounting block which supports C2 and L3. C — Dimensions for L3 and its connecting strips (see text).

It may be more in the static condition, as it will drop some when the amplifier is actually running, and loaded.

If neutralization is needed, run wires from the grid terminals of the socket up to the top of the chassis on feed-through bushings, and then bring wires up alongside the tube envelope adjacent to each plate. The wires are crossed over under the chassis, and the desired feedback is obtained by varying the position of the top wires with respect to the tube plates.

A lamp load may be connected across J2 for a rough indication of power output, though a good dummy load and a power-indicating watt-meter or SWR bridge is much to be preferred. Apply plate and screen power, tune C2 and C3 for maximum indication, and then adjust the position of L4 with respect to L3 carefully, retuning each time the loop is moved. Coupling should be the loosest that will give satisfactory power transfer. The lamp load will be of no value in the adjustment, as it represents a load of far different impedance than will be used ultimately with the transmitter.

829-B Operating Conditions

Service	E_p (Max.)	I_p	E_{sc}	I_{sc}	E_g (minus)	I_g
Class C — cw	750 V	160 mA	200 V	17 mA	50 V	7 mA
Class C — a-m	600 V	150 mA	200 V	16 mA	60 V	7 mA
Class AB$_1$ — ssb	600 V	110 mA	200 V	26 mA	18 V	0
no sig.		40 mA	(reg.)	4 mA		

Maximum plate input for a-m linear: about 40 watts, Class AB$_1$

KILOWATT AMPLIFIERS FOR 50 AND 144 MHZ

The amplifiers shown in Fig. 6-38 were designed for versatility. Though capable of running at the maximum legal power for amateur stations, they operate efficiently at much lower levels. They work well as linears, for use with a-m or ssb, or they can be modulated or keyed in high-efficiency Class-C service. Though the tube type shown is expensive when purchased new, an effective substitute is commonly available on the surplus market at much lower cost. Operated as a rack-mounted pair, as pictured, the amplifiers offer convenient band-changing from 50 to 144 MHz, merely by snapping on the appropriate heater voltage switch, and changing the air connection from one to the other.

The external-anode type of transmitting tube has many variations. The family originated with the 4X150A many years ago, and tubes of the early type are still available, and widely used. A later version, with improved cooling, is the 4X250B, capable of higher power but otherwise very similar to the 4X150A. More recently the insulation was changed from glass to ceramic, and the prefix became 4CX. All the general types thus far mentioned were made with variations in basing and heater voltage that will be apparent to any reader of tube catalogs. The 4CX250R used here is a special rugged version, otherwise very similar to the 4CX250B, and interchangeable with it for amateur purposes. Similar types are supplied by other makers as the 7034/4X150A 7203/4CX250B and 7580. There is another version for linear-amplifier service only, called the 4CX350A.

If one then goes to other basing arrangements similar power capabilities may be found in the 4CX300A, 8122 and others, but differences in tube capacitance might require modification of the circuit elements described here. The air-system sockets (required for all external-anode tubes mentioned) may be the same for all types in the second paragraph, but those just above require different sockets.

Both amplifiers take a kilowatt on cw or ssb with ease. The 144-MHz model must be held to 600 watts input for plate-modulated service to stay within the manufacturer's ratings. On 50 MHz the three tubes in parallel loaf along at 1000 watts in the low-duty-cycle modes. The permissible input on a-m phone is 900 watts. Class C efficiency is on the order of 75 per cent, over a wide range of plate voltages. It is possible to run all the way from 800 to 2000 volts on the amplifier plates without altering screen voltage or drive levels appreciably.

Mechanical Layout

The amplifiers are similar packages, to mount together harmoniously, though this is of only incidental interest to the fellow concerned with one band or the other. They are built in standard 4 by 10 by 17-inch aluminum chassis, mounted open side up and fitted with shield covers. In the author's station a single blower is used for all transmitters. This explains the air-intake sleeve seen on the back of each amplifier. An air hose from the remote blower is pushed into the amplifier being used.

The transmitters are all hooked up together, to meters, power circuits, audio equipment and power supplies common to all. Changing bands involves

Fig. 6-38 — The kilowatt amplifiers for 50 and 144 MHz in a rack made from aluminum angle stock. At the bottom is a meter panel with controls for meter and mode switching.

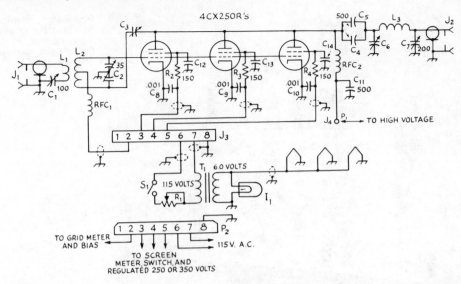

Fig. 6-39 — Schematic diagram and parts information for the 50-MHz amplifier.

C1 — 100-pF miniature trimmer (Hammarlund MAPC-100).

C2 — 35-pF per section split-stator (Hammarlund HFD-35X).

C3 — Neutralizing capacitance — see text.

C4, C5, C11 — 500-pF 5000-volt transmitting capacitor (Centralab 858S-500).

C6 — Tuning capacitor made from 3-inch aluminum disks — see text and Fig. 6-40.

C7 — 200-pF variable, .03-inch spacing (Johnson 167-12 or 200L15).

C8, C9, C10 — .001-μF disk ceramic.

C12, C13, C14 — Bypass built into special air-system socket.

I1 — Green-jewel pilot lamp holder.

J1, J2 — Coaxial chassis receptacle.

J3 — 8-pin male power fitting.

J4 — High-voltage power connector female (half of Millen 37501).

L1 — 1 turn insulated wire about 1-inch dia. Make from inner conductor of coax running to J1.

Strip jacket and braid back about 4 inches. Insert between center turns of L2.

L2 — 8 turns No. 14, 5/8-inch dia, 1-1/4 inches long, center tapped.

L3 — 3 turns 2 inches dia, 3 inches long, 1/4-inch copper tubing.

P1 — High-voltage power connector, male (half of Millen 37501).

P2 — 8-pin cable connector to match J3, female.

R1 — 20-ohm 10-watt slider-type resistor. Set so that heater voltage is 6.0 at socket.

R2, R3, R4 — 150-ohm 1/2-watt resistor. Connect at socket screen terminal.

RFC1 — No. 32 enamel wire closewound full length of 1-watt resistor, 10,000 ohms or higher.

RFC2 — No. 28 dsc or enamel, wound 1-3/4 inch on 1/2-inch Teflon rod. Space turns 1 wire dia for 8.3 μH. For winding information see Chapter 16.

S1 — Spst toggle.

T1 — 6.3-volt 8-A. Adjust R1 to give 6.0 volts.

mainly the switching on of the desired heater circuits, and the insertion of the air hose in the proper intake sleeve. Separate antenna relays are provided for each final stage, and power switching and plugging and unplugging are largely eliminated.

Tube sockets are the air-system type, mounted on 4-inch high partitions with folded-over edges that are drawn up tightly to the top, bottom, front and back of the chassis with self-tapping screws. Air is fed into the grid compartments at the left side, as viewed from the front. Its only path is through the sockets and tube anodes, and out through screened holes in the right side of the chassis. Panels are standard 5 1/2-inch aluminum. Controls for the amplifiers are similar, though their

locations are slightly different. No attempt was made to achieve symmetry through mechanical gadgetry, since the unbalance of the front panels is not unpleasing. The rack shown in Fig. 6-38 was made up from aluminum angle stock to fit the job. Several screen and bias control arrangements were tried before the circuit shown in Fig. 6-43 was settled upon. Meters read driver plate current, and amplifier grid, screen and plate currents. Switches enable the operator to check the grid and screen currents to each tube in the 144-MHz amplifier separately, and the screen currents in the 50-MHz amplifier likewise. A mode switch provides proper screen operating conditions for a-m, linear, or cw service.

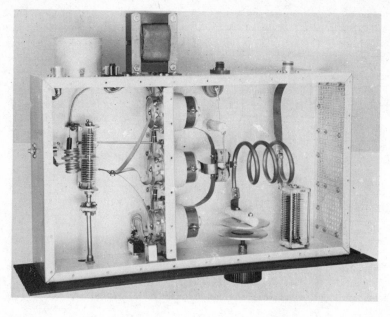

Fig. 6-40 — Interior of the 50-MHz amplifier. Note method of paralleling grid and plate connections.

The 50-MHz Amplifier

The use of three tubes in parallel in the 50-MHz amplifier was an experiment, tried with the expectation that parasitics, unbalance, excessive tank circuit heating and all manner of troubles would develop. These problems never materialized; use of paralleled tubes seemed to introduce no problems on its own, and extensive experience with the amplifier has confirmed the worth of the idea. This happy state of affairs involves a few basic considerations that should be stated here.

1) Paralleling straps in the grid and plate circuits were made "three of a kind." The two going to the outer grids were bent identically, and then the one for the middle tube was bent back on itself as necessary to use the same total length of strap. The same was done in the plate circuit.

2) The grid circuit was split-stator tuned, to get a reasonably-sized grid coil, even with the combined input capacitance of the three tubes plus circuit capacitance — some 60 pF or more. This also provided a means for easy neutralization.

3) The pi-network plate circuit is tuned with a handmade disk capacitor. This has a far lower minimum C than the more conventional tuning capacitor, and it is devoid of the side bars and multiple ground paths that are so often the cause of parasitics in vhf amplifiers. No parasitic resonances were found in this amplifier, other than one around 100 MHz introduced apparently by the rf choke. This caused a blowup when grid-plate feedback developed with a similar choke in the grid circuit. The problem was solved easily by use of a low-Q choke of different inductance in the grid circuit. Do *not* use a high-quality rf choke for RFC1!

4) All power leads except the high-voltage one are in the grid compartment, and made with shielded wire. Where the high voltage comes into the plate compartment it is bypassed at the feed-through fitting.

5) The plate circuit is made entirely of copper strap and tubing, for highest possible Q and low resistance losses. It may be of interest that the entire tank circuit was silver-plated after the photographs were made. Efficiency measurements made carefully before and after plating showed identical results.

Looking at the interior view, Fig. 6-40, we see the grid compartment at the left. The coaxial input fitting, J1 in Fig. 6-39, is in the upper left corner of the picture. Coax runs from this, out of sight on the left wall, terminating in a loop, L1, made from its inner conductor. This is inserted between turns at the center of the grid coil, L2. The series capacitor, C1, is just visible on the left chassis wall. It is not particularly critical in adjustment, so no inconvenience results from its location away from the front panel.

Screen voltage, bias, and 115 volts ac come through an 8-pin fitting, J3, mounted between the air intake and the heater transformer, T1. On the front panel are the heater switch, S1, and the pilot-lamp holder.

The three air-system sockets (Eimac SK-600, SK-620, SK-630, Johnson 124-110-1 or 124-115-1, with chimneys) are centered on the partition, spaced so that there is about 1/4 inch between their flanges. The small angle brackets that come with the sockets should be tightened down with their inner ends bearing against the ceramic chimneys, to hold them in place. Note that the 150-ohm isolating resistors R2, R3, and R4 are connected right at the screen terminals.

Both grid and plate straps are cut from flashing copper 5/8-inch wide. Lengths are not critical, except that all grid straps should be the same length, and all plate straps identical. The plate straps are made in two pieces soldered together in T shape, to wrap around the anode and join at the coupling capacitors, C4 and C5. These T-shaped connections could be cut from a sheet of copper in one piece, with a little planning.

The copper-tubing plate coil, L3, is mounted on stand-off insulators not visible in the picture. Connections to the coupling capacitors, the tuning capacitor, C6, and the loading capacitor, C7, are made with copper strap. It will be seen that these various pieces are bolted together, but the straps were also soldered. The connection from C7 to the output fitting, J2, is a single strap of copper, bolted and soldered to L3.

The disk tuning capacitor can be made in several ways. Flashing copper is easy to work, and the 144-MHz capacitor was made of this material. A more sturdy disk can be made from 1/8-inch aluminum. Those shown in Fig. 6-40 were 3-inch meter cutouts from an aluminum panel. Disk-type neutralizing capacitors (if you can find them; they're not common catalog items these days) provide ready-made disks and lead screw for tuning. For the latter we used 3-inch 1/4-20 brass screws from a neighborhood hardware store. A panel bushing with brass nuts soldered to it provided the lead-screw sleeve. The stationary disk is supported on 1/2-inch-diameter Teflon rod, a material also used for the rf choke form. Teflon works easily and is unexcelled for insulating applications where high temperatures are encountered. We found it reasonably priced, in various diameters, at a local plastics house.

The plate rf choke, RFC2, is important. You'll probably have to make it to get one of sufficiently good quality. For more on this see information under Fig. 6-39 and "RF Chokes for the VHF Bands," Chapter 16. Two coupling capacitors were paralleled because we've experienced trouble with exploding capacitors in pi-network plate circuits in

the past. Maybe one would have handled the job, but two do for sure.

Some Possible Variations

It is always risky to suggest variations on a design unless they have been checked out in use, as bugs may develop in unforeseen ways. The following are ideas only, to be used at the builder's risk, since they have not been tested by the designer.

You might not care for three tubes in parallel. Two should work well, handling a kilowatt except in a-m linear or plate-modulated service. Many builders report success with 2 tubes.

For those who can afford it, a vacuum variable capacitor should be ideal for C6. One with about 10 pF maximum capacitance should do nicely.

For lower tube cost, 4X150As from surplus should work without mechanical changes. Use plenty of air, if you intend to push the ratings of the 150As. A 100-cfm blower is not too much. The ability of the anode structure to withstand heat is the main difference between the 150A and later versions of this tube, and some people have gotten away with 250 ratings with 150-type tubes. In this connection, the 50-MHz amplifier will take a kilowatt at 1200 to 1500 volts, if your power supply will handle the current. This approach plus plenty of air, is preferable to using plate voltages much in excess of the 4X150A ratings.

The 144-MHz Plumber's Special

Use of 1 5/8-inch copper tubing for a 2-meter tank circuit is by no means new.* We simply went one step further and made the entire circuit from standard plumbing components. All the heavy metal you see in the plate compartment of Fig. 6-41 came from the plumbing counter of the local

* "High-Efficiency 2-Meter Kilowatt," *QST*, Feb., 1960, p. 30. "Top Efficiency at 144 Mc. with 4X250Bs," Breyfogle, *QST*, Dec., 1961, p. 44.

Fig. 6-41 — Interior of the 144-MHz amplifier, showing the plate circuit made from standard plumbing components. Brass pipe junctions make connection to the anodes, and T fittings are modified to form the short at the end of the line.

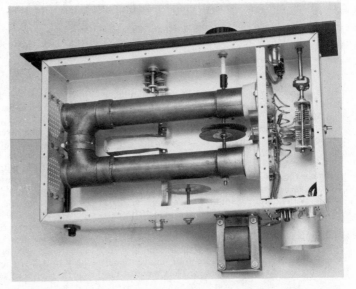

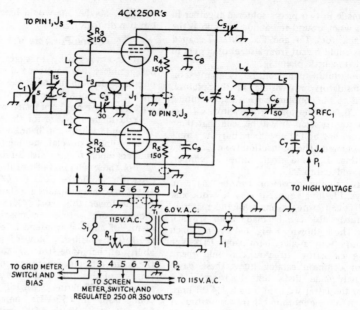

Fig. 6-42 — Schematic diagram and parts information for the 144-MHz amplifier.

C1 — 5-pF differential trimmer (Johnson 160-303 or 6MA11).

C2 — 15-pF per section split-stator (Hammarlund HFD-15X). Leave rotor ungrounded.

C3 — 30-pF miniature trimmer (Hammarlund MAC-30).

C4 — Tuning capacitor made with 3-inch disks. See text and Fig. 6-41.

C5 — 3-inch disk movable with respect to L4. See text and Fig. 6-41.

C6 — 50-pF variable (Hammarlund MC-50).

C7 — 500-pF 5000-volt (Centralab 858S-500).

C8, C9 — Bypass capacitor built into air-system socket.

I1 — Green-jewel pilot lamp holder.

J1, J2 — Coaxial chassis receptacle.

J3 — 8-pin male chassis connector.

J4 — High-voltage power connector, female (half of Millen 37501).

L1, L2 — 3-1/2 turns No. 14, 5/8-inch dia, turns spaced 1/2-inch. R2 and R3 tap on about 1 turn in from grid end. See text.

L3 — 1-turn inner conductor of coax from J1,

about 3/4-inch dia. Remove jacket and braid about 3 inches. Adjust position with respect to L1, L2 for maximum grid current.

L4 — Plate line 1-5/8-inch copper pipe, with junctions and T fittings. Exposed portion of pipe is 8 inches long. Cut right end of T fittings to 1/4-inch shoulder, and joined ends to 3/8-inch shoulders.

L5 — 1/2-inch strap of flashing copper, U portion 4 inches long and 1-1/4 inch wide. Make loop and connections from single piece. Support L4 and L5 on standoffs of ceramic or Teflon.

P1 — High-voltage connector, male (half of Millen 37501).

P2 — 8-pin female cable connector to match J3.

R1 — 20-ohm 10-watt slider-type. Adjust for 6.0 volts at socket.

R2, R3, R4, R5 — 150-ohm 1/2-watt resistor.

S1 — Spst toggle.

T1 — 6.3 volt 8 A. Adjust R1 for 6.0 volts.

RFC1 — 2.15 μH rf choke. No. 22 enamel closewound 1-3/16 inch on 1/4-inch Teflon rod.

Sears store. The picture and Fig. 6-41 should be largely self-explanatory.

At the tube end of the plate line, L4 in Fig. 6-42, we have brass castings normally used to join sections of the copper pipe. They make a nice sliding fit over the tube anodes. For tighter fit, cut thin brass shim stock and insert as much as needed between the anode and the sleeve. The end of the fitting can be slotted and then clamped firm on the anode with a hose clamp, as an alternative. The short at the B-plus end of the line is made with two T fittings, with their flanges cut down to 1/2 inch and slipped over a short section of the pipe that is not visible. Joints throughout the assembly were silver-soldered with a torch, but conventional soldering should do equally well. The flanges at the

open ends of the T fittings are cut down to about 1/4-inch in length.

The last instruction and the information about the plate line given under Fig. 6-42 apply only if the fittings are identical to those obtained by the builder. Since there are several types of fittings available from plumbing supply houses, the following overall dimensions should be heeded: tube end of the plate line to center-line of short — 10 3/8 inches; spacing of pipes center to center — 3 1/2 inches.

In using tube types other than those specified, it may be that some change in plate circuit inductance will be needed. A simple check will show if this is needed. Slip the castings and pipe together without soldering, and assemble the plate circuit temporarily. Check the tuning range by means of a grid-dip meter. No plate or heater voltage is needed for this rough check, but it is well to have the coupling loop in place, and a 50-ohm resistor connected across J2.

The coupling loop, L5, is cut from a single piece of flashing copper 1/2 inch wide. This delivered slightly more output to the load than was obtained with loops of wire of various lengths tried. The loop should be positioned so that the bottom edge is approximately flush with the bottom of the pipes. Optimum coupling to a 50-ohm load is achieved when the closed end of the "U" is about 1/4 inch lower than the open end. Looking down at the plate-line assembly, the coupling loop is centered between the pipes.

The loop and plate line are supported on Teflon rod insulators. The rf choke is also wound on Teflon. Note its position *outside* the U of the plate line. First mounted inside the loop, it went up in a furious burst of smoke when high power was applied to the amplifier.

Our tuning disks are 3-inch sheets of flashing copper. For nicer appearance and better mechanical stability, use 1/8-inch aluminum as in the 50-MHz model. Three-inch brass 1/4-20 screws are threaded through the pipe fittings. The rear one is held in place with a lock nut, and the other is rotated by the tuning knob, a bakelite shaft coupling, and a length of 1/4-inch Teflon rod running in a panel bushing.

A third disk is mounted adjacent to the rear portion of the tank circuit. Its position is adjusted to achieve perfect balance in the tank circuit, but in practice this turned out to have no measurable effect. It is felt that a really good choke at RFC1, and careful adjustment of C1, can practically eliminate the effect of any slight unbalance if the point of connection of RFC1 to the tank circuit is not bypassed to ground.

The 144-MHz grid circuit, L1L2, looks like two coils, but actually is a coiled-up half-wave line. This is somewhat more compact than a half-wave line with its conductors out straight, and it seems equally effective. The grids are connected to the outer ends and the tuning capacitor to the inner. The point of connection of the bias-feed resistors should be determined in the same way as with the usual half-wave line: by coupling in 144-MHz energy and touching a pencil lead along the inductance while watching the grid current. The correct point for final connection of the resistors is that at which no reaction on grid current is observed. Isolating resistors here, and for feeding screen voltage to the sockets, are preferable to rf chokes. The inner conductor of the coaxial line is used to make the coupling loop, L3, which is placed between the inner ends of the grid circuit.

Balanced drive is maintained by adjustment of the differential capacitor, C1, connected in parallel with C2, and mounted on the side of the chassis adjacent to it. The series capacitor, C3, is out of sight under the tuning capacitor, which is mounted on standoff insulators. It is adjusted by inserting a small screwdriver in a hole in the side of the chassis, but if we were doing it again we'd mount C3 on the side wall, just under C1, to make it more readily adjustable. Note that the rotor of C2 is ungrounded.

About Neutralization

These amplifiers were tested without neutralization and we almost got away with it, but use of all modes, particularly a-m linear and ssb, imposes strict requirements on stability. Conventional cross-over neutralization employed in the 144-MHz amplifier is omitted from Fig. 6-42 in the interests of clarity. The schematic representation, C3 in Fig. 6-39, is not very informative either.

In the 50-MHz amplifier the lead visible in Fig. 6-40, attached to the rear stator terminal of C2, runs to a polystyrene feedthrough bushing (National TPB) mounted in the partition between the rear and middle sockets. Even this bushing's wire stub projecting into the plate compartment turned out to be too much "C3" and it was trimmed off 1/16th inch at a time, until minimum feedthrough was indicated on a wavemeter coupled to L3 and tuned to the driving frequency.

Similar feedthrough bushings are used in the 144-MHz amplifier, but here a small wire had to be added to each one. The wire connected to the grid of the front tube is aimed toward the anode of the rear tube, and vice versa. Small sheets of this brass or copper should be fastened under the adjacent edges of the sockets, and bent up at right angles to the partition. These 3/4-inch high barriers act to shield the screen rings of the tubes from the feedback "capacitors" and assure that the coupling is from grid to opposite plate, and not to the screen.* Length and position of the feedback wires are adjusted for minimum feedthrough of driver energy to the plate circuit, as described above. About a half inch of wire was needed in addition to the terminal stub in this case.

When used as linear amplifiers the tubes must be biased to permit them to draw considerable plate current with no drive, so perfect neutralization is a "must." Properly neutralized, the amplifiers will be stable when run at or near maximum safe plate dissipation with no drive, even when the grid and plate circuits are swung through their entire ranges. If they will not pass this test the amplifiers are not ready to be used for linear service.

Controls and Metering

Almost everyone who builds his own equipment has a favored way of controlling it, so the system shown schematically in Fig. 6-43 may not suit everyone. It is for use in a station where power supplies are actuated by closing the primary circuits to all that the operator wants to have come on for transmitting purposes. They are mounted away from the transmitting position, and a cable carries the various voltages to the rf position. At the left, J1, J3, J4, and J5 are terminals carrying all voltages from the power-supply position. These are distributed through meters, controls and output fittings, J6, J7, and J8, to various transmitters.

* Air-system sockets are now available with built-in shielding of the screen ring. The Eimac numbers are SK-620 and 630.

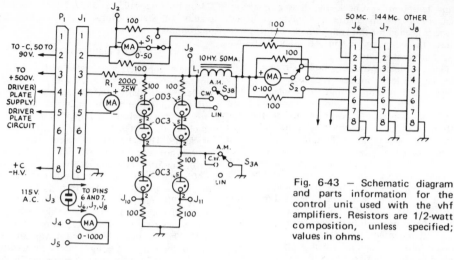

Fig. 6-43 — Schematic diagram and parts information for the control unit used with the vhf amplifiers. Resistors are 1/2-watt composition, unless specified; values in ohms.

J1 — 8-pin male power connector.
J2, J9, J10, J11 — Tip jack.
J3 — Ac connector, male.
J4, J5 — High-voltage feedthrough connector (Millen 37501).
J6, J7, J8 — 8-pin female power connector.
L1 — 10-H 50-mA choke. Must be shorted out for other than plate-modulated service.
P1 — 8-pin female cable plug.

R1 — 2000-ohm 25-watt resistor. Value may be reduced to as low as 1000 ohms if regulation at high values of screen current is desired, provided current measured in J10 and J11 does not exceed 40 mA under low-screen-current conditions.
S1 — Single-pole 2-position switch.
S2 — Single-pole 3-position switch.
S3 — Double-pole 3-position switch.

Circuit breakers at the supply position are used to turn everything off when the station is closed down.

Adjustable bias, 50 to 90 volts negative, is brought in through Pin 2 to a 50-mA meter and appropriate shunts that keep the circuit that is not being metered closed. The switch S1 enables the operator to read the grid currents separately in the 144-MHz amplifier. Grid voltage may be read when required, at J2.

Similarly, a 500-volt positive source is connected through Pin 3, a voltage-regulating system, an audio choke, a 100-mA meter and a 3-position switch, S2, to the screens. Currents can be read separately here, too, and this facility is important in determining that all tubes are running within ratings. The VR system is switched by S3A to provide regulated 250 or 350 volts to the screens. Ganged to it is S3B, which shorts the audio choke for all modes except plate-modulated a-m. This must be done, as the choke will cause trouble on the other modes. The series-parallel VR-tube bank is by no means an ideal regulating system, but it prevents soaring of the screen voltage under conditions of low or negative screen current. These occur only in linear operation, and on cw when the key is up. It is not particularly important that screen voltage be held constant for high screen current, as in plate-modulated a-m and key-down cw conditions with low plate voltage. The screen voltage will be kept down by the heavy load on the supply at such times. Actually a single string of three regulator tubes will do the job quite well, and both amplifiers have been worked successfully with this simpler screen arrangement. Current through

the regulator tube strings can be measured between J10 or J11 and ground.

Operation

Because a variety of tubes may be used, with a wide range of conditions as to plate voltage and drive, we're not going to be too specific here. If you follow the tube manufacturer's recommendations for the plate voltage you intend to use you won't be far wrong. All tubes of this class are quite versatile as to drive level and plate voltage; unless you are running close the maximum plate-input ratings the principal factor to watch is screen dissipation, as far as safety of the tubes is concerned. Set up your amplifier with a dummy load and then try the various conditions given in tube data sheets, observing the operation on all meters. In this way you'll soon learn your way around. A few words of preliminary advice may, however, be in order.

First, don't feel that you have to run a kilowatt right off the bat. Put a Variac in your final plate supply primary and run the voltage down for initial testing, or use a lower-voltage supply until you become familiar with the way the rig works. Watch the screen current closely, particularly at low plate voltage or with high grid drive or light loading. The provisions for checking individual screen currents is important, otherwise you may learn too late that one tube has been taking all or most of what you have seen on a meter that reals total screen current only. In the push-pull amplifier it may be advantageous to balance screen currents by C1, rather than grid currents, if balance of both screen and grid currents does not occur at one setting.

Tune up for Class C and get the feel of the amplifiers before trying linear operation. Then, if linears are unfamiliar to you, read up on them below, and in chapter 5 before jumping in. Use a scope; there is no sure way to set up and operate a linear without one. The Heath Monitor Scope, HO-10 or SB610, is ideal for this job because of its built-in tone oscillator and in-the-transmission-line features. Running a linear, either sideband or a-m, without a scope check is inviting trouble.

Finally, is you must use an a-m linear, don't expect 70 percent efficiency from it. Don't expect 50. Expect and see that you *get*, no more than 35 percent from a Class AB1 linear, or no more than about half the rated plate dissipation for the tubes used. This means 350 watts out of our 50-MHz amplifier with a kilowatt in, even though you can

get 750 watts out of it in Class C. For the 144-MHz amplifier, 200 watts out with 700 in is about the safe maximum for a-m linear service. These are optimum figures; you may get less, but you can't get more and be *linear*.

For higher plate efficiencies go to ssb, cw, or plate-modulated a-m. In any of these modes these amplifiers will give you the biggest legal signal around, if that's what you want. Or they'll throttle down nicely to 300 watts input or less, merely by lowering the plate voltage. They'll work efficiently at much lower inputs if the screen voltage is dropped appropriately. Chances are that you'll still have a signal that will stand out in most neighborhoods, on either 6 or 2, and you'll have no worries about over heating.

TIPS ON A-M LINEAR AMPLIFIERS

It is no small wonder that the a-m linear amplifier appears attractive to the neophyte looking for his first step up the vhf power ladder. At first glance it seems almost too good to be true. A Class AB1 linear, the type most often used, requires *no driving power at all*. Class AB1 is operation without the amplifier drawing grid current at any time. With the amplifier consuming no power from the driver stage, only a mere handful of exciter is needed. You could use a one-watt transistor rig, and have output to spare.

This applies whether the amplifier runs 100 watts input or 1000, so it can be seen that the linear is most attractive in the high-power bracket. The inevitable price to be paid is low efficiency. Thus, there is hardly any point in building a linear for less than about 200 to 300 watts input; you won't get enough step-up in power to make the project worthwhile. And since any amplifier is a fairly expensive undertaking, it may be well to build it for kilowatt capability, even if you don't expect to push it that far right away. The amplifiers of Fig. 6-38 through 6-43 can be run as low as about 300 watts input if you wish. At this level they deliver about 100 watts to the antenna — no mean signal on a vhf band. There is plenty in reserve when you need it, and the final tubes hardly know they're working.

As its name implies, a linear amplifier is one which reproduces the wave form of its driver stage exactly, but at higher power level. This requires considerable attention to details. Everything has to be *right*, or the signal quality suffers, and it will occupy far more space in the band than a signal should. Grid bias, drive level and antenna loading are all critical. Regular use of an oscilloscope is a must. Meters alone are not enough, if you want to be sure that your signal is above reproach.

About Driver Stages

Obviously the driver stage is important in the linear picture. If we are going to amplify it in exactly its original form, the signal had better be good to start with. A distorted splattering signal

fed to a linear results in more of the same; lots more! The exciter should be stable and its output stage as perfectly modulated as we can make it. Since the driver operates at very low level, this is not hard to do. If an exciter is being built especially to drive a linear, it might be well to go with a neutralized-triode output stage, with no more than about 5 watts input. A Class-A modulator employing inverse feedback and some form of output limiting would be good. Peak limiting is important, to keep the average modulation percentage high and prevent overmodulation.

Most vhf transmitters will have a lot more output than is needed, so the drive applied to the amplifier must be reduced in some way. Detuning the driver output circuit or the amplifier grid circuit will not do, as it may leave the driver without a proper load, and impair its modulation quality. A simple solution is to connect a 50-ohm dummy load parallel with the driver output. A coaxial T fitting is connected to the driver output receptacle. The dummy load is connected to one side of the T, and the amplifier grid input to the other. The amplifier grid circuit still may have to be detuned slightly, if the exciter output is more than 2 or 3 watts, but this will not be harmful for only a small reduction in drive. Driver output may also be reduced by lowering its plate or plate-and-screen voltage, though it is well to check the quality to be sure that linear modulation characteristics are being obtained in the driver.

Checking Signal Quality

The Heath Monitor Scope, Model HO-10 or SB610, is ideal for use with a vhf linear, as it may be left connected to the transmission line for continuous monitoring. Some modification may be necessary for effective use of this scope on 144 MHz, though it works nicely on 50 MHz and lower bands as is. Two coaxial receptacles of the SO-239 type are mounted on the back of the scope, with their inner terminals joined by a wire about 1 1/2 inches long. The transmitter is connected to one receptacle and the antenna coax to the other. The

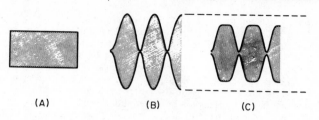

(A)   **(B)**   **(C)**

Fig. 6-44 — Typical oscilloscope envelope patterns for amplitude modulation. Unmodulated carrier is shown at A. The single-tone pattern for 100 percent modulation is shown at B. Peaks should rise to twice the envelope-pattern height, and valleys should just reach the center line. The effects of excessive drive or too-light loading, or both, on a linear amplifier are shown at C. Note the flat-topping and small increase in amplitude over the unmodulated envelope.

unshielded wire inside the scope causes an appreciable impedance bump in a 144-MHz line. This may be corrected by connecting a coaxial T fitting to one of the terminals, and using its two arms to make the above connections from transmitter to antenna line. Internal scope connections and functions remain intact, and the impedance bump is held to manageable proportions.

The scope, milliammeters in the grid, screen and plate circuits of the amplifier, and a power-indicating device in the coaxial line are useful in setting up the linear for maximum effectiveness. The power meter will tell you if you are getting all you should from the amplifier. If you're getting too much, the scope will tell you. The meters are necessary to assure operation at both safe and optimum conditions.

The tube manufacturers' data sheets give typical operating conditions for various classes of service, usually including a-m linear. These are the best guides available and you'll do well to follow them closely, especially when just learning your way around with a linear. They do not tell the whole story, however. They are merely "typical"; there may be other combinations that will work well, if you know how to read the indications your meters and scope provide. Conversely, it may be possible to radiate a less-than-admirable signal, when meter indications alone seem to be in order. You'll need that scope!

In using the 6- and 2-meter linears of Fig. 6-38 the plate voltage can be almost anything, provided that the amplifier is adjusted carefully whenever the plate voltage is changed. From 800 to 2000 volts has been used on 4CX250Rs and Bs. Screen voltage should be what the sheet calls for; in this case 250 volts for Class C and 350 volts for Class AB1. Bias should be variable and adjusted so that the tube or tubes will draw the recommended no-drive plate current. In this instance it's about 100 mA per tube. It is well to start with bias on the high side (no-drive plate current low) to be on the safe side until set up correctly.

With the amplifier running in this fashion, feed in enough drive to make the plate current rise and output start to appear. Tune the final plate circuit and adjust the loading control for maximum output, as indicated by the height of the scope pattern or by the power-indicating meter in the transmission line. Disregard the final plate current, so long as it is at a safe value. (Do not tune for dip;

tune for maximum output.) Run up the drive now to the point where grid current just starts to show, and then back it off slightly. Readjust the plate and loading controls for maximum output. Be sure that you're putting every watt you can into the transmission line for this amount of grid drive. Maximum loading is a must for linear operation.

Try modulating the driver, while watching the scope pattern. It should look like the patterns shown in Fig. 6-44, A and B. These are envelope patterns, which are most readily obtained with the Monitor Scope. Unmodulated carrier is shown at A. The Heath scope has a built-in tone oscillator. Using this or a steady whistle into the microphone should produce a pattern like the one at B, when the modulation level is 100 percent. The peaks and valleys are sharp, and the valleys (negative peaks) just reach the zero line. Positive peaks are just twice the total height of the unmodulated envelope, Pattern C shows effects of excessive grid drive or too-light loading, or both. Note the flat-topping, and the lower height of the positive peaks. If you don't have some form of negative-peak limiting, watch out for excessive modulation in that direction. That's where the splatter comes from first if audio and rf operation is clean otherwise. In watching your voice modulation beware of the bright flashes at the zero line of the modulation pattern that indicate over-modulation on negative voice peaks.

Practice the adjustment routine with a dummy load connected to the transmitter, and you'll soon get the hang of it. Deliberately over-drive the amplifier and see how quickly you can detect the results (pattern 6-44C) on the scope pattern. Observe the meter action, too. You'll see that you can't draw *any* grid current without spoiling the picture. You'll also see that when the scope picture is right the plate current stands still on all modulation peaks. The screen current will probably be just a bit negative. Output will absolutely not exceed 35 percent of the input. If it does, you've got some meter inaccuracies, or you're cheating on the interpretation of the scope pattern. The scope is the final authority; you *have* to believe it.

Now, once over lightly again. Loading is all-important. Keep it at the maximum output you can get for a given value of grid drive. Recheck it for every frequency change or change in plate voltage. Grid current will *always* be zero. Grid drive can be lower than optimum as regards output, but never more than optimum. (You can read grid *vvoltage* for a reference on amount of grid drive, if you like.) The scope will tell you very clearly the minute you go too high. So will the sound of the signal, but this may be hard to determine, if your receiver overloads on your own signal. Most receivers will. Final plate current will rise with increasing grid drive, but it must stand still during modulation. If it kicks on modulation peaks, you've got distortion, and very likely splatter.

All adjustments react on one another to some extent, and each time you change any operating condition you have to go through the routine completely again. This sounds as if you'd spend the rest of your life tuning the rig, but once you get the hang of it you can make the necessary corrections in seconds.

Using SSB and Other Modes

Since a-m linear is the most critical of all, it is in order to switch to any other mode without making any adjustments, if you want to switch instantly. A good linear is more versatile than this, however. It's possible to do a lot better than the a-m conditions on sideband, and still stay in the AB1 mode. Efficiency on cw will shoot up markedly with just a slight increase in grid drive, with no other changes. Same for fm, which is identical to cw, as far as the tubes in the final are concerned. If you want the ultimate in cw or fm output, switch to 250 volts on the screen, and run up the grid drive some more. Drive level is very uncritical, so about all you have to watch for is to keep the final input below the kilowatt level, and avoid swinging the plate current on fm. Readjustment of the plate tuning and loading will be needed for top efficiency. Plate-modulated voice service is quite similar to the cw conditions, except that the maximum plate voltage permissible is lower with most tubes. Grid drive requirements are usually slightly higher for good plate modulation conditions than for cw or fm, and the bias should be juggled for best modulation characteristics. Scope indication should be like Fig. 6-44B.

GROUNDED-GRID 50-MHZ AMPLIFIER

Increasing use of 50-MHz transceivers and transmitters having outputs of 25 watts or more has created a demand for amplifiers to be used with such equipment as the driver. The grounded-grid amplifier of Fig. 6-45 is designed for this use. With 30 watts or more of driving power it will deliver 600 watts cw output. As a Class-B linear, single-tone conditions, its rated PEP output is 750 watts.

Circuit

The Eimac 3-500Z triode is designed for grounded-grid service. As may be seen from Fig. 6-48 driving power is applied to the filament circuit, which must be kept above rf ground by means of high-current bifilar rf chokes, RFC1, and RFC2. These are a central feature of the bottom view, Fig. 6-47. The input impedance is low, so the input circuit, L1C1, tunes broadly, and the 50-ohm line from the exciter is tapped well up on L1. The plate circuit is merely a coil of copper tubing, L2, inductively tuned by means of a "shorted turn" of copper strip, rotated inside its cold end. See Fig. 6-46. Tuning is smooth and the rotating loop avoids many problems commonly encountered in tuning high-powered amplifiers by conventional methods. Plate voltage is shunt-fed to the tube, to prevent the high dc voltage from accidentally appearing on the output coupling loop or on the

antenna line. Most of the lower part of the schematic diagram has to do with control and metering, and is largely self-explanatory. The exciter voice-control relay shorts out R1, allowing grid current to flow, and making the amplifier operative, if the filament and primary-control switches, S1 and S2, have been closed. Feeding ac voltage to the plate-supply relay through J4, J5, and P1 makes application of plate voltage without the filament and blower being on impossible.

Fig. 6-45 — Table-top 50-MHz amplifier of grounded-grid design, only 10 X 12 inches in size. Grid and plate current are monitored simultaneously. Knobs at the right are for input tuning, bottom, amplifier loading, center, and plate tuning, top.

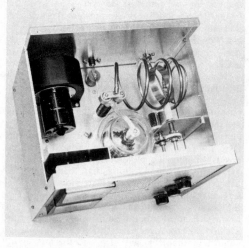

Connections to the grid terminals (on opposite sides of the socket) are made with short 1/4-inch copper straps soldered to the pins and bolted to the chassis with No. 6 screws, nuts, and lockwashers. Be sure that a clean tight rf ground results.t

In Fig. 6-46 it will be seen that the hot end of L2 is supported on the top of the two blocking capacitors, C3 and C4, which, in turn, are mounted on the Teflon rod that serves as the form for RFC3. The ground end of L2 is supported on a vertical post made of 3/8-inch copper tubing, 1-3/8 inches high. The end of the coil can be fitted with a heavy copper lug, or pounded flat. A hole is drilled in the flat portion and a 2-inch brass bolt runs through it and the post and chassis. Be sure that there is a permanent solid rf ground at this point.

The shunt-feed rf choke is effectively across the tuned circuit, so it must be a good one. Hand-winding as described below is strongly recommended, as no ready-made choke is likely to be as good. Teflon is slippery, so a light thread cut in the form will help keep the winding in place. If this cannot be done, prepare and wind two wires, as for the filament chokes. Feed the wire ends through one hole in the form, and wind a bifilar coil. Pull the other ends through the finish hole, bending one back tightly at the hole edge. Remove the other winding, which should leave a tight evenly spaced coil that makes an excellent vhf choke.

The blocking capacitors, C3 and C4, are mounted between brass plates, one of which is fastened to the top of the rf choke form with a sheet-metal screw. The other plate is connected to the hot end of L2 by means of a wrap-around clip of flashing copper. The lead to the tube plate cap is made with braid removed from a scrap of coax. A strip of flashing copper about 1/4 inch wide is also good for this. Use a good heat-dissipating connector, such as the Eimac HR6.

The shorted-turn tuning ring is centered between the first two turns of L2. The ring is attached to a ceramic pillar, and that to a 1/4-inch shaft, the end of which is tapped for 8/32 thread. This shaft runs through a bearing mounted in a bracket 4 inches high and 2-3/4 inches wide, fastened to the chassis and the side of the enclosure. The output loading capacitor, C6, is also mounted on this bracket. It is one inch above the chassis, and the tuning-ring shaft is 3-1/4 inches

Construction

The amplifier chassis is aluminum, 10 by 12 by 3 inches in size, with the tube socket centered 3 1/8 inches from the front edge. The sheet-aluminum panel is 10 inches high. The decorative edging is "cove molding," used by cabinet makers for counter tops. Sides and back are also sheet aluminum. Where they need not be removable, parts are fastened together by pop-riveting. Tools and rivets for this work can be found in most hardware stores. Perforated aluminum (cane metal) is used for the top, and for covering the panel viewing hole.

Stretch the wire for the bifilar rf chokes, before winding. Then, with the wires side by side, under tension, wind them on a form of wood or metal. This is left in until the choke ends are soldered in position. Then remove the form and coat the windings with coil cement, to help maintain turn alignment.

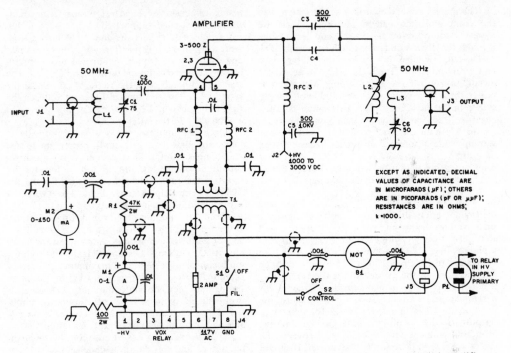

Fig. 6-48 — Schematic diagram and parts information for the 50-MHz grounded-grid amplifier.

B1 — Blower, 15 ft³/min or more.
C1 — 75-pF variable (Johnson 167-4).
C2 — 1000-pF dipped mica.
C3, C4 — 500-pF 5-kV transmitting ceramic (Centralab 858S-500).
C5 — 500-pF, 10-kV or more, TV "Doorknob."
C6 — 50-pF variable (Johnson 167-3).
J1 — BNC coaxial receptacle.
J2 — High-voltage connector (Millen 37001).
J3 — Type N coaxial receptacle.
J4 — 8-pin male power connector, chassis-mounting.
J5 — Ac receptacle, chassis-mounting.
L1 — 4 turns No. 12 enam., 1 inch long, 1-inch dia. Tap 2-1/2 turns from ground end.
L2 — 3-1/2 turns 1/4-inch copper tubing, 3-1/2-inch dia, 5-1/4 inches long. Diameter is finished dimension, not that of form used for winding. See text and photo for turn spacing. Tuning

ring is closed loop of 1/2-inch copper strip, 2-5/8-inch dia.
L3 — 1 turn, 3-inch dia, and leads, made from one piece of 1/8-inch copper tubing or No. 8 wire.
M1 — Dc meter, 0-1 A (Simpson Wide-Vue, Model 1327).
M2 — 0-300 mA, like M1.
P1 — Ac plug, on cable to power supply.
R1 — 47,000-ohm 2-watt resistor.
RFC1, RFC2 — 21 turns each, No. 12 enam., 1/2-inch dia, bifilar.
RFC3 — 30 turns No. 20 enam., spaced wire dia, on 3/4-inch Teflon rod, 3-3/4 inches long. Drill end holes 1/2 and 2-3/4 inches from top.
S1, S2 — Spst, rocker-type, neon-lighted (Carling LT1L, with snap-in bracket).
T1 — Filament transformer, 5 V, 15 A, (Stancor P6433; check any electrical equivalent for fit under 3-inch chassis).

above the chassis. The input tuning capacitor, C1, is mounted under the chassis, with equal spacing between the three, for symmetrical appearance.

The output coupling loop, L3, is just inside the cold end of L2. It can be adjusted for optimum coupling by "leaning" it slightly into or out of L2. Be sure that it clears the shorted turn throughout movement of the latter.

The coaxial output jack, J3, is on the rear wall of the enclosure. A small bracket of aluminum grounds it to the chassis, independent of the bonding between the chassis and the enclosure. Plate voltage enters through a Millen 37001 high-voltage connector, J2, on the rear wall, and is

bypassed immediately inside the compartment with a TV "doorknob" high-voltage capacitor, C5.

The blower assembly in the left rear corner of the chassis draws air in through a hole in the back of the compartment, and forces it down into the enclosed chassis. The only air path is then back up through the socket and chimney (Eimac parts SK-410 and SK-406 recommended) and out through the top of the enclosure. The data sheet for the 3-500Z specifies an air flow of at least 13 cubic feet per minute, when the tube is operated at 500 watts plate dissipation. The ac leads for the blower motor come into the enclosure on feed-through capacitors.

The meters are enclosed in a shield fastened to the front and side panels. Meter terminals are bypassed for rf inside the shield, and leads come through the chassis on feedthrough capacitors. The rocker-type switches just below the meters have built-in illumination. The high-voltage switch is not meant to control the plate supply directly, but rather through a relay, as in the 3000-volt supply shown in the *Handbook*. The plate meter is in the negative lead, so be sure that your supply is compatible with this arrangement. Do not use this system where a potential difference exists between the amplifier and power supply chassis. All power leads are made with shielded wire (Belden 8862) and all exposed points are bypassed to ground.

Adjustment and Use

Do not apply drive to the 3-500Z without the plate voltage being on. Also, it is recommended that initial testing be done with low drive, and with a plate voltage of 1500 or less. With a 50-ohm load connected to J3, apply 1000 to 1500 volts through J2, and turn on the driver. Adjust the tuning ring inside L2 for a dip in plate current. Tune C1 for maximum grid current. Tune C6 and adjust the position of L3 with respect to L2 for maximum output. If the amplifier seems to be running properly, connect an SWR bridge between the driver and J1, and check reflected power. It should be close to zero. If otherwise, adjust the tap position on L1.

Tuning range of the plate circuit can be checked with a grid-dip meter, with the power off the amplifier. The range is affected by turn spacing overall, and at the cold end. The closer the first two turns are together the greater the effect of the tuning ring. No other tuning device is used, so some experimentation with diameter and length of L2 may be needed if you want other than the 49.8 to 52.7 MHz obtained with the graduated turn spacing visible in the interior view. The highest frequency is reached with the ring in a vertical

plane. Dimensions that affect tuning range are as follows: grounded support for L2 — 1-1/8 inches from right side of chassis, and 3-1/4 inches from rear. RFC3 mounting position — 4 inches from rear and 5-1/2 inches from left. Shorted turn approximately centered between turns 1 and 2 of L2. The start of L3 bends from the stator of C6 to near the start of L2. The end toward J2 passes between the first two turns of L2, clearing the tuning ring in any position of the latter.

Once the amplifier seems to work normally at moderate plate voltages, apply higher, up to the maximum of 3000. Plate current, with no drive, should be about 160 mA. It can be lowered by inserting 0.1 to 0.4 ohm in series with R1 and the filament center-tap. A Zener diode, 2 to 9 volts, 10 watts, could do this job, as well.

Keep the amplifier tuned for maximum output. Do not decouple to reduce output; cut down drive and/or plate voltage instead. Adjustment for linear operation requires a scope. Maximum output, minimum plate current, and maximum grid current should all occur at the same setting of the plate tuning. If they do not, the output loading is over-coupled, or there is regeneration in the amplifier. The plate-current dip at resonance is noticeable and smooth, but not of great magnitude.

Typical operating conditions given by the manufacturer, and in the tube-data section of the *Handbook*, are guides to good practice. The amplifier works well with as little as 1000 volts on the tube plate, so varying the ac voltage to the plate-supply transformer is a convenient way to control power level. It is seldom necessary to run the maximum legal power in vhf communication, so some provision for this voltage control is recommended. With just one high-voltage supply needed, and no critical tuning adjustments, power variations from 100 to 600 watts output are quickly and easily made. This amplifier was built by Tom McMullen, W1SL, and first described in *QST* for November, 1970.

KILOWATT AMPLIFIER FOR 144 MHz

The 144-MHz amplifier of Fig. 6-49 can be run in Class AB1, for a-m or ssb linear service; or Class C, for high-efficiency a-m, cw, or fm. Driver power output should be 2 to 3 watts for AB1, and 10 watts or more for Class C. For more on operating conditions, see information on linear amplifiers in this chapter, the tube manufacturer's data sheets, or the tube data section of the *Handbook*.

Construction

The principal difference between this amplifier and its many predecessors using similar tubes lies in the plate-circuit design. The inductor is cut from flat sheet brass, in the form of a U. The circuit is tuned by a simple handmade variable capacitor that avoids problems commonly encountered in this part of a high-powered vhf amplifier. The circuit is practically identical to several previously described in *QST*, this Manual, and recent editions of the *Handbook*.

Fig. 6-49 — The 144-MHz amplifier is built in conventional rack and panel style, with the entire top of cane metal, to provide free air flow. Controls are grid-circuit tuning, C2, lower left; output loading capacitor, C5, center; and plate-circuit tuning, C4, with vernier dial, right. The slotted end of the Teflon shaft on C1 is visible as a white spot just below the loading control.

Fig. 6-50 — Interior of the 2-meter amplifier, showing the brass plate-inductor and vane tuning system. Note the position of RFC1, at the far left, out of the main rf field. The output coupling loop, L4, just below the plate line and barely visible here, is connected to the output jack, J4, on the rear wall with a short section of coax; and to the loading capacitor, C5, on the front panel by means of copper strip.

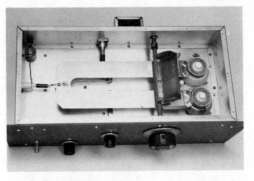

The amplifier is built on a 17 X 8 X 3-inch aluminum chassis, fitted with a bottom cover which completes the shielding and directs the flow of cooling air. The top portion of the enclosure is of similar size, except that it is 3-3/4 inches high, and it has a cane-metal top. It was made by bending up the necessary sheet aluminum, but angle stock and flat sheets could be used equally well. Angle stock along the back of the front panel completes the enclosure. The gray-wrinkle aluminum panel is 7 inches high.

The tube sockets are mounted 2 inches in from the right side, as seen in the photographs, and 2-5/8 inches apart, center to center. The Eimac SK620A sockets, with their integral screen-ring shielding, are recommended. Other sockets may require slightly greater spacing, and some modification of the plate-circuit dimensions. The raised screen-ring shield is also a great aid in neutralizing the amplifier. Some form of shield should be added if early flat sockets are used. This need is particularly acute if the amplifier is to be operated in the Class AB1 mode, which is characterized by very high power sensitivity.

The halfwave-line grid circuit, L2, is tuned at the end away from the tubes by the split-stator variable, C2, and balanced to ground by means of C3, a differential capacitor. This is supported on its stator tabs, which are soldered directly to L2, immediately adjacent to C2. A strap of 1/4-inch copper connects the rotor of C3 to the chassis, in the shortest practical manner. The slotted shaft of C3 is reached through a hole in the bottom cover of the chassis. This hole is sealed with black plastic tape after the adjustment is completed, in order to avoid air leakage.

The input coupling loop, L1, is mounted between and just below the grid lines, with its closed end near the midpoint of the lines. The end toward the panel is soldered directly to its tuning capacitor, C1, and the other to an insulating tiepoint, which also has the center conductor of the RG-58/U coax to J1 connected to it. The position of L1 with respect to L2 can be adjusted by means of an insulating rod, through a hole in the bottom plate near the closed end of the loop. This hole is also taped over to prevent air leakage.

Fig. 6-51 — The principal feature of the bottom view is the half-wave grid circuit. Its split-stator capacitor, C2, is at the left end of the line, L2. The differential balancing capacitor, C3, is also across the line, just to the right of C2. Isolating resistors in the grid circuit, R1 and R2, are near the middle of the picture. The screen isolating resistors, R3 and R4, run to tiepoints on the right wall of the chassis.

Leads to the neutralizing tabs, C9 and C10, are tapped on the grid lines at a point 1-3/4 inches from the grid end. Feedthrough bushings (not visible in the photographs) are under the lines. The crossover is made by copper strips from the lines to the bushings. Variable capacitance to the plate line is provided by copper tabs 1/4 X 5/8 inch in size, soldered to the top ends of the bushings, just below the plate line, L3. Adjusting their position with respect to L3 provides the required neutralizing capacitance.

Connections to the grid ends of L2 are wraparound copper clips slipped over the tubing ends and fastened to the grid posts of the tube sockets with screws. They are soldered to the line ends, for permanence. The connections to C2 are made in somewhat the same way, except that the tabs are soldered to the stator lugs. Note that the rotor of C2 is not grounded. It is supported on ceramic standoffs 5/8 inch high.

The grid-circuit isolating resistors, R1 and R2, are connected to L2 by means of spring clips which are slid over the line before assembly. These can be tube grid clips, if available. They are moved along the line to the point of minimum rf voltage, using the familiar lead-pencil test.

The shaft of C2 is rotated through an insulating shaft, fitted with an insulating flexible coupling, to minimize any tendency to unbalance in the grid circuit. The shaft from C1 is also insulating material, and it has a flexible coupling. The capacitor is not adjusted often, so the shaft end is slotted, and is allowed to protrude through the front panel. It is just visible in the front view, below the output-loading control.

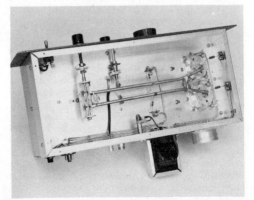

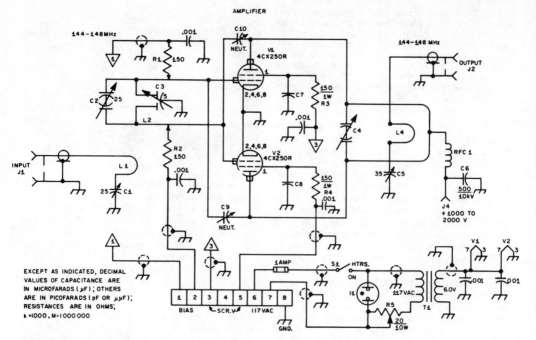

Fig. 6-52 — Schematic diagram and parts information for the 144-MHz amplifier. Capacitors not described are disk ceramic.

C1 — 25-pF miniature variable (Hammarlund MAPC-25B).
C2 — 25-pF per section split-stator (Hammarlund HFD-25).
C3 — 1.5- to 5-pF differential (Hammarlund MAC-5-5).
C4 — Vane-type tuning capacitor; see text and photos.
C5 — 35-pF variable (Hammarlund HF-35).
C6 — 500-pF 10-kV TV "doorknob."
C7, C8 — Screen bypass; part of Eimac SK-620A socket.
C9, C10 — Neutralizing tabs 1/4 X 5/8-inch sheet copper, soldered to top of National FTB bushing.
I1 — 115-volt neon pilot lamp.
J1 — BNC coaxial jack.
J2 — Type N coaxial jack.

J3 — 8-pin power connector, male.
J4 — High-voltage power connector (Millen 37501).
L1 — Copper strip 1/4 X 4 inches. See Fig. 6-54.
L2 — 1/4-inch copper tubing 10-1/2 inches long, 15/16 inch center to center. Bend to Y shape 2 inches from tube end.
L3 — .065-inch sheet brass; see text and Fig. 6-53.
L4 — Copper strip 15/16 X 7-1/2 inches, bent to roughly elliptical shape. See text and Fig. 6-54.
R1, R2 — 150-ohm composition, 1/2 watt.
R3, R4 — 150-ohm composition, 1 watt.
R5 — 20-ohm 10-watt, slider type.
RFC1 — 32 turns No. 24 enamel, closewound on 1/4-inch Teflon rod. See mounting position in interior photo.
S1 — Spst toggle switch.
T1 — 6.3-V 6-A filament transformer (Merit P-2947).

All power leads are made with shielded wire, bonded together by frequent spot-soldering, and to the chassis by means of grounding lugs. Exposed terminals are bypassed wherever necessary, to prevent rf pickup.

Each cathode pin on the socket is grounded through a separate lug, and nothing else uses these lugs for a ground path. Minimum cathode-lead inductance is important. Even the shortest lead shared with another circuit can cause unwanted coupling in a vhf amplifier.

The plate inductor, L3, is made of sheet brass, in the form of a U. Principal dimensions are given in Fig. 6-53. The stator plates of the tuning capacitor, C4, part A, are soldered to the plate line with their right edges 5/8 inch from the tube anodes. Connection to the latter is made with two brass tabs, part B, at the tube ends of the line. These were omitted from the drawing of the

assembly in the interest of clarity, but their position is clearly visible in the photographs. These tabs are curved slightly after bending, to provide more contact surface to the anode. Clamping rings made of flashing copper wrap around the anode structure and hold the tabs tightly to it. This is a point of low rf current, so a large contact area is not vital.

The plate line was made flat originally, but when the amplifier was tested it was found that this did not allow room to adjust the output coupling loop, L4, to the optimum position. The half-inch offset shown in Fig. 6-53 (but not in the photographs) netted a marked improvement in efficiency. The entire plate circuit was silver-plated after the photography. Careful checks on performance indicated no difference, before and after plating. Plating may be desirable on a long-term

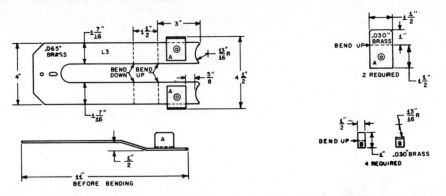

Fig. 6-53 — Principal dimensions of the brass parts of the amplifier plate circuit. The U-shaped inductor is shown in both top and side views, with the stator plates of C4 in place. These plates (A) are shown before bending, at the upper right. The small brackets (B) make contact with the tube anodes. Slight curvature, to fit tube anode, can be imparted by tapping with a small hammer, against a 1-1/2-inch pipe or rod, used as an anvil.

basis, as silver oxide is a good conductor and other oxides are not.

The "stators" and the tabs for the anode connection were silver-soldered to L3. Ordinary soldering will be adequate, but it might be well to use screws to hold the tabs onto L3, as a precautionary measure. The stator plates have flat-head screws running through them and L3, into the insulating supports for the latter. These are 1-inch ceramic pillars. The closed end of the loop is supported on a 1-1/2-inch pillar.

The holes for these supports can be made slightly oval, to position the assembly so that no strain on tubes or sockets is caused when the anode rings are tightened. The mounting hole in the closed end of L3 is also elongated. The screw that holds the line on its support has Teflon washers above and below L3, to permit the line to move on its support, if expansion and contraction with heating and cooling of the line should be appreciable.

The rotor of C4 is in the form of a shallow box made of flashing copper. It is shown in flat form in Fig. 6-54, along with other copper parts of the plate circuit. Its ends, 1 inch high, provide the variable capacitance to the stator plates on L3. After the box is bent to the desired form, its adjoining surfaces are soldered for additional strength and rigidity. The edge away from the tube anodes is supported on a fiber glass rod with 4-40 screws, the rod surface having been filed flat in this area previously. Reducing couplers at each end of the rod permit use of a 1/4-inch shaft bearing at the rear, and a National Velvet-Vernier dial mechanism at the front. Do not use heat-sensitive rod such as Lucite or Plexiglas. Nylon and some types of Bakelite are unstable in strong rf fields, and are also unsatisfactory. Teflon is probably good, but the fiber glass rod is stronger and easy to work. It is 6-3/8 inches long and may be 1/2- or 3/8-inch diameter.

Mechanical stops for the rotor are provided at both ends of its normal travel. A 3/8-inch Teflon rod 1-3/8 inches high, fastened to the chassis between the neutralizing feedthrough bushings, stops the rotor in the horizontal position. The rotor is prevented from "going through the roof" by a 1-inch setscrew in the vernier-drive hub, and a longer-than-normal screw for the lower left mounting screw for the drive assembly.

The rotor in its horizontal position is approximately 1/4 inch above L3, and the spacing at the ends of the rotor is also 1/4 inch. The tubes are fitted with Eimac SK626 chimneys. The under surface of L3 should just clear these. If it does not, raise it by putting washers on the screws that run into the 1-inch pillars.

The output loop, L4, is supported under L3 by two 1/2-inch ceramic insulators. If the threaded holes go the whole length, be sure that the mounting screws do not ground the loop, or come close enough to allow arcing to ground. Connection to the coaxial output jack, J2, is made with a short piece of RG-8/U coax, using a shielding cone at the J2 end. The coax shield is grounded to chassis with a copper strap at the L4 end also, to make the rf path to ground independent of the chassis bonding. The rotor of C5 is also grounded independently. A copper strap connects the stator of C5 to the end of L4. After the final form and size of L4 have been determined, the connection to the strap should be soldered, to maintain a good rf bond. These circuits carry high rf currents, and permanent low-resistance connections are important. The performance of many amplifiers falls off with aging, because factors like this were overlooked.

An adequate supply of cooling air must be provided. The manufacturer stipulates 4.6 cubic feet per minute, per tube, minimum, but much more should be available. The blower used here has a 3-inch diameter wheel, turning at 3300 rpm. It is connected to the rear of the chassis by way of an automotive defroster hose 2-1/8 inches in diameter.

Adjustment

Heater voltage (at the socket) should be 6.0 volts. This is adjusted by means of the slider on R5. Set the sliding clips on L2 at the approximate

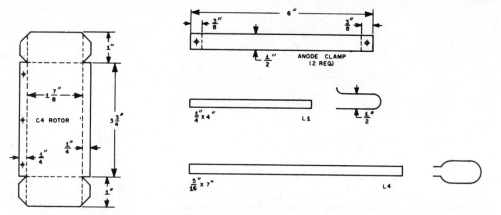

Fig. 6-54 — Flashing-copper parts used in the 2-meter amplifier. Broken lines indicate 90-degree bending required. The surfaces of the C4 rotor are soldered together after bending, for rigidity. The anode clamps, upper right, wrap around the tube cooling ring, and hold the brass tabs (Fig. 6-53) firmly in place. L1 and L4 are shown in the approximate shape, after bending, at the right.

midpoint. Now apply 1 to 2 watts drive to the grid circuit, adjusting the position of L1 and the tuning of C1 and C2 for minimum reflected power, indicated on an SWR bridge connected between the exciter and J1.

With enough drive so that grid current will be measurable, meter each grid separately, and adjust the balancing capacitor, C3, for as near to the same value for each grid as possible. Readjust C2 for each change. When the currents are approximately equal, the neutralization should be adjusted. With a 50-ohm load connected to J2, and with the screen and plate circuits having some dc path to ground, such as through power supply bleeders, couple a sensitive rf indicator to L3. Still with no plate or screen voltage applied, tune C2 and C4 for maximum indication, then adjust the positions of the neutralizing tabs, C9 and C10, carefully for *minimum* rf feedthrough. Recheck the grid circuit balance and tuning each time a tab setting is changed.

The points of connection of the resistors R1 and R2 on the lines comprising L2 are not critical, unless the exciter is low on output, but they should be near the points of lowest rf voltage on the line. Check by running a pencil lead along the line and watching the grid current. The point at which there is no change in the meter indication is where the clip should be. Recheck all adjustments.

The approximate tuning range of the plate circuit can be checked with a grid-dip meter, with no power on the amplifier. It should tune more than the width of the 2-meter band. Now, with an output indicator and a good 50-ohm load connected to J2, the amplifier is ready for power.

For initial tests, the plate voltage should be 800 to 1000 volts. Screen voltage should be no more than 250, preferably regulated. There will be little difference in tuning or output with the cover on or off, so, with due regard for safety, leave it off, at first. Never reach inside the plate compartment when high voltage is applied. To be sure that it is off, short the plate inductor to ground with an insulated screwdriver or other safe shorting device. Do this every time before touching anything inside the compartment in any other way. Play it *safe!*

Apply plate and screen voltage, in that order. Adjust bias so that the plate current is about 150 mA. Apply drive, and tune C4 and C5 for maximum power output. With enough drive for about 5 mA grid current per tube, the plate efficiency should approach 70 percent, after the position of L4 with respect to L3 is adjusted with some care. Loop position and all tuning adjustments change with plate voltage and drive level, so in linear service all adjustments should be made under the conditions for which you want best linearity.

The shape and position of L4 are quite critical. Best efficiency was obtained with the loop roughly elliptical in shape, and about 3/8 inch below L3. Best results show at plate voltages between 1200 and 1800. The tube maker's typical operating conditions are the best guide to efficient operation, but they are only *typical*. If safe levels of grid, screen, and plate dissipation are not exceeded, many variations are possible. See "Tips on Linears" earlier in this chapter.

This amplifier was built by W1SL, and described in February, 1971, *QST*.

References

The 50- and 144-MHz amplifiers described incorporate features from many previous *QST*, *Handbook*, and *VHF Manual* projects.

Maer, "Perseids Powerhouse," *QST*, Oct., 1959 (dual-band amplifier for 50 and 144 MHz).

"High-Efficiency 2-Meter Kilowatt," *QST*, Feb., 1960 (PP 4CX300As).

Breyfogle, "Top Efficiency at 144 Mc. with 4X250Bs," *QST*, Dec., 1961.

"Kilowatt Amplifiers for 50 and 144 Mc.," *QST*, Feb., 1964. Basic information also in this Manual, all editions, and in the *Handbook*, 1966 through 1970. Metering and control information applies to the 144-MHz amplifier described here.

Chapter 7

Vhf Stations – Transceivers, Transverters, and Transmitting Converters

Buy or build? This question faces every new amateur, and it is likely to remain with him as he advances in the art. Though there is nothing wrong with the all-commercial station, if its owner is well informed technically and he operates intelligently and with consideration for others, there are still sound arguments for building one's own equipment, or at least some of it. Many hams new and old still play the game that way.

Parts cost money and may be hard to come by, but building your own gear can save you money on the total station cost. This results from the choices open to the builder. Unlike the buyer of commercial gear, he can have the station *he* wants, which will do best the things he wants most to do. A station covering 80 through 6 meters, for example, is a waste of money for the vhf enthusiast having no interest in the hf bands. The vhf-only approach is sure to deliver more watts-per-dollar and better reception for the money than the multiband station. Perhaps more important, there may be nothing commercially available that really fits his requirements. The continued popularity of high-efficiency one-band kilowatt amplifier designs such as those described in Chapter 6 is proof of this.

But most important is the nature of the hobby itself. Despite all easy approaches, vhf hamming is still essentially a technical avocation. The fellow who learns his way around through building his own equipment and making it work at topnotch efficiency is sure to get more out of it than the mere purchaser of boxes. Finally, there is the personal pride and satisfaction in operating something you built yourself. It is *your* station, in a sense that no manufactured package can ever be, and you will be a better ham for having done the job yourself!

"Nobody builds ham gear any more?" Don't you believe it! Constructional articles, particularly those dealing with vhf, bring in thousands of letters from readers of *QST*, the ARRL *Handbook*, and this *Manual*. Prospective builders order bales of templates for constructional projects, whenever they are offered. Fm items described in Chapter 11 are current best-sellers. The better projects have an amazingly long life. Components of the "Two-Band Station for the VHF Beginner," pictured herewith, are still being built from the original *QST* series published more than a decade ago, and from descriptions of parts of the station that have appeared in the *Handbook* and this *Manual*, in past editions. A reprint of the *QST* articles is still a brisk seller, even though it describes all-tube designs, in what is admittedly the age of the

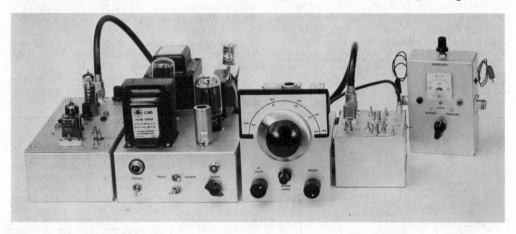

7-1 — A complete two-band station, shown here set up for 50 MHz. The transmitter, left, and converter, right, have companion plug-in units for 144 MHz. The control unit, left center, contains the power supply and modulator, and all units of the station draw their power from it. The simple tuner, right, may be omitted if the builder has a communications receiver. At the far right is an SWR bridge that doubles as a test meter.

transistor and the integrated circuit. Today the series stands as the most-used vhf material ever published, and one of the classic successes in the history of *QST*.[1]

Station Planning

Too often, amateur stations "just grow," rather than developing along planned lines to make the best use of the considerable financial outlay they usually represent. This applies to equipment purchased ready made, as well as to that built at home. We accumulate transmitters, receivers, converters, modulators, and so on down the line, with little thought as to their integration into a working unit for vhf communication. Some commercial gear leans to the opposite extreme − the one-box station that may be neat and unobtrusive, but is often lacking in versatility.

Amateurs are individualists. We like our stations to be unique, tailored to our special needs. With some advance planning we should be able to assemble a station that is both effective and versatile, without its necessarily becoming elaborate or tremendously expensive. With these objectives in mind, most of the equipment we describe here is built unit-style, with few built-in heavy items like power supplies and modulators. These tend to be static in design; long-term investments that can be used with a succession of rf units we may wish to build and try. Subassembly design has much to recommend it, and cost is by no means the only consideration. The ability to try different circuits without becoming involved in the kind of rat's nest all too often seen in amateur stations should rate high in our planning.

The beginner's two-band station, shown set up for 50-MHz operation in Fig. 7-1, demonstrates that a home-built setup can be neat, yet versatile. Though some components may be considered obsolete by present-day transistor standards, the transmitter and converter units of this station are still representative of good vacuum-tube technique. The block diagram of the station, Fig. 7-2, helps to show how a low-powered a-m and cw station for 50 and 144 MHz can be set up. All units plug

1 For a reprint of the 4-part *QST* series describing equipment shown in Fig. 7-1 send 50 cents (no stamps) to ARRL, Newington, CT 06111.

together, so completely new elements of the station can be tried without abandoning the entire project. Such a station can be made the basis for a more advanced setup quite readily, since the transmitters can serve as drivers for higher powered amplifiers, and the converters can be used with a communications receiver, replacing the simple tuner shown.

If the would-be vhf operator wishes to build all or part of his station unit-style, he is advised to go over the basic information given in other chapters. Receiving basics are discussed in Chapter 3, with the special aspects of fm reception added in Chapter 10. Practical receiving units are shown in Chapters 4 and 11. Transmitter design is mainly in Chapter 5, with fm factors in Chapter 10. Transmitting equipment you can build is in Chapters 6 and 11.

This chapter is devoted mainly to one-package applications of information in the above chapters. Most of it is the result of the trend to ssb operation in the vhf bands, which has had an incidental dividend in the form of good cw capability, almost inherent in the qualities needed for good ssb. Examples of simple a-m portable transceivers are also included.

It should be emphasized that, as far as their rf circuitry is concerned, there is little difference between a-m and fm transmitters. The prospective builder of vhf transmitters for other than fm use should not, therefore, overlook the transmitting units for fm described in Chapter 11.

The Transverter

Heterodyning, which is basic to the modern communications receiver and to most ssb transmitters, is being used increasingly in vhf stations. For review, two frequencies combined in any way produce two other frequencies, equal to the sum and difference of the original two. Either product of the mixing process can be used, or both may be. See "Heterodyning," Chapter 5.

Typical vhf applications of heterodyning are shown in Fig. 7-3. The receiving use, A, involves vhf signals, in this instance at 50 MHz and higher, a 36-MHz energy source, a mixer, and a communications receiver which acts as the detector system for

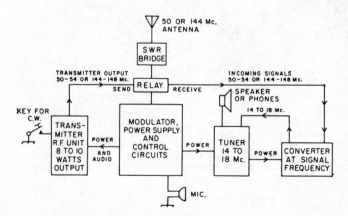

Fig. 7-2 − Block diagram of an a-m and cw unit-style station. A central unit contains the speech equipment, power supply, and control circuits. The antenna connects to a send-receive relay on the back of this unit through a standing-wave bridge. Transmitter rf assemblies for 50 or 144 MHz plug into the left side of the control unit, and a tuner for 14 to 18 MHz into the right side. Converters for 50- or 144-MHz reception plug into the right side of the tuner. The various units may be interconnected with cables, instead of being plugged together, if operating convenience so dictates.

Fig. 7-3 — Typical examples of heterodyning in vhf communication. Use of a 50-MHz converter with a 14-MHz receiver is shown at A. The same frequencies are used in transmitting, B. A single oscillator serves both transmitting and receiving functions in C, permitting operation on a vhf band with a transceiver designed for lower frequencies.

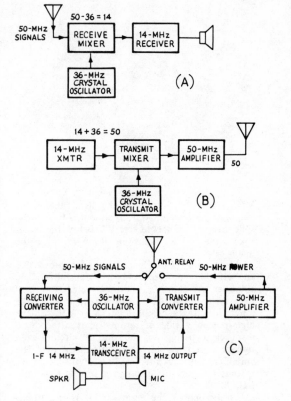

the heterodyned signals. The same frequency combinations are used in transmitting, 7-3B. Here a 14-MHz transmitter and the 36-MHz energy source feed a mixer, and the output is a 50-MHz signal having (hopefully) the same characteristics as the 14-MHz driving signal. The devices described are usually known as *receiving* and *transmitting converters*. As far as the functions we're discussing are concerned, the transmitted or received signals can be of any mode: cw, ssb, a-m, fm, or whatever.

Since the same frequencies are involved in both converters, it follows that a single energy source can be used for both heterodyning jobs. This is done in the *transverter*, Fig. 7-3C, a device increasingly familiar on the vhf scene.

The Transmitting Converter

Receiving converters discussed extensively in Chapters 3 and 4 are essentially unchanged when they perform the receiving function in a transverter. Our concern in this chapter will be with complete transverters and transmitting converters. Remember, in considering the heterodyning approach to vhf transmitting equipment, that it has two basic advantages: The low-level signal can be modulated or keyed in any manner before mixing, and the resultant signal on the vhf band has the same stability and modulation characteristics as the original, if the process is handled properly.

There are problems, too, the most important being that the heterodyning process can very easily result in radiation of unwanted products, which can cause interference if not properly suppressed. It is very important that the mixing frequencies be

as free of harmonic content as possible, and that they be chosen to keep unwanted mixing products far away from the desired frequency range, so that they can be rejected with the inherent circuit selectivity of the system, or by suitable filters added for this purpose.

Another major consideration in mixer design is that the mixing frequencies be applied in such ways and at such power levels that the mixer does not have excessive distortion products that may cause poor signal quality or excessive transmitted bandwidth, or both.

A TRANSMITTING CONVERTER FOR 50 TO 144 MHz

If you have a 50-MHz transmitter that operates to your satisfaction, you can have the same kind of signal on the 144-MHz band quite readily, through use of the transmitting converter of Fig. 7-4. Though this 3-tube rf unit was built primarily to develop ssb and cw drive on 144 MHz with a Heathkit HX-30 50-MHz sideband exciter, it works well with other modes used on these bands. If the 50-MHz rig is VFO-controlled, the 144-MHz signal will have the same stability as the 50-MHz one, and the dial calibration will be the same for both bands.

Though only the transmitting circuits are included, the first stages could also be used to generate the injection voltage for receiving, if one is interested in 144-MHz operation with a 50-MHz

transceiver. Ideas for doing this can be picked up from a transverter described later in this chapter.

Circuit and Layout

The schematic diagram, Fig. 7-5, and the bottom view, Fig. 7-6, may be "read" from left to right. First we have a simple triode crystal oscillator, V1A, on 47.0 or 47.5 MHz, depending on the crystal, Y1. The 47-MHz plate coil, L1, and its tuning capacitor, C1, are in the upper left corner of the picture. The second triode of V1 is a doubler to 94 or 95 MHz. Its tuned circuit, L2C2, is seen adjacent to the oscillator, but with its axis perpendicular to L1. Inductively coupled loosely to L2 is L3, the grid circuit of a 94-MHz amplifier,

Fig. 7-4 — Transmitting converter for duplicating a 50-MHz signal on 144 MHz. Two tubes at the left and center comprise the oscillator, multiplier, amplifier, and mixer stages. At the right is the 144-MHz output amplifier. Provision is made for metering all stages by means of tip jacks and test points. Note crystals taped together to prevent loss of the one not in use.

V1C. On the right side of the first tube is the amplifier plate circuit, L5C3, straddled by L6, the split grid coil of the mixer, V2. Below the mixer tube is the 50-MHz input circuit connected to the mixer cathodes.

From here on the layout and circuit look like any other low-powered 144-MHz transmitter. The amplifier grid coil, L8, is purposely made too small to resonate in the 144- to 146-MHz region with the input capacitance of the 6360, V3. Being on the high-frequency side of resonance, it offers little feedback coupling to the output circuit, even though there is no shielding between the two. The amplifier plate circuit, L9C7, is at the far right. Output is taken off through a series-tuned link, L10C8.

Positioning of the various coils is important. Note that coils are placed so that unwanted coupling between circuits is kept down, even with a fairly compact layout. It is suggested this principle be followed unless the builder is willing to cope with a new set of neutralization problems.

The oscillator and doubler circuits are standard practice. In the grid circuit of the 94-MHz amplifier, the input capacitance of the 6M11 pentode was too high to permit resonating L3 at 94 MHz in the usual way. Some checks with a variable series capacitor showed that a coil of the same size as in the previous plate circuit could be resonated at 94 MHz with about 10 pF in series, so the fixed capacitor shown in Fig. 7-5 was used. Only a small amount of energy is needed for the mixer grids, so neither the tuning nor the coupling between circuits is at all critical.

Getting the 94-MHz amplifier to operate in a stable manner is mainly a matter of achieving ground potential for rf at the screen. This is done with the series circuit, L4C4, the setting of which is not particularly fussy. Coupling between L5 and L6 should be adjusted to the minimum that will provide satisfactory output from the mixer. Make sure that both circuits actually tune, as it is possible to get enough output with one or the other not actually peaking. Best rejection of unwanted frequencies will not be assured unless the circuits are tuned to the desired frequencies.

Coupling between L7 and L8 should also be as loose as it can be and still provide adequate drive for the 6360. Drive requirements depend on the class of operation of the output amplifier. For

anything but Class-C conditions adequate drive is very easily achieved. Here again, be sure that L7 actually tunes *through* the desired frequency, in order that rejection of unwanted frequencies will be at a maximum.

Construction is on a standard 5 × 10-inch aluminum plate and 3-inch chassis. A layout drawing, Fig. 7-7, is given for those who wish to make an exact duplicate. To check every circuit during the adjustment phase of the project, an unusual combination of feedthrough bypasses and tip jacks is used. Oscillator plate current is measured by plugging a meter into J1 and clipping to the exposed terminal of C9. All other plate currents may be read by plugging one side of the meter into J2 and connecting to C10, for doubler plate current, C11, for 94-MHz amplifier plate current, C12, mixer plate and screen current, or C13, amplifier plate and screen current. Amplifier grid current, if any, is checked at J3 and J4. A table of operating conditions is given later.

Bias for the mixer and output amplifier is obtained from a small 22-1/2-volt battery. Builders may prefer some other bias source, but the battery does the trick simply and inexpensively. There is no current drain, and it may even be charged a bit when the amplifier runs into Class-C conditions, so life should be long and voltage constant. Just be careful not to short out the battery when working on the unit. Information on suitable bias supplies may be found in any edition of the ARRL *Handbook.*

The 6360 amplifier operated satisfactorily without external neutralization, but a small amount was added when a slight reaction on amplifier grid current was noted as the plate circuit was tuned through resonance with voltage off. The grid and plate leads are crossed over inside the 6360, providing inherent neutralization in the vhf range, so only a tiny amount of additional capacitance is needed. A half-inch wire is soldered to each grid terminal and bent over toward the adjacent plate terminal. The position is adjusted until reaction on amplifier grid current is eliminated. For circuit simplicity, this neutralization is not shown in Fig. 7-5.

Adjustment and Use

It should not be taken for granted that the heterodyning approach is for the sideband operator alone. Given any of the popular small 50-MHz transmitters, homebuilt or commercial, this heterodyne unit will duplicate its signal on the 144-MHz band at a comparable power level. You'll need no big batch of crystals or two separate VFO

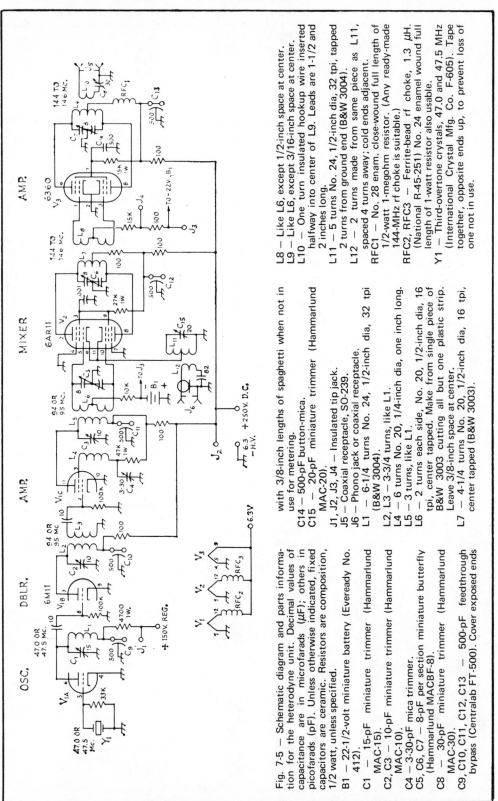

Fig. 7-5 — Schematic diagram and parts information for the heterodyne unit. Decimal values of capacitance are in microfarads (µF); others in picofarads (pF). Unless otherwise indicated, fixed capacitors are ceramic. Resistors are composition, 1/2 watt, unless specified.

B1 — 22-1/2-volt miniature battery (Eveready No. 412).

C1 — 15-pF miniature trimmer (Hammarlund MAC-15).

C2, C3 — 10-pF miniature trimmer (Hammarlund MAC-10).

C4 — 3-30-pF mica trimmer.

C5, C6, C7 — 8-pF per section miniature butterfly (Hammarlund MACBF-8).

C8 — 30-pF miniature trimmer (Hammarlund MAC-30).

C9, C10, C11, C12, C13 — 500-pF feedthrough bypass (Centralab FT-500). Cover exposed ends with 3/8-inch lengths of spaghetti when not in use for metering.

C14 — 500-pF button-mica.

C15 — 20-pF miniature trimmer (Hammarlund MAC-20).

J1, J2, J3, J4 — Insulated tip jack.

J5 — Coaxial receptacle, SO-239.

J6 — Phono jack or coaxial receptacle.

L1 — 6-1/4 turns No. 24, 1/2-inch dia, 32 tpi (B&W 3004).

L2, L3 — 3-3/4 turns, like L1.

L4 — 6 turns No. 20, 1/4-inch dia, one inch long.

L5 — 3 turns, like L1.

L6 — 2 turns each side, No. 20, 1/2-inch dia, 16 tpi, center tapped. Make from single piece of B&W 3003 cutting all but one plastic strip. Leave 3/8-inch space at center.

L7 — 4-1/4 turns No. 20, 1/2-inch dia, 16 tpi, center tapped (B&W 3003).

L8 — Like L6, except 1/2-inch space at center.

L9 — Like L6, except 3/16-inch space at center.

L10 — One turn insulated hookup wire inserted halfway into center of L9. Leads are 1-1/2 and 2 inches long.

L11 — 5 turns No. 24, 1/2-inch dia, 32 tpi, tapped 2 turns from ground end (B&W 3004).

L12 — 2 turns made from same piece as L11, spaced 4 turns away; cold ends adjacent.

RFC1 — No. 28 enam. close-wound full length of 1/2-watt 1-megohm resistor. (Any ready-made 144-MHz rf choke is suitable.)

RFC2, RFC3 — Ferrite-bead rf choke, 1.3 µH. (National R-45-251) No. 24 enamel wound full length of 1-watt resistor also usable.

Y1 — Third-overtone crystals, 47.0 and 47.5 MHz (International Crystal Mfg. Co. F-605). Tape together, opposite ends up, to prevent loss of one not in use.

units to give coverage of both bands. If you're a Technician or Novice at present, use only the 47.5-MHz crystal in the oscillator-multiplier. Heterodyning from 50-MHz frequencies will start your coverage at 145 MHz. A crystal that gives operation on 50.2 MHz will put you on 145.2 MHz, and so on. A VFO that covers 50 to 51 MHz (not for Novice use, of course) will give you coverage of 145 to 146 MHz, which can be extended to 144 MHz with the insertion of the 47-MHz crystal at a suitable time.

The output stage of the conversion unit can be run as a linear amplifier for sideband, cw, or a-m, or it can be driven into Class-C conditions for higher efficiency on cw. Plate modulation may be applied in the usual way for high-efficiency a-m service. The linear way will probably be the more attractive to most users, however, as it eliminates the heavy and power-consuming audio equipment. If your 50-MHz rig is plate modulated, you can make provision for switching the audio power over from its final stage to that of the conversion unit.

Cathode Injection

Initially we ran the 50-MHz energy into the mixer grids and applied the 94-MHz injection to the cathodes, but it was easy to saturate the grids with the swinging drive from the 50-MHz sideband rig. With the circuits·swapped around as shown, the mixer takes the full output of an HX-30 (about 2 watts a-m or 6 watts ssb) without flat-topping. Output is several times what it was with the other arrangement, and linearity is extremely good. Every circuit tunes uncritically, and it is possible to set up almost on-the-button merely by peaking the circuits to approximate frequencies with a grid-dip meter.

The various operating voltages are brought to a terminal strip visible in the upper center portion of Fig. 7-6. In firing up the unit apply plate power to one stage at a time, beginning with the oscillator. This stage works simply, showing the usual sudden downward kick in plate current from about 12 to 5 mA when the crystal starts oscillating. Set C1 so that oscillation starts every time voltage is applied.

If you have a grid-dip meter you can set all following circuits close enough without applying power to the unit. The dip meter can also be used to indicate power output relatively from the various stages, and to determine that output is on the desired frequencies.

The pentode amplifier should be checked for stability by removing power from the preceding stages briefly and watching the amplifier plate current while tuning C3. Should any fluctuation appear, adjust C4 to stop it.

We are now ready to "mix" and to obtain output on 144 MHz. Feed 50-MHz power into J6. With power on V1 and V2, check for output on 144 MHz at L7. A pilot lamp connected to a loop of insulated wire wrapped around L7 may be used temporarily as an output indicator. When output has been obtained, connect a one-mA meter to J3 and J4, and look for amplifier grid current. Leave plate and screen voltage off the 6360 for the moment.

The lead from J3 can be removed from the negative terminal of the bias battery and connected to the chassis, to make it easier to obtain grid current for purposes of adjustment, if necessary. Peak all adjustments for maximum grid current, making sure that this drive is on the desired frequency. You'll need something larger than a one-mA meter if everything is working correctly, or you can reconnect the bias battery once you

Fig. 7-6 — Interior of the 144-MHz heterodyne exciter. 47- and 94-MHz circuits are at the left, the mixer in the center, and 144-MHz amplifier at the right.

Fig. 7-7 — Layout drawing showing principal hole locations and sizes, for those wishing to make a duplicate unit. Hole sizes: A—1 inch, B—3/4 inch, C—1/4 inch; others 1/8 inch. Chassis and plate are 5 X 10 inches.

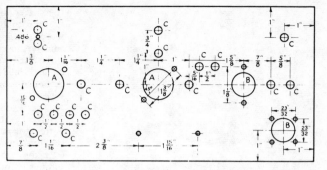

have obtained a reasonable current reading. Operation of the amplifier from here on is exactly like it would be in a conventional transmitter.

When the conversion unit is used for sideband or a-m, the 6360 operates as a Class AB1 linear amplifier. Thus the drive must be kept below the level at which grid current starts to flow. In driving an amplifier like the 144-MHz 4CX250 amplifiers described in Chapter 6, it is not necessary to drive the 6360 into grid current for any class of service. On cw, for example, it is possible to develop 600 watts output from the 4CX250s with the 6360 stage running Class AB1 (no grid current). If a harder-to-drive final stage is used it may be necessary to push the 6360 into Class-C conditions for full-power cw work. This will also be necessary if the 6360 is to be plate modulated.

In practice, it is convenient to use the output control on the 50-MHz exciter as the sole means of controlling the operation of the conversion unit, whether the mode of operation be sideband, cw, or a-m. Keying for cw is done in the 50-MHz exciter, and modulation of the signal is also done there. We have encountered no linearity problems in the mixer or its following amplifier at any level of operation needed with the 4CX250 push-pull amplifier running at power output levels from 50 to 600 watts.

The conversion unit is plugged into a power supply of conventional design. Power is left on the setup during all operating time, as the current drain without 50-MHz drive is well below the rated dissipation of all tube elements.

Tube and Circuit Alternatives

Experience with this exciter has turned up several desirable alternatives. Perhaps you prefer other tube types. If so, individual or dual tubes of characteristics similar to those of the Compactrons can be used. The functions of the double-triode-pentode 6M11 can be performed by a 12AT7 dual triode for V1A and B, and a 6AK5 in place of V1C. Or a single triode for V1A and a 6U8 or other triode-pentode for V1B and C will do nicely. Some differences in layout will be needed either way.

The 6AR11 was used for the mixer mainly as an economy, compared with the cost of a 6360. The latter dual tetrode makes an excellent push-pull mixer, as well as amplifier, and little or no change in layout is required for this substitution.

A higher amplifier output level can be obtained with other dual tetrodes for V3 than the 6360. This tube's larger brother, the 8458, is an excellent candidate, delivering up to 25 watts output at 400 volts on the plates.

Operating Conditions

With the exciter as described, any power supply capable of delivering 250 to 300 volts at 100 mA and 150 volts, regulated, should be satisfactory. Some typical operating conditions are:

Oscillator plate current: 12 mA without crystal oscillating; 5 mA with.

Doubler plate current: 8 mA.

Amplifier plate current: 10 mA.

Mixer plate and screen current: 15 mA with no 50-MHz drive; up to 20 mA with maximum drive.

6360 Amplifier plate and screen current: 25 mA with no 50-MHz drive; 48 mA for operation as linear amplifier; 70 mA max. for Class-C cw.

Amplifier grid current: None, except for Class-C operation; about 1.5 mA max.

Output: 6 watts cw, sideband, or plate-modulated a-m; 2 watts a-m linear.

A 50-MHz TRANSVERTER

With the increase in use of ssb on the vhf bands, there is much interest in adapting hf ssb gear to use on higher frequencies. The transverter of Fig. 7-8 will provide transceiver-style operation on 50 MHz, when used with a low-powered 28-MHz transceiver. The output of the transmitter portion is about 40 watts, adequate for much interesting work. It can be used to drive an amplifier such as the grounded-grid 3-500Z unit described later in this chapter. The receiving converter combines simplicity, adequate gain and noise figure, and freedom from overloading problems.

Circuit Details

The receiving front end uses a grounded-gate JFET rf amplifier, Q1 in Fig. 7-10, followed by a dual-gate MOSFET mixer, Q2. Its 22-MHz injection voltage is taken from the oscillator and buffer stages that also supply injection for transmitter mixing. The difference frequency is 28 MHz, so the

7-8 — The 6-meter transverter, with shield cover in place. Large knobs are for amplifier tuning and loading. Small knob, lower right, is for a meter sensitivity control. The meter switch is just above it.

Fig. 7-9 — Top view of the transverter. The receiving converter is inside the shield at the left. The 22-MHz crystal oscillator and buffer are in the lower left portion of the chassis. In the right corner is the transmitting mixer. Above it is the first amplifier. The 6146 output amplifier is in the shielded compartment at the upper right.

transceiver dial reading bears a direct 28-50 relationship to the 50-MHz signal being received. For more detail on the converter construction and adjustment, see Fig. 4-15 and associated text. The transverter uses the grounded-gate rf amplifier circuit, while the converter referred to above has a grounded-source, but they are quite similar otherwise.

The triode portion of a 6LN8, V1A, is a 22-MHz crystal oscillator. The pentode, V1B, is a buffer, for isolation of the oscillator, and increased stability. Injection voltage for the receiving mixer is taken from the buffer output circuit, L8, through a two-turn link, L9, and small-diameter coax, to gate 2 of the mixer, through a 10-pF blocking capacitor.

The grid circuit of the 6EJ7 transmitting mixer, V2, is tuned to 22 MHz and is inductively coupled to the buffer plate circuit. The 28-MHz input is applied to the grid circuit through a link around L11, and small-diameter coax. The mixer output, L12, is tuned to the sum frequency, 50 MHz, and coupled to a 6GK6 amplifier, V3, by a bandpass circuit, L12 and L13. The 6GK6 is bandpass-coupled to the grid of a 6146 output stage, V4. This amplifier employs a pi-network output stage.

The 6146 plate dissipation is held down during the receiving periods by fixed bias that is switched in by relay K1. The mixer and driver tubes have their screen voltage removed during receiving, by the same relay, which also switches the antenna and 28-MHz input circuits for transmitting and receiving. The relay is energized by grounding pin 7 of P1 through an external switch, or by the VOX relay in the transceiver.

Construction

A 7 × 9 × 2-inch aluminum chassis is used for the transverter, with a front panel 6 inches high, made of sheet aluminum. The top and sides are enclosed by a one-piece cover of perforated aluminum. The output-stage tuning control, C5, is on the upper left of the panel, 2 inches above the chassis. The loading control, C6, is immediately below, under the chassis. The meter, upper right, monitors either 6146 plate current or relative output, as selected by the switch, S1, immediately below it. A sensitivity control for calibrating the output-metering circuit completes the front-panel controls.

The output connector, J2, is centered on the rear apron of the chassis, which also has the input jack, J1, the 8-pin connector, P1, and the bias-adjusting control mounted on it.

The meter is a 1-mA movement, with multiplier resistors to give a full-scale reading on a current of 200 mA. The front cover snaps off easily, to allow calibration marks to be put on as desired.

An enclosure of perforated aluminum, 3-1/4 inches high, 4 inches wide and 4-3/4 inches long shields the 6146 and its plate circuit. There is also an L-shaped shield around the 6146 socket, under the chassis.

The receiving converter is built on a 2-1/2 × 4-1/4-inch etched board, and mounted vertically in a three-sided shield of sheet aluminum.

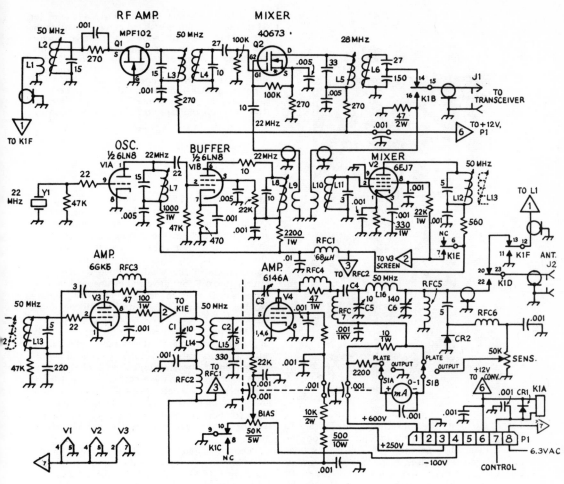

Fig. 7-10 — Schematic diagram and parts information for the 50-MHz transverter.

C1 — 10-pF subminiature variable (Hammarlund MAC-10).

C2 — 5-pF subminiature variable (Hammarlund MAC-5).

C3 — 2-1/2-inch length No. 14 wire, parallel to and 1/4 inch away from tube envelope. Cover with insulating sleeve.

C4 — 500-pF 3000-volt disk ceramic.

C5 — 10-pF variable (Johnson 149-3, with one stator and one rotor plate removed).

C6 — 140-pF variable (Millen 22140).

CR1 — 1N128 diode.

CR2 — 1N83A diode.

J1 — phono jack.

J2 — Coaxial jack, SO-239.

K1 — 6-pole double-throw relay, 12-volt dc coil.

L1 — 2 turns small insulated wire over ground end of L2.

L2, L3, L4 — 10 turns No. 24 enamel closewound on J. W. Miller 4500-4 iron-slug form.

L5, L6 — 12 turns No. 24 enamel on J. W. Miller 4500-2 iron-slug form.

L7, L8, L11 — Iron-slug coils adjusted for 4.1, 5.5, and 5.5 µH, respectively (Miller 4405).

L9, L10 — 2 turns small insulated wire over ground ends of L8 and L11.

L12, L13 — 1-µH iron-slug coil J. W. Miller 4403, 3 turns removed.

L14 — 7 turns No. 20, 1/2-inch dia, 1/2 inch long (B&W 3003).

L15 — Like L14, but 6 turns.

L16 — 6 turns No. 20, 5/8-inch dia, 3/4 inch long (B&W 3006).

P1 — 8-pin power connector.

RFC1 — 68-µH rf choke (Millen 34300).

RFC2 — 8.2-µH rf choke (Millen J-300).

RFC3 — 5 turns No. 22 on 47-ohm 1/2-watt resistor.

RFC4 — 4 turns No. 15 on 47-ohm 1-watt resistor.

RFC5, RFC6 — 8.2-µH rf choke (Millen 34300).

S1 — Dpdt toggle.

Y1 — 22-MHz overtone crystal (International Crystal Co., Type EX).

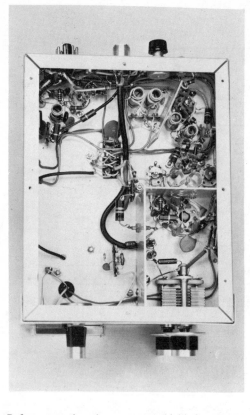

Fig. 7-11 — Bottom of the transverter, with the 6146 socket inside the shield compartment at the right. Three sets of inductively coupled circuits are visible in the upper-right corner. The first two, near the top of the picture are on 22 MHz. Next to the right and down, are the mixer plate and first-amplifier grid circuits. The self-supporting 6GK6 plate and 6146 grid coils are just outside the amplifier shield compartment. The large variable capacitor is the loading control.

Before mounting the converter shield, be sure to check for clearance with the terminals on the meter. Remember, the meter has full plate voltage on it when the switch is set to read plate current, even when the transverter is in the receiving mode.

Testing of the transverter was done with the General-Purpose Supply for Transceivers, described in the power supply chapter of the ARRL *Handbook*. Separate provision must be made for 12 volts dc for the receiving converter.

Injection voltage, signal input, and i-f output connections to the converter are made with small-diameter coax. These and the 12-volt wiring are brought up through small holes in the chassis, under the converter. As seen in Fig. 4-19, the input JFET, Q1, is on the left. The mixer is near the center. The 28-MHz output coils, L5 and L6, are just to the right of Q2.

Note that there are two sets of relay contacts, K1D and K1F, in series in the receiver line. This guarantees high isolation of the receiver input, to protect the rf amplifier transistor. Another protective device is the diode, CR1, across the coil of the relay. If there are other relays external to this unit that use the same 12-volt supply, it is advisable to put diodes across their coils also. Spikes of several volts can be induced with making and breaking of the coil circuits.

Adjustment

A dip meter is very useful in the preliminary tuning. Be sure that L7 and L8 are tuned to 22

MHz and L12 and L13 are tuned to 50 MHz. The driver and output circuits should also be tuned to 50 MHz. Check to be sure that slug-tuned coils really tune *through* the desired frequency. Quite often troubles are eventually traced to coils where the circuit is only approaching resonance as the core centers in the winding. Such a circuit will appear to work, but drive will be low, and spurious outputs will tend to be high. This is a common trouble in overtone oscillators, with slug-tuned coils.

Once the circuits have been set approximately, apply heater and plate voltage to the oscillator, and tune L7 for best oscillation, as checked with a wavemeter or a receiver tuned to 22 MHz. Connect a 28-MHz receiver to the input, J1, and apply dc to the converter. It should be possible to hear a strong local station or test signal immediately. Peak all coils for best reception, then stagger-tune L5 and L6 for good response across the first 500 kHz of the band.

Before applying plate voltage to the 6146, it is advisable to protect the tube during tuneup by inserting a 1500- or 2000-ohm 25-watt resistor in series with the plate supply. Connect a 50-ohm load to the output jack, and energize K1. Adjust the bias control for 25 to 30 mA plate current. Apply a small amount of 28-MHz drive. A fraction of a watt, enough to produce a dim glow in a No. 47 pilot lamp load, will do. Some output should be indicated on the meter, with the sensitivity control fully clockwise. Adjust the amplifier tuning and loading for maximum output, and readjust all of the 50-MHz circuits likewise.

After the circuits have been peaked up, adjust the bandpass circuits by applying first a 28.1-MHz input and then a 28.4-MHz input, and peaking alternate coils until good operation is obtained over the range of 50.0 to 50.5 MHz. Most ssb operation currently is close to 50.1 MHz, so uniform response across a 500-kHz range is not too important, if only this mode is used. If the 10-meter transceiver is capable of a-m operation, and you want to use this mode, coverage up to 50.5 with uniform output may be more desirable. Adjust the position of the neutralizing wire, C3, for minimum rf in L16, with drive on, but no screen or plate voltage on the 6146.

Now apply full plate voltage, with no drive, set the bias adjustment for a 6146 plate current of 25 to 30 mA. With the dummy load connected, experiment with the amount of drive needed to reach maximum plate current. Preferably, use a scope to check for flat-topping as the drive is increased. An output of 40 watts, cw, should be obtainable. The quality of the ssb signal is determined first by the equipment generating it, but it can be ruined by improper operation. Over-driving the mixer or the 6146, and improper loading of the amplifier will cause distortion and splatter. Contin-

uous monitoring with a scope is the best preventive measure.

Because of the frequencies mixed, and the bandpass coupling between stages, the output of the transverter is reasonably clean. Still, use of an antenna coupler or filter between the transverter and antenna is good insurance. The same treatment of the transverter output is desirable when driving a linear amplifier.

A 144-MHz TRANSVERTER

The transverter of Fig. 7-12 is designed to be used with any 14- or 28-MHz ssb exciter capable of delivering approximately 20 watts peak output. It can provide up to 20 watts PEP output at 144 MHz — sufficient for driving a pair of 4CX250 tubes in Class C for cw operation, or the same pair of tubes can be operated AB1 to provide 1200 watts PEP input with this unit as a driver.

It is not recommended that beginners attempt this project since vhf ssb circuits require special care in their construction and operation, a requirement that may be a bit beyond the inexperienced builder.

How It Operates

Starting with V1A, the oscillator, Fig. 7-13, a 43.333-MHz or overtone crystal is used at Y1 to provide the local-oscillator signal for the exciter. Output from V1A is amplified by V1B to a suitable level for driving the tripler, V2. 130-MHz or 116-MHz energy is fed to the grids of V3, a 6360 mixer, by means of a bandpass tuned circuit, L3C1, and L4C2. The selectivity of this circuit is high, thus reducing unwanted spurious energy at the mixer grids.

Output from the exciter is supplied through an attenuator pad at J1 and is injected to the mixer, V3, at its cathode circuit, across a 270-ohm resistor. The attenuator pad can be eliminated if a very low-power exciter is to be used. The values shown in Fig. 7-13 were chosen for operation with a Central Electronics 20-A exciter operating at full input, or nearly so. The driving power needed at the cathode of V3 is approximately 4 or 5 watts PEP.

After the 130-MHz and 14-MHz signals are mixed at V3, the *sum* frequency, 144 MHz, is coupled to the grids of V4, the PA stage, by means of another bandpass tuned circuit — further reducing spurious output from the exciter. PA stage V4 operates in the AB1 mode. Its idling plate current is approximately 25 mA. The plate current rises to approximately 100 mA at full input.

If cw operation is desired, the grid-block keying circuit in the mixer stage (J3) can be included. If ssb operation is all that is contemplated, the minus 100-volt bias line can be eliminated along with J3, R1, and the shaping network at J3. In that case the 15,000-ohm grid resistor from the center tap of L4 would be grounded to the chassis.

Fig. 7-12 — Panel view of the 2-meter transverter. This version is patterned after a transmitting converter design by K9UIF. The on-off switches for ac and dc sections of the power supply are mounted on the front panel of the unit as are the pilot lamps and plate meter for the PA stage. The tuning controls for the various stages are accessible from the top of the chassis.

The receiving section uses a low-noise uhf MOSFET as the rf amplifier and a second dual-gate MOSFET as the mixer. See Fig. 7-15. The gate 1 and drain connections of the rf amplifier are tapped down on the tuned circuits so that unconditional stability is achieved without neutralization. Oscillator energy is sampled with a two-turn link wound over L3. A short length of RG-58A/U carries the injection energy to Q2. The converter is built in a 5 × 2-1/4 × 2-1/-inch box constructed from four pieces of double-sided circuit board that have been soldered on all abutting edges. The unit is mounted on the transverter front panel.

Construction Notes

The photographs show the construction techniques that should be followed for duplicating this equipment. The more seasoned builder should have no difficulty changing the prescribed layout to fit his particular needs, but the shielding and by-passing methods used here should be adhered to even if changes are made.

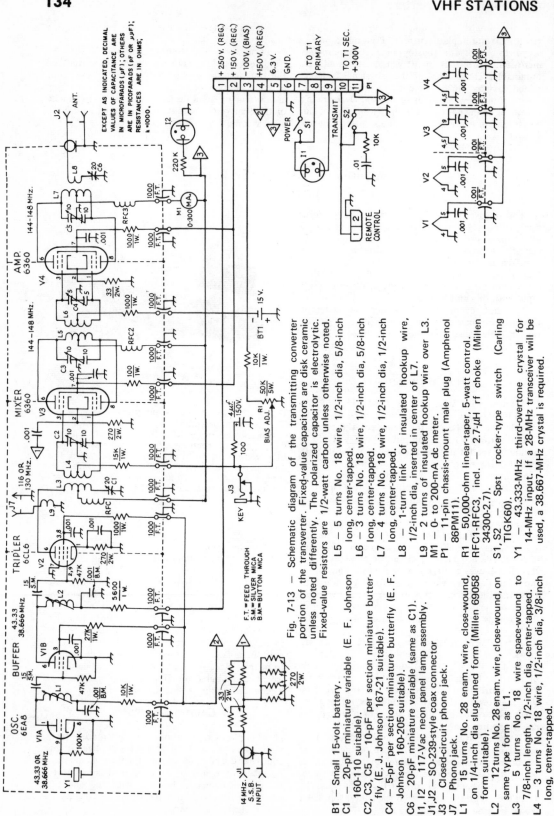

Fig. 7-13 — Schematic diagram of the transmitting converter portion of the transverter. Fixed-value capacitors are disk ceramic unless noted differently. The polarized capacitor is electrolytic. Fixed-value resistors are 1/2-watt carbon unless otherwise noted.

B1 — Small 15-volt battery.

C1 — 20-pF miniature variable (E. F. Johnson 160-110 suitable).

C2, C3, C5 — 10-pF per section miniature butterfly (E. J. Johnson 167-21 suitable).

C4 — 5-pF per section miniature butterfly (E. F. Johnson 160-205 suitable).

C6 — 20-pF miniature variable (same as C1).

I1, I2 — 117-Vac neon panel lamp assembly.

J1,J2 — SO-239-style coax connector.

J3 — Closed-circuit phone jack.

J7 — Phono jack.

L1 — 15 turns No. 28 enam. wire, close-wound, on 1/4-inch dia slug-tuned form (Millen 69058 form suitable).

L2 — 12 turns No. 28 enam. wire, close-wound, on same type form as L1.

L3 — 5 turns No. 18 wire space-wound to 7/8-inch length, 1/2-inch dia, center-tapped.

L4 — 3 turns No. 18 wire, 1/2-inch dia, 3/8-inch long, center-tapped.

L5 — 5 turns No. 18 wire, 1/2-inch dia, 5/8-inch long, center-tapped.

L6 — 3 turns No. 18 wire, 1/2-inch dia, 5/8-inch long, center-tapped.

L7 — 4 turns No. 18 wire, 1/2-inch dia, 1/2-inch long, center-tapped.

L8 — 1-turn link of insulated hookup wire, 1/2-inch dia, inserted in center of L7.

L9 — 2 turns of insulated hookup wire over L3.

M1 — 0- to 200-mA dc meter.

P1 — 11-pin chassis-mount male plug (Amphenol 86PM11).

R1 — 50,000-ohm linear-taper, 5-watt control. RFC1-RFC3, incl. — 2.7-μH rf choke (Millen 34300-2.7).

S1, S2 — Spst rocker-type switch (Carling TIGK60).

Y1 — 43.333-MHz third-overtone crystal for 14-MHz input. If a 28-MHz transceiver will be used, a 38.667-MHz crystal is required.

EXCEPT AS INDICATED, DECIMAL VALUES OF CAPACITANCE ARE IN MICROFARADS (μF); OTHERS ARE IN PICOFARADS (pF OR μμF); RESISTANCES ARE IN OHMS; k =1000.

F.T.= FEED THROUGH
S.M.= SILVER MICA
B.M.= BUTTON MICA

Fig. 7-14 — Inside view of the converter. Shields are used between the rf amplifier input and output circuits, and between the latter and the mixer input circuit. The cable entering the bottom side of the enclosure carries the oscillator injection energy. Output to the associated receiver or transceiver is taken through the jack to the left.

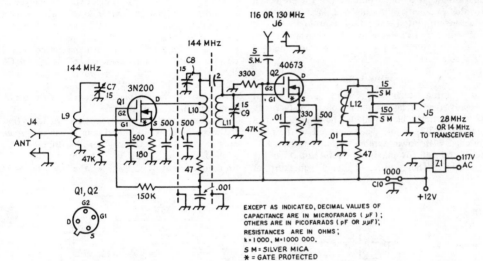

Fig. 7-15 — Diagram of the converter section. Resistors are 1/4-watt composition and capacitors are disk ceramic, except as noted otherwise.

C7-C9, incl. — Air variable, pc mount (Johnson 189-505-5)

C10 — Feedthrough type.

L9 — 4-1/2 turns, No. 18 tinned wire, 1/4-inch ID. Tap at 1-1/2 turns up from the ground end for the antenna connection, and at 3 turns for the Q1 gate.

L10 — 4-1/2 turns, No. 18 tinned wire, 1/4-inch ID. Tap at 3 turns up from the cold end for the Q1 drain connection.

L11 — 5 turns No. 18 tinned wire, 1/4-inch ID.

L12 — 1.99-2.42-μH slug-tuned coil, pc mount, for 28-MHz output (J. W. Miller 46A226CPC); or, for 14-MHz output, 7.3-8.9-μH (J. W. Miller 46A826CPC).

J4-J6, incl. — Phono type.

Q1, Q2 — RCA dual-gate MOSFET.

Z1 — 12-V miniature power supply, transistor radio type.

Fig. 7-16 — Looking into the bottom of the chassis, the rf section is enclosed in a shield compartment made from flashing copper. Additional divider sections isolate the input and output tuned circuits of the last three stages of the exciter. Feedthrough capacitors are mounted on one wall of the copper compartment to provide decoupling of the power leads.

An 8 × 12 × 3-inch aluminum chassis is used for this equipment. An internal chassis, 5 inches wide, 3 inches deep, and 12 inches long, is made from flashing copper and installed along one edge of the main chassis. This method makes it possible to solder directly to the chassis for making positive ground connections rather than rely on mechanical joints. Shield partitions are made of copper and are soldered in place as indicated on the schematic diagram and in the photo. An aluminum bottom plate is used to enclose the underside of the chassis for confining the rf.

Feedthrough capacitors are used to bring power leads into the copper compartment. Though this adds somewhat to the overall cost of the project, it provides excellent bypassing and decoupling, thus reducing unwanted interstage coupling. It also contributes to TVI reduction. Most surplus houses stock feedthrough capacitors, and offer them at reasonable cost.

Tune Up

An antenna-changeover relay and a set of normally open relay contacts, both operated by the exciter, must be provided. The remote control leads, from P2, should be connected to the relay contacts. With power applied to the converter, L12 should be set for maximum noise input to the transceiver. Then, using a signal generator or off-the-air weak signal, peak L9, L10, and L11 for best signal-to-noise ratio.

The transmitter section can be powered by the circuit of Fig. 7-17, or the builder can design a supply of his own choice. Regulated voltages are recommended for best operation.

With a dummy load connected to J2, apply operating voltage. Couple a wavemeter to L1 and tune the oscillator plate for maximum output. Then, detune the slug of L1 slightly (toward minimum inductance) to assure reliable oscillator starting. Couple the wavemeter to L2 and tune for peak output. With the wavemeter applied to L4, adjust C1 and C2 for maximum indicated output.

The next step is to connect the transceiver to J1 and supply just enough drive to cause a rise in PA plate current of a few milliamperes. Tune C3 and C4 for maximum indicated plate current at M1, then adjust C5 and C6 for maximum power output to the dummy load. C1, C2, C3, and C4 should be readjusted at this point for maximum plate current of the PA stage. Use only enough drive to bring the PA plate current up to 100 mA at maximum dc input power.

A closed-circuit keying jack is used at J3 so that the mixer stage is not biased to cutoff during voice operation. Inserting the key permits full bias to be applied, thus cutting off V3. R1 should be adjusted for complete cutoff of V3 when the key is open.

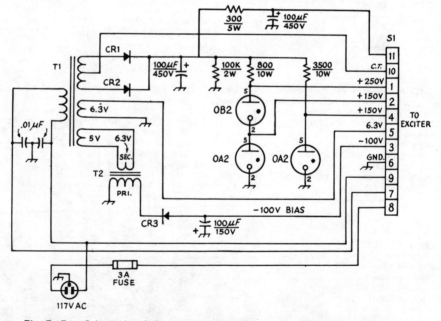

Fig. 7-17 — Schematic of the power supply section. On-off switches for the ac and dc circuits are mounted in the rf deck along with the pilot lamps. Polarized capacitors are electrolytic, others are disk ceramic. CR1 and CR2 are 1000-volt, 1-ampere silicon diodes. CR3 is a 200-PRV 600-mA silicon diode. T1 is a power transformer with a 540-volt ct secondary at 120 mA. Filament windings are 5 volts at 3 A, and 6.3 volts at 3.5 A. T2 is a 6.3-volt, 1-ampere filament transformer connected back to back with the 5-volt winding of T1. S1 is an 11-pin socket (female). A 10,000-ohm resistor and a .01-μF disk capacitor are connected in series between the center tap of T1's secondary and ground for transient suppression when S2 is switched to on. The suppressor is mounted at S2, in the rf deck.

ADJUSTING DRIVE LEVEL TO VHF TRANSVERTERS

In using hf exciters to drive vhf transmitting converters and transverters, the problem of maintaining optimum drive level is often troublesome. Many hf sideband rigs are in the 100-watt category, yet the more desirable mixers require no more than a few watts of drive. This problem is complicated by the necessity for running the ssb exciter at full load, if the quality and carrier suppression of the signal are to be maintained. Reduction of the voice level (to keep down the ssb peak output) is not recommended, as this tends to destroy the effective carrier suppression in the driving signal.

Several solutions are possible. In some hf exciters drive can be taken from a stage preceding the output amplifier; though this is not popular with owners of commercially built rigs, since it requires modification of the circuitry. In some output amplifiers it may be possible to remove the screen voltage, or greatly reduce it, and still get enough output to drive the vhf mixer. The most popular method is to run the hf exciter more-or-less normally, and swamp out most of its output in a dummy load.

This approach is shown in Fig. 7-18A. A coaxial T fitting is inserted in the line between the exciter and the mixer, and a shielded dummy load is connected in parallel. The input tuning of the transmitting mixer can then be used as a level control to some extent, if the power is still too high, or an attenuator can be inserted between the dummy load and the transmitting mixer, to adjust

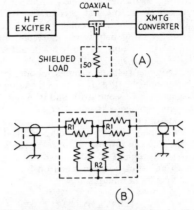

Fig. 7-18 — Methods of attenuating the signal from an hf exciter used with a transmitting converter requiring low driving power. A conventional 50-ohm dummy load is connected across the driver line, in A. An attenuator capable of dissipating up to 15 watts ssb or cw power is shown in B. This is inserted in the driver line. All resistors are 2 watts, R1 33 ohms, R2 270 ohms.

the drive to the desired level. Where the hf exciter output level is moderate, as with the Central Electronics 10B and 20A, the attenuator of Fig. 7-18B alone may serve the purpose, without use of the dummy load.

THE A-M TRANSCEIVER — IS IT OBSOLETE?

Rapid increases in use of fm and ssb in vhf communication have tended to create the impression that amplitude modulation is obsolete. It may be almost gone from the busy hf bands, where the narrower spectrum of ssb is an overpowering advantage, but where there is plenty of room for it, a-m is by no means dead. And it should not be. If we examine all the qualities of all known forms of modulation, we may well conclude that a-m has legitimate roles in the vhf realm that other modes handle poorly, or not at all.

The vhf bands have always been great territory for the do-it-yourself beginner, but if vhf operation goes to more complex modes completely, at the expense of a-m, much of this quality could be lost. Amplitude modulation is the only mode with which the ultimate in simple receivers, the superregenerative detector, can be used effectively. An a-m transmitter, at least in the low-power brackets, is easy and inexpensive to build. No mode can match A2 (keyed-tone modulation) for on-the-air code practice; it is easy to generate, and easy to copy on *any* receiver. There are no critical stability problems, transmitting or receiving, in an a-m system. Finally, good a-m can be very good indeed, even with home-built equipment that is within the capabilities of the average tinkerer-type ham.

Meaning no disparagement of other modes, each of which has qualities that make it unique in its field, we express here the hope that enthusiasm for them will not cause an untimely demise of the a-m transceiver. In what other way could we match the simplicity, versatility, and low cost of the two portable stations that follow these lines? They do some things well that are difficult, expensive, or impossible with competing modes. Most important, they are great fun!

These two portables were chosen for use here not because they are either new or optimum designs, but rather because they are basically simple, yet effective. Many other items appearing in *QST* in recent years will suggest methods you may prefer in building your own "mountain-topper." We suggest a check on references below, before you start.

Tilton, "Featherweight Portable 50-MHz Station," *QST*, November, 1964.

Utz, "Miniwatt 2-Meter Transceiver," *QST*, October, 1967.

Campbell, "A 1969-Model 50-MHz Transistor Transceiver," *QST*, January and April, 1969.

Becker, "More Power on 144 MHz with Transistors, *QST*, August, 1969.

Preiss, A 2-Meter QRP Mountain-Topper," *QST*, May, 1970.

TRANSISTOR PORTABLE STATION FOR 50 MHz

Though "working portable" from the high spots has been an integral part of the vhf game since the earliest times, it remained for the age of transistors to bring lightweight portable vhf stations into the realm of full practicality. The 50-MHz station in Fig. 7-19 is complete, including even the antenna system and microphone, yet it is a mere 5-pound handful. It delivers a good-quality voice signal of up to one watt, and its receiver will pick up any a-m signal that you could hear on the best home-station setup, yet the station will operate for many hours on its self-contained pack of D cells. You can run the rig from the car battery when it is convenient to do so, but you can also take it to any spot you can reach on foot and be ready to operate in minutes.

What's Inside

The handmade sheet aluminum box is 4-3/4 × 6 × 9 inches in size. Inside are separate units for transmitting, receiving, modulation, and power, any of which can be changed without dismantling the others. The receiver is a small imported pocket broadcast set, with a crystal-controlled converter ahead of it. The converter is seen in the left foreground of Fig. 7-20. Its adjustments are reached through holes in the right side of the case, as viewed from the front. The broadcast receiver, attached to the front panel, shows in the left rear corner of Fig. 7-20. At the right rear, in back of the battery pack, is the transmitter rf unit. Just above this assembly is a readymade 1-watt audio amplifier, modified for modulator service. Each of these units will be described in detail.

With the transceiver, in Fig. 7-19, are the microphone, a 35-foot "long-wire" antenna, a dummy load for testing the transmitter, and a small antenna coupler built into a plastic parts box.

These items, a Minilog and miscellaneous small tools and spare parts are carried in a zippered plastic "gym bag" 5 × 9 × 12 inches in size. A lightweight portable 3-element beam that makes this little station "really talk" is described in Chapter 9.

Transmitter Rf Unit

The transmitter is shown in Figs. 7-21 and 7-23, with its circuit diagram in Fig. 7-22. Parts are mounted on an aluminum plate made from a sheet 3 × 7 inches, with 3/8 inch folded up at the bottom. This fastens to the transceiver bottom plate with self-tapping screws. The oscillator and buffer stages use 2N706 transistors, or similar vhf npn types. These are at the left side of Fig. 7-21 and the right of Fig. 7-23. Aluminum shields 2 × 2-1/2 inches are mounted on spade lugs at 2 and 4 inches in from the left side, as seen in Fig. 7-21. Leads from L2 and L4 run through these shields and are insulated from them by sleeves of polyethylene made by removing the conductors from small pieces of RG-58 or 59 coax.

The output stage has two silicon vhf power transistors in parallel. Several types are usable, and bargains may be found occasionally in surplus flyers. RCA's 2N3553, 2N3866, and 2N4427 also work well and can be run at higher input than quoted here, if drive for them is available. 2N706s work well in the final, but will not stand amplitude modulation voltage peaks encountered with 12 volts on the collectors. Nearly all silicon vhf transistors will do for the oscillator and buffer, but the 2N706 has a higher dissipation rating than most. They also can be obtained for as low as five for a dollar from surplus sources.

The safe dissipation rating for transistors can be raised by even the simplest of heat sinks. A strip of thin brass or flashing copper 3/16 inch wide can be

Fig. 7-19 — The 50-MHz portable station, complete with all necessary operating accessories — total weight: under 5 pounds. Accessories grouped around the transceiver: the microphone, miniature antenna coupler, pilot-lamp dummy load, and a 35-foot "long-wire" antenna.

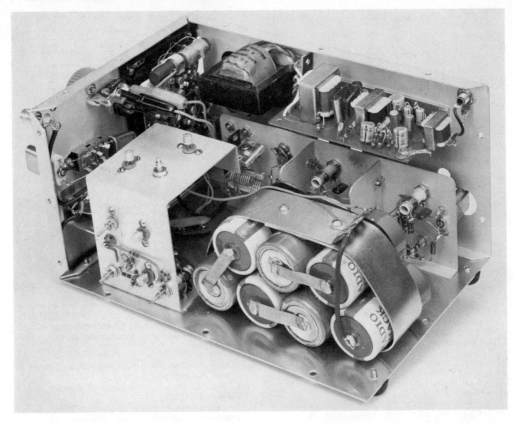

Fig. 7-20 — Interior of the 50-MHz transistor transceiver, with top plate, right side and rear panel removed. Parts of the switching circuits and the small broadcast receiver used for the i-f system are seen on the front panel. The C-shaped subassembly at the left is one of several converters tested in the transceiver. The transmitter rf assembly is seen in back of the package of 7 "D" cells. At the upper part of the left-side panel is the modulator.

Fig. 7-21 — Transmitter portion of the 50-MHz transistor rig. At the left side are the crystal oscillator and buffer stages. The two transistors in the output stage are connected in parallel by means of two brass plates, which also serve as a heat sink. The amplifier collector circuit is tuned by means of the knob at the lower right, the surface of which is slotted to permit adjustment with a screwdriver, through a hole in the left side of the transceiver case. The crystal and the two tuning slugs are also provided with access holes.

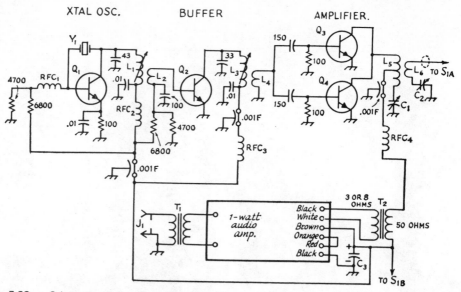

Fig. 7-22 — Schematic diagram and parts information for the transmitter portion of the 50-MHz transceiver. Resistors are all 1/4 watt. Decimal values of capacitance are in μF; others in pF. Suffix F indicates feedthrough type. All others not described are Mylar or dipped-mica, 50-volt rating or more. The modulator is shown in outline form only, since it is a ready-made unit. Lead colors given are for Radio Shack audio amplifier, type 277-038, having a 1-watt rating.

C1 — 35-pF subminiature variables (Millen 25035E).
C2 — 180-pF mica trimmer (Arco 463).
C3 — 5-μF 25-volt electrolytic.
J1 — Phono jack.
L1, L3 — 5 turns No. 24 enamel, closewound on 1/4-inch iron-slug form. (Miller No. 4501, with 3 turns removed or wind on No. 4500 form.)
L2, L4 — 2 turns insulated wire wound near bottom end of L1 and L3, respectively.
L5 — 10 turns No. 20, 16 tpi, 1/2-inch dia, center tapped (B&W No. 3003 Air-Dux 416T, PIC 1730).
L6 — 2 turns insulated wire around center of L5.
Q1, Q2 — 2N706 or equiv. See text.

Q3, Q4 — Silicon vhf power transistor, 1-watt or higher dissipation. See text.
RFC1-RFC4, incl. — 8.2-μH iron-core rf choke (Millen J300-8.2).
T1 — Input transformer, high-impedance microphone to amplifier input, 200k to 1000 ohms (Archer 27-1376).
T2 — Output transformer; 45 to 50-ohm primary, 3.5 or 8-ohm secondary. Connect low-impedance winding to amplifier output, and run final-stage collector current through 50-ohm winding (Knight 54D4147).
Y1 — Third-overtone crystal, 50.11 to 54 MHz (International Crystal Mfg. Co. Type F-605).

bent into keyhole shape and slipped over the 2N706 case for this purpose. The brass plates holding the final stage transistors together (Fig. 7-21) serve the dual purpose of heat sink and parallel collector connectors. Dimensions are not critical, but ours are 0.041 × 5/8-inch brass, about 1-3/4 inches long. Aluminum would be equally good. Be sure that these do not touch the mounting plate or the socket-mounting screws at any point, as the collector and case are connected together in power transistors, and thus the case has the supply voltage on it. Center-to-center spacing of the holes should be the same as that of the transistor sockets, one inch in this case.

Various output circuits were tried, with the series-tuned center-tapped arrangement shown in Fig. 7-22 working out best for this setup. Output is taken off through a series-tuned loop, L6, wound around the midpoint of L5. The series capacitor, C2, is a high-minimum mica trimmer, visible directly over the tank coil in Fig. 7-23. It can be

adjusted for optimum transfer to a 50-ohm load and left set thereafter, since adjustment is not critical.

Modulation

The audio amplifier used for the modulator (Radio Shack 277-038, 1-watt rating) has an output transformer with a low-impedance secondary. This must be replaced with one suitable for modulation purposes, or a step-up transformer can be added. We chose the latter, as it was easier to find than one designed specifically for modulator service. An input transformer to match the high-impedance microphone must also be added. The extra transformers, T1 and T2, in Fig. 7-22, are visible in Fig. 7-20, mounted at opposite ends of the amplifier. The modulation transformer is connected "back to back" with the output transformer of the amplifier, and has the collector current of the final stage of the transmitter running through its 50-ohm winding.

Fig. 7-23 — Back view of the transmitter, with the output stage at the left. Partitions isolate the three stages; crystal oscillator at the right, buffer at the middle.

The amplifier has pnp transistors, so it is set up for positive ground, as is the broadcast receiver. In using the transceiver in negative-ground cars (U.S. standard) the "ground" side of the amplifier and broadcast receiver must be isolated from the transceiver case. The amplifier is mounted on an aluminum bracket, making sure that the mounting screws do not come in contact with the positive-voltage circuits of the module. Parts of the amplifier circuit that connect to the positive lead (brown lead in the unit used here) are bypassed to the transceiver case with an electrolytic capacitor, C3, in Fig. 7-22.

The amplifier unit is intended for 12-volt service, but it works well at lower voltages. Its output tracks with the input to the final stage of the transmitter as the supply voltage is changed, so the modulation percentage remains about the same regardless of the power source used.

Signal quality and modulation percentage depend on many factors. With our operating conditions the best modulation is obtained with audio applied only to the collectors of the amplifier stage, and with the final collector circuit detuned slightly on the high-frequency (low capacitance) side of resonance. When tuned for maximum output the stage shows little upward modulation, and when C1 is detuned to the high-capacitance side the quality is poor and the modulation distinctly downward. The amount of detuning needed depends on the collector voltage, increasing with voltage level.

Output capability is about one watt at 9 volts and two watts at 13 volts, but the stage must be detuned to one-half and one watt, respectively, for

good modulation. About 300 milliwatts output is possible, with good modulation, at 6 volts.

Transmitter Adjustment

Tuneup is very simple. Checking individual stages for current drain is desirable, and adjustments can be made at lower than rated voltages initially. Operation at 6 volts is similar to that at higher voltages, and it may be safer in the check-out phase. Apply voltage through the oscillator feedthrough capacitor only, at first, and check the current drain. As the slug in L1 is moved there will be a downward dip in collector current as the crystal begins oscillating, to around 10 mA at 6 volts. At 9 volts the oscillator current is 15 to 20 mA. Output is enough to light a 2-volt 60-mA pilot

Fig. 7-24 — Front view of the converter portion of the 50-MHz transceiver. Core studs at the right side are for adjusting the rf amplifier collector circuit, the mixer base circuit, and the oscillator collector circuit. The rf stage input circuit is at the lower left.

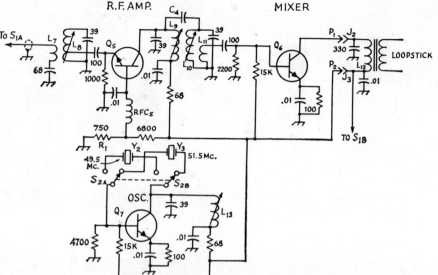

Fig. 7-25 — Schematic diagram and parts information for the transistor converter. Decimal values of capacitors are in μF; others in pF. All are Mylar or dipped mica, 50-volt rating or more. Resistors are 1/4-watt composition. Parts are numbered serially following those of the transmitter.

C4 — Leads of insulated hookup wire twisted together 4 turns. See text.

J2, J3 — Insulated tip jack (Johnson 105-800).

L7 — 2 turns of the inner conductor of the lead to S1, wound over bottom turns of L8. See text and Fig. 7-26.

L8, L9, L10, L13 — 6 turns No. 24 enamel, on 1/4-inch iron-slug ceramic form (Miller 4500, or 4501 coil with 3 turns removed). L8 is tapped at 2 turns from ground end. If made from prepared coil, unwind, clean insulation at tap point, solder on tap, and rewind. Space out turns on any coils if needed to obtain resonance within core range.

L11 — 2 turns No. 24 enamel, wound over bottom turns of L10.

L12 — About 8 turns No. 24 enamel, wound over turns of built-in loopstick of broadcast receiver. Position and number of turns not critical. 330-pF capacitor also uncritical.

P1, P2 — Insulated solderless tip plug (Johnson 105-300).

Q5, Q6, Q7 — Silicon vhf transistor (RCA 40235 used; 40236 through 40240 also tried).

R1 — 680 and 68-ohm 1/4-watt in series. Check different values for optimum amplifier performance.

RFC5 — 8.2-μH rf choke (Millen J300-8.2).

S2 — Two-pole two-position slide switch.

Y2 — Third-overtone crystal, 49.5 MHz International Crystal Mfg. Co. Type F-605.

Y3 — Same as Y2, but 51.5 MHz, or as desired; see text.

---

lamp dimly, if a loop of wire is soldered to its terminals and slipped over L1. Set the slug in L1 for the highest output at which the oscillator starts readily each time voltage is applied.

Now apply voltage to the buffer through RFC3, and check current drawn by Q2. It will rise as the oscillator is tuned toward maximum output, and the pilot lamp load should glow fairly brightly when coupled to L3. Adjust the stud in L3 for maximum output. Current drain will be 20 to 30 mA with the stage working correctly.

Check the amplifier similarly, applying voltage through RFC4. The current to this stage will be practically nil until drive is applied, after which it is proportional to the drive level. A 6-volt 150-mA pilot lamp (brown bead, No. 40, 40A, or 47) makes a good dummy load when the rig is intended to work into 50 ohms. Other lamps will light up, but they do not approximate 50 ohms at normal brilliance. Solder short wires to the base and plug these into the BNC fitting, or temporarily solder the lamp across the coax lead connected to L6. A

lamp mounted in a BNC fitting is a desirable accessory.

Tune C1 and C2 for maximum lamp brilliance, at first. Recheck the settings of L1 and L3 also. The lamp will light very brightly at 9 to 10 volts, indicating about one watt output. Peak C2 for maximum output, and leave it that way. When modulation is to be applied, detune C1 on the low-capacitance side while talking into the microphone, detuning only enough to get a good upward modulation indication in the lamp. Note the final collector current under these conditions. At full output it will be 150 to 200 mA at 9 volts, with detuning to 125 to 150 mA for best modulation. At 12 volts the best setting will be around 150 to 175 mA.

If you have several 2N706s, try various ones in the oscillator and buffer stages, selecting the ones that drive the final collector current to the highest value at the maximum-output tuning condition.

When the detuning procedure outlined is followed the resulting modulation characteristics are at least as good as those of any small pentode or tetrode tube transmitter for the vhf bands. Voice quality is good and "talk power" is high, as there is some inherent clipping effect that tends to prevent excessive modulation and splatter.

THE RECEIVER

Use of a simple crystal-controlled converter working into a pocket broadcast receiver for the i-f and audio system gives more than adequate sensitivity, and the selectivity is good. A friction-drive vernier, to be described later, provides smooth tuning. There are weaknesses however, as in any very-simple approach. The main problem is spurious responses. Image rejection is inherently low, with such a low intermediate frequency, but this is turned to an advantage by setting up the converter injection so that it can be on either the high or the low side of the signal frequency.

Converter Circuit Features

The schematic diagram, Fig. 7-25, makes most circuit details self-evident. Most silicon vhf transistors work well in these stages. The rf amplifier, Q5, is a common-base stage. Its collector circuit is band-pass coupled to the mixer, Q6. The mixer collector circuit is a few turns of wire wound over the built-in antenna (loopstick) of the broadcast receiver. The oscillator, Q7, has one crystal (Y2) wired to a selector switch, S2A. The other side of the switch, S2B, is connected to a crystal socket on the front panel, so that crystals may be plugged in for Y3, to do any of several jobs. The crystal socket is omitted from Fig. 7-25 for simplification.

When crystal Y2 is selected by S2 the injection frequency is 49.5 MHz. Beating with incoming signals, this produces intermediate frequencies between 500 and 1500 kHz for a signal range of 50 to 51 MHz. The broadcast receiver may not go down to 500 kHz unless its oscillator padder is fudged a bit, but the lowest frequency usable for voice in this country, 50.1 MHz, comes in at 600 kHz. If you don't care about tuning as high as 51.1 MHz the crystal frequency for Y2 can be modified to suit your desires.

Use of a crystal on 51.5 MHz for Y3 permits tuning of the first megahertz of the band in the reverse direction on the broadcast dial. The low end appears at 1500 kHz and 51 MHz is at the 500 kHz end. This provides a quick solution to image problems that may crop up locally, since image rejection is much better at the 1500-kHz end of the receiver's tuning range. Mobile services around 48 MHz ride through strongly as images when Y2 is used, but disappear when Y3 is switched in. A local MARS net just below the band edge takes over the receiver when Y2 is used, but gives no trouble with Y3. On the other hand, Y3 puts most of the band occupancy in the part of the dial where tuning rate is least favorable. Signals in the upper half of the band (if there are any) appear as images in the tuning range when Y3 is used. So it boils down to using whichever crystal does the best job under conditions of the moment.

Plugging other crystals in for Y3 provides coverage of any one-megahertz segment in or near the 50-MHz band. For ranges other than 50 to 51 MHz the rf circuits must be repeaked for optimum reception, but this is done readily enough by moving the core studs in L8, L9, and L10. Repeaking these lower in frequency gives 48 to 49 MHz with Y2. Running them out and switching in Y3 gives 52 to 53 MHz.

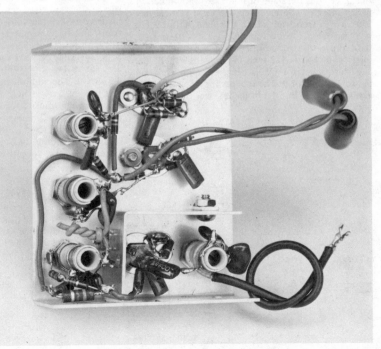

Fig. 7-26 — Rear view of the 50-MHz converter. The rf amplifier transistor socket and the input coil are isolated from the rest of the converter by an L-shaped shield, lower right. Leads at the top run to the crystal switch. Those with tips attached plug into jacks connected to the mixer collector winding on the loopstick. Coax at the lower right goes to S1A.

Receiver Construction

From Figs. 7-19 and 7-20 it will be seen that the broadcast receiver is mounted on the front panel of the transceiver, with the back of its case removed and the speaker facing forward. No specific dimensions can be given as there is an almost unlimited variety of small receivers available. We recommend that one of the better types be used; agc action and audio quality are considerably better in most 8-transistor models than in the very cheap 6-transistor ones.

Most pocket sets use pnp transistors, and so have opposite battery polarity to that required for the npn transistors in the transmitter and converter. This poses no real problem, as the receiver cases are plastic and there is no "ground" as such. We drilled holes near the four corners of the case for mounting. With some sets it may be necessary to install wire screening inside the speaker hole to prevent pickup of broadcast stations, but this was not needed with the receiver used here.

A vernier drive for the broadcast receiver dial can be made quite simply. A 1/4-inch panel bearing (E. F. Johnson 115-255) is used with a drive shaft of 1/4-inch tubing or rod. A small rubber grommet with a 1/8-inch hole is stretched to slip over the shaft in a position to bear against the edge of the small circular dial of the receiver. The mounting hole for the bearing can be filed slightly oval in shape, to permit adjusting the pressure of the grommet on the dial. One grommet will stand up for months of operation.

The converter chassis is a C-shaped piece of aluminum, cut to 2-1/2 X 5 inches and then bent over one inch top and bottom. The physical layout is not particularly critical, except that the holes for the three coils (left side of Fig. 7-26) should be 3/4 inch center to center. They are on a vertical line 3/8 inch in from the side of the plate, with L9 1/2 inch up from the bottom. Next above it is L10, with the oscillator coil, L13, at the top. The rf input coil, L8, is 1/2 inch in from the other side, and the socket for Q5 is centered approximately between L8 and L9. The sockets for Q6 and Q7 are along a vertical line 1-1/8 inches over from that of

the three coils. Q6 is midway between the center lines of L10 and L13 (3/8 inch up from L10), and Q7 is the same distance above the level of L13. The rf amplifier is isolated from the rest of the converter by means of an L-shaped shield mounted on spade lugs. The amplifier collector lead runs through this shield to L9. The converter assembly is held on the bottom plate by two self-tapping screws.

The antenna coupling winding, L7, is made from the inner conductor of the RG-174/U coax used for the lead to S1A. Strip the braid back about two inches and leave the polyethylene intact except for about 1/8 inch at the end, for soldering to the series capacitor. Wrap the insulated conductor around the winding in the same direction as the bottom turns of L8, and solder the braid and one side of the series capacitor to a ground lug under the coil mounting. Leave some surplus length in the coax, so that the converter can be removed with the connection to S1A left intact for minor adjustments.

The common positive supply lead and the mixer collector lead are fitted with solderless tip plugs (E. F. Johnson 105-300) which fit into matching jacks (105-800), to permit easy disconnecting for converter removal. (This maker's tiny Rib-Loc plugs and jacks would be fine here.) The jacks are soldered to a tie-point strip visible in Fig. 7-20, just adjacent to the top of the broadcast receiver. The oscillator base and collector leads running to S2A and S2B are made just long enough to reach the terminals of the switch, and must be unsoldered to remove the converter.

PACKAGING AND POWER

Presumably the transceiver could be fitted into some standard-size case, but the metal work involved in making your own is not extensive. The front and back panels are 4-3/4 X 6 inches, with 3/8 inch folded over on all sides. Metal size before bending: 5-1/2 X 6-3/4 inches. Sheets for the sides are cut 5-1/2 X 9-3/4 inches, and bent up to 4-3/4 X 9. Top and bottom plates are 6 X 9 inches. Self-tapping screws hold the case together. Access holes for the transmitter and receiver adjustments, and holes for the microphone jack, transmitter crystal, and receiver audio gain control should be located according to the parts used. Jacks for metering in the negative lead, and for internal-

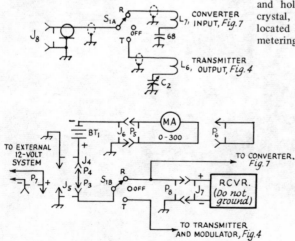

Fig. 7-27 — Switching and power circuits for the transceiver.

BT1 — 7 or 8 "D" cells in series.

J4, J5, J6 — Phono jack.

J7 — Polarized power plug on receiver battery lead (part of broadcast receiver).

J8 — Coaxial socket, BNC type.

P3, P4, P5, P6, P7 — Phono plug.

P8 — Similar to J7, but polarity reversed. Can be removed from top of 9-volt transistor radio battery.

S1 — 2-pole 3-position wafer switch, miniature type.

external power selection (see Fig. 7-27) can be mounted wherever convenient on the rear wall.

The send-receive switch is a wafer type with horizontal lever action, though any small 3-position 2-pole rf switch will do. The crystal switch is an ordinary slide type. Antenna leads are small-size coax (RG-174/U) throughout.

The seven or eight "D" cells are wired in series with strips of metal or stiff wire. They are in layers, wrapped with electrical tape to hold them in place, and clamped in a wrap-around metal strip that is screwed to the bottom plate.

The cells shown are inexpensive, and stand up very well. Transistors have a great advantage over tubes in overall efficiency, and even smaller batteries can be used if light weight is the primary consideration. Mercury, alkaline, and nickle-cadmium cells are more uniform and longer-lived than ordinary "D" cells, but because of the intermittent nature of the load, and their recuperative powers, the cheaper cells make a logical choice for most users.* Another transistor "plus" is that, with no critical filament temperature to be maintained, the efficiency of the transceiver remains constant over a wide range of battery voltage. Output drops off with fading voltage, of course, but the quality of the signal holds up until the batteries are almost dead.

The transceiver may be run from a car battery or other external power source by removing the jumper (P3 and P4, Fig. 7-27) and plugging P7 into J5. A cigarette lighter plug and cable to P7 is handy for operation from a car battery. The car's electrical system must be negative-ground, the U.S. standard. In case you're worried about running 12 volts on a 9-volt transistor radio, this has been tried with several different types with no apparent damage resulting. If you still want protection, it's a simple matter to install a 9-volt Zener regulator on the receiver line.

Adjustment and Use

Adjustment of the transmitter was described earlier. Monitoring of the total drain can be done with a milliammeter plugged into J6, Fig. 7-27. If the meter is removed a phono plug with its contacts shorted (P6) is plugged into J6. A 150-mA lamp is a must for a dummy load, used as described earlier.

The tuned circuits of the transmitter and converter are broad enough so that repeaking is not necessary in the course of normal use between 50 and 51 MHz, except for the retouching of C1 in the transmitter. With the twisted-wire coupling capacitor, C4, made as described, receiver response is nearly flat from 50 to 51 MHz.

As with most receivers using bipolar transistors, it is important to use a properly tuned and matched antenna system, to avoid overloading problems from out-of-band signals. A well-matched 50-MHz beam accomplishes this ordinarily, and something like our 50-MHz portable job (see Chapter 9) is highly recommended. When a beam

* A review of the various types of batteries suitable for use with transistor gear is given in *QST* for September, 1967.

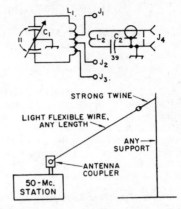

Fig. 7-28 — Circuit of the antenna coupler and its application in feeding a long wire in portable work. Tip jacks J1 and J2 may be used for a balanced-line system. Any of the three jacks may be used for random-length long wires, merely by checking for best reception. Peak C1 for maximum signal on receiving. Gain and directivity of the long wire will depend on length and slope.

C1 — 11-pF per section butterfly variable (Johnson 160-211 or 11MB11).
C2 — Fixed ceramic capacitor, 39 to 68 pF. Check with variable temporarily, if possible.
L1 — 18 turns No. 24, 1/2-inch diameter, 32 tpi. Tap at 5 turns from each end and 1-1/2 turns from one end (B&W No. 3004).
L3 — 2 turns insulated hookup wire around center of L1.
J1, J2, J3 — Tip jack.
J4 — BNC cable fitting. Connect J4 and rotor of C1 with copper strip.

cannot be used, various "long wires" are effective, if properly tuned and matched to the transceiver input. Wire antennas and the little plastic-case antenna coupler of Fig. 7-28 will be found very superior to the collapsible whip type of antenna so often used with hand-carried equipment. Tilted wires respond to various polarizations, and they have some gain and directivity.

Various wire lengths can be plugged into the tip jacks connected to taps on L1. A balanced line, or even an improvised V or rhombic, can be plugged into J1 and J2. Anything will work, but usually the longer the better. Tune in a signal on the receiver and peak the coupler for maximum signal strength.

The coupler can be connected directly to the BNC fitting on the transceiver, or a length of coax can be used. The support for the far end of the wire can be a fire tower, tree, building, or whatever happens to be handy. If there is room to maneuver, walk around (maypole fashion) until maximum signal is found. Contacts have been made at distances up to 125 miles on several occasions employing this haywire but effective approach.

The above information is a condensation of a two-part *QST* article, "50-Mc. Transistor Transceiver, Mark II," February and March, 1967.

SELF-CONTAINED PORTABLE FOR 144 MHz

Originally described by DeMaw as "The Connecticut Bond Box," in August, 1968, *QST*, the 2-meter transceiver of Fig. 7-29 represents the simple approach to 2-meter portable gear as well as anything before or since. It can be operated from its own D cells, from a car battery, or from an ac-operated 12-volt supply. It has a 3-transistor transmitter, a superregenerative receiver with isolating rf amplifier stage, and an audio module that serves both portions of the station. Construction is the circuit-board type, and templates for board layout work are available from ARRL, for 25 cents and a stamped addressed envelope.

Receiver Section

A JFET grounded-gate rf amplifier provides some isolation for the IGFET superregenerative detector. The insulated-wire "gimmick" capacitor, C19, in Fig. 7-31, provides light adjustable coupling between the rf amplifier and the detector. Quench-frequency voltage is provided by R14C26, in the source lead of the detector. The output of the detector passes through a quench filter consisting of C24, C25, RFC5, and C27. L9 isolates the af signal from the B+ line. Drain voltage is varied by R15, for regeneration control. R16 is the audio gain control.

When soldering the IGFET, Q5, into the circuit, be sure to connect a clip lead between the tip of the soldering iron and a good earth ground. This

Fig. 7-29 — The 2-meter transceiver is housed in a legal-bond box. A dial-calibration chart for the receiver is pasted on the inside of the lid. Two plastic cable clamps serve as holders for the two-section 1/4-wavelength whip antenna (inside lid) when the unit is not in use. The antenna is held together at the center by a 1/4-inch-diameter threaded coupling.

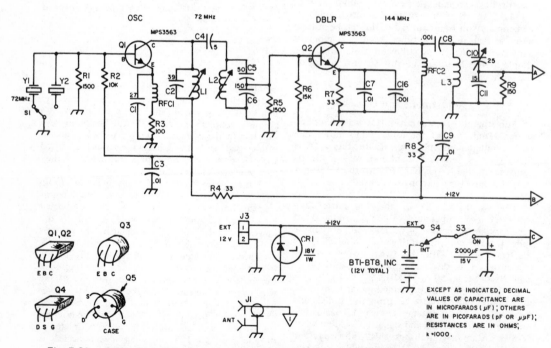

Fig. 7-31 — Schematic of the 2-meter transceiver. Fixer-value capacitors are disk ceramic except those with polarity marking, which are electrolytic. Resistors are 1/2-watt composition. Component numbering is for identification of parts on the circuit-board templates. Significant parts are listed below in the usual manner.

AR1 — 200-milliwatt audio module (Round Hill Associates Model AA0100*).

BT1-BT8, incl. —Eight size-D flashlight cells, series connected and mounted inside box by means of four Keystone No. 176 dual-battery clips.

C10, C12 — 5 to 25-pF ceramic trimmer, Erie 822-CN or equiv. (Midget 3- to 30-pF mica trimmer also suitable.)

C15 — 8- to 50-pF ceramic trimmer, Erie 822-AN or equiv. (Midget 8- to 60-pF mica trimmer also suitable.)

C19 — 3 turns insulated wire, wrapped around low end of L8.

C20 — 15-pF subminiature variable (E. F. Johnson 160-107).

C22 — 5-pF min. variable (Hammarlund MAPC-15B, all but one rotor and one stator plate removed).

CR1 — 18-volt 1-watt Zener diode (used for transient protection during mobile operation).

J1 — SO-239 coax fitting (chassis mount).

J2, J3 — Two-terminal single-contact audio connector (Amphenol 75PC1M or similar.

L1, L2 — 3 turns No. 22 enam. wire spaced to occupy 1/2 inch on 1/4-inch-dia ceramic slug-tuned form (J. W. Miller 4500-4*).

L3 — 4 turns No. 20 bare wire, 1/2 inch long, 5/16-inch inside diameter.

L4 — 6 turns No. 20 bare wire, 1/2 inch long, 5/16-inch ID.

L5 — Same as L3.

L6 — 8 turns No. 20 bare wire, 1 inch long, 5/16-inch ID. Tap 5 turns from source lead of Q4.

L7 — 5 turns No. 22 enam. wire, closewound on 1/4-inch dia ceramic slug-tuned form (J. W. Miller 4500-4).

L8 — 4 turns No. 10 bare copper wire, 1 inch long, 3/8-inch ID. (The tap shown is not a physical one; see description of C19.

L9 — Total primary winding of 500-ohm ct transistor output transformer. 8-ohm secondary winding not used. (Argonne AR-164 or similar.)

R15-R17, incl. — 100,000-ohm audio-taper carbon control.

RFC1 — Miniature 50-μH choke (Millen 34300-50*).

RFC2-RFC4, incl. — Miniature 2.7-μH rf choke (Millen 34300-2.7).

RFC5 — Subminiature 10-mH rf choke (J. W. Miller 73F102AF).

RFC5 — Subminiature 10-mH rf choke (J. W. Miller 73F102AF).

S1, S4 — Spdt slide switch.

S2 — 4-pole 2-position phenolic single-section rotary wafer switch (Mallory 3142J).

S3 — Spst slide switch.

Y1, Y2 — 72-MHz overtone crystal (International Crystal Co. in HC-6/U holder.*).

* Round Hill Assoc., Inc., 434 Sixth Ave., New York, N.Y. 10011

*J. W. Miller CO., 19070 Reyes Ave., Compton, CA 90221.

* International Crystal Co., 10 N. Lee St., Okla. City, OK 73102.

* James Millen Mfg. Co., 150 Exchange St., Malden, MA 02148.

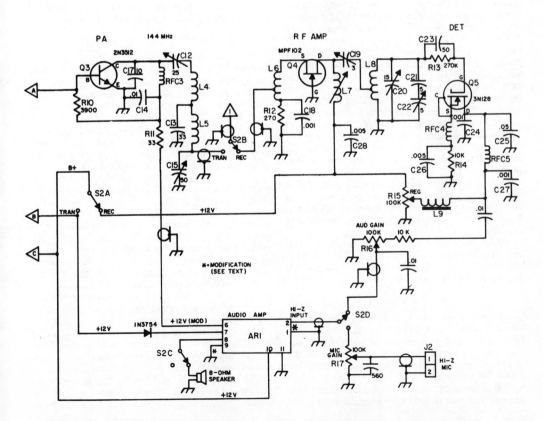

Fig. 7-30 — Top-chassis layout of the transceiver. The receiver section is at the left. Controls for regeneration and modulation are in the foreground near the center of the chassis. The audio module is at the lower right, and the transmitter board is near the panel, directly under the loudspeaker. The home-made heat sinks are visible at the left end of the audio board.

will help prevent damage to the gate of the 3N128 should static charges be present. Also, *do not handle* the leads of Q5. The leads should be removed from their shorting collar by means of a wooden toothpick. Once Q5 is soldered in place, it should be quite safe from static-charge damage.

The transmitter portion has a 72-MHz crystal oscillator, Q1, in which the C1 and the internal capacitance of the transistor control the feedback. Bandpass coupling and a capacitive divider provide optimum coupling at the intended frequency and impedance matching, for minimum harmonics in the drive to the doubler, Q2. The oscillator and doubler transistors are inexpensive Motorola types, but other vhf transistors should be usable. The RCA 2N3512 is a low-cost type that works well, and may be easier to stabilize than higher beta transistors might be. A heat sink is recommended for Q3. (Wakefield Engineering NF205 used.)

Another capacitive divider, C10C11, matches the output of the doubler to the base of the amplifier, Q3, with C10 tuning the circuit. The amplifier is biased for Class AB conditions, for maximum low-drive output. The combination *L* and pi network in the amplifier collector circuit provides optimum harmonic rejection. Tuning is done by C12, with C15 serving as the loading capacitor.

Power leads are decoupled by means of C3, C9, and C14, in combination with R4, R8, and R11. The three 33-ohm resistors also serve as current-limiting devices for the transistors.

Audio Section

The audio unit, AR1, is a ready-made import assembly with two input impedances, 50 ohms and 100k ohms, and two output impedances, 8 and 500 ohms, the latter used for modulation of the amplifier collector voltage. The audio assembly has a 200-mW rating at 9 volts, but this can be raised to 300 or more by using 12 volts, and adding heat sinks to the two output transistors. Several audio

assemblies of this general type are available, and numerous modifications of them have been shown in *QST* articles of this type, including the 50-MHz transceiver immediately preceding this text.

Because the module is designed for a positive-ground bus (pnp transistors are used), it is necessary to "float" the entire assembly above chassis ground to prevent short-circuiting the power supply. Information on the mounting techniques and some modifications to the board is given later.

Building the Transceiver

The packaging of this circuit can be up to the builder. In this instance a standard legal-bond box was chosen. It measures 5 X 6 X 11-1/2 inches.

The chassis and panel are made from 16-gauge aluminum sheeting. The chassis measures 11-1/4 X 4 X 1 inch. The panel is 11-1/4 X 4-3/4 inches. After the panel holes are drilled, a coating of zinc chromate should be sprayed on it. Then, after thorough drying, a coat of spray-can enamel or lacquer can be added for the final touch.

The receiver and transmitter are built on etched-circuit boards, but point-to-point wiring could be used if done neatly and with short connections. AR1 is insulated from the main chassis to prevent short-circuiting the power supply. It has a plus-ground bus; the rest of the transceiver circuit uses a negative ground. A piece of cardboard is mounted between the circuit board and the chassis to prevent accidental contact between AR1 and the chassis. AR1 is bolted to the chassis at four points. The four mounting holes in the main chassis contain small rubber grommets, each serving as an insulator. Terminals 1 and 9 of the audio board are common to its plus-ground bus. These terminals must be disconnected from the ground bus by removing the thin copper connecting strip which joins the circuits.

To operate AR1 at 12 volts it is necessary to add heat sinks to the two transistors nearest the output transformer. The sinks can be made from

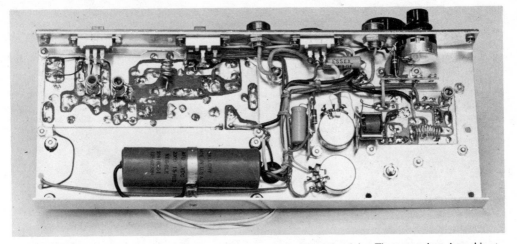

Fig. 7-32 — Bottom view of the chassis. The receiver board is at the right. The transmitter board is at the upper left. A 2000-μF 15-volt electrolytic is mounted near the rear lip of the chassis.

pieces of thin brass, copper, or aluminum. They are 1-1/2 inches long, formed by warping the stock around a drill bit which is slightly smaller in diameter than the body of the transistor.

All interconnecting rf leads are made with subminiature coax cable, RG-174/U (Belden 8216). Shielded audio cable should be used for all af wiring which is more than a couple of inches in length. A bargain-house import is used for the receiver tuning dial. No slippage was noted with the 2-inch-diameter model used here. The next smaller model is not recommended because it may not handle the torque of the tuning capacitor. A 2-1/2-inch-diameter loudspeaker is used. Its protective grille can be made from perforated aluminum.

Two 3-inch-long brass angle brackets, each with 3/4-inch sides, mount the panel-chassis assembly inside the box. Two 6-32 hex nuts are soldered to the bottom side of each bracket, directly under No. 10 access holes. Four 6-32 X 3/8-inch screws hold the transceiver in place. The brackets are attached to the sides of the box with 4-40 hardware.

Tune Up and Use

The receiver should be tested first. With an antenna connected to J1, apply operating voltage and adjust R15 until a rushing noise is heard in the speaker. Do not advance R15 beyond this point as the sensitivity of the receiver will decrease. Next,

tune in a weak signal on the air or from a signal generator and tune L7 for a peak response. Chances are that when the peak is reached, the detector will stop oscillating. If this happens, advance R15 until the hiss returns. If it does not, detune L7 slightly until a compromise is reached (L7 usually loads the detector somewhat when it is tuned to the operating frequency). Alternatively, a 1000-ohm swamping resistor can be connected across L7 to reduce its effect on the detector. Trimmer C20 is used to set the tuning range of C22. The turns of L8 can be spread or compressed for additional frequency adjustment.

A No. 49 pilot lamp makes a suitable dummy load for visual tune-up of the transmitter, though somewhat reactive at 144 MHz. First, determine

Fig. 7-33 — Eight size-D cells are series connected to provide 12 volts. They are mounted in Keystone holders on the back wall of the bond box. The 1/4-inch-diameter hole in the front of the cabinet (upper right of photo) permits final calibration of the receiver (C20) after the installation is completed. The hole is opposite the shaft of C20.

that the oscillator, Q1, is operating by coupling a wavemeter (or grid-dip meter in the diode-detector position) to L1 and look for an indication of output. Adjust the slug in L1 for maximum output, then turn the transmitter on and off a few times to make sure the crystal always kicks in. If not, detune L1 slightly toward the high-frequency side of resonance until the oscillator does start each time. Next, peak L2, C10, C12, and C15 for maximum indication on the bulb. There will be some interaction between the circuits, so the foregoing steps should be repeated a few times to assure maximum output. Final adjustments should be made with the antenna connected, and with an SWR indicator in the line.

A sensitive SWR indicator is needed at this power level. One of the Monimatch indicators with a 4-inch-or-longer line (air-dielectric element type) can provide full-scale readings if a 100-μA meter is installed. Alternatively, see *QST*, August, 1967, for a low-power bridge. Also, see the "Monimatch Mark II," *QST*, February, 1957.

Chapter 8

Antennas and Feed Systems

Every radio station since the first one has had an antenna, but what a bewildering array these skywires represent! Antenna experimentation has long been a favorite pursuit for the amateur and for good reason. Probably by no other effort can the average ham so improve his results, at so little cost, as by putting up a better antenna. But what is a better antenna? Though numerous books have been published on every aspect of antenna design and talk about beams is heard wherever hams gather, there is probably more misinformation about antennas than about any other subject in amateur radio.

In the following pages we will attempt to sort the wheat from the chaff, but the reader is cautioned not to look for simple all-purpose answers. There is no one antenna or feed system that "has everything." Nowhere are better antennas more needed than on the vhf scene, but making an intelligent choice involves more than a perusal of performance figures found in antenna manufacturers' catalogs.

As in our equipment chapters, we will discuss principles first, presenting information that will be helpful whether the reader intends to build an antenna or buy one ready made. This will be followed by practical examples, for the fellow who wants to build his own arrays.

OBJECTIVES

Choice of a vhf antenna system begins with some decisions about the type of work we want to do best, since there is no antenna that does all things well. Does highest possible gain overrule other considerations? Is broad frequency response important? Can we live with a sharp beam pattern, or would something broader and less critical in aiming serve our needs better? How about omni-directional coverage? Can we go all-out for size, or must there be some compromise with what simple mounts and inexpensive rotators will handle? What is the nature of nearby terrain? Are there trees, wires, and buildings to be cleared? Is there a neighbor problem? Let's think about these and other points a bit before we get down to how-to-build-it details.

About Gain

Sad to relate though it may be, we should recognize the fact that antenna gain figures are often on the optimistic side. Even when given accurately, and with the best intentions, gain information may be in terms confusing to the average reader. True measurement of gain is difficult; few amateurs can do it accurately. On-the-air evaluation is also far from simple. It is entirely possible to get several contradictory observations in as many tries, and usually only long-term comparisons will show if a new antenna is doing what we wanted it to do. What really counts is whether or not an antenna provides a stronger and more consistent signal at distant points than was possible before. If a new installation does not yield this result, impressive numbers have little meaning.

There is no magic about antenna gain. It is achieved only by taking radiation from some portions of the antenna's field where it may serve no useful purpose, and putting it into areas where it will do some good. A logical way of expressing antenna gain, therefore, is to compare the field

strength in the favored direction with that of an antenna that would radiate equally in all directions. Such an antenna exists in theory only, since it would have to be a point source. Called an *isotropic radiator*, it has a special appeal for the man who would have his antenna look good on paper. If it has a gain of 1, a half-wave dipole has a gain of 2.14 dB. "Gain over isotropic" is a handy and legitimate way of stating antenna performance, and it is coming into more general use in antenna literature. But remember that figures so quoted are more than 2 dB higher than those for the more familiar half-wave dipole comparison. Unless otherwise stated, gains mentioned in this text are with respect to a half-wave dipole, a comparison we can measure.

Frequency Response

Antenna gain is often achieved at the expense of frequency coverage, especially in arrays having

TRANSMISSION-
LINE LOSS MAY NULLIFY
HEIGHT GAIN

usually not obtained with the same antenna adjustment that gives maximum forward gain, however. It is another of those factors that you obtain in trade for something else. Usually the choice is between highest gain and optimum front-to-back ratio.

Omnidirectional Coverage

There are several ways of building up gain without losing a circular pattern in the horizontal plane. Compression of the vertical angle is involved here. Since radiation at angles other than those close to the horizon ordinarily does the vhf man little good, trading off the high-angle power loss for gain along the ground looks almost like something for nothing. Omnidirectional antennas have many uses, and we'll be describing practical systems later on, but they, too, have their drawbacks. Gain achieved without modifying both horizontal and vertical patterns is limited to a few decibels, even when high and somewhat cumbersome stacks are involved. More important to the man in the midst of high vhf activity concentration, interference problems multiply as omnidirectional gain is built up. Noise problems increase, and heterodynes and cross-talk seem to grow as if by magic.

Height Gain vs. Line Loss

In nearly every instance, the higher the vhf antenna the better. Clearing obstructions in the immediate vicinity is of utmost importance. Wires, trees, and buildings in the line of fire can ruin the antenna pattern, absorb power, and aggravate TVI and other interference problems. Putting the vhf antenna up high enough so that its main radiation pattern is completely above nearby TV antennas may be one of the best TVI-prevention measures that can be taken.

As may be seen from the height-gain information of Chapter 2, increased height may do as much for you as putting up a much larger antenna at rooftop height. But how you get the added height is important. Particularly at 144 MHz and higher, the added transmission-line loss may be considerable. An antenna installed at the top of a hill nearby may be a useful approach, but it probably will entail some special attention to feed methods.

And so it goes. Working with antennas is always interesting and often rewarding, but the important thing is to remember that there is more to it than a choice that promises the most decibels for the least dollars.

many parasitic elements. As will be shown later, the gain of even a small antenna of this kind is available over only a narrow frequency range, whereas an array of the same stated gain built with more driven elements may work well over all or most of a vhf band. This point is of little concern to the 2-meter DX enthusiast who is interested only in the first few hundred kHz at the low end of the band, but to the fellow who wants to work effectively over a wide frequency range it could be the deciding factor in a choice between two very different antenna systems having the same advertised gain. The broad-band array will be larger and perhaps somewhat more difficult to handle and install, but with several times the bandwidth it may be a better investment, depending on one's operating habits.

Pattern Shape

An antenna with very high gain inevitably has a main lobe shaped like a cigar or a baseball bat. This can be both good and bad. In areas of high vhf activity, a narrow antenna pattern is fine, if it helps to hold down the level of some of the local signals you have to work through. It may be helpful in nulling out man-made noise, if the sources of such noise lie mainly in one direction. On the other side of the ledger, a very narrow main lobe imposes stiff requirements on the rotator and direction-indicating devices, and it may keep you from hearing some choice DX that pops up a little off your line of fire. The local rag-chewer won't get his money's worth from really sharp beams.

Front-to-back ratio is allied to sharpness of pattern, but antennas can be built and adjusted to have high rejection off the back and still retain a broad frontal lobe. High front-to-back ratio is

TYPES OF VHF ANTENNAS

The simplest antenna commonly used in vhf work consists of a single driven element. It may be called a dipole, a whip, a halo, or some more fancy name. It may be horizontal, vertical, or something in between. It always has some gain over that theoretical isotropic antenna we spoke of earlier, but never very much. It is handy for getting on the air quickly and unobtrusively, but it will never give

you a very large sphere of influence, unless perchance you live on the top of the highest mountain in your state — and maybe not even then. We'll go into dipole design later.

To build up antenna gain we do various things with dipoles. We may make several, hang them in a curtain arrangement, and feed them all in phase. This is called a *collinear* array. We'll have many practical examples in Chapter 9. Or we may line up one or more elements in the same plane with the dipole, in front or in back of it, but not connected to the feedline. These are called *parasitic* elements. They may be *directors* (one or more, shorter than the driven element, and placed ahead of it) or *reflectors* (usually only one, longer) placed in back. Such an antenna is called a Yagi, in honor of its Japanese co-developer.

Both systems have their uses in vhf communication. In either, gain is related to size. To double the gain of a collinear array (increase it by 3 dB) we must use twice as many elements, in a frontal area roughly twice as large. The size-gain relationship in a Yagi is more complex, involving length as well as number of elements, but a significant improvement always means a much larger antenna. To double the Yagi gain we must nearly double the number of elements, and more than double the length. Approximately 3 dB gain can be achieved by stacking two similar antennas side by side or one above the other, and feeding them in phase. The spacing for optimum gain increases with the length of the Yagi antenna. Pairs of antennas can be stacked, as can be pairs of pairs, and so on, but the size-doubling requirement for increasing the gain by 3 dB makes it obvious that increasing-gain projects reach the point of diminishing returns quite quickly.

YAGI ANTENNA DESIGN

Though it is possible to make a 2-element parasitic array bidirectional by adjustment of its element lengths or spacings, the objective in making a Yagi is usually a pattern that is essentially unidirectional. Whether the parasitic element operates as a reflector or a director is determined by the relative phase of the currents in the driven and parasitic elements. With element spacings commonly used (1/4 wavelength or less) the current in the parasitic element will be the right phase to make it act as a reflector when it is tuned to the inductive or low-frequency side of resonance. In other words, it will be longer than the driven element. To act as a director, the element must be tuned to the high-frequency side of resonance, by making it somewhat shorter than the driven element.

Element Lengths and Spacings

The maximum gain that is theoretically possible with a 2-element parasitic array is shown in Fig. 8-1. The gain obtainable at various director and reflector spacings is also given. It is assumed that the length of the parasitic element is adjusted for each change of spacing, as it must be if it is to deliver maximum gain. The curves of Fig. 8-1 are for 2-element antennas only, and results in practice may not work out exactly as shown. To see why we look at Fig. 8-2, which shows the radiation resistance at the center of the driven element when the parasitic element is adjusted for the conditions of Fig. 8-1. Note that the radiation resistance goes very low at close element spacings.

With the low feed impedance of the close-spaced array, the rf current is very high, so ohmic losses go up. The bandwidth of the system goes down, and the difficulty of feeding the antenna properly rises. The result is that, for practical purposes, and especially with more than one parasitic element, some modification of these theoretically optimum spacings is necessary for best overall results. Thus we find the "wide-spaced" array in common use where three or more elements are involved.

Exact analysis of what happens in a Yagi antenna is difficult if not impossible, and it would serve little use here since optimum arrangements have been worked out experimentally by many workers. There are many ways to make a good Yagi, particularly a long one. Numerous combinations of element lengths and spacings give almost identical results. You can have an interesting time of it proving this for yourself, if you are experimentally inclined. If you aren't you can make a vhf array by following the tables given herewith, and be assured of good results, provided you have a few simple instruments to check system performance.

In practical terms, the element lengths and spacings in a Yagi array, even a long one, are by no means so critical as some harried workers would have you believe. If you can match the antenna to its transmission line and transfer power to it efficiently, it will perform well, even if element lengths vary by as much as 1 percent and element spacings by 5 percent from the recommended values. The reflector length is more tolerant on the long side and the director lengths on the short side of the table values. A small error in these directions increases the antenna's bandwidth with only a very minor effect on gain. Error in the opposite directions can ruin Yagi performance much more quickly. This is the same as saying that frequency response of a Yagi is broader on the low side than on the high side of resonance, a fact that is well to bear in mind in deciding on an optimum frequency for the array.

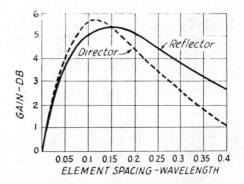

Fig. 8-1 — The maximum possible gain obtainable with a parasitic element over a half-wave antenna alone, assuming that the parasitic element tuning is adjusted for greatest gain at each spacing.

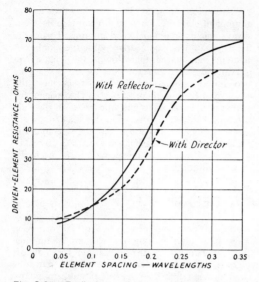

Fig. 8-2 — Radiation resistance at center of driven element as a function of element spacing, when the parasitic element is adjusted for the gains given in Fig. 8-1.

Recommended dimensions given later take this into account, but remember, if you want more bandwidth make the reflector longer and the directors shorter. If for some reason you want to try close parasitic-element spacing, make the director nearest the driven element *longer* and the reflector *shorter* than the recommended values, by 1 to 2 percent, depending on the closeness of the spacing. This is in line with the point made above that frequency response sharpens with closer spacing.

There is little point in pursuing the matter further, as these points are covered in interesting detail in all modern editions of the *ARRL Antenna Book*. A study of that manual, and some of the references it cites, is recommended to the experimentally inclined amateur.

Yagis — Short and Long

Element spacing of 0.15 to 0.2 wavelength is recommended for small Yagis (up to 4 elements) commonly used in 50-MHz work. With convenient tubing and boom sizes the following figures apply for all vhf parasitic arrays:

$$Driven\ Element\ Length,\ Inches = \frac{5600}{Freq\ (MHz)}$$
$$(1)$$

Reflector – 5 percent longer
Director – 5 percent shorter
Second Director – 6 percent shorter

Fig. 8-3 — Length factor for the range of conductor diameters used in practice. This curve applies to either quarter-wave (grounded or ground-plane antennas) or half-wave antennas.

A perceptible increase in gain can be had by spacing the second director 0.25 wavelength from the first, though the difference may not be worth the extra boom length in some instances.

Uniform element spacing can be continued for more elements, but some improvement in gain can be achieved by going to graduated spacing. Here each successive director is spaced somewhat greater than the previous one, until a spacing of about 0.4 wavelength is reached, after which all directors are spaced this much. A good rule of thumb for medium and long Yagis is:

Dipole to D1 – 0.15 wavelength (λ)
D1 to D2 – 0.18 λ
D2 to D3 – 0.25 λ
D3 to D4 – 0.35 to 0.42. All directors beyond D4, to be the same spacing.
Dipole to Reflector - 0.2　　　　　　　(2)

The 5-percent-longer, 5-percent-shorter rule applies. For slightly more bandwidth, start with D1 at 4 percent shorter than the driven element and take off 0.5 percent for each succeeding director. Lengths of individual elements are sufficiently tolerant that you can change by 0.5 percent one way or the other and find only a barely measurable difference in gain. A listener at the other end of a communications circuit would not know that anything had happened. Even at 432 MHz, where half-wave elements are only about a foot long, it is possible to change *all* elements by as much as 1/16 inch without much effect, if the matching system is readjusted after the change is made.

Element Diameter

Information given in (1) applies with tubing sizes commonly used in vhf antennas. Elements 1/2 to 1 inch in diameter are customarily used at 50 MHz. For 144 MHz, 1/8 to 3/8 inch is common.

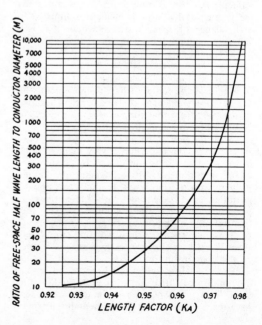

Fig. 8-4 — Design information for Yagi antennas. Curve A shows the optimum boom length in wavelengths for any number of elements. Curve B shows the maximum gain that can be expected when the design information of Curve A is used.

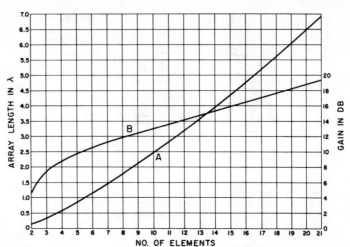

For 220 and 420 MHz, we may go as small as 1/16 inch, and anything larger than 1/4 inch is seldom used. There may be exceptions however, and appreciable changes in element lengths must be made for large variations from the above practice.

The larger the element diameter the broader the frequency response, so variations on the large side may not be too critical, but when elements much smaller than standard practice are involved it is well to check the antenna performance carefully. Some idea of the practical extent to which small element diameter can affect element length can be seen in a 50-MHz portable beam described in Chapter 9. In planning construction of antennas having unusual length/diameter ratios the information of Fig. 8-3 can be used to good advantage. Here the vertical scale is the free-space half wavelength divided by the conductor diameter. The horizontal is the percentage of a free-space half wavelength that should be used for a driven element.

The standard-practice range of element sizes mentioned above represents only about 1 percent change in element length, from lowest to highest K factor. The 50-MHz portable array mentioned above has a factor of nearly 2000, if the diameter near the ends of the telescoping elements is used.

The elements in this array had to be extended 6 inches beyond the usual lengths before this array worked properly. This is an increase even greater than that indicated by the graph of Fig. 8-3.

Gain and Size in Yagi Arrays

As mentioned earlier, there is an optimum boom length for a given number of elements in a Yagi array. This is obtained from Fig. 8-4, curve A. Note that a 4-element array is about a half wavelength long. A 6-element beam of optimum length is *twice* as long, and an 8-element array should be *four times* as long as one with 4 elements.

What these combinations should yield in gain is given by curve B. Our 4-element Yagi is capable of just under 9 dB. The 6-element goes over 10, and the 8-element to about 12. There is no limit to the gain that can be achieved with longer booms of practical length, as has been demonstrated by experimenters willing to build Yagis 50 feet or more in length for 144 MHz, but after the first 13 to 15 elements it becomes a rather dubious business.

Optimum element placement is given in Table 8-I. As may be seen from these figures, this is not

TABLE 8-I

Optimum Element Spacings for Multielement Yagi Arrays. DE — driven element; R — reflector; D — director.

No. Elements	R-DE	DE-D1	D1-D2	D2-D3	D3-D4	D4-D5	D5-D6
2	0.15λ-0.2λ						
2		0.07λ-0.11λ					
3	0.16 -0.23	0.16 -0.19					
4	0.18 -0.22	0.13 -0.17	0.14λ-0.18λ				
5	0.18 -0.22	0.14 -0.17		0.17λ-0.23λ			
6	0.16 -0.20	0.14 -0.17	0.16 -0.25	0.22 -0.30	0.25λ-0.32λ		
8	0.16 -0.20	0.14 -0.16	0.18 -0.25	0.25 -0.35	0.27 -0.32	0.27λ-0.33λ	0.30λ-0.40λ
8 to N	0.16 -0.20	0.14 -0.16	0.18 -0.25	0.25 -0.35	0.27 -0.32	0.27 -0.33	0.35 -0.42

N = any number; director spacings beyond D6 should be 0.35-0.42λ.

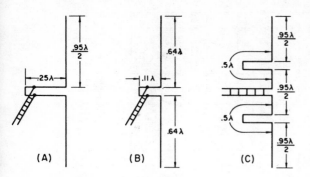

(A) **(B)** **(C)**

Fig. 8-5 — Vertical collinear antennas for vhf use. Antennas A and B use the same total length of wire, A being arranged as two half-waves in phase, and B as an "extended double-Zepp." Antenna C is three half-wave elements in phase. All give some gain over a single half-wave radiator, without directivity in the horizontal plane.

particularly critical. These graphs and table and the information of (1) are all one needs to design effective Yagi arrays.

Collinear Arrays

The collinear (elements along a common line) is one of the oldest forms of directional arrays. The "Two Half-Waves in Phase," the "Extended Double-Zepp," and other simple collinears are almost as old as short-wave radio. They and their larger multielement relatives that grow on some of our best vhf antenna farms are still among the most useful. Because the collinear is made up of many driven elements, with only reflectors for parasitic elements, it is much more frequency-tolerant than a Yagi of the same gain. A 2-meter collinear can be cut and matched for the middle of the band and it will work over the entire four megahertz with only moderate variation in gain.

Properly designed, a collinear system is easy to feed with common types of transmission line. It can be strung together with sticks and wire, hauled up into a tree, and rotated by pulling on ropes — and it will work. One of the first and most renowned vhf beams ever built was handled in just that way. See Chapter 1. This is not to infer that

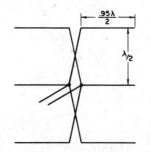

Fig. 8-6 — Bidirectional collinear array using 6 half-wave elements in phase. Parasitic reflectors or a screen may be placed in back of the driven elements for increased gain and unidirectional pattern.

the collinear is useful mainly where ham haywire is the order of the day. Care in design and construction pays off in performance, but the collinear is tolerant of amateur methods; considerably more so than the Yagi.

Nondirectional Collinears

Simple vertical collinears like those of Fig. 8-5 provide some gain over a vertical half-wave dipole, without introducing directivity in the horizontal plane. At A we have two half-waves in phase, fed by means of a folded half wavelength at the center. A balanced transmission line is shown, but coax and a balun could be used equally well. Slightly increased gain and lowered radiation angle result from lengthening the radiating portions and shortening the stub, as in the extended double-Zepp, B. The total wire length is the same: 3 half-wavelengths. Three or more half-wave vertical elements, kept in phase by means of quarter-wave stubs, C, is another common omnidirectional vertical antenna.

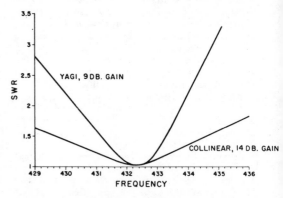

Fig. 8-7 — Comparison of the frequency responses of a small Yagi antenna and a large collinear array. A Yagi of comparable gain would have a still sharper frequency response.

Directional Arrays

Larger arrays with 4, 6, 8, or more half-wave elements stacked side-by-side and one above the other are what most vhf men think of when they hear the term, "collinear." These may be driven elements only, as in Fig. 8-6, wherein a bidirectional pattern is obtained, or reflectors may be added for unidirectional characteristics, as in several examples shown in Chapter 9. Directors can be added, but this is seldom done. Large arrays with directors are better arranged and fed as combinations of Yagi bays, rather than as collinears.

Reflectors in a collinear array are usually parasitic in nature, but a reflecting metal plane can be used. This can be of sheet metal, though more often wire mesh is used, in the interest of decreased wind resistance. Spines of wire or small tubing are also usable, so long as the spacing of the spines is well under 0.1 wavelength. To be fully effective, the plane reflector should be at least a quarter wavelength larger in both dimensions than the curtain of driven elements it backs up.

An interesting comparison between the bandwidth of a 6-element Yagi and that of a collinear array having 8 half-wave elements in phase, backed by a screen reflector is shown in Fig. 8-7. The Yagi, with a gain of about 9 dB, has a much sharper frequency response than the collinear, with a gain of 14 dB. Both antennas were matched carefully between 432 and 433 MHz. The collinear shows an SWR under 1.8 over a range of 7 megahertz, while the Yagi exceeds this mismatch in less than 3 megahertz. Had the Yagi in question been a long one, with a gain similar to that of the collinear, its useful frequency range would have been very much sharper still. A typical 2-meter long Yagi may be expected to work well over about 1 megahertz, while a collinear of large size for this band will work nicely over at least 3 times as much frequency range.

POLARIZATION

The wave emitted by an antenna perpendicular to the earth is said to be "vertically polarized." Radiation from an antenna parallel to the earth's surface is termed "horizontal." In the space age these terms may mean nothing. Once we lose the reference of ground there is no longer any "horizontal" or "vertical," but merely what is more accurately called *plane polarization*. The radiation from any straight wire or rod is mainly plane-polarized, but it can be horizontal, vertical, or anything in between.

Much of the time it *is* something in between so the horizontal-vertical argument that raged for years without ever being entirely settled tends to be a specious one. There is no one "best" polarization, and going along with what others in a given area are using offers the best hope for good vhf coverage. Because a vertical dipole or whip has an essentially omnidirectional pattern in a horizontal plane, vertical antennas were employed for most of the early vhf communication, before the days of high-gain arrays. When beams began to take over the burden of vhf work it was only natural to mount them in a horizontal position. Gradually then vhf men went over to horizontal antennas, except in a few areas where mobile work was a major factor. In mobile fm communication, with repeaters, vertical is the accepted standard in most areas.

Horizontal or Vertical?

There is no consistent large difference in coverage between horizontal and vertical, so long as the same polarization is used at both ends of the path. Reflections and the passing of the wave over intervening hills modify polarization to a marked extent. Probing with mobile antenna installations will show the polarization shifting with a car movement of a wavelength or less. Discrimination between horizontal and vertical may amount to 20 dB or more, and at 144 MHz or higher it can be found to reverse itself at times in a matter of inches of travel. The results of this are familiar to any vhf mobile worker, in the form of "mobile flutter" that is so pronounced at certain car speeds, in anything but the most wide-open terrain.

In vhf mobile communication our effective working range is nearly always limited by noise, mostly ignition racket from our own car and others. Such noise tends to be vertically polarized, so in areas of appreciable motor traffic horizontal antennas yield considerably higher signal-to-noise ratios than vertical ones. This has led to adoption of halos, turnstiles, and other horizontally polarized mobile antennas, despite the concern of some family passengers who may not be sold on the esthetic virtues of these devices.

In other vhf work not involving mobiles noise is still a factor, but it may or may not be predominantly vertical in nature. In general polarization is not an important consideration, as far as signal-to-noise ratio is concerned, other than with mobiles. Long experience has shown that if there is any signal-strength advantage it usually lies with horizontal polarization. This is probably because of a combination of the vertical nature of some noise and the observed tendency of polarization to roll over to horizontal in passing over hilly terrain. This is hard to pin down, however, and some vhf men with extensive experience in high-mountain country insist that vertical is superior to horizontal in working with mobiles. This may well account for the predominance of verticals in California and preference for horizontals in most other areas, where the terrain is either open or rolling in character.

Near saturation of the country with television, which employs horizontal polarization, introduces a factor not present when the move to horizontal standardization for amateur vhf work began in the late 1930s. Because polarization shift is slight in the immediate vicinity of the transmitting station, horizontal polarization for both home TV and

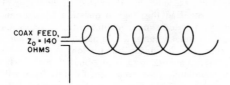

COAX FEED,
$Z_0 = 140$
OHMS

Fig. 8-8 — Schematic drawing of a helical antenna. Circumference should be one wavelength, diameter 0.32 wavelength, turn spacing 0.22 wavelength, and reflector diameter 0.8 wavelength.

amateur work does increase the possibility of TVI of the front-end-overload variety. It should not be assumed that changing back to vertical would be a cure-all for TVI problems however, for the causes and cures of TVI are much more involved than this. Furthermore, since interference that may result from matched polarization is due to receiver deficiencies and is not the fault of the amateur, he should not be required to sacrifice communications efficiency as a TVI expedient.

We had interference problems when everyone used vertical vhf antennas. We still have them in areas where verticals are predominant today. TVI resulting from harmonic radiation and the all-too-common audio-rectification problem would be largely unaffected by changing the polarization of the amateur antenna. Cross-polarization has demonstrated no marked TVI cure-all properties in Great Britain, where television is vertical and amateur vhf antennas are horizontal.

Space-Age Polarization

A third type of polarization is coming into widespread use in communication involving natural and artificial satellites, because of the constantly varying polarization encountered in this work. Called *helical* or *circular* polarization, this is best symbolized by a screw thread, with the wave boring through space in the manner of a bolt being turned into a threaded hole. A circularly polarized system will accept waves of any plane polarization, as well as circularly polarized waves, so it is useful in amateur vhf communication in areas where both horizontal and vertical are in use. It suffers a 3-dB penalty for its universality, however, so it is usually not as good as matched plane polarization in such circumstances.

Two-way work involving circular polarization at both stations should be equal or superior to matched plane polarization, and it may be used on paths where there is marked polarization shift, over land as well as in space communication. There is a polarization-matching problem with circular systems also: the direction of rotation or "sense," must be the same for both stations. A right-hand-polarization wave encounters approximately the same barrier in a left-hand-polarized antenna as does a horizontal wave at a vertical antenna, the discrimination amounting to 20 dB or more.

A further complication is introduced in work via reflection paths, as in the earth-moon-earth route: the reflection produces a reversal of polarization sense. To receive our own signal reflected from the moon, we must reverse the sense of antenna polarization between transmitting and receiving. The problem is lessened for two stations communicating by way of the moon or a reflecting satellite, since one merely needs to use right-hand and the other left.

Circular polarization is inherent in the helical antenna, Fig. 8-8, in which the driven element is a coil or wire or tubing, fed at one end and usually backed up by a screen reflector or "ground plane." Dimensions of the helix are not critical, so it is useful over a very wide frequency range. Each turn of the helix is one wavelength at the midpoint of its useful frequency range. Combinations of horizontal and vertical elements placed at right angles to one another and fed in the proper phase also produce circular polarization. The sense can be reversed by reversing the feed system in such an array.

OFF THE BEATEN PATH

Collinear and Yagi antennas of conventional design are so universally used in vhf communication that most amateurs give little consideration to other systems. To a degree, antenna principles are the same regardless of frequency, so it may be to the vhf man's advantage to try methods used on other frequencies, both higher and lower than his accustomed stamping ground.

The Quad

An antenna very popular among DX men on 10, 15, and 20, but little used in vhf work, the Quad has interesting possibilities. It can be built from sticks and wire, if need be, so its cost can be close to the ultimate low for beams. It is an antenna that is readily adjusted, since all elements can be stub-tuned. It has an appreciable frontal area, and it is inherently a lower-angle radiator than a Yagi of the same height above ground. A quad can be built with any number of elements, in the manner of a Yagi, or several driven elements can be arranged in sets fed in phase, much like the collinear. The same basic stacking and feeding principles apply for quads as for Yagis.

Long-Wire Antennas

An amateur with a wire antenna for lower bands never need wait for the erection of a vhf beam before operating on 50 MHz or higher bands. Antennas for 80, 40, or 20 are not often well adapted to vhf use, but they can always be made to work, after a fashion. On rare occasions they may be outstanding, for a long wire operated on its high harmonics has interesting properties. Two-meter men the length of the Atlantic Seaboard fondly recall the booming signal put out for years by W4CLY, using a 75-meter dipole that sloped down from the lighthouse at Cape Henry, Virginia. More

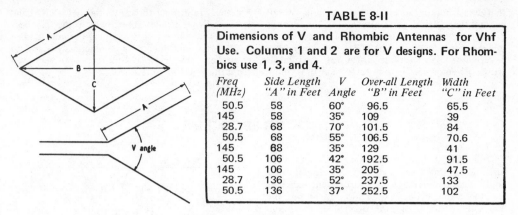

TABLE 8-II

Dimensions of V and Rhombic Antennas for Vhf Use. Columns 1 and 2 are for V designs. For Rhombics use 1, 3, and 4.

Freq (MHz)	Side Length "A" in Feet	V Angle	Over-all Length "B" in Feet	Width "C" in Feet
50.5	58	60°	96.5	65.5
145	58	35°	109	39
28.7	68	70°	101.5	84
50.5	68	55°	106.5	70.6
145	68	35°	129	41
50.5	106	42°	192.5	91.5
145	106	35°	205	47.5
28.7	136	52°	237.5	133
50.5	136	37°	252.5	102

often, the low-band wire will show its best properties in the least-useful directions, but there's no harm in trying.

Principles that make the V and rhombic useful on lower frequencies still apply at vhf. If designed for lower bands these antennas will not have dimensions that are optimum for 50 or 144 MHz, but they can be pressed into service in a pinch. With side lengths and angles adjusted for a vhf band they may do very well. A rhombic large enough for appreciable gain at 50 MHz may fit on a residential lot, and if it can be aimed to take care of major activity areas it may be worth a try. Unterminated, the rhombic is bidirectional, which may help in this. A main problem with wire arrays is getting them high enough to make them really pay off in vhf work. Practical V and rhombic dimensions are given in Table 8-II.

Plane and Parabolic Reflectors

Looking higher in frequency, the vhf man can borrow techniques from uhf practice. Plane, corner, and even parabolic reflectors begin to be attractive at the upper end of the vhf range. Large nonresonant reflector systems offer broad frequency response, clean pattern, and noncritical adjustment, but from the standpoint of gain for a given size, they are not outstanding. A corner-reflector array having a gain of 10 dB, for example, is larger and more difficult to erect than a Yagi or collinear of the same gain.

The flat-plane reflector backing up collinear elements may have more potential. A light frame covered with chicken wire, window screening, or hardware cloth, with sets of elements for two bands on opposite sides of the structure is a convenient way of operating on 220 and 420, or 420 and 1215 MHz with one rotating array. Except as it affects impedance, spacing of the corner or flat-plane reflector from its driven elements is not particularly critical. The impedance of the driven element for various spacings (D) from the vertex of

corner angles 45 to 180 degrees (flat plane) is given in Fig. 8-9. Gain with the flat-plane reflector remains nearly constant from 0.1 to 0.25 wavelength, so it can be seen that varying the spacing may be a convenient way of accomplishing an impedance match.

The parabolic reflector produces a very sharp and clean pattern, if it is large in terms of wavelength. A reflector diameter of about 10 wavelengths is the minimum for appreciable focusing effect, which is the basis of the system. This means about a 25-foot "dish" for 432 MHz which may look like the hard way to develop an outstanding signal at that frequency. Where the reflector can be set up at or near ground level, as for moonbounce work, a sizeable installation is well within the capacities of the kind of workers who are apt to band together for a group project in this field.

Because of constant improvement in reflector design for military and scientific needs, some large reflectors have become available to amateurs through surplus channels. Several of the larger amateur installations have used surplus dishes, but other individuals and groups have demonstrated

Fig. 8-9 — Feed impedance of the driven element in a corner-reflector array, for various corner angles of 180 (flat sheet), 90, 60, and 45 degrees.

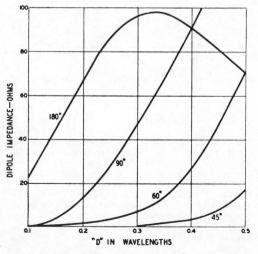

that construction of a suitable parabola is not beyond the realm of possibility.

A reflector as small as 6 feet in diameter can be pressed into service at 420 MHz, but it will have large minor lobes and low gain. A Yagi or collinear array of equal or better performance is more practical. In general therefore, the 1215-MHz band is the dividing line above which the parabola becomes a thoroughly practical approach. For 2300 MHz and higher it is practically standard equipment, and even a 4-footer works very well from this point on up.[1]

STACKING PROBLEMS

In stacking horizontal Yagis one above the other on a single support, certain considerations apply whether the bays are for different bands or for the same band. As a rule of thumb, the minimum desirable spacing is one-half the boom length for two bays on the same band, or half the boom length of the higher frequency array where two bands are involved.

In the stacked two-band array of Fig. 8-10, the 50-MHz 4-element Yagi is going to "look like ground" to the 7-element 144-MHz Yagi above it, if it has any effect at all. It is well known that the impedance of an antenna varies with height above ground, passing through the free-space value at a quarter wavelength and multiples thereof. At one-quarter wavelength and at the *odd* multiples thereof, ground also acts like a reflector, causing considerable radiation straight up. This effect is least at the half-wave points, where the impedance also passes through the free-space value. Preferably, then, the spacing S should be a *half* wavelength, or multiple thereof, at the frequency of the smaller antenna. The half-the-boom-length rule gives about the same answer in this example. For this length of 2-meter antenna, 40 inches would be the minimum desirable spacing, but 80 inches would be better.

The effect of spacing on the larger array is usually negligible. If spacing closer than half the boom length or a half wavelength must be used, the principal thing to watch for is variation in feed impedance of the smaller antenna. If the smaller

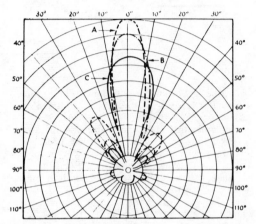

Fig. 8-11 — Approximate horizontal patterns of a 32-element 2-meter collinear, showing the effect of increasing spacing between the inner element ends. Pattern C (solid line) is with the element ends two inches apart, the procedure normally used in such arrays. Pattern B resulted when the spacing was increased to 1/4 wavelength. Pattern A was taken with 5/8-wavelength spacing between inner element ends. Note that the main lobe is longer and sharper with the wider spacings. Minor lobe content also increases, and this is a limiting factor in bay spacing in all types of arrays. A bay spacing of 5/8 wavelength is optimum for short Yagis, as well.

antenna has an adjustable matching device, closer spacings can be used in a pinch, if the matching is adjusted for minimum SWR. Very close spacing and interlacing of elements should be avoided, unless the builder is prepared to go through an extensive program of adjustments of both element lengths and matching.

Stacking for Gain

In stacking bays for the same band fed in phase, the minimum spacing for appreciable gain is a half wavelength for Yagis of up to four elements or so. For such small Yagis, and for dipoles and omni-directional systems such as the Big Wheel and the turnstile, a spacing of 5/8 wavelength will give appreciably more gain. This is convenient in that an electrical full wavelength of coax may be used

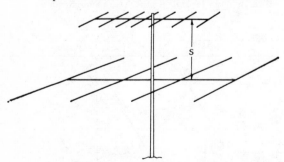

Fig. 8-10 — In stacking Yagi arrays one above the other the minimum spacing between bays, S, should be about half the boom length of the smaller array. Wider spacing is desirable, in which case it should be a half wavelength, or some multiple thereof, at the frequency of the smaller array. If the beams shown are for 50 and 144 MHz, S should be 40 inches minimum, with 80 inches preferred. Similar conditions apply for stacking bays for a single band.

[1] A comprehensive discussion of parabolic antenna theory and practice, prepared by WA9HUV, is available from ARRL for $1.00 per copy. A condensation appeared in *QST* for June, 1971, p. 100.

for phasing. We'll get into phasing and feed problems later.

As bay spacing is increased in directional arrays the main lobe becomes sharper, but minor lobe content also increases. This becomes self-defeating if carried too far. Small Yagis spaced a half wavelength show a beautifully clean pattern, but only moderate gain from stacking. For Yagis up to two wavelengths long, a bay spacing of one wavelength is good, though minor lobes are quite pronounced when individual bays have 6 elements or less.

For arrays of more than two wavelengths, keep that half-the-boom-length minimum in mind, but space them wider if you can. It can be seen from this that stacking of long Yagis makes for large and ungainly structures, but gain never comes easily once you get into the upper brackets.

Stacking Yagis one above the other increases gain without sharpening the horizontal pattern — usually a desirable objective. In stacking another pair beside the first two, the optimum spacing depends on the length of the bays. One wavelength center-to-center is ordinarily used with booms less than one wavelength long. The half-the-boom-length minimum applies with longer ones.

Pattern effects with stacking are illustrated in Fig. 8-11, made with two 16-element collinears mounted side by side. Note that the pattern is markedly sharper with each wider spacing between halves of the array. The gain is also higher, but minor-lobe content increases rapidly at the wider spacings. Pattern A, made with 5/8 wavelength between the inner element ends, shows excellent gain, but the pattern is extremely sharp, and minor lobes are larger than for B, which was made with the bays spaced to leave 1/4 wavelength between inner element ends (3/4 wavelength between bay centers).

Going beyond 5/8 wavelength would result in no improvement in gain, for the minor lobes would be much larger. These would grow from here on, at the expense of the main lobe. A likely compromise between the maximum obtainable gain and the risk of large minor lobes is between 1/4 and 1/2 wavelength between inner element ends, depending on what the builder wants most from his effort.

Also apparent from these patterns is the fact that with large collinears, as with large Yagis, it is not to our advantage to fill up an array with elements. Spacing out the inner element ends to a half wavelength probably nets as much as putting another set of elements in the space between the bays. The 48-element collinear array for 432 MHz, Fig. 9-64, is probably at least as effective as would have been a 60-element collinear of the same frontal area — and the former is much easier to build and feed properly.

Phasing and Feedpoint

Arrangement of phasing lines and the point of connection of the main transmission line are important factors in the performance of large arrays. Balance of currents about the central feedpoint is the critical point here, as the driven elements must be in phase if the system is to

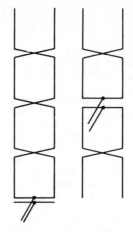

Fig. 8-12 — Arrays of several driven elements should be fed at the center of the system, so that currents will be balanced about the feed point. Array at the left was ineffective until the feed was changed to the center connection, as in the right-hand sketch.

function properly. The author learned this the hard way years ago with a curtain array of 8 vertical half-wave elements in phase. This bidirectional system was first erected as shown at the left in Fig. 8-12. This was desirable mechanically, but the array worked very poorly. Changing the feed point to the center of the phasing system corrected the current unbalance, and turned this admittedly rather haywire arrangement into an effective vhf array.

The more driven elements there are in a phased system the more difficult it is to keep them in balance. Thus it is often desirable to break up a large driven system into several sets of elements, interconnected with phasing lines. The 48-element 432-MHz array mentioned above is an example. Ordinarily no more than 8 elements should be in a single set, and breaking these up into two sets of 4 each may be better. See Fig. 8-13.

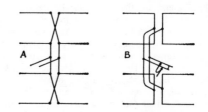

Fig. 8-13 — In phasing large arrays no more than 8 elements should be connected to one line terminal, as at A. Even with 8 half waves in phase, it may be desirable to break the systems up into two parts, as at B, joining their midpoints with a phasing line. The phasing harness so used should be a half wavelength or multiple thereof each side of the main feed point. The universal stub, Fig. 8-18D, is very useful for feeding such a system.

TRANSMISSION LINES

The best antenna is of little value if it cannot be made to accept power from the transmitter or transfer signals it intercepts to the receiver. Thus, selection of the right transmission line and an effective method of matching it to the antenna are of utmost importance. These factors are more vital to the vhf man than to the occupant of lower frequencies, for even with the best lines losses run higher in vhf installations than in the 80-through-10 station. It is easy to waste more than half our transmitter power in heating up the transmission line, and still more can be lost in radiation from it that should have gone on to the antenna itself. Many 144-MHz installations are at least this bad, and on higher bands power and received-signal losses may run up to 90 percent, with some lines that are fairly common in vhf circles!

Coax, Twin-Lead, or Open-Wire

There are three principal types of transmission line commonly used in vhf installations today. Each is obtainable in many styles and sizes, and each has its strong and weak points. There is no one "best" line, or we would not still be using all three. Choice of the right one begins with the line-loss information, Table 8-III, but this is by no means the whole story. These figures are for new lines, properly installed, and used in dry weather. Under average amateur-station conditions losses will almost certainly be greater than the table indicates.

Coax has relatively high loss in the tables. RG-8, perhaps the most commonly used line, reputedly has a loss of about 2.5 dB per hundred feet at 144 MHz — if the line is working perfectly. At 420 MHz, the same line, in new condition and perfectly installed, will dissipate 70 percent of your transmitter power and received-signal strength in a 100-foot run. Discouraging as these figures may seem, they are not the whole story. Transmitter power loss can be made up to some extent by increasing power, at least up to the legal limit, but in receiving the signal lost can never be recovered.

Good coax, on the other hand, is tolerant of installation. It is almost impervious to weather changes, and it can be installed anywhere. Tape it to a steel tower, or bury it; let it wrap around the tower and unwrap again as the beam is rotated — the loss will stay the same, almost regardless of conditions that adversely affect other types of lines. A prime advantage of coax that is often ignored is the fact that it permits measurement of the system performance readily, and with fairly inexpensive equipment. You can measure your SWR and line loss, and the effects of any adjustments are immediately apparent. This is not easy with other types of line.

Twin-Lead is inexpensive and convenient to use. Its advertised losses look good on paper, compared with coax. The best grade of tubular Twin-Lead, transmitting type, is quoted at 1.25 dB

per hundred feet at 144 MHz and 2.3 dB at 420 MHz, but losses go up markedly in wet weather, and performance is very erratic. Flat ribbon gives the most trouble, but even the best tubular line will show fluctuating loading in heavy-rain conditions. Cheap lines with small conductors and thin insulation should be avoided entirely, unless the line is to be indoors or no more than a few feet long.

Book figures make open-wire line look best of all. If a good open line has only 0.2 dB loss at 144 MHz, why doesn't everyone use it? Even at 420 MHz, the loss per 100 feet can be under 1 dB. This picture has the biggest "ifs" of all, however. Such fine results are achieved, if ever, only under the most carefully controlled conditions. The conductors must be large, yet spaced closely so that radiation from the line will be negligible. Wire alignment must be kept constant, yet with a minimum of insulating spreaders and supports. There can be no sharp bends in the line, and it must be positioned so that it is balanced to ground.

These conditions definitely are *not* met in most amateur installations. We use TV-type lines, with too-small conductors and spacings generally too wide, at least for 420 MHz. There are spreaders every few inches. The line is often run close to a metal tower or eavetroughs, with little or no consideration of balance to ground. Nearly always there are bends of a sharpness that can be very harmful. One 220-MHz line installed with reasonable care and using half-inch spaced open TV line showed a measured loss of 4 dB in a 125-foot run. This represents a transmitter power loss of 60 percent, yet it was probably a better-than-average amateur installation.

The potential low-loss qualities of open line can be realized in amateur work if sufficient care is taken in the construction and use of the line. Large conductors are a must; never less than No. 14, and No. 12 or larger is better. Spacing must be close in terms of wavelength; not more than 1 inch at 144 MHz and proportionately less at higher frequencies if at all possible. Teflon is preferred for spreaders, and they should be several feet apart. If bends must be made, keep them to very obtuse angles, or in a continuous arc of large radius.

Baluns (about which more later) should be made and used with care. A 100-foot straight run of No. 12 enamelled wire, spaced 5/8 inch center-to-center with Teflon spreaders every 6 feet, fed with baluns at each end, was measured for loss, including baluns, at 144, 220, and 432 MHz. It showed 1.1, 1.35, and 1.56 dB, respectively, on these frequencies. By comparison a 1/2-inch TV line tested on 432 MHz under identical conditions showed a loss of 2.3 dB. These losses are somewhat higher than those of Table 8-III, but they represent the best that can be expected in a practical amateur installation. They also demonstrate the worth of good open-wire line, when it is used properly. If the line must be long, a good open-wire installation is probably the best way to do the job at moderate cost.

TABLE 8-III CHARACTERISTICS OF COMMONLY USED TRANSMISSION LINES

Type of Line	Conductor Size	Z₀ Ohms	Velocity Factor	Coax OD Inches	Attenuation in dB/100 ft MHz: 50	144	220	420	Power Rating, Watts MHz: 50	144	220	420
Open wire[1]	12	400-600	0.975		0.13	0.25	0.5	1	Over 1 kW			
Open-Wire TV Line, 1/2-inch[2]	18	400	0.95		0.3	0.75	1	1.8	Over 1 kW			
Open-Wire TV Line, 1-inch[2]	18	450	0.95		0.3	0.75	Not recommended		Over 1 kW			
Parallel-Conductor Solid-Dielectric Twin-Lead[3]												
Standard Flat (214-056)	7/28	300	0.82		0.85	1.55	1.9	2.8	Over 1 kW when dry			
Tubular (214-271)	7/28	300	0.82		0.85	1.55	1.9	2.8	Over 1 kW when dry			
Tubular, Transmitting Type (214-076)	7/26	300	0.82		0.68	1.25	1.6	2.3				
Extra-Heavy Flat (Federal K-200)[2]	7/22	200	0.82		0.5	1	1.3	2	Over 1 kW			
Coax, Solid-Dielectric												
RG-58/U[4]	20	53.5	65.9	0.195	3	6	7	15	350	175	125	90
RG-59/U	22	73	65.9	0.242	2.3	4.2	5	8	500	250	180	125
RG-8/U	7/21	52	65.9	0.405	1.5	2.5	3.5	5	1500	800	650	400
RG-11/U	7/26	75	65.9	0.405	1.55	2.8	3.7	5	1500	800	650	400
RG-17/U	0.188	52	65.9	0.87	0.5	1	1.3	2.3	4500	2300	1900	1200
Foamed RG-8A/U	7/21	50	75	0.405	1.22	2	2.75	3.9	1500	800	650	400
Aluminum-Jacket Foamflex												
3/8-inch[5]	0.117	50	75	0.435	0.85	1.5	2	3	2200	1200	900	600
1/2-inch[5]	0.162	50	75	0.60	0.65	1.2	1.5	2.3	3000	1600	1100	800
3/8-inch[5]	0.077	70	75	0.435	0.82	1.5	1.9	2.9	similar to 50-ohm types			
1/2-inch[5]	0.108	70	75	0.60	0.62	1.2	1.5	2.3				

[1] Spreaders at least 3 feet apart. Maximum spacing between conductors 1-1/2 inches for 50 MHz, 1 inch for 144, 3/4 inch for 220, 1/2 inch for 420. Loss figures neglect radiation.
[2] Estimated loss, neglecting radiation.
[3] Numbers with 214 prefix are American Phenolic Corp.
[4] With all coax listed except RG-58; letter A, B, or C after number signifies noncontaminating jacket. With 58, only RG-58/U has this type jacket.
[5] Not including vinyl jacket.

Tips on Selecting Coax

Coaxial line comes in two principal impedances: 52 and 72 ohms. There are small variations either side of these nominal figures, but they are of no significance for our purposes. Other impedances are available, but are seldom found in amateur installations. From the standpoint of overall effectiveness there is no preference between the above impedances, but practical factors tend to make the 52-ohm types the more useful. Most test equipment is set up for 52 ohms, for example. On the other hand, 72-ohm coax and a balun of the same material provides a good match to the 300-ohm balanced load that some vhf antennas represent.

Losses in any line are related to conductor sizes and types of insulation. The small sizes of coax, with inner conductors of No. 22 wire or smaller, are bound to have high losses, regardless of quality or price. An inner conductor of No. 14 wire or its equivalent in stranded wire is about the minimum that should be used, except for short runs. Coax like RG-58 or 59 is convenient, but it should never be used for vhf applications where the run is more than a few wavelengths. There is no easier way to waste power and lose receiving effectiveness!

Any coax costs money and good coax is quite expensive, but all things considered the best may turn out to be a good investment. Cheap coax is likely to be old, and its measured loss may be higher than figures given in the table. More important, older types of coax and some inexpensive new ones deteriorate quite rapidly when used outside. Be sure to find out whether or not the coax of your choice will stand up in outdoor service. "Non-contaminating" is the word for it. Coax guaranteed for 15 years of use, underground or otherwise exposed, is now available at moderate cost.

Coax is available in infinite variety. Worth looking for is the "polyfoam" version of standard types. These cost slightly more than solid-dielectric types, but losses are typically one-third less. Watch the velocity factor. An electrical half wavelength will be a greater portion of a physical half wavelength with foam or other low-density dielectric than with solid.

Various lines are made with semiflexible sheathing, usually aluminum, and with spiral wrap or foam insulation. These are fairly costly, but they deliver excellent results and are fine for permanent installation. Flexible sections for rotation are needed with these, and a good way to handle a multiband installation is to put in a remotely operated coaxial switch to permit the use of one line for all antennas.

About Coaxial Fittings

If you go to the expense of a good coaxial line, it is approaching the ridiculous to pinch pennies on the fittings to be used with it, particularly on 220 MHz and higher. The so-called "UHF" fitting isn't to be trusted in the uhf range, especially if you want to be able to measure antenna and feed-line performance with any degree of accuracy.

Probably the best fitting, for most of us, is the series N, a constant-impedance type that can be bought at moderate prices on the surplus market. It gives a constant impedance through the connection and can be had in all types required. Properly installed, it is weatherproof.

Series C fittings provide constant impedance and are weatherproof. In addition, they are quick-disconnect and very handy on that account. However, they are not on surplus and are quite expensive.

The BNC Series is nice, but too small for the RG-8-size line. The Type HN is a constant-impedance series, for the larger sizes of coax. Whatever series you select, be sure that the installation job is done properly. Water leaking into fittings will ruin the best system in short order. A sprayed coating of lacquer, and tape wrapping, help to prevent moisture absorption.

G-Line

Most uhf amateurs are aware that there is a single-conductor transmission line, invented by Goubau, and called "G-Line" in his honor. Papers by the inventor appeared some years ago, in which seemingly fantastic claims for line loss were made; under 1 dB per hundred feet in the microwave region, for example. Especially attractive was the statement that the matching device was broad-band in nature, making it appear that a single G-Line installation might be made to serve on both 420 and 1215 MHz.

When uhf TV first appeared on the scene, a G-Line kit was put on the market. Mainly because of its high cost (about $30.00, plus installation) it never sold well for home TV use, but G-Line has since come into its own in cable TV systems. Here very long lines must be run, and losses must be held to a minimum, so the G-Line principle looks more attractive.

The basic idea is that a single conductor can be an almost lossless transmission line at ultra-high frequencies, if a suitable launching device is used. A similar launcher is placed at the other end. Basically the launcher is a cone-shaped device which is a flared extension of the coaxial feedline. In effect, the cone gets the energy accustomed to travelling on the inner conductor, as the outer conductor is gradually removed. The inner conductor should be large and heavily insulated. No. 14, vinyl covered, is supplied with the kit.

Since the kit was designed for home TV use, the small end of the horn launcher has a balun of sorts for conversion from unbalanced to balanced line. This can be removed for amateur purposes and the system fed directly with 72-ohm coax. The G-Line is very sensitive to bends. If any must be made, they should be in the form of an arc of large radius, this being preferable to even an obtuse-angle change in the direction of run. The line must be kept several inches away from any metal and should be supported with as few insulators as possible.

A 100-foot run using direct 72-ohm feed to the launchers measured for loss at 432 MHz showed 2.7 dB, which may have been mainly in the launchers, since they were much too short to be really effective at this frequency. Theory states

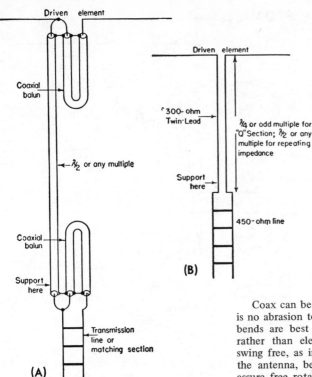

(A)

(B)

Fig. 8-14 — Flexible sections for rotatable arrays. Coax may be used, as at A. If the coax section is any multiple of a half-wavelength, the antenna impedance will be repeated at the bottom end. Twin-Lead may be used either as a *Q* section or as an impedance repeater, as shown in B.

that the cones should be at least 3 wavelengths long, and the kit type is less than one wavelength at 432 MHz. Since loss in the line itself is presumably very low when properly installed, the G-Line idea should be useful where very long runs are required in uhf and microwave work.

Practical Line Installations

It is one thing to quote losses for a straight Twin-Lead or open-wire line, without bends or insulating supports, and well away from metal or semiconducting objects such as trees, roofs, and walls. It is quite another to put up a practical installation for an amateur station, where a line must be run from inside the house, be fastened to a tower part way up, and then allowed to swing free as the antenna is rotated. The inevitable losses and mechanical troubles that result from compromises inherent in the amateur approach, particularly with rotatable arrays, make a strong case for coax. But with any line these problems must be dealt with, and how we handle them can make a good many decibels difference in our signal reports, sending and receiving.

If coax is used it is best to support it frequently throughout the run and not depend on strain to keep it up out of harm's way. Burying coax is fine, provided that it is the noncontaminating variety. Lines of this type have a letter following the number. Example: RG8A/U is the noncontaminating version of RG8/U. The letter may be A, B, or C, depending on other characteristics. Most coax made today is noncontaminating, but the buyer should watch this point in picking up "bargains."

Coax can be taped to a tower, so long as there is no abrasion to cut through the insulation. Sharp bends are best avoided, but only for mechanical rather than electrical reasons. Where coax must swing free, as in the portion that will rotate with the antenna, be sure that enough slack is left to assure free rotation without additional strain. An extra turn or two around the tower, near the point of attachment to the beam, is usually desirable. Make all supports extra strong, to take care of extra loads imposed by ice and wind.

Properly handled, coax makes the best available rotating section for antennas that are fed with other types of line that may be more critical as to proximity to metal. Open-wire lines are particularly susceptible to breakage or shorting out unless special precautions are taken. Usually some form of insulated flexible line is connected between the antenna proper and a stationary support at the top of the tower or mast on which the antenna is mounted.

Such a flexible section can take several forms, and it can be made to do double duty as a matching device. Probably the most satisfactory method for arrays that are not to be fed directly with coax, is to use a flexible section of coax with baluns at each end, as shown in Fig. 8-14A. If the flexible section is made any multiple of a half wavelength electrically the impedance of the array will be repeated at the bottom of the flexible section.

A similar method is to use Twin-Lead for the rotating section, as shown in Fig. 8-14B. The 300-ohm tubular transmitting-type line is recommended. Here again, halfwave sections repeat the antenna impedance at the bottom end. Such a rotating section can also be made any odd multiple of a quarter wavelength, to act as a *Q* section, giving a step-down between a 450-ohm open line and a 200-ohm antenna impedance. More on these applications will be found in the text relating to matching devices that follows.

IMPEDANCE MATCHING

We know, or can determine, the impedance of the transmission line we want to use. If we knew the impedance of the antenna with equal certainty, matching one to the other would be a simple matter and one of our major vhf antenna problems would be solved forever. Unfortunately, the actual impedance of an antenna is subject to so many variations that it is seldom possible to put a precise value on the impedance the transmission line must work into. Some kind of adjustable matching device is, therefore, a very useful tool.

Matching systems are many and varied, but all perform one basic function: that of impedance transformation, so that the feedline will "see" an impedance similar to its own, regardless of the actual antenna impedance. Matching may be combined with other functions, such as conversion from an unbalanced line (coax) to a balanced load (center-fed antenna element). Matching may be included in the phasing lines connecting the bays of stacked arrays. The matching element may also be used to tune the system to resonance. We'll get to examples of all these methods shortly, but first a bit more about what they are going to be called upon to do.

About Antenna Impedance

This was discussed briefly earlier, but to review, a half-wave dipole in free space has an impedance of about 72 ohms. When the dipole is close to ground, or objects that simulate ground, its impedance changes. In the first half wavelength from the ground up, the impedance swings from a few ohms near ground, through the free-space value near 0.25 wavelength to as much as 100 ohms at 0.3 wavelength, and then back to 72 ohms at the half-wave point. Beyond here it drops off to 60 ohms and rises through 72 ohms again to nearly 85 ohms, then drops back to 72 ohms again at one wavelength. The effect of ground on impedance becomes relatively insignificant beyond two wavelengths, as shown in Fig. 8-15, but it can be seen that in situations most hams encounter in putting up antennas the impedance of a dipole is anything but a sure thing.

Ground is only one factor. Adding parasitic elements drops the impedance, but how much is anyone's guess, especially in arrays with both reflector and director elements. Length, diameter, and spacing of these elements can effect great

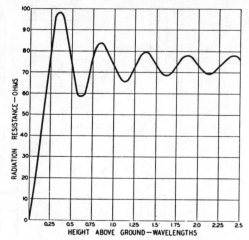

Fig. 8-15 — Variation in radiation resistance of a horizontal half-wave antenna with height above perfectly conducting ground.

changes in the impedance of the driven element, to the point where it is almost impossible to predict what the feed impedance of a Yagi array will be. The best course, then, is to make the antenna first, determine its impedance by estimate or experiment, and then make a matching device to fit the requirements. If we can make a reasonable guess at the impedance, we can make an adjustable matching device of small range that will do the job.

If our antenna is just a half-wave dipole, Fig. 8-16A and B, we can assume 72 ohms, knowing from the curve of Fig. 8-15 that it cannot vary much more than 30 ohms either way. Adding a reflector will bring the impedance down — to 40 or 50 ohms, on the average. Putting on directors will lower it further, to something around 20 ohms. All these are for a feed point of the split dipole, A. At the center of a dipole that is unbroken, Fig. 8-16B, the rf voltage between the element and ground is zero. This point can thus be grounded, as in all-metal arrays, and the impedance matched by tapping the line out on the element in various ways.

Rf voltage and impedance at the ends of half-wave elements are very high. So is the feed

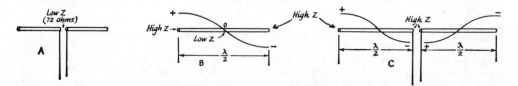

Fig. 8-16 — The halfwave dipole, A, is fed at its center, the point of lowest impedance. For a dipole in free space, and at certain heights above ground, this impedance is 72 ohms. Rf voltage on a halfwave dipole is shown by the curved line in B. Since there is no voltage to ground at the center of an unbroken dipole, this point can be grounded to the metal support. Rf voltage and impedance are high at the ends of two collinear dipoles in phase, as at C.

impedance of two dipoles fed in phase at their inner element ends, Fig. 8-16C, the simplest collinear array. The feed impedance of an "H" array of four half-waves in phase is somewhere around 600 ohms. The popular vhf collinear 16-element array (8 halfwaves in phase as in Fig. 8-13, but with reflectors) gets down to around 200 ohms — *maybe!* Remember that there are modify- ing factors, including that of coupling between elements, but 200 ohms is a good starting point for setting up a matching system for this type of array.

All these assumptions are valid approximations only for the frequency at which the system is resonant. If the array is out of tune all bets are off. We then must have some means of tuning the system before we can match it.

COMMON MATCHING METHODS

We will not describe all kinds of matching systems, but will consider only those commonly used in vhf work, or those that should get more attention.

The Delta

First there is the *delta* or *Y-match*, Fig. 8-17A. Here the transmission line is fanned out and tapped onto the driven element at points equidistant from the center. The taps can be adjusted until an impedance match is achieved, and then fastened permanently in place. One of the first impedance-matching devices ever employed, it still has its merits, not the least of which is simplicity. Chief fault is the likelihood of radiation from the fanned-out portion, if it is not properly propor- tioned. It is also quite frequency sensitive.

The delta works well with a balun made of coax, or an antenna coupler of some kind. A coaxial balun connected at the base of the delta is shown at B. If this is made of 72-ohm coax there could be a 300-ohm line of any convenient length between the balun and the delta. Adjustment is very easy when the delta is combined with coax feed. You merely insert an SWR bridge in the coaxial line near the balun and adjust the delta side length and spread for zero reflected power. If the balun or balanced line is connected directly to the delta as shown in Fig. 8-17A and B, the lines can be of any impedances commonly available. More on baluns below.

Gamma and T-Match

Variations of the tapping-out idea are seen in the *gamma* and *T-match*, C and D of Fig. 8-17. The gamma is fine for coaxial feed, while the T is most often used with balanced line. A balun and coaxial feed could be used with the T, of course, just as with the delta. The series capacitor, C1, is used to tune out the inductive reactance of the gamma

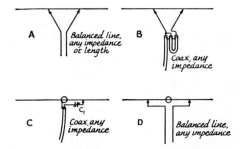

Fig. 8-17 — The transmission line and antenna impedances may be matched by tapping the feedline out on the dipole in various ways. The delta or Y-match is shown at A. A variation for coaxial feed, using a balun, is given at B. The gamma match, C, is popular where coax feed is used. The T-match, D, may be fed with balanced line, or through a balun as in the case of B.

arm. Without it the gamma system cannot be made to work perfectly, as a slight unbalance is always present. The gamma arm is usually made of tubing of about the size of the driven element, and a sliding clip is used between the two, to facilitate adjustment. The capacitor can be at either end of the arm.

Once the proper value is found for C1, it can be removed and a fixed capacitor substituted. An assumed value for your line can be taken, and only the point of connection of the arm made adjust- able. Suitable fixed values for 50 ohms are as follows: 50 MHz — 65 pF, 144 MHz — 20 pF, 220 MHz — 15 pF, 432 MHz — 8 pF.

Fig. 8-18 — A single conductor may be bent as at A to form a folded dipole, giving an impedance four times that of a simple split dipole. It may thus be fed with 300-ohm balanced line, or 72-ohm coax and a balun. Higher impedance step-up can be achieved by making the unbroken portion of the dipole of a larger conductor, as at B. A quarter- wavelength matching transformer, or Q section, is shown at C. A matching device that is useful for any balanced load is the universal stub, D. The transmission line can be coax or balanced line, any impedance.

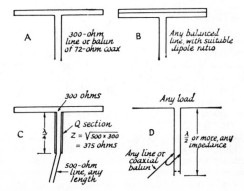

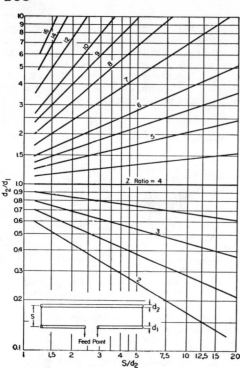

Fig. 8-19 — Impedance step-up ratio for the two-conductor folded dipole, as a function of conductor diameters and spacing. Dimensions d_1, d_2, and S are shown on the inset drawing. This information is not reliable for use on amateur bands above 148 MHz.

Strictly speaking, series capacitors should be used with the T system too, but since omitting them does not upset the balance of the dipole, as it would with the one-sided gamma, they are not always used.

Folded Dipole

One of the most commonly used matching devices is the *folded dipole*, shown in various forms in Fig. 8-18. When a single conductor is bent around as shown at A, the impedance seen by the transmission line is quadrupled. Thus a folded dipole made from one size of conductor throughout has an impedance of 4 X 72, or 288 ohms, and it can be fed with 300-ohm line, or with a balun and 72-ohm coax, without appreciable mismatch. The dipole element can be made from a piece of Twin-Lead, with each outer end shorted and one conductor broken at the midpoint, for connecting the transmission line. This is a convenient arrangement for temporary or indoor use.

Additional impedance step-up can be obtained by making the unbroken portion of the dipole of larger cross-section than the fed portion, as shown in Fig. 8-18B. This is widely used in parasitic arrays, where the feed impedance is nearly always much lower than 72 ohms. Impedance step-up depends on the ratio of the conductor sizes, and on the spacing between them. If the approximate impedance of the antenna is known, a suitable

element can be made for 50 or 144 MHz by using the nomogram, Fig. 8-19.

Where the spacing between the portions of this type of dipole is an appreciable portion of a wavelength, as it must be at 220 or 420 MHz, the information of Fig. 8-19 is no longer reliable. A better method of matching arrays for these frequencies is to use the universal stub, Fig. 8-18D, or the Q section, Fig. 8-18C. For more on matching Yagis for 220 and 432 MHz, see practical examples in Chapter 9.

A problem with folded dipoles is that one must know the impedance to be matched in order to design one to do the job. Educated guesses may come close enough for most practical purposes. For example, if we assume the feed impedance of a Yagi array to be 20 ohms, we can use a folded dipole with a 15-to-1 step-up as the driven element, and feed the array with 300-ohm Twin-Lead. The mismatch will be slight, even if the dipole impedance turns out to be 15 ohms, or 25 ohms, instead of 20. The SWR will be only about 1.2 to 1 in either case. We could use a 10-to-1 dipole and a 50-ohm balun equally well.

The folded dipole is easy to make, and it is somewhat more frequency tolerant than some other matching systems. It is very useful in stacked-Yagi arrays having open-wire phasing lines. A fairly high value of dipole impedance is desirable

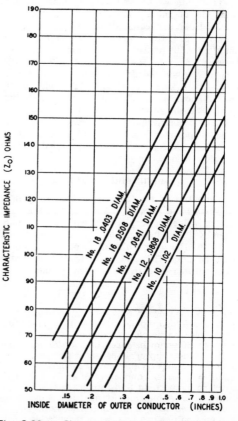

Fig. 8-20 — Characteristic impedance of typical air-insulated coaxial lines.

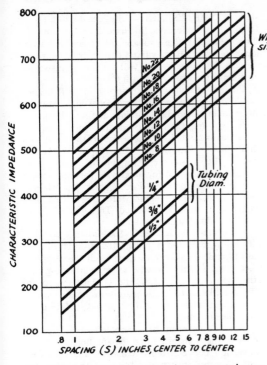

Fig. 8-21 — Characteristic impedance vs. conductor size and spacing for parallel-conductor lines.

Fig. 8-22 — Clip for use in adjusting the point of connection of a balun, or the adjustable short of Fig. 8-18D, made from a piece of perforated aluminum. Balun leads are soldered to the lug. When the adjustment process is completed, the clip may be removed and the connection soldered permanently to the line.

here, but the exact value is not important, as matching will be taken care of where the main transmission line connects to the phasing section.

The Q Section

A quarter wavelength of transmission line has the property of acting as a matching transformer between two different impedances. Such a transformer is called a *Q* section, and an example is given in Fig. 8-18C. Here a 300-ohm dipole is matched to a 500-ohm line by using a *Q* section whose impedance is equal to the square root of the product of the two impedances to be matched. A 375-ohm section is required here, but the principle may be applied to many vhf matching problems. The impedance obtainable with various conductor sizes and spacings is obtainable from Fig. 8-20 for coax, and 8-21 for balanced lines. Our 375-ohm *Q* section could be two No. 10 wires spaced 1-1/4

inches apart, or two 1/4-inch rods 2-3/4 inches apart, to show two examples.

An adjustable *Q* section is a convenient way of matching two impedances that are known only approximately. Two 1/4-inch rods can be made to provide impedances of about 210 to 400 ohms, by varying their spacing from 3/4 to 3 inches. The system can be used to step up as well as down, and it works with coaxial or parallel conductors. We'll have examples later.

The Corrective Stub

Probably the most useful matching device of all is the universal stub of Fig. 8-18D. Because the matching stub must be a half wavelength or more to start, it is cumbersome at 50 MHz or lower, but it is ideal for 144 MHz and higher bands. No impedances need be known to utilize it, and within limits the system to be matched does not have to be resonant. The short on the line is adjusted to resonate the system to be fed, and then the transmission line is tapped onto the stub at the matching point. The load can be any impedance, the stub can be any convenient wire or tubing size, and any spacing. The feedline can be coaxial or balanced, any impedance. A balun is used with coax as indicated in the sketch. The shorting bar can be grounded, and the unused portion of the stub cut off, once adjustment is completed.

Two variables are involved, which complicates the adjustment procedure a bit, but with a standing-wave bridge in the line the job is quite simple. You merely move the position of the short and the point of connection of the transmission line until zero reflected power is indicated on the SWR bridge. Coupling *at the transmitter* is then adjusted for the desired loading.

Where the point of connection of a balun or shorting bar must be made adjustable, a small clip of perforated aluminum, Fig. 8-22, is handy for a

Fig. 8-23 — Circuit and parts information for the vhf antenna couplers.

C1 — 100-pF variable for 50 MHz, 50-pF for 144 MHz (Hammarlund MC-100 and MC-50).

C2 — 35-pF per-section split-stator variable, 0.07-inch spacing (Hammarlund MCD-35SX). Reduce to 4 stator and 4 rotor plates in each section in 144-MHz coupler for easier tuning; see text.

J1 — Coaxial fitting, female.

J2 — Two-post terminal assembly.

L1 — 50 MHz: 4 turns No. 18 tinned, 1-inch diameter, 1/8-inch spacing (Air-Dux No. 808T) inside L2.
    144 MHz: 1-1/2 turns No. 14 enam., 1-inch

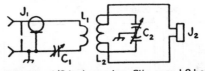

diameter, 1/8-inch spacing. Slip over L2 before mounting.

L2 — 50 MHz: 7 turns No. 14 tinned, 1-1/2-inch diameter, 1/4-inch spacing (Air Dux No. 1204). Tap 1-1/2 turns from each end.
    144 MHz: 5 turns No. 12 tinned, 1/2-inch diameter, 7/8 inch long. Tap 1-1/2 turns from each end.

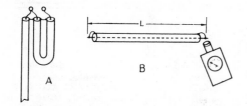

Fig. 8-24 — A balun for working from coaxial to balanced line is shown at A. Impedance at the balanced end, top, is four times that of the coaxial line used. The loop is an electrical half wavelength. Its resonant frequency may be checked with a dip meter as shown at B.

temporary connector. The holes are already made, and with some tension on the clip the edges of the aluminum bite into the conductor slightly, assuring good contact. Small Fahnstock clips are also useful. When adjustment is completed, remove the clip and solder the connection permanently, using the same overall lead length.

Making and Using Baluns

As its composite name implies, a balun is a device for working between an unbalanced line (coax) and a balanced line or load. It can take several forms, some of which also include the function of impedance matching along with the unbalanced-to-balanced conversion.

The Antenna Coupler Probably the most versatile of baluns, the antenna coupler, Fig. 8-23, can be made to work from any impedance of coaxial line at J1 to any impedance balanced load at J2. The low-impedance input circuit, L1C1, is series resonant at the operating frequency, and inductively coupled to the balanced circuit, L2C2. The balanced output, connected to J2, is tapped down on L2 an equal amount from each end.

Component values in the antenna coupler are not critical, and it will handle a wide range of impedance combinations merely by adjusting the capacitors. Changing the tap positions on L2 extends the range of impedances still further. The values of L1 and C1 should be roughly those that have inductive and capacitive reactance equal to the value of the coaxial line impedance. Since the value of capacitance is the more readily estimated, it is customary to aim for this and adjust the size of L1 to resonate with it. Approximate values for the various bands are as follows: 50 MHz — 65 pF, 144

MHz — 25 pF, 220 MHz — 15 pF, and 420 MHz — 10 pF. A variable capacitor used for C1 should be chosen so that these values can be reached with some to spare. Often a fixed capacitor of approximately the above value will suffice, adjustment then being made entirely with C2.

For adjustment of the coupler an SWR bridge should be connected in the coaxial line between the antenna changeover relay and J1. The two capacitors are then adjusted for zero reflected power, as indicated on the bridge. If this results in unsatisfactory transfer of power from the transmitter, the loading control in the transmitter should be readjusted for maximum forward power on the bridge meter. Do *not* adjust the antenna coupler for maximum forward power reading; always set it for zero reflected. This applies in any matching adjustment.

Connected as described, the antenna coupler will aid in reception, reducing the strength of any out-of-band signals before they reach the receiver, where they might otherwise cause overloading and other spurious responses. The coupler is also an effective filter, attenuating any unwanted frequencies present in the transmitter output, before they reach the antenna.

The coupler can be connected at any point between the transmitter and the antenna where the conversion between the unbalanced and balanced lines is desired. Because of the need to retune the coupler for appreciable frequency excursions, it is usually mounted within easy reach of the operating position.

A versatile 2-band antenna coupler (Transmatch) of the type shown in Fig. 8-23 is described in detail in Chapter 14. It is also capable of working between unbalanced lines of different impedance, and it includes a built-in SWR indicator.

4-to-1 Baluns Broad-band baluns of several types are readily constructed. Bifilar-wound coils can be used in the same manner as on lower frequencies, but this method is seldom used above 30 MHz. The most common balun for vhf service is made from an *electrical* half-wavelength of coax, usually the same type as used for the main transmission line, folded back on itself and connected to the main line and the antenna as shown in Fig. 8-24. This balun provides an impedance step-up of 4 to 1, while handling the unbalanced-to-balanced conversion.

The physical length of the balun loop will vary with different types of coaxial lines. With solid-

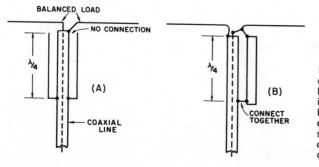

Fig. 8-25 — Two types of baluns, for conversion from a coaxial line to a balanced load. The coaxial sleeve, A, is the preferred type, and it also can be used as a matching device, as described in the text. Both serve the same main purpose: prevention of current flow on the outer conductor of the coaxial line.

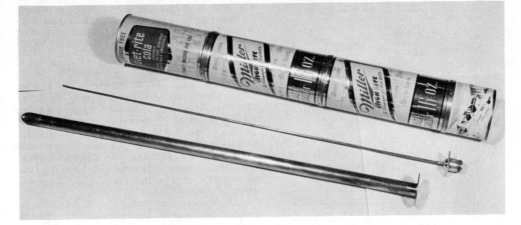

Fig. 8-26 — Coaxial-sleeve balun for 144 MHz, showing the parts that make up the air-dielectric matching section.

TABLE 8-IV

Lengths for the decoupling sleeve, A, and copper pipe outer conductor, B, for 144, 220, and 432 MHz.

	A	B
144 MHz	19-3/4"	20-5/16"
220 MHz	12-1/2"	12-29/32"
432 MHz	6-1/4"	6-31/32"

dielectric coax the loop will be about 65 percent of the free-space value for a half wavelength. Less dense insulation such as foamed polyethylene may increase this to as much as 80 percent of the free-space value, so it is well to check the loop for resonance. Using the length of leads that will be involved in the eventual connections, short the ends as shown in Fig. 8-24B, and couple the dip meter to one end.

The coaxial balun is cumbersome for use below 50 MHz, and it ceases to be practical above 450 MHz. At the lower frequency the loop can be rolled into a coil if desired. Usually it is taped to the main transmission line in U shape. It is best to run the balun perpendicular to the load, which would mean dropping it vertically from the boom of a horizontal Yagi. The main line can be looped back to the boom and taped in place, if this is desirable mechanically. A permanent position for the balun with respect to its load is particularly important at 220 or 420 MHz. The loop for the latter frequency is only about 8 inches overall, so mechanical variations can throw the balance the loop is supposed to provide quite a bit off.

Small coax such as RG-58 or 59 is not recommended for baluns. Soldering weakens and distorts the insulation, making shorts likely, and the small conductors break very easily. Losses in small-coax baluns often run prohibitively high. RG-8 or similar sizes are much better, if the balun is made and mounted with care.

The impedance at the end of the balun is 4 times that of the coax used. A balun with 52-ohm coax will match a 200-ohm load, and 72-ohm coax and a balun match a 300-ohm load.

1-to-1 Baluns The unbalanced to balanced conversion can also be made without an impedance change, using the balun shown schematically in Fig. 8-25A. Here a split dipole or other balanced load is fed directly with coax. This would make for unbalance and rf flow on the outer conductor of the line, but for the detuning sleeve (or *bazooka*) that has been added to the last quarter-wavelength of the line. Being open at the top and shorted to the outer conductor at the bottom, this sleeve presents an infinite impedance to rf at the resonant frequency, effectively choking off current flow and preventing radiation from the line.

A similar effect can be achieved with the bazooka in B, wherein a quarter-wave line section shorted at the bottom is formed by connecting an additional piece of coax or tubing as shown. This is less effective than the sleeve method however, and is seldom used above the 50-MHz band. It is used occasionally for vhf mobile antennas wherein it

TABLE 8-V

Inner conductor wire sizes to be used with 9/16-inch ID copper pipe outer conductors, for various impedance-matching jobs commonly encountered in vhf work. The impedance of the main coaxial transmission line, Z_s, is given in the left column. Next is the balanced load, Z_r, to be matched.

Z_s, ohms	Z_r, ohms	Wire Size, A.W.G.
50	72	4
50	200	10
50	300	12
50	450	18
75	200	12
75	300	18
75	450	24

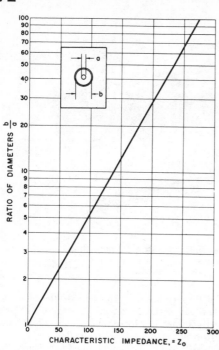

Fig. 8-27 — Characteristic impedance of coaxial matching sections for various conductor diameter ratios. The outside diameter of the inner conductor and the inside diameter of the outer conductor are used.

balun. Examples are the beer-can baluns of Figs. 8-26 and 28, made by K6HCP and WA6GYD. These are assemblies to which the main coaxial line run is attached by means of standard coaxial fittings. By making the inner portion of the balun of the right combination of conductor sizes it is made to act as a coaxial Q section. Construction of the balun is detailed in Fig. 8-28. Lengths of the sleeve and coaxial section for 144, 220, and 432 MHz are given in Table 8-IV.

The inner coaxial portion of the balun can be made to continue the line impedance, or transform it to other impedances. If standard wire sizes are used for the inner conductor, load impedances from 70 to 450 ohms can be matched by using 9/16-inch ID copper pipe for the outer conductor. The matching combinations for various wire sizes are given in Table 8-V. You can choose your own combinations for various Q-section impedances by using the graph of Fig. 8-27. Remember, the formula for finding the needed Q-section impedance, Z_o, is

$$Z_o = Z_s Z_r \qquad (3)$$

where Z_s is the impedance of the main transmission line, and Z_r is the impedance to be matched.

The load to be matched can be either balanced or unbalanced, but if it is the latter the outer sleeve is not needed. The diameter of the detuning sleeve is not critical; it just happens that beer cans work out conveniently. Let's say we want to match 50 to 300 ohms, a frequently encountered situation that cannot be handled with a flexible balun. From formula (3) we find that we need a Q section with an impedance of 122 ohms. Fig. 8-27 tells us that a b/a ratio of 7.5 is needed. With standard 9/16-inch ID plumbing copper pipe and a No. 12 wire we can take care of this job nicely. Many other usable combinations can be worked out, using pipe and wire sizes that are readily available.

may be convenient for feeding a split driven element directly with coax. In this application the bazooka is usually a piece of small coax similar to the main line. Taping the two pieces together leaves the issue of true electrical length somewhat in doubt, and other feed methods are generally preferable.

Impedance-Matching Balun Since the sleeve assembly of Fig. 8-25A is a quarter-wavelength long, it is a simple matter to make it serve well as a Q section for impedance matching, as well as a

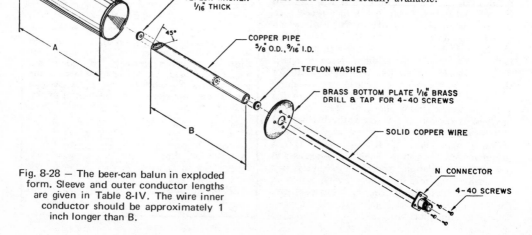

Fig. 8-28 — The beer-can balun in exploded form. Sleeve and outer conductor lengths are given in Table 8-IV. The wire inner conductor should be approximately 1 inch longer than B.

FEEDING STACKED AND PHASED ARRAYS

If individual bays of a stacked array are properly designed they will look like noninductive resistors to the phasing system that connects them. The impedances involved can thus be treated the same as resistances in parallel, if the phasing lines are a half wavelength or a multiple thereof. The latter point is important because the impedance at the end of a transmission line is repeated at every half wavelength along it.

In Fig. 8-29 we have three sets of stacked dipoles. Whether these are merely dipoles or the driven elements of Yagi bays makes little difference for the purpose of these examples. Two 300-ohm antennas at A are one wavelength apart, resulting in a feed impedance of approximately 150 ohms at the center. (It will be slightly less than 150 ohms, because of coupling between bays, but we can neglect this for practical purposes.) This value holds regardless of the impedance of the phasing line. Thus, we can use any convenient type of line for phasing, so long as the *electrical* length is right.

The velocity factor of the line must be taken into account. As with coax, this is subject to so much variation that it is well to make a resonance check if there is any doubt. The method is the same as for coax, Fig. 8-24. A half wavelength of line is resonant both open and shorted, but the shorted condition (both ends) is usually the more readily checked.

The impedance-transforming quality of a quarter-wavelength of line can be employed in combination matching and phasing lines, as shown in B and C of Fig. 8-29. In B, two bays spaced a half-wavelength are phased and matched by a 400-ohm line, acting as a double Q section, so that a 300-ohm main transmission line is matched to two 300-ohm bays. The two halves of this phasing line could each be 3 or 5 quarter-wavelengths long equally well, if these lengths serve any useful purpose. An example would be the stacking of two Yagis, where the desirable spacing is more than one-half wavelength.

A double Q section of coaxial line is illustrated in Fig. 8-29C. This is useful for feeding stacked bays which were originally set up for 52-ohm feed. A spacing of 5/8 wavelength is optimum for small Yagis, and this is the equivalent of an electrical full wavelength of solid-dielectric coax, such as RG-11/U. If our phasing line is made one quarter-wavelength on one side of the feed and three quarters on the other, one driven element should be reversed with respect to the other to keep the rf currents in phase. If the number of quarter-wavelengths is the same on either side of the feedpoint, the two elements should be in the same position, not reversed as shown in C. See "5-over-5 for 50 MHz," Chapter 9.

One marked advantage of coaxial phasing lines is that they can be wrapped around the vertical support, taped or grounded to it, or arranged in any way that is convenient mechanically. The spacing between bays can be set at the most desirable value, and the phasing line placed anywhere necessary to use up the required electrical length.

Making Adjustments

Wherever adjustable matching devices are used, any really effective adjustment procedure must be carried out either with the antenna in the position in which it will eventually be used, or under conditions simulating the eventual installation. The thought of making adjustments at the top of a tower is often a bit staggering to the budding big-antenna enthusiast, but fortunately such a high-wire act is not really necessary. There are right and wrong ways to do the job at ground level, however. From preceding discussion of the effect of ground on antenna impedance it is easy to see that matching adjustments made with an array close to ground could be quite a bit off when the array is hoisted to its eventual resting place 50 feet or more in the air. Furthermore, even if there were no impedance change from the effect of ground, objects quite some distance out in front of the

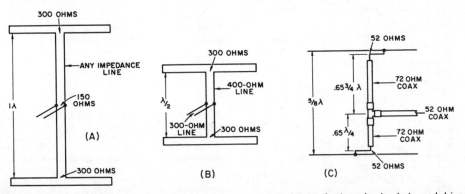

Fig. 8-29 — Three methods of feeding stacked vhf arrays. A and B are for bays having balanced driven elements, where a balanced phasing line is desired. Array C has an all-coaxial matching and phasing system. If the lower section is also 3/4 wavelength, no transposition of bays is needed.

array may reflect enough power back to it so that an appreciable reflected-power reading is observed from effects other than actual mismatch. The bigger and sharper the array, the more troublesome these reflections become.

The solution to this problem is obvious, but not too many antenna workers seem to think of it: aim the beam straight up, with the reflectors close to ground. If the front-to-back ratio is 20 dB, the amount of power that will be radiated downward with the beam in the straight up position is negligible, and so is the effect of ground on the antenna impedance. This lazy-man approach has been used many times, on bands from 50 through 432 MHz, and on each occasion it has resulted in very close to optimum matching when the array was finally installed in the tower position. Very much better results are possible in this way than with the array's line of fire parallel to and near the ground.

How Important is Matching?

Due mainly to over-exposure to the term, a good many hams tend to worship perfect matching. To have a 1-to-1 SWR is the ultimate achievement, for them. But is it so very important? Not necessarily! It depends on what you're going to do. As may be determined from Fig. 8-30, a 100-foot line of RG-8 coax at 144 MHz will have its loss increased by less than 0.5 decibel with a 2:1 SWR compared to a perfectly matched line. If the loading on the transmitter is adjusted properly and the line is trimmed for length, if necessary, a listener at a distant point would not be able to tell the difference. Note that this line trimming is to achieve a resonant condition and proper loading. *It does not affect the SWR!*

Mismatch is important in some ways, and it can tell you things about your antenna system. Make a frequency run, measuring SWR at 144, 144.5, 145, 145.5, 146, and so on. If your SWR dips to near 1:1 at 147 MHz and is 3:1 at 144, you need some work on your array. You're sure to be getting less

than top performance at the low end. But if 2:1 is as low as you can get, and it is around the frequency you work most often, you don't need to worry too much if the transmitter loads satisfactorily.

With high power a high SWR runs you into the danger of flash-over of the line, but this doesn't happen very often in vhf circles, at least with any coax worth using.

Exact matching *is* important in making measurements of antenna performance. If you would learn anything from attempted gain measurements you have to know *exactly* how much power you're putting into the antenna, or at least you have to know that you're using the same power every time. Forward-power readings with the usual SWR bridge are useless for antenna evaluation purposes, unless the system is perfectly matched. This means adjusting for *zero* reflected power, every time a comparison or measurement is made.

Much of the conflicting evidence reported in articles on antennas over the years has resulted from a lack of understanding of the importance of this precaution. Just putting up a field-strength meter and then pruning the elements or adjusting their spacing for maximum meter reading may result in your having a fairly good antenna, but it is a wholly unreliable way to make measurements. If you find the element lengths and spacings recommended in much of the literature on antennas confusing, failure to keep the radiated power constant, or inability to determine it accurately, may well be at the bottom of most of the inconsistencies.

Using the SWR Bridge

Coaxial feed is recommended, if only for the reason that it permits easy monitoring of the matching process. You merely connect a standing-wave bridge in the coaxial line and adjust the matching device for lowest possible reflected power. This should be zero, or very close to it. All that is left then to make your antenna radiate effectively is to adjust the coupling at the transmitter for maximum forward power on the bridge meter. Note that you do *not* adjust the matching device for maximum forward power; you adjust for *zero* reflected.

Where the bridge is inserted in the line is important. Many hams are happy about their antenna systems because a bridge connected in the

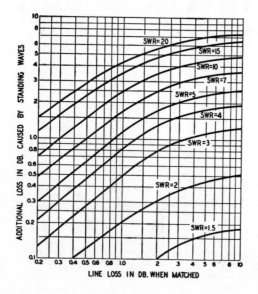

LINE LOSS IN DB. WHEN MATCHED

Fig. 8-30 — Increase in line loss because of standing waves. To determine the total loss in decibels in a line having an SWR greater than 1, first determine the loss for the particular type of line, length and frequency, on the assumption that the line is perfectly matched (Table 8-III). Locate this point on the horizontal axis and move up to the curve corresponding to the actual SWR. The corresponding value on the vertical axis gives the *additional* loss in decibels caused by the standing waves.

line at the transmitter output shows zero reflected power, but they may be in a fool's paradise. If the transmission line is long in terms of wavelength, and lossy (all coaxial lines are lossy enough to throw us off) the line may, in effect, be self-terminating. That is to say you can have the world's worst mismatch at the end of a 100-foot run of RG-8 on 432 MHz and you'll never know it if the bridge is connected at the transmitter. Try a direct short on the end of your line, or disconnect the antenna entirely, and see how little difference it makes on *your* line. Remember these are the ultimate extremes of mismatch! The bridge must be connected at or near the antenna, when making matching adjustments.

There is no way to adjust an antenna properly without an SWR indicator. Don't try to do without one, for it is probably the most important instrument you can own. It need not be fancy or "commercial." Very simple units are described in Chapter 14. The one built into the two-band Trans-match should work well on all vhf bands. The "line-sampler" rivals expensive in-line devices in versatility and accuracy, and it can be made to work from at least 50 through 1300 MHz. Both types are inexpensive to build.

DANGER — HIGH RF FIELD STRENGTH!

For years we have been reminded to "Switch to Safety," and techniques for doing this are well established, at least as far as dangerous ac and dc voltages are concerned. But how about strong rf fields? At what level is there any real danger to humans in exposure to uhf power?

There is much difference of opinion, but rough guidelines are available. Dick Knadle, K2RIW, discusses the problem in some detail in his *QST* treatment of the kilowatt amplifier for 432 MHz, described briefly in Chapter 14. He reports that the US Government has set a limit of 10 mW/cm² averaged over a 6-minute period as the safe maximum for human exposure. More than this causes thermal heating of skin tissue. Heating effect is especially dangerous to the eyes. There exists possibility of disturbances to the human nervous system, as yet unconfirmed in this country, which has caused some other authorities to set standards from 2.5 microwatts/cm² to 1 mW/cm² as allowable limits.

K2RIW feels we should be on the conservative side, and treat any radiation from high-power uhf transmitters with healthy respect. He recommends staying at least 30 feet away from the front of a 432-MHz antenna carrying 700 watts of rf power, and he would not climb a tower carrying this antenna, while power was on. He probed the kilowatt amplifier, running at full legal input, and found no more than one milliwatt, and that only within 1/4 inch of the air-exhaust screening, on the cover plate.

Chapter 9

Building and Using V H F Antennas

To some extent an antenna is an antenna, regardless of frequency. Certain basic principles apply all across the rf spectrum, but the wavelength factor makes for very large differences in practical problems encountered in building and erecting antennas, even within the vhf range. Mainly for this reason, the explanatory material of Chapter 8 may not be enough for many vhf enthusiasts who would like to try their hands at building their own beams.

Arguments in favor of building rather than buying are not greatly different for antennas than for other equipment we need for communication, except perhaps that fabrication of antennas may be more within the capabilities of the home craftsman than other equipment phases of the game. The hardest part of the job, the erection of the antenna, has to be done by the amateur in any case, so he is more likely to go the whole way and build the skyhook himself. Any able-bodied ham with a few simple tools can build and erect his own antennas, and usually he will enjoy the work and learn much from it. Very likely he will stretch his dollars somewhat further too, for good antennas come rather high these days.

Material for the construction of arrays may be costly, depending on where you do your shopping, but there are many ways for the ingenious ham to adapt inexpensive items to his purposes. Serviceable beams have been made by coating wooden dowels with conducting paint, or even by wrapping them with aluminum foil. Neither of these techniques is recommended, but they are examples of what can be done in a pinch. Salvage should not be overlooked, if costs are really important. Lumber yards; electrical; welding, or plumbing-supply houses; metal-smelting companies; junkyards and surplus lots – these are a few places in addition to the usual channels where we may find usable metal products. Hardware stores often have stocks of aluminum and accessories useful in vhf antenna construction.

Almost anything that is strong enough can be used for booms and supporting frames, whether it is insulating or conducting material, and there is no law requiring that elements be round in cross-section, so long as they are of a metal that is a reasonably good conudctor. And though electrical rotation systems have become almost standard equipment in amateur antenna practice, there is much to be said for simple "armstrong system" rotating devices.

Rotating provision of some kind *is* important, however. In earlier days at least, much of the magic ascribed to a ham's first beam was actually the

TABLE 9-I

Dimensions for Vhf Arrays in Inches

Freq (MHz)*	50*	144*	220*	432*	
Driven Element	111	38-5/8	25-7/16	13	* Dimensions are for *most-used* sections of each band: 50 to 50.6 MHz, 144 to 145.5 MHz, 220 to 222 MHz, and 432 to 434 MHz. The element lengths should be adjusted for each megahertz difference in frequency by the amount given in the third line of the table. Example: if optimum performance is wanted much above 145 MHz, shorten all elements by about 1/4 inch. For above 146 MHz, shorten by 1/2 inch. See text.
Change per MHz*	2	1/4	1/8	1/32	
Reflector	116-1/2	40-1/2	26-3/4	13-1/2	
1st Director	105-1/2	36-5/8	24-1/8	12-11/32	
2nd Director	103-1/2	36-3/8	24	12-9/32	
3rd Director	101-1/2	36-1/8	23-7/8	12-7/32	
1.0 Wavelength	236	81-1/2	53-5/8	27-1/4	
0.625 Wavelength	149	51	33-1/2	17	
0.5 Wavelength	118	40-3/4	26-13/16	13-5/8	
0.25 Wavelength	59	20-3/8	13-7/8	6-13/16	
0.2 Wavelength	47-3/4	16-1/4	10-3/4	5-7/16	
0.15 Wavelength	35-1/2	12-1/4	8	4	

Element spacings are not critical, and table figures may be used, regardless of element lengths chosen. Parasitic element lengths are optimum for collinear arrays and small Yagis, having 0.2-wavelength spacing.

result of its having been the first antenna he ever put up high and in the clear, and equipped with some form of rotator. Even a simple dipole with these attributes is not a bad antenna, but the bigger and better a vhf array is, the more it needs a rotator and some means of telling where the antenna is headed. If these requirements can be handled adequately by pulling on ropes and looking out the window, then there is no reason to be ashamed of doing it that way.

Because the band for which they are designed makes such a difference in the size and structural details of vhf antennas, our practical constructional information is given by bands. It should be stressed that the following are *examples*; they by no means cover the range of possibilities. Nor should it be inferred that, because a particular antenna is shown for only one band, it cannot be used, in principle at least, for others. These are ideas, to be adapted as the reader may see fit. The true ham will "take it from there."

To aid those who like to work strictly on their own, as far as materials and mechanical construction are concerned, Table 9-I gives the principal dimensions needed in building antennas for 50 through 450 MHz. Note that a most-used portion of each band is used for this information. Line 2 of the table is a change factor to be applied to table element lengths when other parts of a band are to be emphasized. Only element lengths are ordinarily this critical. Element spacings and phasing-line lengths can be left as given, or midband values used.

In the practical construction examples the dimensions of the original are given. Where the array is one that will be highly frequency-sensitive, as in a long Yagi, the portion of the band where the antenna works best is stated. The change factor of Table 9-I can be applied if some other band segment is to be favored. When in doubt, check back through Chapter 8, for basic information.

ANTENNAS FOR 50 MHz

Nearly everyone, at one time or another, has need for something simple and/or inexpensive for an antenna. This means a half-wave dipole of some sort, ordinarily. It can be any of the arrangements described in Chapter 8, so we will consider here only those that are most commonly employed in 50-MHz work.

The Folded Dipole

Probably the most universally useful 50-MHz dipole, all things considered, is the folded variety. It is broad in frequency response and not critical as to construction or adjustment. It can be made of a wide range of conductor sizes and materials, and it is adaptable to various mounting arrangements. It can be fed directly with 300-ohm balanced line (Twin-Lead or open-wire) or coax and a balun.

A folded dipole can be suspended from rope or wires or supported on a mast, depending on how the element is made. The center of the element can be grounded for lightning protection, or left floating electrically. The dipole of Fig. 9-1A can be made entirely of Twin-Lead, ready-made open-wire, or of any wire you may have on hand. When made of Twin-Lead, it is occasionally tacked or taped to a wall, when a temporary and unobtrusive antenna is the principal requirement.

Where it is to be mounted on a support such as a rotating mast, the dipole of 9-1B is preferable. The conductor size is not critical, except that both the broken and unbroken halves should be the same size. The unbroken portion can be attached to or run through a metal pipe or tubing support, in which case only a small cross-arm, or perhaps none at all, will be needed. The wire dipole, A, can be supported on a wooden "T," using vinyl-insulated screw eyes or the type sold for TV installations. The inner ends of the broken portion of either dipole, where the feed line connects, should be insulated from the support. The upper

and lower parts of dipole B are connected at the outer ends by means of metal pillars or sleeves. If the tubing is sufficiently flexible it can be bent around as in dipole A, but this is usually done only in dipoles for the higher bands, where small conductors are stiff enough to be self-supporting.

The feed line can be Twin-Lead or open-wire. If the latter, the half-inch-spaced type is preferable to the 1-inch, as it is closer to 300 ohms impedance. Coax and a balun can also be used. If this is done, 72-ohm coax will give a better match than 52-ohm, though even with the latter, the SWR will not be more than about 1.5 to 1, which is not serious.

The "J" Antenna

Center-fed systems like the folded dipole are well adapted to horizontal polarization, but the need for running the feed line perpendicular to the

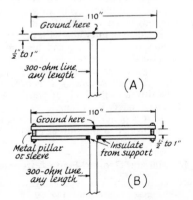

Fig. 9-1 — Folded dipoles for 50 MHz. Either may be fed with 300-ohm line, or 72-ohm coax and a balun. Dipole A is made of wire or Twin-Lead; dipole B of any convenient size tubing. Either can be grounded at the center of unbroken portion.

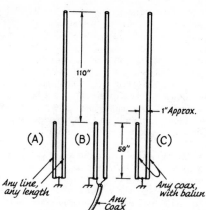

Fig. 9-2 — Three versions of the "J" antenna, with dimensions for 50-MHz operation. Grounding for lightning protection may be done as indicated by the ground symbol.

dipole for some distance makes them cumbersome for most vertical applications. The "J" system of Fig. 9-2 is more useful for vertical polarization. This is a vertical dipole with the matching arrangement at the bottom end, for convenience. It may be fed in various ways.

Antenna A has a balanced-line feed. This can be any impedance, as the point of connection is moved along the stub portion until a match is achieved. Antenna B is fed at the bottom end with coaxial line. This is a good approximation, if the antenna is to be erected and used without attention to matching. Though it may not be a perfect match, it will be close enough for practical purposes. Antenna C is for use where adjustment for match is desired. As in A, the coaxial line and balun are moved along the stub until an SWR bridge in the line shows zero reflected power. The bottom end of the system can be grounded for lightning protection in either A or C. In B, the bottom of the stub portion can be grounded.

The basic idea of the "J" is that the stub should not radiate, but in actual practice it does, to some extent. This radiation interferes with that from the main portion of the antenna and may result in raising the effective radiation angle. For this reason other matching methods are preferable, though the "J" has the virtue of simplicity. It is occasionally used as the driven element about which parasitic elements are rotated in a simple vertical Yagi. Except in B, it is preferable to run the feed line as nearly perpendicular to the stub as possible, for at least a quarter wavelength.

Coaxial and Ground-Plane Antennas

Particularly where the supporting structure is metal, the coaxial antenna, Fig. 9-3, and the ground-plane, Fig. 9-4, are superior to the "J" for omnidirectional vertical use. Both are intended primarily for coaxial feed, and the line can be run up inside the pipe mast, if one is used. The upper element is, in effect, an extension of the inner

conductor of the coax. The radials of the ground-plane and the skirt or lower element of the coaxial are connected to the outer conductor, and to the support, if desired. The skirt of the coaxial antenna should be so connected only at the top; the rest of it must be insulated from the coax and the support. Element and skirt lengths are not critical in the coaxial antenna. About 54 inches should be suitable for work across the whole 50-MHz band.

The ground-plane is perhaps the best all-purpose vertical antenna for coaxial feed. As the name implies, the horizontal radials simulate ground; consequently the impedance of the antenna is little affected by variation in height above actual ground and the nature of the supporting structure.

A simple and often-used version would be as shown schematically in Fig. 9-4A, except fed entirely with 52-ohm coax, without a matching section. The feed impedance of a ground-plane is low; of the order of 30 ohms, so there will be some mismatch when it is fed with 52-ohm line. The SWR is under 2 to 1, however, and performance should be satisfactory.

Matching can be achieved in several ways. A simple method is shown at A, but it requires that the main line be 72-ohm coax. The quarter-wave *Q* section of 52-ohm line makes an almost perfect match, and it can be connected very simply. The lower end of the *Q* section and the upper end of the main line can be fitted with coaxial connectors, and a coaxial junction used between them. The length of 38 inches for the matching section is for solid-dielectric coax with a velocity factor of 0.65. Foam and other low-density insulation will make the matching section longer. Means for checking resonant lengths are outlined in Chapter 8. See Fig. 8-24.

Another method for matching with 52-ohm line is to shorten the radiating element slightly, and then tune out the reactance so introduced by

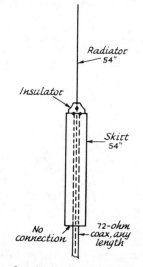

Fig. 9-3 — Coaxial vertical antenna for 50 MHz. A supporting pipe mast can run up inside the skirt portion.

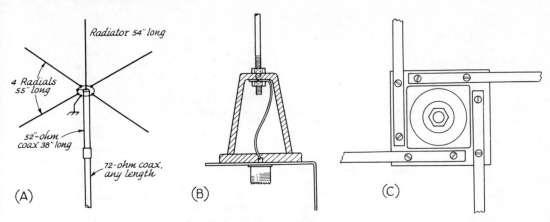

Fig. 9-4 — The ground-plane antenna, shown with Q matching section, A. One method of making the antenna, with a metal mounting bracket and ceramic insulator is shown at B. Radials, omitted from B in the interest of clarity, are shown attached to the metal mounting bracket in C.

connecting a closed-end stub in parallel with the antenna. If the antenna assembly includes a coaxial T fitting at the base of the driven element, the stub can be connected at will, and trimmed for length until a perfect match is achieved. With a 53-inch radiator the stub should be about 21 inches, if made with 52-ohm coax, but it is well to start with one somewhat longer and trim for match. Remember to short the far end of the stub each time a check is made.

Another matching trick with the ground-plane is to droop the radials downward, adjusting their angle below the horizontal until the antenna feed impedance becomes 52 ohms. This usually occurs at about a 45-degree angle. The antenna ceases to be a true ground-plane under these circumstances, but the method is often a satisfactory compromise. There will be some radiation from the radials in the drooping position, but this is not necessarily bad. Mixed polarization could be a "mixed blessing" under some propagation conditions.

Ground-planes can be made in many ways. One is shown in Fig. 9-4B. The vertical radiator is 1/4-inch rod, threaded at the bottom end, held in the top of a ceramic standoff insulator with nuts above and below the top of the cone. Before the insulator is bolted to the angle bracket that serves as a mounting, a wire or flexible strip of copper is fastened under the nut. It is left long enough so that it can be soldered to the coaxial fitting mounted on the angle bracket, before the insulator is bolted in place.

Radials are omitted from B in the interest of clarity. They can be fastened to the angle bracket, as shown in 9-4C. The angle bracket can be fastened to any vertical support, of wood or metal. A metal support preferably should be grounded independently of the outer conductor of the coax, for lightning protection.

Omnidirectional Horizontals

Often it is desirable to maintain uniform field strength in all directions about the station when horizontal polarization is used. In 50-MHz work this is usually accomplished with a halo or turnstile antenna. Basically, the halo is a half-wave dipole, bent around into a circle or some other shape that will give it fairly uniform radiation in the horizontal plane. Any of the common matching systems described in Chapter 8 can be used with the halo.

Where the halo is used for 50-MHz mobile work the total length of the ring is usually reduced by capacitive loading between the ends, as shown in Fig. 9-5. The circumference of the ring so formed is usually 60 to 70 inches.

The gamma matching system is convenient for mobile halos, as it permits matching to coaxial line and the use of an unbroken driven element. The step-up type of folded dipole is also used in halos, though the mechanical work involved has limited this type of feed mainly to manufactured antennas. A three-ring model of this kind has long been a fixture on the 6-meter mobile scene.

The capacitively loaded halo is a high-Q device, and it must be tuned with care or it will be all but useless. Usually some provision is made for varying the end-to-end capacitance, C1. If a gamma-matching system is used, the series capacitor, C2, and point of connection of the gamma arm to the element should be made variable, at least temporarily. Adjust these and the tuning capacitor, C1,

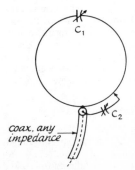

Fig. 9-5 — The halo antenna is a half-wave radiator bent into circular shape for nearly uniform radiation pattern. Capacity plates, C1, permit use of a small radiator for 50 MHz. Gamma match and series capacitor, C2, are for coaxial feed.

for minimum reflected power in an SWR bridge connected in the transmission line. This is made easier if the element is first resonated roughly at the middle of the desired operating range with C1, checking resonance with a grid-dip meter. The best point for coupling the dip-meter coil is near the feed point, just to the left of the coaxial line ground point in Fig. 9-5. Variation of the effective capacitance of C1 is usually done by mounting a small disk on an adjusting screw, equipped with lock nuts, to one of the plates, and then adjusting its position with respect to the other plate.

Halos can be stacked one above the other in a vertical line, to lower radiation angle and build up gain. This is done occasionally for fixed stations where omnidirectional coverage and something better than a single halo are required. Matching and feeding can be done in the same ways as with any two 50-ohm antennas. See Chapter 8, and below.

The optimum spacing for stacked halos is 1/2 to 5/8 wavelength.

Two 50-MHz halos adjusted individually for 50-ohm feed can be stacked physically 5/8 wavelength apart by connecting them with half-wave (77-inch) sections of 52-ohm coax, with a T fitting. A 38-inch 52-ohm Q section at this point will then match a 72-ohm transmission line. Specific halo designs follow in the mobile section, later in this chapter. For more stacking details see Fig. 9-44.

The turnstile antenna, shown for 144-MHz use in Fig. 9-39, can be adapted readily to 50-MHz service. It is larger physically than the halo, and it should provide slightly more gain and considerably broader frequency response. A stacked turnstile system makes a very good omnidirectional antenna for home-station use. Stacking methods similar to those outlined for halos and other coax-fed antennas can be employed with turnstiles.

YAGI ARRAYS FOR 50 MHz

Fig. 9-6 — A lightweight 3-element 50-MHz array. Feeder is 52-ohm coax, with a balun for connection to the folded dipole driven element. Balun loop may be coiled as shown, or taped to the supporting pole.

The Yagi antenna is almost ideally suited to 50-MHz operation. Usually only a relatively small portion of the band is covered so the Yagis limited frequency response presents no problems, and arrays having gains of up to 10 dB are easily built and erected. Except under the most severe weather conditions, rotation of 50-MHz Yagis of up to at least 6 elements can be handled with inexpensive TV-type rotators, provided means are taken to prevent the entire weight of the structure from bearing on the rotator driving mechanism. Some rotators have thrust bearings available as accessories, for this purpose.

3-Element Lightweight Array

The 3-element 50-MHz array of Fig. 9-6 weighs only 5 pounds. It uses the closest spacing that is practical for vhf applications, in order to make an antenna that could be used individually or stacked

in pairs without requiring a cumbersome support. The elements are half-inch aluminum tubing of 1/16-inch wall thickness, attached to the 1-1/4-inch dural boom with aluminum castings. (Kirk Electronics Yagi clamps.) The mounting method of Fig. 9-14 is also usable. By limiting the element spacing to 0.15 wavelength, the boom is only 6 feet long. Two booms for a stacked array can thus be cut from a single 12-foot length of tubing.

The folded-dipole driven element has No. 12 wire for the fed portion. The wire is mounted on 3/4-inch cone standoff insulators and joined to the outer ends of the main portion by means of metal pillars and 6/32 screws and nuts. When the two halves are pulled up tightly and wrapped around the screws, solder should be sweated over the nuts and screw ends to seal the whole against weather corrosion. The same treatment should be used at each standoff. Mount a soldering lug on the ceramic cone and wrap the end of the lug around the wire and solder the whole assembly together. These joints and other portions of the array may

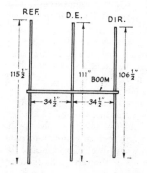

Fig. 9-7 — Dimensions of the 3-element array of Fig. 9-6, for working in the lower portion of the 50-MHz band. Driven elements are 1/2-inch aluminum tubing. The folded dipole driven element uses No. 12 wire for the fed portion.

Fig. 9-8 — Closeup view of the boom mounting for 50-MHz arrays. A plate of aluminum about 6 inches square is backed up by wood or Masonite. TV-type U clamps hold the boom and vertical support together at right angles. The aluminum casting shown here for mounting the beam elements is no longer sold, but suitable substitutes are available.

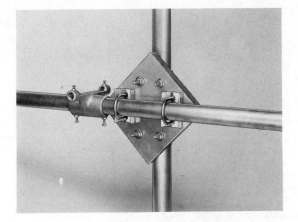

be sprayed with clear lacquer as an additional protection.

The aluminum casting shown in Fig. 9-8 is no longer sold but Kirk Yagi Clamps (Kirk Electronics, 134 Westpark Road, Dayton, OH 45459) serve equally well. The inner ends of the fed portion of the dipole can be supported on ceramic cones, whose mounting screws go through the 1/2-inch element at points equidistant from the midpoint, the actual separation being determined by the element-mounting hardware used. Any inner-end separation from 1-1/4 to 3 inches should be usable. The plane of the two portions of the

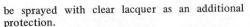

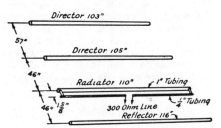

Fig. 9-9 — Dimensions of a 4-element 50-MHz array having maximum forward gain in the lower part of the band. The folded dipole details are for 300-ohm balanced feed.

folded dipole is unimportant. It need not be vertical, as in Fig. 9-6.

The element lengths in Fig. 9-7 are for best operation between 50.0 and 51 MHz. The reflector and director are approximately 4 percent longer and shorter than the driven element. The close spacing of the parasitic elements (0.15 wavelength) makes this deviation from the usual 5 percent desirable. For higher parts of the band, shorten all elements by 2 inches per megahertz higher in frequency.

The folded dipole gives a single 3-element array a feed impedance of about 200 ohms. It may be fed with a balun of the type shown in Fig. 8-25, using 52-ohm coax. A gamma-matched dipole may also be used. See Fig. 8-17C and associated text. A

variable capacitor can be used experimentally and replaced with the nearest-available fixed value, once the needed capacitance is found experimentally. Coaxial variable capacitors, handmade or manufactured, are also usable. Some form of gamma match is especially desirable if two bays are to be stacked. The matching and phasing arrangement, shown later in connection with a 5-over-5 for 50 MHz, is applicable to smaller bays as well.

High-Performance 4-Element Array

The 4-element array of Fig. 9-9 was designed for maximum forward gain, and for direct feed with 300-ohm balanced transmission line. The parasitic elements may be any diameter from 1/2 to 1 inch, but the driven element should be made as shown in the sketch. For a 1/2-inch driven element use the information for the antenna of Fig. 9-6. The spacing between driven element and reflector, and between driven element and first director, is 0.2 wavelength. Between the first and second directors the spacing is 0.25 wavelength.

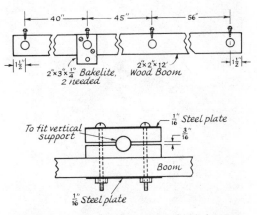

Fig. 9-10 — Suggested construction for an inexpensive 4-element array for 50 MHz using a wooden boom. Dimensions are a slight modification of the optimum given in Fig. 9-9, to fit a 12-foot boom. Mounting arrangement is for clamping to a pipe mast.

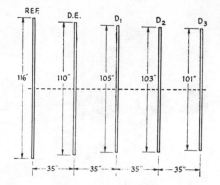

Fig. 9-11 — Five-element 50-MHz Yagi for a 12-foot boom. Dimensions are for working in the lower part of the 50-MHz band.

The same general arrangement may be used for a 3-element array, except that the solid portion of the dipole should be 3/4-inch tubing instead of 1 inch. The boom length would then be about 8 feet.

With the element lengths given, the array will give nearly uniform response from 50 to 51.5 MHz, and usable gain to about 52 MHz.

If a shorter boom is desired, the reflector spacing can be reduced to 0.15 wavelength and both directors spaced 0.2 wavelength, with only a slight reduction in forward gain and bandwidth. A slight modification for mounting on a 12-foot wooden boom is shown in Fig. 9-10. Also included

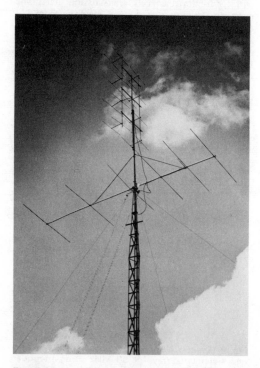

Fig. 9-12 — A 6-element Yagi for 50 MHz, with optimum spacing for forward gain given in Fig. 9-13. Boom is 20 feet long. Antenna at the top is 16-element all-metal collinear array for 144 MHz.

is a method of attaching the boom to a pipe support, using wood blocks. A convenient way of supporting metal-boom arrays on a pipe mast is shown in Fig. 9-8.

5 50-MHz Elements on a 12-Foot Boom

As aluminum or dural tubing is often sold in 12-foot lengths, this dimension may impose a practical limitation on the construction of a 50-MHz beam. A 5-element array that makes optimum use of a 12-foot boom may be built according to Fig. 9-11. If the aluminum-clamp method of mounting elements shown in Fig. 9-14 is employed, the weight of a 5-element beam can be held to under 10 pounds.

The gamma match and coaxial line are recommended for feeding such an array. A folded dipole similar to that used in the 3-element array will provide an approximate match to 52-ohm coax and a balun, but the gamma system is preferable, as it permits adjustment for exact match at the favored frequency range.

Gain and bandwidth of this compromise design are both slightly below optimum, but it represents effective use of a 12-foot boom. It will have a bit more gain than a 12-foot 4-element array, but will be somewhat more critical in frequency response.

LONG YAGIS ON 50 MHz

Once we go beyond the convenient and readily available 12-foot boom appreciably, any structure tends to become cumbersome, so building for optimum performance is usually the main consideration. A 5-element 50-MHz of optimum design is shown as part of the 5-over-5 described later. Yagis of 6 elements, or even longer, need not be heavy or overly difficult to mount and rotate. Choice of materials and judicious use of bracing are important here.

6-Element 50-MHz Yagi

The 6-element arrays of Figs. 9-13 and 9-19 are examples. The 20-foot boom can be made of light aluminum TV masting. This comes in 10-foot lengths which telescope one inside the other for about 6 inches. The joint can be held firm with self-tapping screws. Any light boom more than about 12 feet long should be braced to keep it in alignment, preferably from above the boom, as shown in Figs. 9-12 and 9-14. A method of splicing tubing for long booms is shown in Fig. 9-18.

Dimensions in Fig. 9-13 are for operation in the first megahertz of the band. Set up in this way, the array can be adjusted for perfect match at 50.3 and it will show an SWR under 1.7 to 1 from 50 to 50.6 MHz. Slightly more bandwidth can be achieved by making the directors one-half inch shorter than shown. Additional directors should be spaced 70 inches apart. They may be similar to D4, or each one inch shorter for greater bandwidth.

Elements are mounted in the same way as for the 3-element job, using aluminum castings. The center support is the same as in Fig. 9-8. Elements can be run through the boom and clamped, as shown in Fig. 9-14, but the aluminum-casting

Fig. 9-13 — Dimensions of the 6-element 50-MHz array. If the boom length is limited to exactly 20 feet, reduce spacing of D3 and D4 by 2 inches each. Dimensions are for the low megahertz of the band.

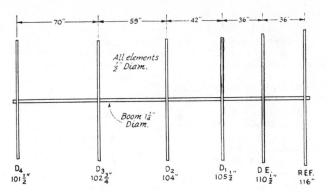

method of mounting is stronger. It is recommended for light boom materials. Matching is by means of a coaxial gamma arrangement shown in Fig. 9-15. Once adjustment is completed the open end of the gamma arm can be wrapped with plastic tape, and it and the joint between the sliding and stationary parts of the gamma capacitor sprayed with clear lacquer. If anyone doubts the ability of this arrangement to withstand weather, the original was used for over seven years, and was working nicely when replaced by that in Fig. 9-19.

The main gamma arm is cut from the same material as the elements. It is suspended parallel to the driven element by means of two 1-inch ceramic standoffs and 4 sheet aluminum clips, as shown in the photograph. The 1/2-inch tube is 15 inches long. Its inner end is connected to the inner conductor of a coaxial fitting, which is mounted on a small bracket screwed to the boom casting. Holes are drilled and tapped in the casting to take

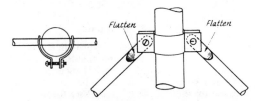

Fig. 9-14 — Method of mounting elements through a metal boom, left, and of bracing the boom to the vertical support, right. Suspension bracing is recommended for long booms. Shorter ones can be braced below the boom. A one-piece wrap-around clamp on the boom takes the angle brace.

two 6/32 machine screws for mounting the bracket.

The sliding arm that is the movable element of the coaxial capacitor is made of 1/4-inch tubing or rod, about 14 inches long. It is maintained coaxial with the main arm by means of two polystyrene bushings. One is force-fitted to the end of the rod that goes inside the main arm. The other is fitted tightly into the far end of the main arm, but reamed out to permit the movable rod to slide freely in and out. These bushings can be made from 3/8-inch polystyrene rod, or they can be fashioned easily from small polystyrene coil forms.

A clip of sheet aluminum makes contact between the driven element and the sliding rod. Be sure that all surfaces at the points of contact are completely clean, as solid low-resistance electrical contact is of utmost importance here.

Proper adjustment of the gamma match requires an SWR bridge. If the work cannot be done with the beam in the position in which it is to operate, set it up temporarily with the boom vertical and the reflector close to the ground. Insert the bridge in the line near or at the antenna. If more than a few watts of power is present in the line, adjustment of the gamma will best be done with gloves on the hands, to prevent rf burns. The operation is twofold; both the point of connection and the value of the series capacitor must be adjusted. Start with the clip set about 16 inches out from the boom, with enough tension on the clip to insure a good electrical connection. Adjust the capacitance and the point of connection for zero reflected power at the midpoint of the frequency range you want to work over effectively.

Fig. 9-15 — Gamma-matching section for the 6-element array, using a coaxial variable capacitor. The sheet aluminum clip at the right and the length of the small rod protruding from the arm are adjusted for minimum reflected power. The movable rod element of the capacitor is about 14 inches long, and is insulated from the fixed portion, of 1/2-inch tubing.

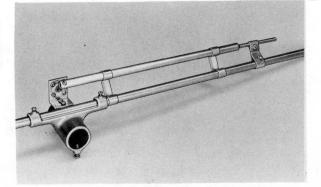

If you are interested only in the first 600 kHz or so of the band, use 50.3 for the adjustment frequency. For good coverage of 50 to 51 MHz, use 50.5. In the latter case, the SWR should be below 2 to 1 over the 1-megahertz range.

STACKED 50-MHz YAGIS

The lower radiation angle resulting from the stacking of two 50-MHz Yagis one above the other has a very beneficial effect on station effectiveness, particularly on long paths. The gain may exceed the theoretical 3 dB obtainable from stacking, where radiation angle is a critical factor. (Low radiation angle can be harmful, too, but the effect is discernible mainly on paths that are not too difficult to cover, ordinarily.) Gain from stacking is achieved without appreciable sharpening of the horizontal pattern, and with little effect on frequency response, whereas gain from using more elements in a single plane tends to make both factors more critical.

Choice between a single long Yagi and a stacked pair of the same theoretical gain thus becomes a matter of operating objectives. Stacking a pair of 3-element bays like that in Fig. 9-6 should give about the same gain as a single optimum-spaced 6-element bay, Fig. 9-12. The 3-over-3 will require less rotating, but the 6-elements-in-line will reject strong signals from off the desired line of fire more effectively.

Stacking Methods

The functions of phasing and matching of two Yagi bays can be handled with open-wire or coaxial lines. Uses of both are discussed in Chapter 8. See Fig. 8-29 and associated text. Antennas designed for balanced-line feed are more readily phased with

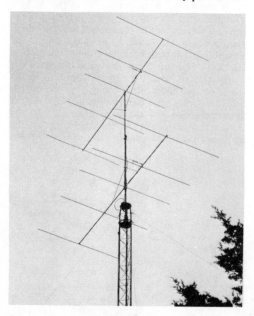

Fig. 9-16 — 5-over-5 stacked-Yagi array for 50 MHz, with all-coax feed.

open-wire line. Coaxial-line phasing and matching is ideal for gamma-matched bays, and it has obvious mechanical advantages. Coaxial phasing tends to result in somewhat cleaner radiation patterns, there being no pickup or radiation from the phasing system. A properly designed balanced-line system should also work well in this respect, but chances for stray signal pickup and phasing-line radiation are greater.

Coaxial matching and phasing are shown in the 50-MHz 5-over-4 that follows. A 4-over-4 using balanced transmission line feed and phasing can be made very simply with two bays of the type shown in Fig. 9-9. A 400-ohm line of No. 12 wire spaced 1-1/8 inches connecting two such bays a half-wavelength apart presents a 300-ohm feed impedance at its center. It can be fed with a main transmission line of 300 ohms impedance, balanced, or with 72-ohm coaxial line and a balun. Half-wave spacing gives somewhat less than optimum gain, but the lowered radiation angle still makes such a 4-over-4 very much worthwhile.

A bay spacing of 5/8 wavelength (12 feet) and all-coax matching and phasing is appreciably better. A full wavelength (20 feet) is optimum for medium-length bays, but it may be more than most vhf-antenna builders want to tackle.

5-OVER-5 FOR 50 MHz

The information provided in Fig. 9-17 is useful for a single 5-element Yagi, or for the stacked pair of Fig. 9-16, either to be fed with a 50-ohm line. The phasing and matching arrangement may be used for any pair of Yagis designed for 50-ohm feed individually. With slight modification it will serve with Yagis designed for 200-ohm balanced feed.

Mechanical Details

Construction of the single Yagi bay or a stacked pair is simplified by use of components that should be available to most builders. Element-to-boom and boom-to-mast mounts are aluminum castings designed for these applications by Kirk Electronics, 134 Westpark Road, Dayton, OH 45459. The gamma matches shown schematically in Fig. 9-17 are of coaxial construction, waterproofed for long life, available from the same supplier.

Booms are made of two 8-foot lengths of 1-1/4-inch aluminum (Reynolds) found in many hardware stores. Reynolds makes a special fitting for joining sections of the tubing, but these are not widely available from the usual hardware-store stocks, so a handmade splice was substituted. A piece of the same-diameter tubing as the booms, 12 inches or more in length, is slotted with a hacksaw, and then compressed to fit inside the ends of the two 8-foot lengths, as seen in Fig. 9-18. If the splice is held in the compressed position with large pipe pliers or a hose clamp, the ends will slide inside the boom sections readily. When the splice is released from compression, the two tubes can be driven together. Self-tapping screws should be run through the tubes and the splice, to hold the assembly firm. Use at least two on each side of the splice.

Elements are 1/2-inch aluminum tubing, Alcoa alloy 6061-T6. Almost any aluminum should be suitable. Kirk Yagi clamps, one-piece aluminum castings designed for this job, are available for 3/8- as well as 1/2-inch elements, and 1-1/4-inch boom. The eyes through which the elements pass are drilled, but must be tapped for 10-32 setscrews to tighten the elements firmly in place, two screws per element. The portion of the clamp that surrounds the boom can be spread slightly to allow the clamp to slide along the boom to the desired point. The interior surface is slightly rough, so tightening the yoke with the screw provided with the clamps makes the element set firmly on the boom. The reflector, driven element, and first director are all in back of the boom splice.

The vertical member of the stacked array is 1-1/4-inch thick-wall anodyzed steel tubing, commonly used in large antenna installations for home TV. Do not use thin-wall aluminum or light galvanized steel masting. The aluminum is not strong enough, and inexpensive steel masting rusts inside, weakening the structure and inviting failure.

Spacing between the bays can be a half wavelength (10 feet), 5/8 wavelength (12 feet), or a full wavelength (20 feet), though the wide spacing imposes mechanical problems that may not be worth the effort for most builders. The 5/8-wave spacing is a good compromise between stacking gain and severe support problems, and is recommended with the materials used here.

The 10-foot lengths of steel masting could be used, with the bottom 8 feet running through the tower bearing to the rotator. A heavier main support is preferable, however, and it is "1-inch water pipe" in this installation. This is iron, about 1-3/8-inch outside diameter, extending about 8 feet out of the tower. The steel masting between the Yagi bays is fastened to the pipe with four TV-type U-clamps, spaced evenly in the overlapping area of the two supports.

The booms are braced to the mast fore and aft, using the longest pieces of element stock left over when the forward directors are cut from 12-foot lengths. Ends of the braces are flattened about one inch, and bent to the proper angle. Outer ends fasten to the booms with two self-tapping screws each. The mast ends are clamped to the support with one TV U-clamp for each pair. This bracing is good insurance against fluttering of the booms and elements, which can cause failures after long periods, even though a structure appears adequately strong.

Phasing and Matching

A single 5-element Yagi can be fed directly with 50-ohm coax, through the Kirk coaxial gamma-match assembly (Type C6M). This has an adjustable coaxial capacitor, and an arm that connects to the driven element with a sliding clip. Both the capacitor and the point of connection should be adjusted for minimum reflected power, at the center of the frequency range most used. Doing this between 50.2 and 50.4 MHz is suitable for most operators, other than those using fm above 52.5 MHz. Each bay of the stacked pair should be set in this way. The pair can then be fed through a

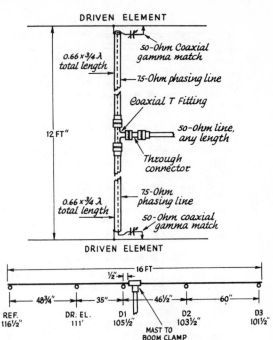

Fig. 9-17 — Principal dimensions of the 50-MHz 5-over-5, with details of the 3/4-wavelength Q-section matching system. The propagation factor of 0.66 applies only with solid-dielectric coax. Gamma-matching assemblies are coaxial-capacitor units (Kirk Electronics C6M).

double Q-section of 75-ohm coax, as shown in Fig. 9-17.

The Kirk gamma-match assembly has an SO-239 coaxial fitting built in, so the phasing lines are fitted with PL-259 coaxial connectors at both ends. The inner ends attach to a matching coaxial T fitting. The main run of 50-ohm line connects to the center of the T, with a coaxial through-connector and a PL-259 fitting. When the antenna is installed all connectors should be wrapped tightly with plastic tape, and sprayed with Krylon or other protective spray. Dow-Corning Silastic RTV-732 sealant is also good for this use. If the coaxial phasing sections are wrapped around the booms and vertical support a few times, they will just reach the T-fitting, when 12-foot spacing is used.

The lines should be any odd multiple of a quarter-wavelength. If both are the same length the gamma arms should attach to the same side of the driven elements. If there is a half-wavelength difference in the lines, the arms should connect to opposite sides. The length given in Fig. 9-17 is nominal for solid-dielectric coax. If foam-dielectric line is used, the propagation factor given by the maker should be substituted for the 0.66 figure. It is best to grid-dip the line sections for resonant frequency, in any case. Cut the line three inches or more longer than the expected length. Solder a loop of wire between the center pin and the mounting flange of an SO-239 connector. Attach this to the PL-259 connector at one end of the

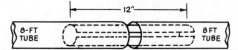

Fig. 9-18 — Details of the boom splices used in the 5-element 50-MHz Yagis. Two 8-foot lengths of 1 1/4-inch tubing are joined to make the 16-foot booms.

line, and couple it to the dip-meter coil. Trim the line length until resonance at the midpoint of the intended frequency range is indicated. This will not change appreciably when the other coaxial connector is attached.

The line used in the model described is RG-59A/U, which is satisfactory for any amateur power level, so long as the SWR is kept low. Larger coax, such as RG-11A/U, is recommended for a greater margin of safety.

Adjustment and Testing

An individual Yagi can be tested and matched properly by mounting it a half-wavelength above ground, in a large area that is clear of obstructions for many wavelengths. The boom can also be tilted up, until the ground-reflected wave is not a factor in the field-strength meter reading. The SWR bridge should be connected at the gamma match, or an electrical half-wavelength therefrom. Apply low power (not over 10 watts) and adjust the gamma capacitor and the point of connection to the driven element for zero reflected power, at the desired frequency range. The model was flat from 50.2 to 50.4 with just perceptible reflected power showing at 50.1 to 50.5. Adjusted in this way the array should work well up to about 51 MHz.

The best way to check operation of the stacked pair is to support the array with the reflectors resting on the ground and the booms pointing straight up. A 6-foot step-ladder can be used for a temporary support. The bays can be fed separately

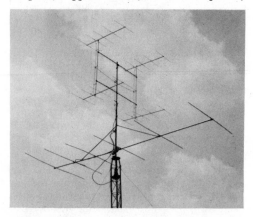

Fig. 9-19 — All metal arrays for 50 and 144 MHz. All parts of both beams can be assembled readily with ordinary hand tools. In this installation the two beams are fed from a single feed line, with a waterproofed coaxial switch at the top of the tower permitting selection of the desired array from the operating position.

with 50-ohm line, in this position, and the gamma settings should be the same as obtained in the first check, described above. Now connect the two 75-ohm phasing lines, and insert the SWR bridge in the 50-ohm line to the T fitting. The SWR should be the same as when the bays are fed separately through the 50-ohm line; close to 1:1. The array can be dismantled and reassembled atop the tower, and matching should remain correct.

The matching-phasing system described is useful for any two loads designed for 50-ohm feed. The 5/8-wave spacing is usable with up to at least 6-element bays, though wider bay spacing is needed for maximum gain with long Yagis. Individual antennas intended for 200-ohm balanced feed can be matched with 75-ohm coax in the phasing harness and baluns at each load.

Bay spacing is not critical. Close spacing gives somewhat lower gain, but a very clean pattern. The main lobe gets sharper and larger as spacing is increased, but minor lobes also increase. These take over from the main lobe if spacing of bays is carried too far. The effect of increasing bay spacing is shown graphically in Fig. 8-11.

144-OVER-50

Stacking of arrays for 50 and 144 MHz, and a method of using a single low-loss transmission line, are illustrated in the two-band system of Fig. 9-19. The 4-bay 144-MHz array will be described in the next section. The 6-element 50-MHz Yagi is very similar to the one already described, except for the simplified gamma matching system and special attention to lightweight element design.

The 50-MHz elements have center sections of half-inch aluminum tubing making up about half their total length. Thin-walled fuel-line tubing inserts in each end keep the total element weight down, and provide a means of adjustment of length, if the builder wishes to experiment with tuning. The entire element can be made of the heavier tubing, though the arrangement described is lighter, and has a bit lower wind resistance. Some shopping around in surplus houses, aluminum smelting places, and hardware and plumbing supply stores, as well as the usual aluminum tubing sources, will turn up several tubing size combina-

Fig. 9-20 — Model showing the method of mounting 1/2-inch elements on a 1-1/4-inch boom without drilling holes through the latter. For strongest permanent assembly, self-tapping screws should fasten the sheet-metal clamps in position.

tions that can be used in this way. The ends of the larger tubing can be slitted with a hacksaw to a depth of about three inches, and then tightened onto the smaller material with a wrap-around clamp. The elements can be mounted through the boom, as in Fig. 9-14, fastened with Kirk Yagi Clamps, as in the 5-over-5 just described, or held in place with sheet-aluminum clamps shown in Figs. 9-20 and 21.

The lips of the clamps should be bent upward at right angles first. Forming the "U" is started by placing the tubing in a vise in a vertical position, and bending the clamp around it. The actual U shape is achieved by opening the vise to slightly more than the width of tubing-plus-clamp, placing the clamp U-down loosely in the vise with the tubing lying in it, and then tapping the tubing lightly with a hammer. Alignment of the holes in the clamps is not fussy, and if they are drilled slightly larger than needed to pass the screws there will be no assembly problem. We used a No. 22 drill and 6-32 screws. The nuts should be pulled up only tightly enough to hold the assembly firmly together. Check the nuts after the array has been in use for a few days and tighten as necessary.

The gamma method is about as simple as you can get: the coax is merely brought along the boom to the driven element, bent at right angles, and run out far enough to match the antenna impedance when fed through a 100-pF fixed capacitor. The point of connection was found experimentally, though 20 inches and 100 pF should do. Put an SWR bridge in the line and move the connection along the element, for minimum reflected power. The outer conductor of the coax should be grounded to the boom at about 54 inches from the capacitor end. Strip a narrow band of the outer covering off, and fasten it to the boom with the "figure 8" clamp of Fig. 9-21D. Waterproof by wrapping with plastic tape and spraying with Krylon. Treat the capacitor similarly. It must stand high rf current. The Centralab 8505-100N is adequate. A variable may be used if mounted in a weatherproof box.

The 144- and 50-MHz arrays can be fed with separate 52-ohm lines, but a single high-quality transmission line was used in this installation. A

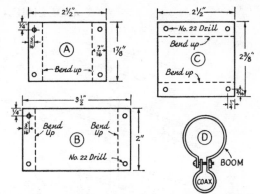

Fig. 9-21 — Dimensions of aluminum plates used to make the assembly clamps in the vhf arrays. Sheet metal should be 3/64 inch or thicker. Two A-type clamps are needed for joining 3/4-inch tubes at right angles for assembling the frame of the 144-MHz array. One B and one C are needed to mount a 1/2-inch element on a 1-1/4-inch boom, as in Fig. 9-20. The "figure 8" clamp, D, made from a 1/2-inch-wide strip approximately 6 inches long, is used to ground the coax to the 50-MHz boom.

hermetically sealed coaxial switch was mounted on the vertical support between the two antennas for this purpose. An ordinary coaxial relay will do, if mounted in a waterproof box. The remote switch operates on 115 volts ac, but to make for a safe installation a 6.3-volt transformer was used in the station, connected to a similar transformer on the tower through rotator cable with pairs of wires in parallel. Low-voltage ac is used for the main run. Antenna selection at the control position is done in the primary circuit at the station end.

The other 144-over-50 combination, Fig. 9-12, is set up for separate open-wire lines. The rotating section of line to the 144-MHz 16-element collinear is 300-ohm transmitting Twin-Lead. The 50-MHz rotating section is coax, terminated in a balun and a Q section, to match the 400-ohm line. Small mismatches in these lines are unimportant, as both main runs are high-quality balanced transmission line. They show no increase in loss when operated with a moderate SWR.

144-MHz ANTENNAS

Though some information in the 50-MHz section may be useful to the builder of 144-MHz arrays, the roughly 3-to-1 difference in size tends to make construction ideas for the two bands mutually exclusive. The 2-meter antenna nearly always has more elements than the one for 6, for two good reasons: size permits it and performance demands it.

Though gain over a dipole comes progressively easier as we go to higher frequencies and smaller elements, overall communications efficiency does not. Regardless of frequency, the *physical size* of the antenna is what really counts in determining how well a station will work out. A 5-element Yagi, properly designed, will have the same gain

whether built for 50 or 144 MHz. It is accepted as quite a good antenna on 6, but if everyone used nothing larger on 2 our results on that band would be dismal indeed. Thus, we find long Yagis and large collinear arrays in common use on 144 MHz and higher bands, but relatively rare on 50 MHz.

Frequency response may be important on 144, too. Most 50-MHz activity is concentrated near the low end of the band, but we spread out more in the 144-MHz band. Its ability to work over a relatively wide frequency range makes the collinear a good choice for many 2-meter men, while those who want optimum performance in one narrow segment probably will go for the long Yagi.

COLLINEAR ARRAYS

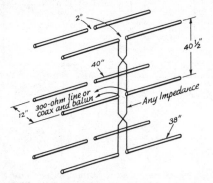

Fig. 9-22 — Schematic drawing of a 12-element collinear array for 144 MHz that may be fed with coaxial line and a balun, or 300-ohm balanced line. The supporting frame of Fig. 9-24 was intended for use with this type of array.

Two collinear systems for 144 MHz and higher bands are shown in Figs. 9-22 and 9-23. Either can be fed directly with 300-ohm balanced line, or with coaxial line and a balun. The actual feed impedance depends on many factors, but if no means of matching is used the SWR on the main line will never be very high. For precise matching, use of the universal stub (Fig. 8-18D) is recommended.

Feed impedance can be controlled to some extent by varying the spacing between the driven elements and the reflectors. In the 16-element array, Fig. 9-23, the impedance tends to be on the low side of 300 ohms, so the reflectors are spaced 0.2 to 0.25 wavelength behind the driven elements. In the 12-element system, Fig. 9-22, the impedance

is higher, due to the lesser number of elements and connection of the main line at the inner ends of the middle pair instead of at the midpoint between two pairs, so the reflectors are spaced 0.15 wavelength to bring the impedance down. There is little gain difference with reflector spacings from 0.15 to 0.25 wavelength.

A supporting frame may be made of wood or metal, if elements are supported at their centers and no insulating mounts will be needed. It is best to keep the supporting structure in back of the plane of the elements insofar as possible, and to avoid use of insulating material near the element ends. All-metal construction is illustrated in Figs. 9-24 through 9-26. All-wood construction is used in 432-MHz arrays described later.

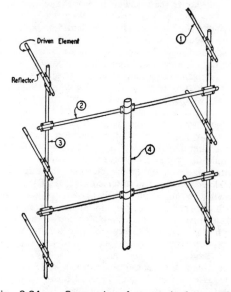

Fig. 9-24 — Supporting framework for a 12-element 144-MHz array of all-metal design. Dimensions are as follows: element supports (1) 3/4 X 16 inches; horizontal members (2) 3/4 X 46 inches; vertical members (3) 3/4 X 86 inches; vertical support (4) 1-1/2-inch diameter, length as required; reflector-to-driven-element spacing 12 inches. Parts not shown in sketch: driven elements 1/4 X 38 inches; reflectors 1/4 X 40 inches; phasing lines No. 18 spaced 1 inch, 80 inches long, fanned out to 3-1/2 inches at driven elements (transpose each half-wave section). The elements and phasing lines are arranged as shown in Fig. 9-22.

Elements should be rigid enough so that light tension on the phasing lines will not bend them appreciably. Aluminum or dural tubing 1/4 to 3/8 inch in diameter is commonly used, and 1/4-inch aluminum rod is good. Frequency response of the collinear array is broad enough so that element lengths and other dimensions can be taken from Figs. 9-22 or 23 or from Table 9-I.

Large collinear arrays should be kept to a maximum of 8 driven elements per set of phasing

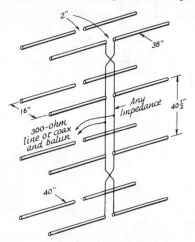

Fig. 9-23 — A 16-element collinear array similar to the 12-element of Fig. 9-22, except that the feedpoint is midway between the middle pairs of elements. Wider spacing of the reflectors results in nearly the same feed impedance. An example of this array is shown above a 50-MHz Yagi in Fig. 9-12.

Fig. 9-25 — Model showing method of assembling all-metal arrays, using clamps detailed in Fig. 9-26.

lines. See Fig. 8-13 and the 432-MHz collinear of Fig. 9-64 for recommended methods of feeding arrays of more than 8 driven elements. Two 16-element 2-meter arrays can be mounted side by side or one above the other, and fed in phase. A side-by-side 32-element setup was used to collect the data of Fig. 8-11, on the effects of spacing between bays. Increasing the bay spacing makes a large array that is hard to handle mechanically, but a very worthwhile improvement in gain and pattern sharpness results.

The feed impedance at the center of the phasing line between two such bays is roughly half that of one bay alone. A Q section with variable spacing, or the universal stub, Fig. 8-18C and Ð, will provide for matching.

All-Metal Construction

Collinear arrays of all-metal design can be very light in weight, yet rugged enough to withstand extreme weather hazards. The 16-element array of Fig. 9-12, built according to Figs. 9-23 through 26, survived four severe winters, mounted 70 feet in the air on a windswept New England hilltop, yet it was in good condition when taken down. It weighed less than 10 pounds and was relatively easy to handle. The entire frame, except for the 1-1/2-inch vertical support, was made of 3/4-inch aluminum tubing. Elements are 1/4-inch tubing, center-mounted. Phasing is done with open-wire TV line soldered to lugs bolted to the inner element ends.

The rotating portion of the transmission line was 300-ohm tubular Twin-Lead, brought to an insulating support just below the tower bearing. Here it joined the main transmission line, which was open-wire pulled up tight on strain insulators at each end. As pointed out in Chapter 8, straight unsupported runs are recommended for low radiation loss with open line. This installation had 125 feet, yet it performed in outstanding fashion.

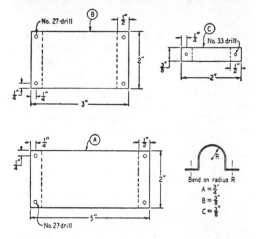

Fig. 9-26 — Clamps used for assembling all-metal collinear arrays. A, B, and C are before bending into U shape. Right-angle bends should be made first, along dotted lines, then the plates may be bent around pipe of the proper diameter. Sheet stock should be 1/16-inch or thicker aluminum.

YAGIS FOR 144 MHz

Where a small antenna with appreciable gain is needed, a Yagi is the usual choice at 144 MHz and higher, as well as at 50. There is normally little point in building 2-meter Yagis with less than five elements, as a 5-element array of optimum design fits handily on a 6-foot boom. With some shopping and make-do methods, an effective 2-meter Yagi can be assembled for almost nothing.

Bamboo or wooden tool handles make excellent booms. Dowelling of up to one-inch diameter is available in most hardward stores and lumberyards. Welding rod and aluminum "picket wire," available almost anywhere, are good for beam elements, which can be held in place with self-tapping or wood screws. TV hardware is useful and inexpensive. Even TV antennas themselves may be of such design as to be readily converted to amateur vhf needs. It is not mandatory to scrimp on vhf antenna costs, and there is a very useful source of top-grade materials and hardware in many stores in the form of Reynolds Aluminum stocks. The methods already outlined for all-metal construction are adaptable to Yagis as well as collinears. In using wood for booms and frames the range of usable methods is as wide as the builder's imagination.

Mounting Vertical Yagis

It is obvious to anyone who has tried to use available 2-meter Yagis that most are designed for horizontal polarization. To use a single Yagi effectively in a vertical position requires a non-metallic support. Closet poles available in lumberyards serve this purpose well for moderately sized

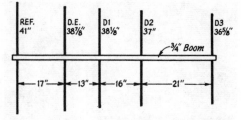

Fig. 9-27 — Optimum design for a 2-meter Yagi, using 5 elements on a 6-foot boom. When used singly, this antenna can be fed as shown in Fig. 8-17B, with 4-inch delta arms connected 3 inches either side of center. The balun loop would be about 27 inches long. With lengths shown, the antenna works well from 144 to above 146 MHz, but gain drops sharply above 147 MHz.

2-meter antennas. Hardwood poles, not so widely available, are recommended if the entire support, through the tower bearing and down to the rotator, is to be of wood. A simpler solution is to clamp the wood pole to a vertical support of strong metal tubing, using wood only for the portion of the vertical member that is to be within a quarter-wavelength of the bottom end of the elements.

Side-by-side stacking of vertical Yagis gets away from this problem and is highly recommended. If the array is to be relatively small in size, two 5-element bays side-by-side would be preferable to a single Yagi of the same theoretical gain, from both mechanical and electrical considerations.

5-Element 144-MHz Yagi

An optimum design for 5-element 2-meter Yagis, to be used singly or combined in stacked systems, is shown in Fig. 9-27. Dimensions given work well from 144 to 146 MHz, if the matching is adjusted at 145. Lengths should be reduced 1/4 inch for each megahertz higher center frequency than 145 MHz. The original elements have center sections of 1/4-inch aluminum tubing with 5/32-inch rod inserts that slide into the center members. One-piece elements of 1/8- to 1/4-inch tubing or rod will work equally well. The larger size will permit fastening in place with self-tapping screws bearing on the elements. For smaller sizes, use a

clamp like that of Fig. 9-14. The booms are 3/4- or 1-inch diameter aluminum. Wood dowelling could be used equally well.

A delta match is used in conjunction with a coaxial-line balun to feed the single 5-element Yagi. Some experimentation with delta dimensions may be required to achieve the best match. (See Fig. 8-17 and detailed description of the delta match in Chapter 8.) Start with dimensions of Fig. 9-28A. This arrangement makes a fine small Yagi that can be dismantled readily, for carrying about in portable work.

5-Over-5

Use of two 5-element Yagis with 1-wavelength spacing is shown in Fig. 9-28A. The phasing harness can be any open-wire line, preferably not spaced more than one inch. Delta dimensions are not critical in this application, as the matching is done with the universal stub at the center of the harness.

5-Over-5s Stacked Side by Side

The 4-bay 20-element system in Figs. 9-19 and 9-28B uses two sets of 5-over-5, connected between centers with another 1-wavelength line. The universal stub is connected at the center of the horizontal section. In each case, the stub length and line-connection point are adjusted for minimum reflected power in the main line.

An interesting phasing method was used in the 4-bay array. Common electric zipcord, available in any hardware store, was split into its two parts. The insulation was left on, and spreaders made of ordinary 1/2-inch wood dowel were used to hold the wires one inch apart. Holes were drilled in these of such size that the zipcord could just be pulled through them. They are held in place with any good cement. If supported with TV-type screweyes that grip the spreaders, such a low-cost line is very durable. The array shown was taken down after two years of use in a very exposed location, and no deterioration was apparent. There was no breakage, even under several heavy ice loads each winter. Using several supports on each harness section is the key to this long life.

The transmission line was switched between the six- and two-meter arrays by means of a water-proofed antenna relay. To avoid the dangers of a 115-volt line run, 6.3-volt transformers were used at each end. This one-line hookup makes it possible to use a good low-loss coaxial line to its fullest potential on two bands.

Wood-Boom 7-Element Yagi

A 7-element Yagi with folded-dipole matching is shown in Fig. 9-29. A good material for booms in medium-length Yagis is round wooden stock available in most lumberyards. Commonly called rug or closet poles, they come in various lengths and diameters. The boom shown is 10 feet long, and 1-1/4 inches in diameter. It should hold alignment without bracing, if properly treated to prevent moisture absorption. Select stock that is thoroughly dry and free of knots. When holes have been drilled, spray or brush on clear lacquer, dry,

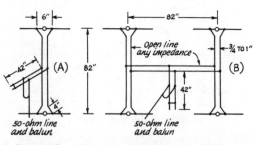

Fig. 9-28 — Stacking details for the 5-element Yagis of Fig. 9-19 and 9-27. The short on the universal stub, and the point of connection of the main transmission line, are adjusted for minimum reflected power in the latter. Balanced line could be connected similarly for the main run.

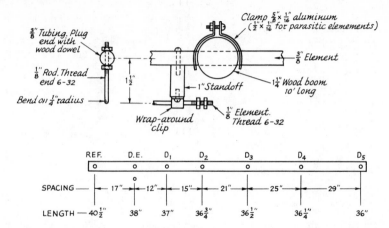

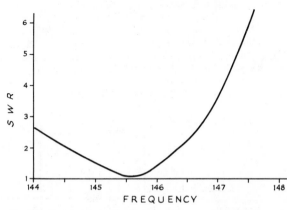

Fig. 9-29 — Dimensions and structural details of a 10-foot wood-boom Yagi for the 144-MHz band. The end view of the folded-dipole driven element is shown at the upper left, and the method of mounting it in the boom, at the right. Dimensions are for feeding with 52-ohm coax and a balun. Element lengths are for optimum performance between 145 and 146 MHz. Detail of the driven element is shown for one side only, in the interest of clarity.

and then brush on outside paint. When all mechanical and electrical work has been completed, the assembled antenna can be sprayed with clear lacquer to prevent corrosion of metal parts.

Parasitic elements can be hard-drawn aluminum wire or welding rod, 1/8 inch or larger, or tubing up to 3/8-inch diameter. The smaller stock is preferable. The 10-foot boom is probably about the longest that will hold up well without bracing, but if a longer beam is wanted it can be braced as shown in Fig. 9-14. Additional directors should be spaced 29 inches apart, and each made progressively 1/4 inch shorter. Element spacings are not particularly critical. The reflector can be anywhere from 12 to 20 inches in back of the driven element, with only a slight effect on performance, provided that the matching system is adjusted to take care of varying feed impedance. Director spacing can be varied plus or minus an inch or so with no noticeable change in characteristics. Element lengths can vary plus or minus 1/8 inch without any change that could be observed except by the most careful check on frequency response.

With the ratio-type dipole shown in Fig. 9-29, the antenna can be fed directly with 50-ohm coax and a half-wave balun. A small range of adjustment can be had by bending the 1/8-inch portion of the folded dipole nearer to or farther from the 3/8-inch portion. The curve of Fig. 9-30 shows the standing wave ratio of the array with the dimensions given, using this method of feed. This is a good setup for the fellow interested mainly in operating above 145 MHz. If optimum performance is wanted near the low end of the band the elements can all be made 1/4 to 1/2 inch longer.

In mounting the elements the boom should be drilled just large enough so that the elements fit tightly into the holes. They can be held in place by wood screws run into the boom and bearing firmly against them. These screws can be bonded together with a wire running down the boom, and this can be grounded, for lightning protection. A better method of holding the elements in place is shown at the upper right of Fig. 9-29. This clamp arrangement works equally well with any round boom, regardless of material used.

Driven-Element Construction

Construction of the ratio-type dipole is shown in Fig. 9-29. The unbroken portion is 3/8-inch tubing, the ends of which are plugged with wood dowels to permit tightening nuts against it to hold the fed portion of the dipole in position. The latter is 1/8-inch wire or rod, with the ends threaded for 6-32 nuts. An alternative method of making end connections, if you do not have a threading die, is to hammer the rod end flat and then drill it to pass a 6-32 screw. The outer end can be bolted to the 3/8-inch portion, and the inner to soldering lugs attached to the ends of the coaxial line and balun.

Fig. 9-30 — Curve of standing-wave ratio taken with the 10-foot Yagi of Fig. 9-29. For optimum matching between 144 and 145 MHz, make all elements 1/4 to 1/2 inch longer, leaving all other dimensions as shown. Note that mismatch rises more rapidly on the high-frequency side.

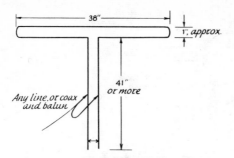

Fig. 9-31 — One-piece folded dipole and universal matching stub for substitution in place of the ratio-type dipole. Adjustment of the stub length and point of connection of the feedline can be made for optimum matching anywhere in the lower half of the band, with the element lengths given in Fig. 9-29.

The two portions of the dipole are held in alignment by means of 1-inch ceramic or teflon standoffs, one on each side of the boom and about one inch out from it. A 6-32 screw running through the 3/8-inch upper portion and a wrap-around clamp of thin metal, also with a 6-32 screw, hold this assembly together as shown in the sketch.

An alternative driven-element design that allows a wide range of adjustment, and use of any type of transmission line, is shown in Fig. 9-31. This is made from a single piece of stiff wire 160 inches long, bent as shown to include both the dipole and the universal matching stub. The sliding short on the stub, and the point of connection of the line or balun, are adjusted for zero reflected power, using a frequency in the middle of the range where optimum performance is desired. Readjusting for various frequencies will extend the useful range of this array beyond that in the SWR curve of Fig. 9-30. The stub matching method can be used to extend the range of the ratio dipole, as well, if desired.

Stacking

Where two of these Yagis are to be stacked the type of dipole used is unimportant, for matching will be taken care of at the central feed point, preferably with the universal stub. The information of Fig. 9-28 can be used. If a ratio-type dipole is used in each bay, with open-wire line for the phasing section, the SWR on this line will be lower than if a uniform-conductor dipole is used, but this is not an important consideration, in view of the short run of phasing line. Two of these 10-foot Yagis stacked should nearly equal the single 24-footer of Fig. 9-32 in gain. The stacked pair will have broader frequency response, and in some circumstances may be easier to install.

Long Yagis for 144 MHz

Though there is no theoretical limit to the amount of gain that can be achieved in making ever longer arrays, the practical limit is reached in 144-MHz Yagis at somewhere around 24 to 30 feet for most of us. If the limited frequency response of arrays this long is not a severe handicap, they are an attractive means of developing outstanding antenna performance.

Optimum element spacings and lengths for long Yagis were worked out experimentally by W2NLY and W6QKI some years ago, and similar work has been done by many others since. These projects have resulted in published figures that appear to be contradictory, but their seeming disparity merely shows that there are many ways to arrange the elements in a Yagi for roughly the same result in gain and bandwidth for a given length. This point explains the variations that will be found in comparing the Yagi systems shown in these pages.

One product of the W2NLY-W6QKI work was a 13-element 144-MHz Yagi that has since become an almost standard long-Yagi design. Lengths and spacings for one version are shown in Fig. 9-32. This antenna is just under 24 feet long, but it can be made very light in weight and easy to handle. With the dimensions given in the drawing (all directors the same length) optimum performance is maintained essentially from 144 to 145 MHz. (The SWR curve will show a rise at the low end, and a steeper rise approaching 145 MHz, but gain and minor-lobe content do not change markedly.)

Polar plots of this antenna at various frequencies are given in Fig. 9-33. At the left are runs at 144 and 145 MHz. Note that the broken line for 145 MHz shows a narrower main lobe, but some increase in size of the minor lobes. Plots at 145.5 and 146 MHz show greatly reduced gain, and at the higher frequency almost no difference between the major and minor lobes. Above 145 MHz appreciably, the array has no practical value.

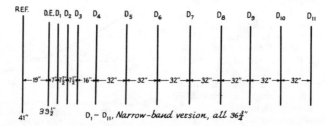

Fig. 9-32 — Element lengths and spacings for a 24-foot high-performance 144-MHz Yagi. Greater bandwidth can be achieved, at some sacrifice in forward gain, by tapering the element lengths as described in the text. Design information is from W2NLY and W6QKI.

Fig. 9-33 — Polar plots made with the long Yagi of Fig. 9-32. At the left are plots at 144 and 145 MHz. Note that at the higher frequency the main lobe is sharpening and minor lobes are larger. At the right we see that the gain is much lower and the minor lobes are much larger in the 145.5-MHz curve, solid line. The array is of little value at 146 MHz, broken line, there being little difference between major and minor lobes.

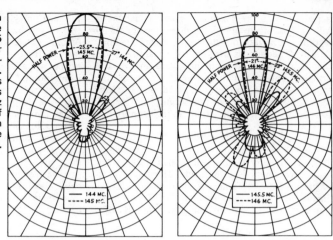

This situation is improved somewhat by tapering the director lengths, as may be seen from Fig. 9-34, showing the relative gain level across the band with elements tapered 1/8 inch (solid line) and 1/4 inch (broken line). The 1/8-inch taper extends the useful range to about 145.5 MHz, and the 1/4-inch to above 146, but both involve appreciable sacrifices in peak gain. When tapered element lengths are employed, the first director, D1, should be 37-3/4 inches, D2 37-5/8, D3 37-1/2, and then each additional director 1/8 or 1/4 inch shorter, depending on the performance desired.

These curves and pattern plots represent the best that can be expected. In practice, the pattern of a long Yagi working above its upper useful frequency limit is little more than a mass of minor lobes and deep nulls. For work over all or most of the band, a collinear array, or a smaller Yagi, is to be preferred.

A convenient way to build a long Yagi is to obtain several telescoping aluminum mast sections, available from radio and TV distributors. These should be pinned together with self-tapping screws. Elements can run through the boom, if clamps such as shown in Fig. 9-29 are used to hold them in place. Hard drawn aluminum wire or rod 1/8 inch in diameter is a good element material. It is strong, and springy enough so that ice does not form on it readily. If an ice load does build up, the elements droop and the ice slides off, after which they spring back to their original position. A long Yagi of this construction, with suitable bracing for the boom, is practically indestructable.

With very long booms it is best to hang the antenna from its braces, though booms up to about 24 feet stand up well with bracing below the boom. The boom bracing of Fig. 9-14 is suitable for suspension. Where braces are below the boom, greater strength can be achieved by leaving the brace material round, and driving a tight-fitting wood plug into the end several inches, so that it will not compress when tightened in place. Lightweight aluminum angle stock also makes good boom braces.

Hauling a long Yagi up to its position may be the most difficult part of an antenna installation. Many antenna workers solve this problem by designing the antenna so that it can be assembled atop the tower. The necessary components can be run up on a pulley rope with ease. This is practical if the boom is made in several sections that telescope together. The method has been used by the author of these lines on many occasions to put up large arrays single-handed.

Feeding the long Yagi presents no special problems, except that one should be sure that it is matched at the frequency to be most often used. Impedance of the array will depend on many factors, but if a basic impedance of about 25 ohms is assumed, and the matching system worked out accordingly, the result will never be very far off. A step-up folded dipole with a half-inch solid portion, and the fed portion of 1/8-inch wire spaced 1-1/4 inches between centers, will give an 8-to-1 impedance step-up, and something close to 200 ohms feed impedance. Typical construction is shown in Fig. 9-29. This can be matched with 52-ohm coax and a balun, or a quarter-wave Q section can be installed at the feedpoint for higher

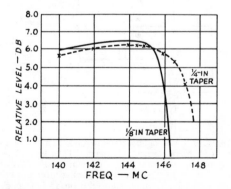

Fig. 9-34 — Relative response of the long Yagi with director lengths tapered 1/8 inch, solid line, and 1/4 inch, broken line.

impedances. If the spacing is made adjustable it will be possible to adjust the impedance of the Q section for perfect match to any desired feedline.

The Q section, if used, and the main feed line can be run along the boom toward the vertical support. This is usually preferable to letting the transmission line dangle, as the feedpoint is a long way from the center of the system, and it puts considerable unnecessary strain on the support.

Stacking

Long Yagis have large "aperture"; consequently they require very wide spacing when stacked, if a real improvement is to be made. There is little to be gained from stacking two 24-foot Yagis closer than 12 feet apart, and 16 to 18 feet is better. In matching stacked systems, remember the rule that the feed impedance of a stacked pair is about half that of one bay, if the phasing line is any multiple of one wavelength long, electrically. If made any odd multiple of a half wavelength, the phasing system will act like a double Q section, when fed at its midpoint.

Because of the mechanical and electrical problems in handling stacked combinations of long Yagis, more bays of shorter Yagis often may be a better solution. As an example, four 24-foot Yagis in a box configuration take roughly 6000 cubic feet of space. It may give 20 dB gain, if the job is done properly. A set of 8 6-element Yagis spaced one wavelength each way takes only about 1000 cubic feet of space, yet it should give almost as much gain, and probably over a wider frequency range.

USING QUADS ON 144 MHz

Though it has not been used to any great extent in vhf work, the Quad antenna has interesting possibilities. It can be built of very inexpensive materials, yet its performance should be at least equal to other arrays of its size. Adjustment for resonance and impedance matching can be accomplished readily. Quads can be stacked horizontally and vertically, to provide high gain, without sharply limiting the frequency response.

The 2-Element Quad

The basic 2-element Quad array for 144 MHz is shown in Fig. 9-35. The supporting frame is 1 X 1-inch wood, of any kind suitable for outdoor use. Elements are No. 8 aluminum wire. The driven element is one wavelength (83 inches) long, and the reflector 5 percent longer, or 87 inches. Dimensions are not particularly critical, as the Quad is relatively broad in frequency response.

The driven element is open at the bottom, its ends fastened to a plastic block, which is mounted

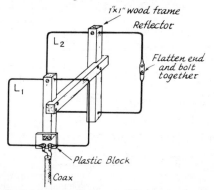

Fig. 9-35 — Mechanical details of a 2-element Quad for 144 MHz. Driven element, L1, is one wavelength long; reflector, L2, 5 percent longer. Sets of elements of this type can be stacked horizontally and vertically for high gain with broad frequency response. Bay spacing recommended is 1/2 wavelength between adjacent element sides. Example shown may be fed directly with 52-ohm coax.

at the bottom of the forward vertical support. The top portion of the element runs through the support and is held firm by a screw running into the wood and the bearing on the aluminum wire. Feed is by means of 52-ohm coax, connected to the driven element loop. For a perfectly nonradiating line the coax should be fitted with a detuning sleeve (see Fig. 8-25) but omission of this precaution does not seriously affect the performance of the Quad.

The reflector is a closed loop, its top and bottom portions running through the rear vertical support. It is held in position with screws, top and bottom. The loop can be closed by fitting a length of tubing over the element ends, or by hammering them flat and bolting them together, as shown in the sketch.

The elements in this model are not adjustable, though this can easily be done by the use of stubs. It would then be desirable to make the loops slightly smaller, to compensate for the wire in the adjusting stubs. The driven element stub would be trimmed for length and the point of connection for the coax would be adjustable for best match. The reflector stub could be adjusted for maximum gain or front-to-back ratio, whichever quality the builder wishes to optimize.

In the model shown only the spacing is adjusted, and this is not particularly critical. If the wooden supports are made as shown, the spacing between the elements can be adjusted for best match, as indicated in an SWR bridge connected in the coaxial line. The spacing has little effect on the gain, from 0.15 to 0.25 wavelength, so the variation in impedance with spacing can be utilized for matching. This also permits use of either 52- or 72-ohm coax for the transmission line.

Stacking Quads

Quads can be mounted side by side or one above the other, or both, in the same general way as described for other antennas. Sets of driven elements can also be mounted in front of a screen reflector. The recommended spacing between adjacent element sides is a half wavelength. Phasing and feed methods can be similar to those employed with other antennas described in this chapter.

Adding Directors

Parasitic elements ahead of the driven element work in a manner similar to those in a Yagi array. Closed loops can be used for directors, by making them 5 percent shorter than the driven element, or about 79 inches. Spacings can be similar to those for conventional Yagis. In an experimental model built by W8HHS the reflector was spaced 0.25 wavelength and the director 0.15. A square array using four 3-element bays worked out extremely well.

Workers using Quads on 144 MHz have reported reduced fading, compared with horizontal Yagis. Possibly this is due to the presence of some vertical polarization with the Quad, making it less affected by polarization changes that tend to occur on long or obstructed paths.

THE SKELETON-SLOT ANTENNA

A novel antenna that is very popular with British vhf enthusiasts is shown in Fig. 9-36. Developed by B. Sykes, G2HCG, and sold by his company, J-Beams, Ltd., on both sides of the Atlantic, this so-called "skeleton-slot" array gets its name from the nature of its driven element, derivation of which is as follows:

Start with two half-wave dipoles spaced 5/8 wavelength, one above the other, as at A. Radiation is mainly from the center portions of these, so the ends are bent toward each other, as in B. Then they are joined with what is essentially a wide-spaced transmission line, C, and fed with a fanned-out Y section and coaxial or balanced line. Balanced-to-unbalanced conversion, for feeding with 75-ohm coax, is accomplished with a coaxial sleeve as detailed in Chapter 8, Fig. 8-25. This is not shown in the sketch. The name of the array comes from the fact that this radiator behaves in much the same manner as a slot in a plane of metal, but in this case the plane is reduced to a closed loop.

Polarization is in the plane of the 15-inch portions, or horizontal in the example. These replace the usual driven elements in a stacked-Yagi system, and parasitic elements are lined up with them in the same way as in a conventional Yagi. Vertical spacing is 5/8 wavelength. Dimensions given are for 145 MHz, and broader frequency coverage is claimed than would be the case for a Yagi of similar dimensions. Up to 7 parasitic elements are commonly used in each half of the array. Element spacing is similar to that employed in Yagi design.

Two or more of these stacked slot-fed systems can be placed one above the other or side by side, and fed in phase in the manner of stacked Yagis. Starting with about 72 ohms for the first set, a stacked pair will have a feed impedance of about 36 ohms, and so on. Spacing of the sets varies between 1 and 3 wavelengths, depending on the length of each bay, following the rules for Yagis set forth in Chapter 8. Slot-fed arrays are common on both 144 and 432 MHz throughout the United Kingdom, and elsewhere in Europe. The foregoing information is published with the kind permission of The Radio Society of Great Britain.

Fig. 9-36 — Derivation of the skeleton-slot vhf array. Only the driven element is shown, in the interest of clarity. Parasitic elements are lined up with top and bottom portions of the driven element, giving the effect of a stacked Yagi with 5/8-wavelength bay spacing.

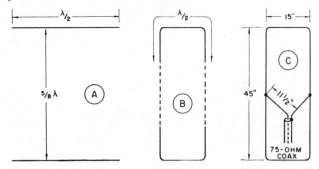

OMNIDIRECTIONAL 2-METER ANTENNAS

Net operation and the rapid growth of vhf repeaters, especially in the 2-meter band, have focussed interest on omnidirectional antenna systems for this band. Repeater work is almost wholly done with vertical antennas, and the trend in 2-meter mobile work has swung back toward vertical on that account. On the other hand, most home-station operation other than above 146 MHz is still horizontal, so there is need for omni-directional systems of both polarizations. The simple forms of vertical antennas described for 50-MHz work in the first pages of this chapter can be duplicated for the 144-MHz band by using dimensions from Table 9-I. Specific designs given here for 144 MHz will be confined to those for which models have been built and tested on this band. Mobile antennas are treated separately later.

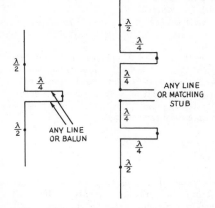

Fig. 9-37 — Basic details of nondirectional vertical collinear antennas. If constructed of stiff rod or tubing, they can be supported at points indicated by dots.

Vertical Collinears

Vertical elements can be stacked end-to-end and fed in phase, to build up gain without introducing horizontal directivity. Any number of elements could be used, but stacks of two or three are common. Fig. 9-37 shows these types, with preferred mounting points indicated with black dots. The midpoints of the stubs can be grounded for lightning protection, if desired.

Either antenna can be made of wire, but a better arrangement involves use of copper pipe and plumbing fittings, which can result in a very rugged

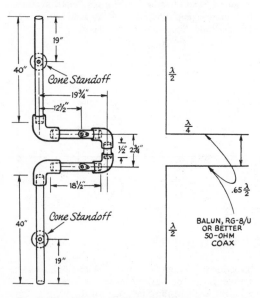

Fig. 9-38 — Mechanical and electrical details of the 2-meter collinear antenna. Element and stub lengths are the actual lengths of tubing required. If adjustment is to be attempted, the connection points for the transmission line, and the position of the short on the stub, should be adjusted for zero reflected power in the transmission line.

array that is almost impervious to the effects of bad weather. Such an all-plumbing vertical two half-waves in phase is shown in Fig. 9-38. Recommended mounting points are shown. Preferably those on the radiating elements would have ceramic stand-off insulators, mounting the antenna to a wooden support.

Initially the matching section at the center was operated in the manner of the universal stub, shown on several other arrays, as at the right. When the optimum shorting and connection points were determined experimentally, the assembly was completed with plumbing fittings as shown. The coaxial line and balun connection points shown should provide a near-perfect match, if the antenna construction follows the sketch. Practically no reflected power could be measured from 145 to 147 MHz with a 52-ohm line and balun connected at the points on the stub indicated. Match should be adequate across the entire 2-meter band.

All parts were obtained at the plumbing counter in a local Sears store. Soldering can be done with a 100-watt or larger iron, or with a small torch.

Very similar construction can be used with the three-element stack shown in Fig. 9-37, except that the feed is at the center of the middle element of three. This antenna can be fed at this point with 300-ohm line with fair matching, or a universal stub can be used. It should be as least a half-wavelength long initially. When the proper point for the short is found experimentally, the unused portion can be cut off. The center points of all stubs can be grounded.

As with all verticals except the end-fed variety, positioning of the transmission line presents a problem, whether it is coax or open line. Ideally, it should run away from the antenna in a horizontal plane, but this is rarely practical. If the supporting structure has metal anywhere above the bottom of the antenna it will probably affect the antenna pattern more than the feedline will, so the position of the latter is unimportant. If possible the structure should be of nonconducting material, where it is near to any part of the antenna proper. In this case, run the line down at least a quarter-wavelength away from the radiator. For more on vertical collinears, as used in repeater work, see Chapter 12.

The two antennas of Fig. 9-37 are useful for some horizontal-polarization situations, such as the need for some gain and directivity in a limited space. Made of wire, they can be strung up in an attic, to give a measure of antenna performance in places where a rotatable beam is impractical. For indoor use, a transmission line of 300-ohm Twin-Lead works very well.

OMNIDIRECTIONAL HORIZONTAL ANTENNAS

Fairly uniform radiation in all directions with horizontal polarization is occasionally needed in vhf stations. The control station of a local net, most of whose members normally use horizontal 2-meter beams, is one example. An Official Bulletin Station in the midst of a large population

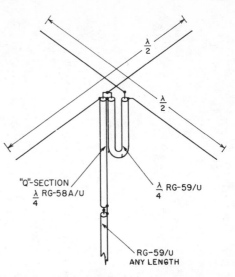

Fig. 9-39 — Schematic drawing of the turnstile antenna. Crossed dipoles (dimensions from Table 9-I) are fed 90 degrees out of phase through a quarter-wavelength loop. The Q section is not ordinarily used in mobile installations where the line is short.

concentration is another. The Headquarters Station, W1AW, has demonstrated the worth of a stacked omnidirectional array on 2 meters for the latter application, for some years now.

Remember that gain is achieved only by taking radiation from some parts of the antenna pattern where it would be wasted for ordinary purposes, and putting it somewhere else, where it will add to the signal in the receivers we want to reach. In an omnidirectional antenna with horizontal polarization, this can be done only through compression of the vertical pattern by stacking two or more antennas and feeding them in phase.

Very few simple horizontal antennas that are called omnidirectional really are, but when they are stacked in a vertical plane they can be oriented differently, so that their individual patterns complement one another, resulting in more nearly uniform radiation in all directions.

The Halo

Being merely a dipole bent into circular shape, the popular halo antenna for 2 meters is far from omnidirectional. Most of the radiation from a half-wave element is from the middle of the radiator, regardless of what is done with the ends. The principal virtue of the 2-meter halo is that it makes possible a horizontal antenna of compact design and convenient shape. The pattern approaches omnidirectional character only when the loop is made small, and the antenna is capacity loaded, as is done in 6-meter installations. This makes the antenna a high-Q device having a very low feed impedance and narrow frequency coverage. Halos of various types, for both 6 and 2 meters, are described in the mobile section of this chapter.

Turnstile for Two

An unobtrusive but effective omnidirectional antenna for 2-meter mobile or fixed-station use is the "turnstile," Figs. 9-39 and 40. This adaptation by W1CUT is two half-wave dipoles crossed at right angles, fed with equal power but 90 degrees out of phase, as shown in Fig. 9-39. The quarter-wavelength stub provides this phasing of the second dipole. Note that this is not the usual coaxial balun; it is a *quarter* wavelength long, not a half wavelength. The pattern of the turnstile is essentially circular in the horizontal plane.

Mechanical details of the turnstile are shown in Fig. 9-40. The insulating support is a 1-inch piece of 1-1/2-inch diameter polystyrene rod, drilled in the center to fit over a 1/4-inch rod used for a support. A setscrew keeps this mount tight on the rod. Tapped holes 90 degrees apart take the four

Fig. 9-40 — Mechanical details of the lightweight turnstile.

dipole elements, each 19 inches long, threaded to fit in the holes in the round block. Lock washers, soldering lugs, and nuts hold the rods tightly in place and provide for connection of the line and stub, in the manner shown schematically in Fig. 9-39. Be sure that the dipole rods do not come in contact with the center support.

The Q-section arrangement shown is desirable if exact matching is important. In a mobile installation, where only a short feed line is needed, direct feed with any convenient small coax will work about equally well.

Though primarily for mobile use, this design may be adapted for neat home-station installation. The block can be fitted to the top of a pipe mast, and the coaxial line run down inside, if desired. Turnstiles may be stacked for additional gain, in a manner similar to that shown for the Big Wheel. Because of the light weight, up to four turnstiles may be stacked vertically with only a relatively small support. In mobile work the turnstile is somewhat superior to the halo, and is broader in frequency response as well.

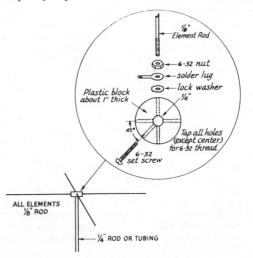

Fig. 9-41 — The Big Wheel, an omnidirectional horizontal antenna for the 144-MHz band designed by W1FVY and W1IJD. Radiating elements occupy an area approximately 40 inches in diameter.

The Big Wheel

A weakness of the halo is its small size, and resultant low gain. It is considerably below a halfwave dipole, compared with the latter's pattern in its favored directions perpendicular to the dipole. The halo is also quite limited in frequency response, particularly when capacitively loaded. The turnstile is somewhat better than the halo, and is much broader in frequency response.

One of the best horizontal omnidirectional arrays yet devised for amateur vhf work, in gain, frequency response, and uniformity of pattern is the "Big Wheel," developed by W1FVY and W1IJD, and shown in Fig. 9-41.

Almost harder to picture and describe than to build, the Big Wheel consists of three one-wavelength elements connected in parallel and arranged in clover-leaf shape. The parallel connection results in a very low impedance, which is raised to 50 ohms with an inductive stub. Frequency response is very broad. With the stub adjusted to the proper length for perfect match at 146 MHz, the SWR is negligible from 144 to 148 MHz. The radiation pattern is not perfectly circular, having slight dips in line with the notches in the antenna.

Elements (A in Fig. 9-43) are 80 inches long, of any convenient size tubing or rod stock. With tubing, the strength and stability of the antenna are improved if wooden plugs are driven into the element ends. One element end is fastened to a grounded angle plate, B in Fig. 9-43. The other connects to a floating triangular plate, C. The two plates are kept in alignment by a ceramic or bakelite insulator about 1-1/2 inches high. The inner conductor of the coaxial line connects to the triangular plate, and the sheath to the angle bracket. The stub connects between these two plates.

Note from the schematic presentation, Fig. 9-42, that the elements are in parallel. Looking down at the antenna, if the left side of one element goes to the angle bracket, its right end goes to the triangular plate. Moving around to the right, the next element connects the same way, and so on, to the third. Only the stub length is critical, and since it is merely a strip of aluminum, several of various lengths can be made and tried. Another method is to slot the mounting hole in one end of the stub, so that its electrical length can be adjusted. Distorting the shape of the stub also will tune it to some extent. The only objective in this is to get an SWR bridge in the line to show zero reflected power at 146 MHz. The SWR will then be just detectable at opposite ends of the band. The size and shape of the elements contribute to the excellent broad-band characteristics.

A single Big Wheel is nearly as effective in all directions as a horizontal half-wave dipole in its favored directions, and it is some 2 to 3 dB better than a single halo. A very marked improvement comes with stacking a pair of Wheels, and this is easily handled electrically and mechanically. A stacked pair, and a pair of pairs, are shown in Fig. 9-44. Physical spacing is 5/8 wavelength. This is not critical; it may be set to whatever the phasing sections make convenient, in the vicinity of 50 inches.

The phasing lines are 1/4- and 3/4-wavelength sections of 75-ohm coax. These act as a double Q section, resulting in 50 ohms impedance at the T fitting junction. An electrical wavelength of solid-dielectric coax works out to be about 5/8 wavelength physically, the optimum stacking dimension. The length of the phasing sections should be checked out with a grid-dip meter, as described in Chapter 8.

The off-center connection for a pair of antennas requires that one be inverted with respect to the other. Polarities for sets of 2 and 4 are shown in Fig. 9-44. In the 4-stack, the feed impedance is kept at 50 ohms through use of two 3/4-wavelength Q sections of 75-ohm coax, joined at the midpoint of the array with a T fitting, and fed there with 52-ohm coax for the main run.

The slight irregularities in the horizontal pattern of a single bay can be smoothed out in a stacked pair by positioning the bays so that the centers of the radiator elements of one line up with the notches of the other in the vertical plane. Coupling between bays of a stacked system re-

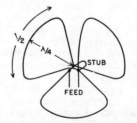

Fig. 9-42 — Schematic representation of the Big Wheel. Three one-wavelength elements are connected in parallel. The resulting low feed impedance is raised to 52 ohms with an inductive stub.

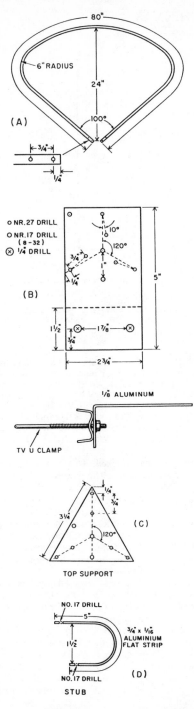

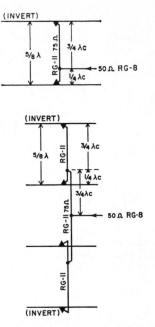

Fig. 9-44 — Stacking arrangements for two and four Big Wheels. Off-center feed in the two-bay system requires that one bay be inverted with respect to the other. In the 4-bay stack the two center bays are the same side up and the two outer ones are inverted. Both systems are for 50-ohm feed. Dimensions given in λc should include the velocity factor of the coaxial line.

Fig. 9-43 — Structural details of the Big Wheel. One element is shown at A. For strength the ends are plugged with wood. The grounded lower support is shown at B. It is fastened to the pipe support with a TV U clamp. One end of each element is connected to this plate, and the other to the triangular plate, C. The tuning stub is shown at D.

quires some modification of stub length for perfect matching. The usual stub length for a single bay is 5 inches. For two bays stacked, the stubs will be 6 inches each. In a 4-bay system, the top and bottom stubs are 6 inches and the inner pair 7 inches. A longer stub than 5 inches may be needed for a single bay mounted near a car top or other large metal body, if perfect matching is to be achieved.

Gain from a stacked pair tends to average well above the 3 dB that theory would indicate, especially where the antennas are not at great height above ground. This probably results from the lowering of radiation angle that comes with stacking. Greatest improvement is observed with a pair, compared with one. With four, the overall gain is more in line with what one would expect, and the improvement over a stacked pair tends to be less than the theoretical 3 dB. The end result, however, is omnidirectional gain roughly comparable to the gain of a small Yagi in its favored direction.

Stacked omnidirectional systems are fine for control-station use in vhf nets, or for situations where erection of a rotatable antenna is not possible, but they are not ideal substitutes for rotatable arrays. Interference problems may become acute when gain is built up in an omnidirectional array. Likewise, the broad frequency response of the Big Wheel is not an unalloyed blessing. The antenna may increase the trouble one has with spurious receiver responses, in a location where other vhf services are operating close by.

VHF MOBILE ANTENNAS

The simpler antennas already described can be adapted to mobile service, to the extent that other users of a family car will permit its disfigurement. A 2-meter Big Wheel or a 3-element array for hidden-station hunting go pretty far in this direction, but they *are* used at times. On the other hand, perhaps the most-used mobile vhf antenna may be the broadcast receiver whip, or a reasonable facsimile thereof.

Some vhf mobile enthusiasts, including the author of this book, like to order new cars with no radio or antenna, and then make their own arrangements for both. Often vhf mobile operation is a casual business, typically a Sunday-afternoon drive with a rig that may also serve the home station. Or operation may be and increasingly is on fm, working through repeaters, which reduces the requirement for mobile-antenna efficiency quite markedly. In any event, with a little thought and planning it is always possible to come up with a pretty fair vhf mobile antenna, even if it also has to serve the car broadcast receiver as well.

No-Holes Mounts

Increasing use of other than amateur communications equipment in cars has led to the development of many types of antenna mounts that can be installed on cars without hole drilling or disfiguration of the vehicle in other ways. It is also quite easy to make your own.

Two detachable whip mounts are shown in Fig. 9-45. At the top is a sheet aluminum bracket with

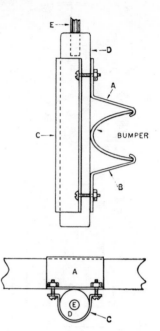

Fig. 9-46 — Top and side views of a bumper mount easily made from sheet aluminum. Clamps A, B, and C, 1/8-inch stock, hold vertical member, D, tightly to the bumper. Vertical support can be tubing, for heavy antennas like a 50-MHz halo, or wood, as shown. The rod E is 1/2-inch aluminum, drilled at the top end to take the turnstile support of Fig. 9-40.

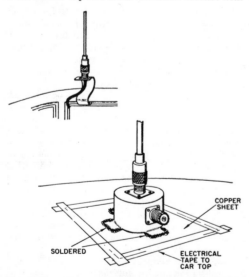

Fig. 9-45 — Two no-holes mounts for vhf mobile whips. The clip, a temporary expedient, is merely a coaxial fitting mounted on a light strip of aluminum, which can be bent over the top of the window or around the edge of the door opening. The turret is cut from a can top, soldered to a thin copper plate. This is taped to the car top. Tape, or a sheet of thin plastic, under the plate will permit easy removal of the assembly, leaving no damage to the surface.

a coaxial fitting attached. This can be bent to fit the car door, or frame. The temporary coaxial lead can run over the top of the window, or in most cars it can run through the door opening, as it will not be subjected to long-term abrasion from opening and closing the door. The weather stripping around most car doors will pass RG-58 or 59 coaxial line easily. Similar arrangements can be made for temporary mountings around the rear deck openings of most cars.

The turret mount of Fig. 9-45 can be left in place as long as desired, and the antenna and line removed when not in use. Its construction from an ordinary can top, soldered to a sheet of copper or brass, should be obvious from the drawing. Plastic tape holds the mount to the car top, permitting removal without damage to the finish. Electrical contact to the car roof is not needed for good operation. The capacitance of the base plate to a metal car top is enough to simulate electrical grounding.

In many years of vhf mobile operation in a variety of cars, the author has always found it possible to work out ways of mounting effective antennas without drilling visible holes. Removable trim and the holes for mounting it have provided means for fastening antenna mounts in place, and bringing in coaxial-line feed. Air vents offered ready-made holes and access to the car interior in

Fig. 9-47 — Three-purpose whip serves for broadcast reception and for 50- and 144-MHz mobile work. Set to optimum 50-MHz length, it works as a 3/4-wave antenna on 144, though performance is improved slightly if length is adjusted when changing bands. Mount is an aluminum bracket fastened inside the well around the gas tank opening.

the case of the all-purpose mount that is just visible in Figs. 9-51 and 53. This takes antennas mounted in a PL-259 plug, or on a 1/4-inch rod or tubing support. A compartment around the gas tank fill pipe was used for the whip bracket of Fig. 9-47. Even the screws and holes already in the car were used for mounting this one, and only a small hole in the side of the compartment, inside the rear deck, was needed for the coaxial line.

A detachable bumper mount for mobile antennas such as the turnstile or halo is detailed in Fig. 9-46. This is handy for supporting portable beams, as well. See Fig. 9-54. It requires only a few pieces of sheet aluminum, a section of round wooden closet pole or broom handle, and an aluminum rod or tubing for the vertical member. Dimensions will vary with each installation, so only the basic ideas are given here. For a 6-meter halo the support should be aluminum masting, and the brackets should be made of 1/8-inch stock. For light 2-meter antennas, brackets of 1/16- or 3/32-inch aluminum should suffice.

Mobile Whips

Where vertical polarization is in general use the whip is quite a satisfactory mobile vhf antenna. It is also used by casual mobiles in horizontal areas, regardless of polarization disadvantage, because of its convenience and unobtrusive appearance. Cross polarization may not pose too severe a problem in mobile operation; the polarization of the received signal is likely to be mixed, as a result of multiple reflections. The vertical whip serves well in working ionospheric DX on 50 MHz, again because of the random nature of the polarization of a reflected signal. Additionally, a quarter-wave antenna working against ground (the car body) tends to be a good low-angle radiator. The chief weakness of the whip is that, like other verticals, it is more susceptible to ignition noise than horizontal systems.

Whips for 144 MHz or higher bands should preferably be mounted near the center of the car roof, as this gives a large ground plane, nearly omnidirectional coverage, and a low radiation angle. Roof mounting is good for 6-meter whips, too, but not everyone likes a 5-foot vertical on a car top. Family circumstances may dictate use of the broadcast whip, or reasonable facsimile. The whip of Fig. 9-47 serves three purposes. It is connected to a coaxial switch on the dash, and leads from this run to the broadcast receiver and to mobile rigs for 6 and 2. Other positions of the switch can be used for testing other gear, without disrupting the "permanent" installations.

Length of a 50-MHz whip is not particularly critical. A field-strength indicator may not show too much variation with changes of an inch or two either way, but the best length should be found experimentally, preferably with a field-strength meter, as it may not be the theoretical quarterwavelength. The position of the antenna on the car may affect both the optimum length and the feed impedance. Do not adjust length for best match, as the nominal impedance of a whip is below 50 ohms. Trim the coax line length, if necessary, for optimum loading.

A 50-MHz whip of optimum length, usually 54 to 56 inches, works reasonably well in the 3/4-wave mode on 144 MHz. If you can extend the whip about 4 inches for 2-meter work, resonance can be obtained for both bands. The radiation angle is high for a 3/4-wave whip, but it is a convenient expedient for casual two-band work. If you work only the 2-meter band, a 19-inch car-top whip will almost certainly be better.

If the antenna mount is made with an SO-239 coaxial jack and 50-ohm-line feed, many different antennas can be pressed into service. The antenna can be changed readily for different bands, and the socket can be used for connecting portable beams having coaxial feed. Such a coaxial setup permanently mounted on the car is a very useful accessory.

Most collapsible whips are small enough so that they can be mounted in a PL-259 coaxial plug, using some kind of insulating sleeve. The impedance is low at this point, so the quality of the insulation is not vital. Even a few layers of ordinary black plastic tape will do nicely. Insulating rod of various kinds can be drilled or turned down, as required. A good way to make a solid connection between whip and plug is to fit a 6-32 brass screw into the whip end, and tap the center connector of the PL-259 plug for 6-32 thread. Soldering the screw into the whip base and into the plug will result in a strong connection.

One versatile type of whip that should not be overlooked is the many-sectioned variety made for use with small portable radios. The whip shown at the left in Fig. 9-48 has 10 sections, and it collapses to 8 inches. It cost two dollars at a local radio bargain counter. Mounting it in a PL-259 plug takes a little doing, but the result is worth some work. It will resonate on any band from 220 through 50 MHz, as it is adjustable from 8 to 54-1/2 inches, and it will stay at any length you set it.

5/8-Wave 2-Meter Whip

Also in Fig. 9-48 is a close-up view of the lower part of a 5/8-wavelength whip for 2-meter mobile work. Such an antenna has a low radiation angle and appreciable gain over any shorter vertical whip. Manufactured versions of the 5/8-wavelength whip are widely used in commercial and 2-meter fm mobile work, but there is no reason why you shouldn't make your own and save some money.

The basic ideas for this antenna were supplied by Vern Epp, VE7ABK, in October, 1965, *QST*. The whip is a lightweight portable-radio type with a base section about 3/16-inch diameter. It extends to a maximum of 37 inches, so a 10-inch base section is added to bring the total to over the optimum for this application, which is around 45 inches. The actual length is not particularly critical, if the capacitor across the matching circuit is variable, as this adjustment can compensate for length variations of several inches. The coil is connected to the sleeve of the coaxial plug at the bottom, and to the whip at the top. The inner

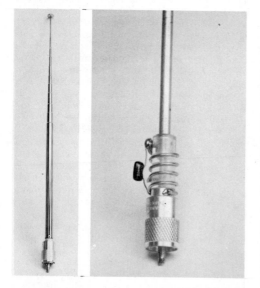

Fig. 9-48 — Detachable whips for vhf mobile use. Both have PL-259 coaxial plugs fitted at the base. At the left is a 10-section portable-radio whip, fastened to a Teflon rod fitted inside the plug sleeve. At the right is a 5/8-wavelength 2-meter whip, with matching circuit mounted on a polystyrene rod.

conductor of the coaxial line is tapped up one turn from the bottom.

The coil is wound on 1/2-inch poly or Teflon rod 2 inches long, turned down to 11/32-inch diameter for the first 3/8 inch of its length, and 3/8-inch diameter for the second 3/8 inch. This leaves a 1-1/4-inch shoulder extending above the fitting, for the coil support. Drill the center of the rod its entire length about 1/8-inch diameter. Drill two No. 35 holes perpendicular to this, one about 1/4 inch from the top and the other one inch from the top.

Drill out the top end of the insulator 1/4-inch diameter, to a depth of 1/2 inch. A 10-inch piece of 1/4-inch aluminum tubing is inserted in this hole, and drilled to match the No. 35 hole in the insulating material. Tap the No. 35 hole for 6-32. A 1/2-inch 6-32 screw runs through the side of the tubing to press against the inner wall on the other side, to assure good electrical contact for the top end of the coil. If a whip that extends to 45 inches or more is available, it can be fitted directly to the insulating coil mount.

A length of No. 22 wire is used for making the tap on the coil. Bend the end upward at 45 degrees, about 1/4 inch, so that the point will come up into the lower No. 35 hole when the wire is threaded into the tip of the coaxial fitting and up into the drilled insulator. It can be bent around the coil wire and soldered. The coil is No. 14 tinned, 4 turns wound on the insulating rod, with turns spaced about 3/16 inch, center to center, and another complete turn around the top of the coaxial fitting, soldered in place. Wrap the top end around the 6-32 screw inserted in the top horizontal hole in the insulator, and solder.

The capacitor shown in the photograph was initially a small 15-pF trimmer, soldered across the coil. Obviously this is not a permanent arrangement, it having been put on to determine the optimum value experimentally. This was found to be about 10 pF, for a total antenna length of 45 inches, for use in the upper half of the 2-meter band. Adjustment of the whip length will take care of other frequencies in the band, with one value of fixed capacitor. Adjustment can be made for minimum reflected power in the coaxial line, or for highest reading on a field-strength indicator. Whip length or coil turn spacing can be adjusted, after the fixed capacitor is installed, as shown in the photograph.

The 5/8-wave whip has only one weakness when compared with other whips mentioned: it is a one-band device, and it will not work for broadcast reception. The grounded matching coil effectively shorts the whip to the car frame at broadcast frequencies. For 2-meter communication it will be considerably better than either 1/4- or 3/4-wave whips.

Using the Broadcast Whip

Many whips installed on cars for broadcast reception can be extended long enough to work well on 50 MHz. If you check on it, you may be able to get a whip of the desired length installed when you buy a new car, and you might even get it put on where you want it. There is likely to be a transmission-line problem with broadcast whips, as installed on cars. The line normally used is a high-impedance type designed for low capacitance. This will not work well in amateur installations set up for 50-ohm lines, unless it happens to be just the right length. Conversely, 50-ohm coax may not be too good for broadcast reception, especially if the run is long. Some broadcast receivers have tunable input circuits that may help to compensate for loading effects of a low-impedance line, but it is best to keep the run from the antenna to the broadcast receiver short, if RG-58 or similar 50-ohm line is used.

The length of line to the vhf rig will not be important, so the best way to use a bc whip is to run a 50-ohm line from the whip mount to a coaxial switch nearby. The line to the bc receiver can be made with the low-capacitance line that came with the whip, and the 50-ohm lines for the ham gear can be any convenient length, as may be needed to run them under carpets and out of the way otherwise. With some thought a whip installation can be made that will work well for both purposes, and the car will show no evidence of its use as a hamshack on wheels. This is a real advantage at trade-in time.

HORIZONTAL MOBILE ANTENNAS

Where horizontal polarization is in use for home stations, the mobile operator must use a horizontal antenna if he is to achieve maximum local coverage on the vhf bands. Aside from the importance of matching polarization, the horizontal antenna pays a considerable dividend in rejection of ignition noise, especially on 50 MHz. In ssb communication it is particularly important to keep down noise input to the receiver, as simple noise-limiting circuits are not effective with the ssb mode. Several practical horizontal antennas are described below.

Novel 2-Meter Halo

A quick-disconnect 2-meter halo that can be dropped onto the broadcast antenna or added to a

Fig. 9-49 — This 144-MHz halo appears to have no transmission line or matching device. Attached off-center to the whip of Fig. 9-47, it uses the whip as a single-wire transmission line. Optimum whip length is approximately 40 inches, so top section is telescoped when the halo is used. Very little vertical polarization is in evidence.

6-meter whip is shown in Fig. 9-49. The brainchild of W3KDZ, it uses the ancient principle of single-wire feed. In this case the whip acts as the transmission line, and is connected to the halo off-center, at the approximate matching point. The halo should preferably be about 40 inches up on the whip, and if possible the whip should not extend above it. Minimum vertical radiation is obtained in this way. The distance off center on the halo should be adjustable, but 3 to 5 inches is a good starting point.

The length of the halo element will depend to some extent on the diameter of the circle. The smaller the circle the shorter the element, because of increasing capacitance end-to-end. The one shown is 40 inches long, and resonates at 145 MHz,

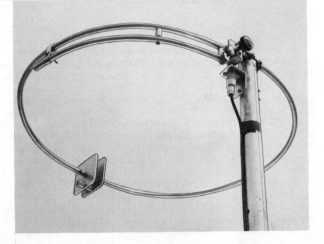

Fig. 9-50 — Halo for 50 or 144 MHz. As shown it is set up for the 50-MHz band. Change to 144 is made by moving connecting clip closer to the center post, and changing the spacing of the capacitor plates by swapping the ceramic insulators.

Fig. 9-51 — Shortened dipole for 50-MHz mobile service. Loading coils are inserted either side of a solid center section. Inserts are 19 inches long, threaded into forms that support the loading coils. See Fig. 9-52.

when bent so that the opening is 9 inches. In the original by W3KDZ the element was 34 inches, and the ends were fitted into a polystyrene insulator about 2 inches long. A grid-dip meter resonance check is desirable, in any case.

Walking around the car with a field-strength meter showed some interesting pattern and polarization variations with the whip-halo combination. With the 55-inch whip alone the 144-MHz polarization was predominantly vertical, with a major lobe off the back of the car, at an angle of about 15 degrees to the right of the line of travel. With the halo at 40 inches up the whip, left in its extended position, the polarization was mixed, with vertical strongest on the main lobe, but with several horizontal and 45-degree lobes elsewhere. With the whip run down to the halo (whip now 40 inches long, thus mismatched in the vertical mode) horizontal was mainly evident, with some energy at 45 degrees, but almost no vertical. In other words, the single-wire feed principle *does* work. The halo is by no means omnidirectional, however; its main lobe is forward and to the left, perpendicular to that portion of the halo near its high-current midpoint. A lesser lobe appears off the back and to the right of the car heading.

2-Band Halo

A halo that can be set up to work on either 50 or 144 MHz is shown in Fig. 9-50. This antenna is customary 50-MHz size, 67 inches in circumference, with 2-1/4-inch square capacitor plates fitted to each end. The gamma matching arm is 14-1/2 inches long, of the same material as the halo, and separated from it by ceramic insulators. A clip of sheet aluminum provides sliding contact between the arm and the halo. As always with the gamma match, be sure that this makes a clean tight contact.

The halo shown was put together mainly to try out the two-band idea, so its mechanical details are not spelled out here. Important points in a permanent installation are the arm-to-halo contact already mentioned, waterproofing of the series

capacitor, and some adequate provision for keeping the halo rigid during driving. Any flopping of the halo causes intermittent detuning, and severe mobile flutter, in addition to that normally encountered.

Operation on two bands is achieved by changing the point of connection on the halo arm, the setting of the variable series capacitor, and the spacing of the square-plate capacitor at the element ends. The plate spacing is changed by using a 3/4-inch ceramic standoff to hold the plates in position for 50 MHz and changing to one 5/8 inch long to bring resonance down to 48 MHz, so that it will operate on its third harmonic.

Resonance must be achieved before the antenna can be matched on either frequency. This can be facilitated by use of a grid-dip meter, coupling to the halo near the vertical support. Resonance does not need to be exact for 144-MHz work, as the antenna tunes more broadly on this band, but it is critical in the 50-MHz band. When it is resonated near the desired frequency range, apply power and move the sliding clip and adjust the variable series capacitor for lowest reflected power. These adjustments must be made with care for either band.

For 50-MHz work the clip connection is near the outer end of the arm. For 144 it works at about 3 to 4 inches out from the capacitor. With a 25-pF capacitor in series with the arm, tuning is near the middle of the range for 50 MHz and close to minimum for 144. Properly adjusted the halo works well over only about 50 to 50.5 MHz without readjustment. In the 2-meter band, satisfactory operation is possible over about half the band without retuning. The range with the antenna set up for 50-MHz service seems to be normal for a halo on 6. On 144, the antenna seems to give somewhat better coverage than the conventional 2-meter halo, probably because of its larger size.

A Neat 50-MHz Dipole

Where a horizontal antenna is needed for 50-MHz mobile, and a halo is too much of an eyesore, the dipole of Fig. 9-51 works reasonably well and is unobtrusive in appearance. If it can be mounted near the middle of the car the element ends will not extend far enough to be dangerous to passersby. Because radiation is largely from the center of a dipole, this design works better than one in which a single loading coil is used at the center of the element. Mounted just back of the rear window, as shown, the antenna has a major lobe to the rear and a lesser one forward. In stationary operation the antenna can be rotated for best signal by loosening the plug sleeve slightly. The connection is maintained, so the received signal can be monitored as the antenna is turned.

As may be seen from Fig. 9-52, the horizontal dipole has loading coils at equal distances either side of center. The dimensions given are one of many possible arrangements. They were dictated by a desire to use 2-meter turnstile elements for the outer portions, and keep overall length to about 50 inches.

The 13-inch rod which is the center portion of the dipole is drilled and tapped at each end for

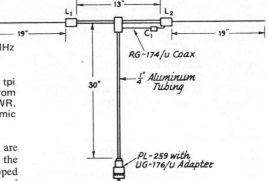

Fig. 9-52 — Principal details of the loaded 50-MHz mobile dipole.

C1 — 15-pF dipped mica.

L1, L2 — 11 turns No. 20, 5/8-inch dia, 16 tpi (B&W No. 3007). L2 tapped 3/4 turn from inner end, or as required for minimum SWR. Coils are supported on 1/2 X 1-inch ceramic pillars (Millen 31001).

6-32 thread. The loading coils, L1 and L2, are made in a manner similar to those used with the two-band antenna. Prepared coil stock is slipped over 1/2 X 1-inch ceramic standoff insulators, and the wire ends are soldered to lugs at each end of the insulators. The element ends are 1/8-inch aluminum welding rod, threaded 6-32 for about one-half inch at their inner ends. A 6-32 nut is threaded onto the element, and this acts as a stop when the element is screwed into the insulator.

The 13-inch center section is supported in a 1/2-inch piece of solid aluminum rod about one inch long, with a setscrew running in from the top to hold the rod tightly in place. The lower portion of the block is drilled to take the vertical support, which is 1/4-inch aluminum tubing. This can be any length that will stand the strain; ours is 30 inches long.

The diameter of the bottom end of the vertical member is filed down just enough so that it can be forced into the UG-176/U adapter, which, in turn, screws into the PL-259 coaxial plug. Small-diameter coax was first used for the feedline, bringing it out through a hole in the vertical support. This turned out to be fragile, so a piece of zip cord (one conductor and its covering discarded) was substituted and found to work just as well.

Adjustment

The top end of the line extending through the hole as shown forms the arm of a gamma match. The series capacitor, C1, was first set up as a variable, permitting the right combination of capacitance and tap position on L2 to be selected experimentally.

First the antenna by itself must be resonated at the center of the desired frequency range. This will be a narrow frequency spread, a limitation not too important, with most 6-meter operation being in the first 500 kHz of the band ordinarily. The resonant frequency can be checked with a grid-dip meter, putting the GDO coil adjacent to the 13-inch center section of the antenna, close to the center block. The trick now is to trim the lengths of the outer elements, or the number of turns in the loading coils, until you hit the desired frequency. It will be a sharp indication; when you approach the desired frequency, do not trim elements by more than one-half inch at a time, or the loading coils by more than 1/4 turn. Whichever you cut, be sure that the same change is made on both halves of the antenna. When you're through, the coils should be identical, and the outer ends of the element the same length.

The antenna used by the writer was trimmed for resonance at about 50.25 MHz. The next step was to find a value of series capacitor, C1, and a point of connection on the antenna or loading coil, L2, that would provide a 50-ohm termination for the coaxial line. This was done experimentally with the antenna support clamped in a vise on the workbench. A recheck of the SWR and operating frequency, when the antenna was installed on the car, showed little change.

Frequency response is about the same as with a capacitively loaded halo. Resonated and matched at 50.25, the dipole is usable from the low end to 50.5 MHz before the SWR rises above 2 to 1, a mismatch that is tolerable in a mobile setup.

2-Meter Dipole with Built-In Balun

A dipole makes a good horizontal 2-meter mobile antenna. Nearly all mobile antennas have some directional characteristics, depending on their position on the car, so the natural bidirectional pattern of a simple dipole may not be too much different from what usually results from the use of a supposedly omnidirectional mobile antenna.

The dipole of Fig. 9-53 is clean in appearance, and it has an invisible built-in balun. Installed on a car top it will have very nearly a true bidirectional

Fig. 9-53 — Horizontal dipole for 2-meter mobile. The vertical support is 1/4-inch tubing, with small coax inside, thus serving as a 1:1 balun.

dipole pattern, without the distorted lobe that usually results from direct feed of a split dipole with coax. It is very easy to make, and is handy for portable as well as mobile use.

The construction is similar to that for a turnstile. A center insulator is mounted at the top of a support made of 1/4-inch aluminum tubing, of any convenient length. The bottom of the support is forced into a UG-176/U adaptor, which screws into a PL-259 coaxial plug. The feedline is RG-58/U or RG-174/U coax, running inside the tubing. The coax should not make contact with the tubing at the top. The outer conductor is connected to one half of the dipole and the inner conductor to the other. The support is made to act like a 1-to-1 balun by running a self-tapping screw in at a point about 18 inches down from the top, to contact the outer conductor at that point.

The screw is not needed if the support is approximately a quarter wavelength high, as the ground will be made automatically by the connection of the coax to the PL-259 plug. In fact, several different lengths have been tried, and the sleeve support seems to work like a balun regardless of length. In the dipole pictured the grounding screw is about 6 inches above the fitting (support just over 2 feet high) and the radiation from the dipole is a good figure 8, whether the screw is contacting the outer conductor or not. It might be useful to be able to ground the outer conductor at this proper point in longer supports, however, and it is a simple thing to do. Be careful that the screw is not run in far enough to puncture the inner insulation, and short out the coax.

PORTABLE ANTENNAS

From earliest times one of the great joys of vhf hamming has been "working portable." Every enthusiast dreams of someday having a station on a mountaintop, with an unobstructed view for miles in every direction. Few of us ever see this dream become a permanent reality, but with the mobility we enjoy today nearly everyone can bring it off for a few hours now and then.

The catch is that even the finest vhf locations have a way of turning out to be somewhat

Fig. 9-54 — Portable beam set up for 144 MHz, using the bumper bracket of Fig. 9-46.

disappointing unless a good antenna is available. Halos, whips, and the like are pretty poor stuff, compared with a beam antenna of even moderate size. Fortunately, fixing up a vhf array so that it can be moved about readily is no great task.

Antennas can be built to encompass many degrees of portability. Probably the simplest are antennas and supports that come apart enough to permit tying to a ski rack or other car-top carrier. Most manufactured beams are shipped knocked-down, so dismantling for some portability is no problem. Yagis made for the TV trade nearly always have folding elements, to make life easier for the serviceman-installer. These can be modified for amateur bands quite readily. Occasionally the element spacings can be left as they were in the original, and the element lengths adjusted according to Table 9-I.

The next step is to make your own boom and supporting structure, using TV masting. This can be cut to the maximum length that your car storage space permits. Usually something around 4 feet maximum length is convenient. Element mounting methods described elsewhere in this chapter can be adapted to portable beams handily. The principal problem then becomes how to feed the array, since two popular matching systems, the folded dipole and the gamma match, do not lend themselves readily to quick dismantling and reassembly.

One thoroughly practical feed method is the delta or Y match, Fig. 8-17A and B, and 9-56. If the connection to the driven element is made with removable clips the delta provides a connecting and matching system that can be coiled up and carried in your pocket. The bottom of the delta can be terminated in a coaxial balun and coax of the desired length, or Twin-Lead can be used for all or any desired part of the main run to the equipment.

If the portable beam is to be used alongside the car the support can be tied or clamped to the door handle or bumper. An example of an effective bumper clamp is shown in Fig. 9-47, and in actual use in Fig. 9-54. A screwdriver or small stake can be driven into the ground to anchor the bottom of the mast.

Lightweights for 6 and 2

If you're satisfied to operate only in high spots that are accessible by car, extreme light weight is of no great interest, so long as the antenna can be taken apart and packed away conveniently in the car. But you really need the performance of a beam when you work a flea-powered transistor portable from some remote mountain top, miles from the nearest road. If you go for this kind of vhf hamming, light weight and easy carrying are of primary importance. The arrays of Fig. 9-55 were designed to be carried on foot. They sacrifice nothing in performance for their lightness, so they also serve nicely for general-purpose portable operating.

Provision is made for a 3-element 50-MHz beam and a 5-element 2-meter one. The booms are duplicates, so that one can be used for either band, or the two antennas can be set up together. All the material for the 2-band setup, with booms, 15-foot vertical support and feedlines, adds up to less than 5 pounds. It stows in a canvas golf bag, as seen in Fig. 9-57. In more-or-less this form they have served the author in vhf portable ventures from Maine to California and the Canadian Rockies to Florida. They evolved gradually, being made ever lighter and easier to set up, until it is felt that they are now near the ultimate in portability and performance.

The 3-Element 50-MHz Yagi

The booms are 3/4-inch aluminum tubing, originally two 6-foot pieces, now cut into 4 3-foot sections. An insert at the center made of 5/8-inch copper pipe joins two 3-foot pieces to make a 6-foot boom. This size is a nice sliding fit inside

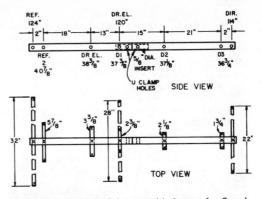

Fig. 9-55 — Details of the portable beams for 6 and 2. One boom can serve for either array, or two sets of hardware can be made, permitting simultaneous operation on two bands. The hole just back of the U-clamp holes is used for both 6- and 2-meter elements.

3/4-inch hardware store aluminum tubing. A TV-type U clamp holds the boom to the vertical support. Drilled as shown in Fig. 9-55 the boom supports the center sections of the elements for either beam. The 50-MHz elements are 1/4-inch aluminum tubing, with their ends drilled one inch deep with a No. 5 drill, to take collapsible whips that make up the balance of each element. Various sizes of these whips can be found in distributor catalogs. Ours are Lafayette Type 99-C-3005, 0.210 inch in diameter at the base, and 47 inches long, extended.

Because these whips are very thin at the outer ends, the elements must be made several inches longer than would be the case for normal element diameters. The driven element is 120 inches, the reflector 124 inches, and the director 114 inches.

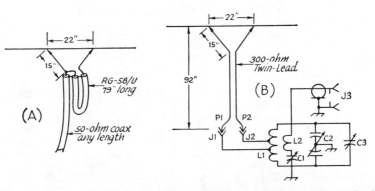

Fig. 9-56 — Two methods of feeding the 50-MHz portable array. A half-wave balun and a delta match of flexible wire are shown at A. The Twin-Lead delta and line, with adjustable antenna coupler, B, permits use of the array over a wider frequency range. With readjustment, it provides a constant load for the transmitter, from 50 to 52 MHz.

C1 — 75-pF miniature variable (Hammarlund MAPC-75B).
C2 — 11-pF miniature butterfly variable (Johnson 160-211).
C3 — 30-pF miniature mica trimmer (ARCO)
J1, J2 — Insulated tip jack.
J3 — BNC fitting.

L1 — 15 turns No. 20, 1/2-inch dia, 16 tpi. Tap at 3-1/2 and 11-1/2 turns.
L2 — 3 turns insulated hookup wire, around center of L1. Coupler is assembled in a 1-5/8 X 2 X 3-1/4-inch Minibox, with the tip jacks at one end and the coaxial connector at the other.

Fig. 9-57 — Beams for 6 and 2 with 15-foot vertical support and all hardware, ready for travel.

With 47-inch whips inserted to a depth of one inch, center sections should be as follows: reflector 32 inches, driven element 28 inches, and director 22 inches. The elements can be held in place with clips in the manner shown for several other antennas in this chapter, or self-tapping screws can be run through the top of the boom, to bear on the element midpoint. The ends of the center sections are slotted with a hacksaw, and a small wrap-around clamp is used to squeeze the ends tightly around the whip.

The array can be fed conveniently in two ways, as shown in Fig. 9-56. The simpler is the delta and balun, A. This works fine at the design frequency, but the SWR rises quickly on either side. If an antenna coupler is used, at B, the useful frequency range of the array can be extended considerably. A small coupler unit can be connected at the bottom of the delta, and coax run from there to the equipment, or part of the transmission line can be Twin-Lead or other balanced line. This can be any length, though the electrical half wavelength shown is a good system.

With the short lines normally used in a portable setup, this array works extremely well, and its gain and directivity are very helpful in working out with low-powered gear. When the coupler is used, and retuned for each frequency change, the system can be matched perfectly over the first two megahertz of the band. Gain is 6 dB or better from 50 to 51.5 MHz, and in excess of 7 dB in the most-used lower part of the band.

The 5-Element 2-Meter Beam

The boom for the 144-MHz antenna can be the one used for 6-meter operation, or it can be another made similarly. The center sections of the 2-meter antenna are 1/4-inch aluminum rods, with their ends drilled and tapped 6-32, to a depth of 1/2 inch. Element extensions are 1/8-inch aluminum wire or welding rod, threaded 6-32 at the inner end. To prevent confusion in assembling the antenna, the extensions are all the same, and the center sections are made progressively shorter, back to front, to give the optimum element lengths. The dimensions given in Fig. 9-55 are for best performance from the low end to about 145.5 MHz.

A delta and balun are used with this array also. The arms of the delta are 4 inches long, including the alligator clips used for connecting to the driven element. Pieces of zip cord make flexible long-lasting delta arms. The balun loop, of RG-58/U coax, is 27 inches long.

ANTENNAS FOR 220 AND 420 MHz

Since physical size must be maintained as we go to progressively higher frequencies, if communications effectiveness is to be maintained, the number of elements in large arrays for 220 or 420 MHz tends to stagger the imagination of users of lower bands. On the other hand, a half wavelength becomes of such proportions (roughly 2 feet on 220, 1 foot on 420) that high-performance beams are not difficult to build and adjust.

Antenna work at these frequencies is an absorbing field in itself. There is no better way to work out pet antenna ideas than with models built for 420 MHz. If reasonable care is used in scaling significant dimensions, models can supply answers in a few hours of interesting work that would take days (and dollars) to work out on some lower frequency — if, indeed, they could be developed satisfactorily there at all, by amateur methods.

We formerly heard the statement, "Yagis don't work on 420!" This completely false notion is mainly the result of the workers having neglected the question of scaling. Yagis and most other kinds of antennas work just as well on 220 and 420 MHz as on any lower frequency, if they are made and fed properly. Anyone interested in working the full band, 420 to 450 MHz, would be foolhardy to use them, but where operation is confined to a narrow segment like 432 to 436 MHz, for example, frequency response should be no problem. This is likely to hold for 220-MHz work as well, as activity is frequently channelled to one part of that band, by mutual local agreement.

Line losses *are* a problem at these frequencies. As pointed out in Chapter 8, the best line may be none too good. Matching is important, particularly if any real antenna evaluation work is to be undertaken. Line radiation is troublesome, and must be countered with every reasonable precaution.

Basic antenna systems already described work well on both 220 and 420. Collinear arrays may be built using the midband dimensions of Table 9-I and the mechanical arrangements suggested for 144-MHz arrays, except that most parts can be of smaller cross-section and lighter in weight. In all-metal construction of collinears or Yagis, element and boom diameters should be kept in scale with the 144-MHz designs, insofar as possible. A

12-inch element running through a 1-1/4-inch metal boom, for example, is out of place in a 420-MHz array. Hard-drawn aluminum wire or welding rod, preferably not larger than 1/8 inch in diameter, is good for elements. Booms no larger than 1/2 inch are recommended, if made of metal.

Matching methods follow the basic principles detailed in Chapter 8, but the small physical proportions of the adjustable Q section, the delta match, and the universal stub make these probably the most desirable matching devices. The ratio-type folded dipole is suspect at these frequencies.

Plane and corner reflectors assume practical proportions. Where broad frequency response and high front-to-back ratio are desired, driven elements backed up by a wire grid or metal screening make a fine antenna. This is particularly inviting where two bands must be taken care of with a single structure, since elements can be mounted on opposite sides of such a reflecting plane. The gain of a screen reflector array is little affected by the spacing of the elements from the reflector, but there is a marked change of impedance when the spacing is changed. (See Fig. 8-9, 180-degree curve.) From this it is clear that matching to a transmission line can often be achieved by selecting a suitable spacing by experiment, if the impedance of the system is not known.

YAGIS FOR 220 AND 432 MHz

Moderate-size Yagis for the 220 and 420-MHz bands can be built at very low cost, and with only simple tools, if the suggestions of Figs. 9-58 and 59 are followed. Booms are 1 X 1-inch wood, available in any lumberyard. (Your dealer will call it "one by one" but the actual size will be more like 3/4 X 7/8 inch.) Be sure that it is straight, dry, and free of knots. Take the man's advice as to which kind of wood will be best for out-door use, as available stocks vary around the country. Ours was red cedar. Prime and paint it well, if you want long life.

An 11-element array is shown for 432 MHz, and a 7-element one for 220 MHz, both using element spacings and lengths that are close to optimum for gain. The antenna should be supported near its mechanical balance point, roughly 2 feet from the reflector end. If a TV-type U clamp is used, it is well to bend up a U-shaped metal plate the width of the boom and about 3 inches long, and slip it over the boom at the point where the holes are to be drilled for the clamp. This protects the boom from crushing when the U-clamp nuts are tightened, and leaves it strong enough to stand up well without bracing. Gusset plates of wood or Masonite make stronger assemblies. See Fig. 9-63.

Parasitic elements in the 432-MHz model are made of 3/32-inch aluminum welding rod, and 1/8-inch is used for the 220-MHz model. This material can be purchased very reasonably at welding supply houses, usually in 3-foot lengths. Any stiff wire or rod up to 1/8 inch diameter will do. Drill the boom with a size that will just take the elements with a force fit, then run a 1/2-inch brass or aluminum screw into the boom to bear on the element and hold it in place. The screws can then be bonded together and connected to ground for lightning protection, if desired.

The driven elements originally tried were step-up folded dipoles similar to those used in the 144-MHz Yagis, but it was found that these did not work well at 220 and 432 MHz. This is probably the result of the spacing between the two parts of such a dipole being a considerable portion of a wavelength at these frequencies. The 432-MHz Yagi was made with a driven element of the same material as the parasitic elements, mounted as shown in Fig. 9-58 A and B. Blocks of insulating material 1/4 inch thick and 1-1/2 inches square are fastened to the boom with two 1-1/2-inch brass screws and nuts. The upper portion of the dipole runs through the boom, just above the center, and the lower is held in place with 4-40 nuts on either side of the insulating plates, as shown in the end view, B. The 3/32-inch rod is easily threaded for 4-40, if this is done before the element is bent. The total length of the wire is about 25 inches. An alternative to threading is to hammer the ends flat, and drill for 4-40 screws.

Fig. 9-58 — Details of a 6-foot 11-element Yagi for 432 MHz. The square boom and one polystyrene mounting block for the driven element are shown at A. The blocks, element, and boom are shown in detail in the end view, B. Matching stub, C, fastens to ends of the driven element, and is mounted under the boom between two poly blocks. Element lengths and spacings for the middle of the 420-MHz band are shown in the side view of the complete array.

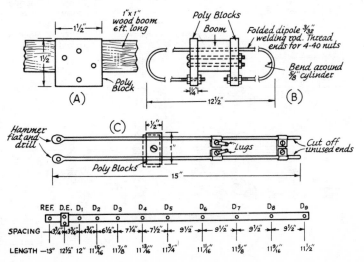

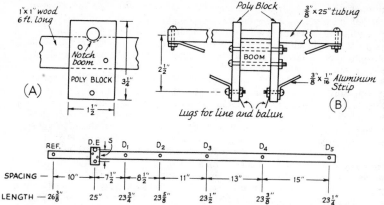

Fig. 9-59 — Element 220-MHz Yagi on a 6-foot wood boom. Poly blocks each side of the boom support the modified folded-dipole driven element. Latter has sloping lower portion, for matching 52-ohm coax and balun, connected to lugs at the bottom of sketch B. With element lengths and spacings given in the side view of the array, optimum performance is obtained over the first 3 to 4 megahertz of the band.

The antenna is matched by means of a universal stub, C, made of the same material as the elements. It should be cut about 15 inches long, and suspended under the boom. An adjustable short and two sliding clips for connecting the transmission line or balun are provided for adjusting the matching. The ends of the stub that connect to the dipole are pounded flat with a hammer, and then drilled to pass the threaded ends of the dipole. These are held in place by the 4-40 nuts shown in B. A ceramic cone standoff insulator (not shown in the drawing) is fastened to the underside of the boom. Two pieces of polystyrene similar to that used for the dipole mounting blocks, one above and one below the matching stub, are fastened to this cone, clamping the stub in place.

The short and the point of connection of the balun are adjusted for zero reflected power, as indicated in an SWR bridge connected in the line.

The bridge should be at a point in the line a multiple of a half-wavelength from the antenna, for the greatest ease of adjustment.

The 220-MHz Yagi can be made in the manner just described, using a dipole made of a single piece of wire. The universal stub for matching should be about 28 inches long, to assure an adequate range of adjustment. A variation of the ratio-type folded dipole was made for the 220-MHz antenna as shown at B in Fig. 9-59. Here a flat strip of aluminum comprised the fed portion of the dipole, and a 3/8-inch tube the unbroken portion. The aluminum strip is bolted to the underside of the tubing at the outer ends. The slope down to the feed point at the polystyrene blocks determines the impedance. With the dimensions shown the array can be fed with 52-ohm coax and a balun, connected to the lugs at the insulating plates. The SWR is under 1.5 to 1 from 220 to 224 MHz, with optimum match at about 221.5 MHz.

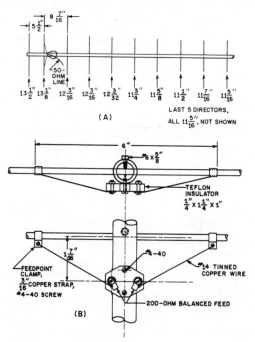

(A)

(B)

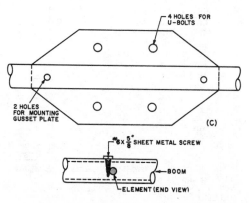

Fig. 9-60 — Details of the 15-element "WØEYE 15-element Yagi" for 432 MHz. Director spacing is uniform throughout. Five forward directors, all the same length, are omitted from (A) for clarity.

Driven-element mounting and feed arrangement are shown in (B). Gusset-plate mounting for the boom is shown in (C). Note method of holding elements in place. Mounting plate dimensions are uncritical.

11-Element 220-MHz Yagi

An 11-element 220-MHz version of the Yagi described for 432 can be made using the dimensions of Fig. 9-59, and adding four more directors spaced about 19 inches apart. This requires a 12-foot boom, which should be heavier stock than the 1 by 1 used for the 6-foot models. The added directors can be all the same length as D5, or tapered 1/8 inch per element, as the others are in Fig. 9-59. An 11-element Yagi of this type was made for 220, using a 3/4-inch aluminum boom, and a combination delta and universal-stub match. If the matching was readjusted for frequency changes it could be made to work uniformly over at least 2 MHz. The effect of the metal boom could be observed. Elements had to be about 1/8 inch longer than with the wood boom, for the center frequency of the array to remain the same, but this is not critical if the matching is adjustable.

WØEYE 15-Element 432-MHz Yagi

Demonstrating the truth of an earlier statement that there are many ways to make an effective Yagi, WØEYE built and tested the 432-MHz antenna of Fig. 9-60, using quite different element spacings. All directors are spaced the same, 8-7/16 inches, on a 116-inch boom, of 3/4-inch aluminum tubing. Element lengths are tapered, except for the five forward directors, not shown in the drawing, which are all 11-5/16 inches long. Aluminum rod 3/16 inch diameter is used for all elements.

Several interesting mechanical and electrical features are included. The delta arms are brought to an insulating block mounted on the boom. Elements are held in position by means of self-tapping screws so placed that they just bear against the elements. A gusset plate and two U clamps hold the boom in position on the vertical support.

Gain has been measured carefully, at over 14 dB over a reference dipole. This can be raised 0.5 dB by the addition of a 3-element reflector, details of which are shown in Fig. 9-61. Note that reflectors 2 and 3, above and below the boom, are 13 inches long, while reflector 1, mounted through the boom, is 13-1/2 inches.

Stacking in pairs or sets of four can use dimensions and methods of Fig. 9-62. Feed is set up for 50 ohms and a 4:1 balun.

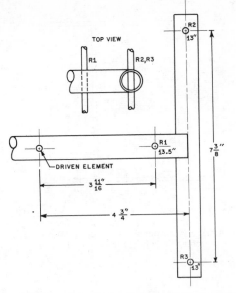

Fig. 9-61 — Gain of the 15-element Yagi can be increased about 0.5 dB by adding directors above and below the plane of the other elements. Note that the in-line reflector, R1, is spaced closer to the driven element when this is done.

2-BAY AND 4-BAY ARRAYS FOR 432 MHz

The 432-MHz Yagis described above can be used effectively in stacked pairs, or in a 4-bay system, as shown in Fig. 9-62. For convenience in stacking, delta-matched driven elements are used, with open-wire phasing lines and a universal stub. All director elements are as in Fig. 9-58. The driven element is 13 inches long, and the reflector is 13-1/4 inches. Essential mechanical details of the supporting frame are shown in Fig. 9-63.

The dimensions of the fanned-out portions of the phasing lines are not particularly critical, so long as all four are the same. The sides of the delta are about 2 inches long, and they fasten to the driven element about 1-3/8 inches each side of the center point. The phasing lines can be 1/2-inch spaced TV line, though No. 12 or No. 14, with a

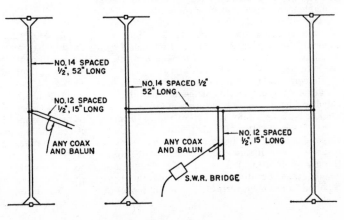

Fig. 9-62 — Phasing arrangements for two and four 432-MHz 11-element Yagis. Bay spacing of approximately two wave lengths is set by the length of the phasing lines. The universal stub matching device may be used with any type of transmission line, as well as with the coaxial line and balun as shown.

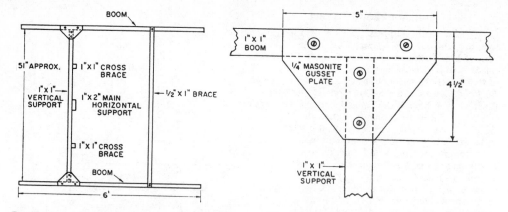

Fig. 9-63 — Mechanical details of the 432-MHz arrays. At the left is a side view of the 44-element system. The Masonite gusset plates used to hold the array in alignment are made as shown at the right. The array is supported on a round wooden closet pole, fastened to the three horizontal members in the sketch at the left, by means of U clamps.

minimum of spreaders, preferably Teflon rod, will be much better and more durable. The lines should be supported on standoffs at several places, to prevent flexing at the connection points.

Construction

All-wood construction was used for low cost, ease of assembly, and freedom from worry over large amounts of metal in the field of the array. Lightweight wood design would be none too strong for large arrays on lower frequencies, but at 432 MHz the wood frames are sturdy enough to stand up longer than most uhf enthusiasts will want to stay with one array.

The wood is mostly 1 X 1 stock. Like all lumber dimensions for width and thickness, this is a misnomer. The actual size is likely to be more nearly 7/8 X 7/8 inches, but this is not important for our purposes. It merely makes it impossible to give precise dimensions for the supporting frame. Get good-quality dry wood, free of knots, and preferably a kind that is not subject to severe warping. Most lumber dealers will be glad to advise you on the best materials for outdoor use, and available woods vary around the country.

The holes for the elements are drilled the size of the elements or slightly smaller, and the elements are forced into place. Half-inch brass wood screws that run in from the top or bottom hold the elements in position firmly.

Bracing can be whatever the wind and weather conditions in your locality demand. The principal details of the array frame are given in Fig. 9-63. At the left is the assembly for two of the 11-element bays. The main vertical member, also 1 X 1, is held perpendicular to the booms by means of gusset plates of 1/4-inch Masonite, as shown at the right. If only an 11-over-11 is to be built, this vertical member can be dispensed with, and the bays clamped to the main vertical support by means of U clamps.

When four bays are to be used additional bracing is needed, and the gusset plates and forward bracing become necessary. The front brace is 1/2 X 1-inch stock, bolted between the two booms to keep them in alignment. The two vertical supports with the gusset plates are tied together horizontally with two 1 X 1-inch cross braces and a 1 X 2-inch main support, as shown. Not shown in the sketch are two 1/2 X 1-inch wood sway braces that run from the mid-points of the two forward vertical braces to the 1 X 2-inch main horizontal member. These are held in place by small brackets cut to fit from sheet aluminum. The main vertical support, not shown, is 1-1/4- or 1-1/2-inch round closet-pole stock. This is inexpensive and strong, and there is no extraneous metal in the array proper.

To make the wood members reasonably durable and waterproof they were sprayed with Krylon before assembly. The Masonite gusset plates were also well soaked with lacquer spray. The whole assembly was painted with ordinary outside white house paint.

Adjustment

Matching the array should be done with the bottom bay at least four feet above ground, if in the position that it will be in use; that is, with the booms horizontal. The region in front of the array should be free of trees, buildings, wires, or any other materials or objects that can reflect 432-MHz energy. A high-gain array has a strong field out front. An appreciable reflection back has a marked effect on its impedance. If you don't have a good large open area, prop the array up with the vertical support in a horizontal position, and the four booms pointing straight up. Ground under the array will have little or no effect on its impedance in this position, as the power radiated off the back is negligible, for this purpose.

Fig. 9-64 — Element details and phasing harness for the 48-element 432-MHz collinear array. Reflectors, not shown, are 13-1/4 inches long, with their inner element ends 3/4 inches apart. Phasing harness, B, should be spaced no more than 1/2 inch. Main transmission line can be coax or balanced line.

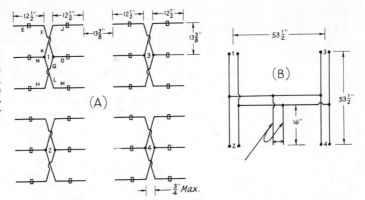

With an SWR bridge in the coaxial line near the antenna (preferably some small multiple of a wavelength away), adjust the short on the universal stub and the point of connection of the balun for zero reflected power. Once the proper points are found, permanent connections can be made.

A 48-ELEMENT COLLINEAR FOR 432 MHz

The high-gain 432-MHz collinear of Figs. 9-64 and 65 is inexpensive and easy to build and adjust. Though light in weight and mostly made of wood, it survived two rough winters in a hilltop location. Materials can be obtained anywhere, and only the simplest tools are needed in its construction.

Basically it is made up of four 12-element collinears, each having six half-wave driven elements, with reflectors. These are arranged in a square and connected by 2-wavelength phasing lines of open TV line, spaced 1/2 inch. To help to clarify this, in Fig. 9-64, the driven-element sets are numbered 1 and 2, at the left, and 3 and 4, at the right. The phasing harness is shown separately, with terminals correspondingly numbered. At the center is a universal stub (see Fig. 8-18), permitting the array to be fed with any balanced line, or coax and a balun.

We have ignored the 24 reflector elements so far, as they are not connected electrically, and showing them only complicates any drawing. They

are 13-1/4 inches long, and placed approximately 5-1/2 inches in back of the driven elements. The latter dimension has little significance as far as performance is concerned.

Most details of the supporting frame are in Fig. 9-65. The four vertical members, A, the two smaller horizontal braces, B, and the 24 element supports, C, are all "1 by 1" stock. This won't cost much, so get the best you can; free of knots and well dried. Take your lumberman's advice as to the kind of wood; the best available varies from one section of the country to another. As with all lumber, the actual size is less than the trade size, so the assembling can be done with 2-inch brass 6-32 screws, washers, and nuts. These are indicated in the front view.

The element supports, C, are held in place with 2-inch brass wood screws. Drill holes in the A pieces just large enough to pass the screws, and in the ends of the C pieces about half the screw diameter. Now drill all the element holes. Paint all surfaces with a priming coat, and let it dry thoroughly. Coat the inner end of the C pieces with a good glue or cement, and screw them in place firmly — but don't overdo it. After the glue is dry, paint the frame again.

The elements can be about any conducting material: aluminum wire, welding rod, or what-have-you. Put in the reflectors first. They are not centered exactly in the supports, but rather are

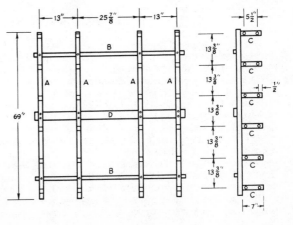

Fig. 9-65 — Details of the wooden supporting frame for the 432-MHz collinear array. Vertical members, A, are 1 X 1 X 69 inches; horizontal braces, B, 1 X 1 X 54 inches. Element supports, C, are 1 X 1 X 7 inches. Center brace, D, is 1 X 2 X 54 inches. Assembly dimensions are given on the drawing.

placed so that their inner ends are about 3/4 inch apart. Put a 1/2-inch brass wood screw into each support to bite lightly into the element and hold it in place. This is also done with each driven element.

Each set of six half-wave elements and interconnecting lines requires only four pieces of wire. At the upper left of Fig. 9-64, E, F, G, and H are one piece, and J, K, L, and M are another. Elements N and O are made from pieces of wire about 13-1/2 inches long. Pound one end of each flat on an anvil, wrap it around a wire or rod of the same diameter, and drill through the overlapping flat portions for a 4-40 screw. This makes a loop that can be clamped tightly to the midpoint of the interconnecting lines.

For E-F-G-H and J-K-L-M, cut pieces about 52 inches long, feed them through the proper holes in the C supports, and bend so that the elements are 12-1/2 inches long, with inner ends about 1/2 inch apart, and the phasing sections are arranged as shown in the sketch. Spacing at the cross-over points can be done with 3/8-inch poly or Teflon rods, about 1-1/4 inches long, and either drilled or notched to pass the phasing wires. Drilling is best, but it creates something of a "threading" problem in assembling the elements and phasing leads. We gave it up after an initial try, and resorted to notched insulators, cemented in place with epoxy glue. They did not come loose in nearly two years on the tower. Spacing of the lines should be maintained at 3/4 inch or less.

Elements N and O are wrapped around the phasing leads and clamped in place. Trim each to 12-1/2 inches over-all length, if necessary. When all elements are in place and they and their phasing sections are lined up properly, put in 1/2-inch brass wood screws bearing on each element to hold it permanently in position in its C support.

The phasing harness, 1-2, 3-4, and connecting line, is made of 1/2-inch open TV line, each piece 53-1/2 inches long, this being 2 wavelengths as checked out for resonance with a dip oscillator at 432 MHz. Connection is made to the four sets of driven elements by soldering to lugs under the nuts that hold the center elements in contact with the aluminum phasing leads. The lines are longer than

needed, physically, but the extra length permits looping them back to supports attached to the frame. TV hardware is useful here. Make all phasing-line bends on as large a radius as possible, and try to keep junctions perpendicular.

The universal stub can be any convenient material. The element wire was used in the original, 16 inches long, with the conductors spaced about 1 inch. When the proper points for the sliding short and the line connection are found, be sure that tight permanent connections are made. The excess of the stub below the short can be cut off, and the stub grounded for lightning protection, if desired. In the original the stub is mounted on brackets attached to the center vertical support, not shown in the sketch.

A U-shaped clamp of sheet aluminum holds the brace D to the supporting mast. Sheets of metal on each side of the brace prevent damage to the wood when it is clamped tightly in its final position. A similar but smaller clamp and plate arrangement was made for the lower B member, to steady the assembly.

Adjustment for matching was done with the beam in a horizontal position, aiming straight up. Two different feed systems have been used: a coaxial line and balun, and a balanced line. With the latter, tubular transmitting Twin-Lead runs from the stub to an anchor at the top of the tower. Here it joins a 100-foot run of No. 12 wire, 1/2-inch spaced on Teflon spreaders, one every 6 feet. This line is pulled up tightly and is straight throughout. At the house end there is a grounded adjustable short, and a balun connection, to complete the run to the antenna relay. The short and balun connection are adjusted for zero reflected power on this short section of coax. A mild SWR exists on the balanced line, but this is of no consequence, the total loss having been measured at under 1.6 dB.

The array has a very sharp main lobe, with two fairly large minor lobes on either side — an inescapable consequence of the wide spacing between bays. Response is sufficiently broad for uniform results over at least 4 MHz in the vicinity of 432 MHz, when the stub is adjusted at the middle of the desired frequency range.

THE CORNER REFLECTOR

Corner and plane reflector principles were discussed in some detail in Chapter 8. The corner requires but one driven element, and is capable of giving a very clean pattern and moderate gain, with very broad frequency response. At 220 and 420 MHz its size assumes practical proportions, and it can even be used at 144, though usually at less than optimum size.

The corner angle can be 90, 60, or even 45 degrees, but the side length must be increased as the angle is narrowed. The driven element spacing from the corner can be anything from 0.25 to 0.7 wavelength for a 90-degree corner, 0.35 to 0.75 for a 60-degree one, and 0.5 to 1 for a 45-degree corner. Feed impedance for various corner angles

and spacings was given in Fig. 8-9. Since the spacing is not critical as to gain, variation of it may be used to achieve impedance matching.

Gain with a 60- or 90-degree corner with 1-wavelength sides runs around 10 dB. A 60-degree corner with 2-wavelength sides has about 12 dB gain. It will be seen that this is not outstanding for the size of such an array, but there are other advantages. A corner may be used for several bands, for example, or perhaps for uhf television reception, as well as for amateur uhf work.

A suggested arrangement for a corner reflector system is shown in Fig. 9-66. Sheet metal or wire mesh may be used with equal effectiveness for the reflecting plane. A series of spines, as shown, is

Fig. 9-66 — Construction of a corner-reflector array. Frame can be wood or metal. Reflector elements are stiff wire or tubing. Dimensions for three bands are given in Table 9-II. Reflector element spacing, G, is the maximum that should be used for the frequency; closer spacings are optional. Hinge permits folding for portable use.

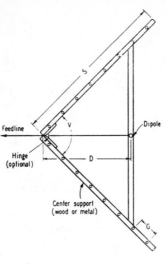

equally good, if the space between them is kept under 0.06 wavelength at the highest frequency for which the reflector is to be used. The frame may be made of wood, with a hinge at the corner to facilitate portable work or assembling atop a tower. Principal dimensions for corner reflector arrays for 144, 220, and 420 MHz are given in Table 9-II. These dimensions are not critical, because of the broad frequency response of any plane-reflector system.

TABLE 9-II

Dimensions of Corner-Reflector Arrays for 144, 220, and 420 MHz

Band (MHz)	Side Length "S" (Inches)	Dipole to Vertex "D" (Inches)	Reflector Length "L" (Inches)	Reflector Spacing "G" (Inches)	Corner Angle "V" (Degrees)	Feed Impedance (Ohms)
144*	65	27.5	48	7-3/4	90	70
144	80	40	48	4	90	150
220*	42	18	30	5	90	70
220	52	25	30	3	90	150
220	100	25	30	screen	60	70
420	27	8-3/4	16-1/4	2-5/8	90	70
420	54	13-1/2	16-1/4	screen	60	70

*Side length and number of reflector elements somewhat below optimum — slight reduction in gain.

BROAD-BAND ANTENNAS

In addition to utilizing harmonic resonances, as in most long-wire antennas, there are several ways to make an antenna work on more than one band. Most are variations of the broad-band dipole principle, in which the radiating element is modified in shape so that it has no precise *electrical* length. The "conical" and "bow-tie" antennas of vhf and uhf TV usage are familiar examples. In all such antennas the net effect is to make the transmission line gradually become the antenna, the point at which this happens varying with frequency.

A would-be vhf enthusiast who must have an unobtrusive antenna that will work on 50 through 220 MHz could do worse than to put up a TV conical. Its pattern will be far from perfect, and its gain low, but it will work after a fashion. Similarly, uhf bow-ties and corner-reflector antennas have been pressed into service on 432 MHz in a pinch. Performance of the TV conical on 50 MHz may be improved slightly by extending the elements 3 or 4 inches.

A 3-Band Log-Periodic Array

A more esoteric idea is the basis of the "log-periodic antenna," now widely used in military and commercial stations where many frequencies must be employed to maintain communication in the hf range. In theory, the frequency range of this type of antenna is almost unlimited, and in

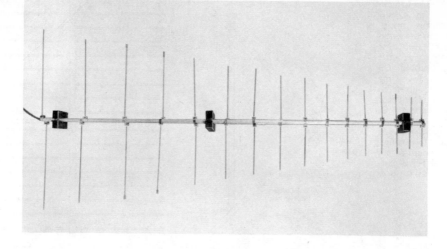

Fig. 9-67 — The log-periodic array for 140 through 450 MHz looks like a Yagi when viewed from top or bottom. Actually it has two electrically separate booms, each with a set of elements arranged as shown in Fig. 9-68. Black objects are wood-block spacers for the booms. Design is by K7RTY.

practice a spread of 4 or 5 to 1 is not uncommon. Arrays of this kind can take many forms. A simple version by K7RTY is shown in Figs. 9-67 through 70.

As author Heslin put it in his June, 1963, *QST* article: "This is an antenna whose resonance transfers smoothly from one element to the next, as the frequency is raised." More on the principle of the log-periodic antenna may be found in a November, 1959, *QST* treatment by Milner, W1FVY.

The version described here is not readily drawn or photographed in its complete form, to show full details. It has two booms one above the other, as shown in the sketch of the short (front) end, Fig. 9-69. Elements are progressively longer and wider spaced as we move toward the back of the array. The array is fed with coaxial line, which runs inside the lower boom its entire length. The outer shield connects to that boom, and the inner conductor to the upper. Each boom has a set of staggered elements, as shown in Fig. 9-68. These are assem-

bled so that when the antenna is viewed from directly above or below it appears somewhat like a long Yagi, as in the photograph. The two booms are maintained 1-1/4 inches apart, by means of wooden blocks.

Frequency response is determined by the shortest and longest elements. The example is quite uniform in gain and feed impedance, from 140 to 450 MHz. Gain over this entire range is roughly what would be expected from a 3-element Yagi for any one frequency.

The element mounts were made from inexpensive TV antenna parts, modified to take an element with a threaded end, as shown. K7RTY used 1/4-inch rod for elements, but other sizes are suitable if a mounting method is available. Note that two assemblies like that shown in Fig. 9-68 are required. These must be held in alignment, but insulated from each other.

An array of similar electrical properties was made by W1CUT, using 1/2-inch aluminum channel stock for the booms, and threaded-end 1/8-inch

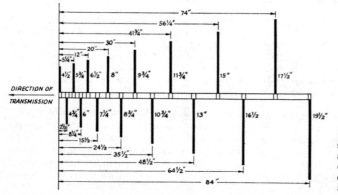

Fig. 9-68 — Dimensions for one section of the log-periodic vhf array. The finished array consists of two of these sections, mounted one above the other, to give the appearance of Fig. 9-67.

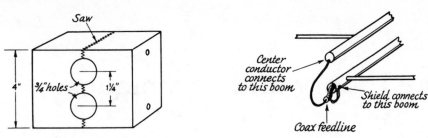

Fig. 9-69 — The two booms of the wide-band array are kept in alignment and insulated from each other by three wooden blocks, left. Short end of the array, right, shows how the array is fed. Lower boom, with coax inside, acts as an infinite balun.

aluminum rod for elements. The coaxial line ran the length of one of the channels, apparently serving as an "infinite balun" in the same way as in the K7RTY version where the coax runs inside the boom. This array was tested and found to have an SWR under 2:1 at 144, 220, and 432 MHz, and gain averaging 6 dB over this range.

The log-periodic, in common with all broad-band arrays, does not give something for nothing. Gain is very low, compared with what a Yagi of the same physical size would deliver on one frequency, but the principal weakness is its broad-band nature. Being almost equally effective across more than a 3-to-1 frequency range, the antenna presents very much more of a problem with spurious receiver responses than does a Yagi, with the latter's inherent selectivity. By the same token, greater care must be exercised in keeping down spurious products in the transmitter. The log-periodic will accept power on any frequency in its wide range, and radiate it with some gain. This is quite a different matter from working with a Yagi that has gain only over a narrow frequency range, and considerable rejection ability on most other frequencies.

Still, if one antenna, with one feedline and one rotator, for several vhf and uhf bands (and perhaps the TV channels in between) is your requirement, the log-periodic will probably fill it as well as any one antenna can.

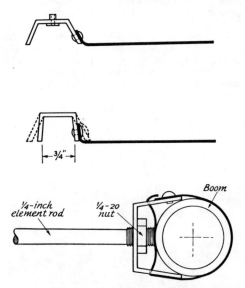

Fig. 9-70 — Element mounts are made from TV line standoffs with stainless-steel straps, top. The insert is knocked or drilled out, and the clamp portion bent as shown at the center. Complete mount, with 1/4-inch element in place, has lock and tension nut inside the clamp, to avoid need for drilling the latter.

STIFFENING ANTENNA TUBING

Lightweight tubing used in antenna work can be made much stronger by inserting a wooden plug at the point where strain is expected. This is particularly effective for a light vertical support for beams, where it runs through the tower bearing. This is the point where the tubing is most likely to collapse. Stuffing it with a wood dowel that is a close fit will strengthen it greatly. A foot or two either side of the tower bearing is all that is needed. Rug-pole stock is available at most lumberyards. Get hard wood for greatest strength. This

may not be so readily available, but it is worth shopping around for.

Also good for this application, though heavy: ordinary thick-wall water pipe. It may bend, but it will not collapse or break. The so-called 1-inch water pipe (inside diameter) is fine. Lightweight steel tubing is probably the least desirable of all, because of its susceptibility to collapsing. Aluminum or dural tubing offers the best compromise between strength and light weight, of readily available materials.

Chapter 10

Fm – Theory and Techniques

Methods of radiotelephone communication by frequency modulation were developed in the 1930s by Major Edwin Armstrong in an attempt to reduce the problems of static and noise associated with receiving a-m broadcast transmissions. The primary advantage of fm, the ability to produce a high signal-to-noise ratio when receiving a signal of only moderate strength, has made fm the ideal mode for mobile communications services and quality broadcasting. The disadvantages, the wide bandwidth required, and the poor results obtained when an fm signal is propagated via the ionosphere (because of phase distortion), has limited the use of frequency modulation to the 10-meter band and the vhf/uhf section of the spectrum.

Fm has some impressive advantages for vhf operation, especially when compared to a-m. With fm the modulation process takes place in a low-level stage. The modulation equipment required is the same, regardless of transmitter power. The signal may be frequency multiplied after modulation, and the PA stage can be operated class C for best efficiency, as the "final" need not be linear.

In recent years there has been increasing use of fm by amateurs operating around 29.6 MHz in the 10-meter band. The vhf spectrum now in popular use includes 52 to 53 MHz, 146 to 147.5 MHz, and 440 to 450 MHz.

FREQUENCY AND PHASE MODULATION

Fig. 10-1 — One advantage of the fm mode is the large amount of surplus equipment which can be converted for amateur use. AREC and civil-defense groups increasingly are using vhf fm for local communications networks because of the low cost and high reliability of surplus commercial gear. Here WA6ECK checks Motorola Handi-Talkies which have been modified for 6-meter operation at the San Fernando Emergency Operating Center during an earthquake emergency.

It is possible to convey intelligence by modulating any property of a carrier, including its frequency and phase. When the frequency of the carrier is varied in accordance with the variations in a modulating signal, the result is frequency modulation (fm). Similarly, varying the phase of the carrier current is called phase modulation (pm). Frequency and phase modulation are not independent, since the frequency cannot be varied without also varying the phase, and vice versa.

The effectiveness of fm and pm for communication purposes depends almost entirely on the receiving methods. If the receiver will respond to frequency and phase changes but is insensitive to amplitude changes, it will discriminate against most forms of noise, particularly impulse noise such as is set up by ignition systems and other sparking devices. Special methods of detection are required to accomplish this result.

Modulation methods for fm and pm are simple and require practically no audio power. There is also the advantage that, since there is no amplitude variation in the signal, interference to broadcast reception resulting from rectification of the transmitted signal in the audio circuits of the bc receiver is substantially eliminated.

Frequency Modulation

Fig. 10-2 is a representation of frequency modulation. When a modulating signal is applied, the carrier frequency is increased during one half cycle of the modulating signal and decreased during the half cycle of opposite polarity. This is indicated in the drawing by the rf cycles occupying less time (higher frequency) when the modulating signal is positive, and more time (lower frequency) when the modulating signal is negative. The change in the carrier frequency (frequency deviation) is proportional to the instantaneous amplitude of the modulating signal, so the deviation is small when the instantaneous amplitude of the modulating signal is small and is greatest when the modulating signal reaches its peak, either positive or negative. As shown by the drawing, the amplitude of the signal does not change during modulation.

Phase Modulation

If the phase of the current in a circuit is changed there is an instantaneous frequency change during the time that the phase is being shifted. The amount of frequency change, or deviation, depends on how rapidly the phase shift is accomplished. It is also dependent upon the total amount of the phase shift. In a properly operating pm system the amount of phase shift is proportional to the instantaneous amplitude of the modulating signal. The rapidity of the phase shift is directly proportional to the frequency of the modulating signal. Consequently, the frequency deviation in pm is proportional to both the amplitude and frequency of the modulating signal. The latter represents the outstanding difference between fm and pm, since in fm the frequency deviation is proportional only to the amplitude of the modulating signal.

Fm and Pm Sidebands

The sidebands set up by fm and pm differ from those resulting from a-m in that they occur at integral multiples of the modulating frequency on either side of the carrier rather than, as in a-m, consisting of a single set of side frequencies for each modulating frequency. An fm or pm signal therefore inherently occupies a wider channel than a-m.

The number of "extra" sidebands that occur in fm and pm depends on the relationship between the modulating frequency and the frequency deviation. The ratio between the frequency deviation, in hertz, and the modulating frequency, also in hertz, is called the modulation index. That is,

$$\text{Modulation index} = \frac{\text{Carrier frequency deviation}}{\text{Modulating frequency}}$$

Example: The maximum frequency deviation in an fm transmitter is 3000 Hz either side of the carrier frequency. The modulation index when the modulating frequency is 1000 Hz is

$$\text{Modulation index} = \frac{3000}{1000} = 3$$

At the same deviation with 3000-Hz modulation the index would be 1; at 100 Hz it would be 30, and so on.

In pm the modulation index is constant regardless of the modulating frequency; in fm it varies with the modulating frequency, as shown in the above example. In an fm system the ratio of the *maximum* carrier-frequency deviation to the *highest* modulating frequency used is called the deviation ratio.

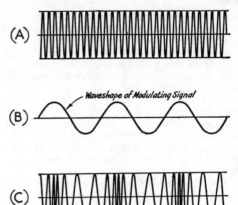

Fig. 10-2 — Graphical representation of frequency modulation. In the unmodulated carrier at A, each rf cycle occupies the same amount of time. When the modulating signal, B, is applied, the radio frequency is increased and decreased according to the amplitude and polarity of the modulating signal.

Fig. 10-3 shows how the amplitudes of the carrier and the various sidebands vary with the modulation index. This is for single-tone modulation; the first sideband (actually a pair, one above and one below the carrier) is displaced from the carrier by an amount equal to the modulating frequency, the second is twice the modulating frequency away from the carrier, and so on. For example, if the modulating frequency is 2000 Hz and the carrier frequency is 53,000 kHz, the first sideband pair is at 52,998 kHz and 53,002 kHz, the second pair is at 52,996 kHz and 53,004 kHz, the third at 52,994 kHz and 53,006 kHz, etc. The amplitudes of these sidebands depend on the modulation index, not on the frequency deviation.

Note that, as shown by Fig. 10-3, the carrier strength varies with the modulation index. (In amplitude modulation the carrier strength is constant; only the sideband amplitude varies.) At a

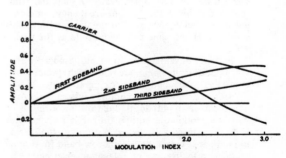

Fig. 10-3 — How the amplitude of the pairs of sidebands varies with the modulation index in an fm or pm signal. If the curves were extended for greater values of modulation index it would be seen that the carrier amplitude goes through zero at several points. The same statement also applies to the sidebands.

modulation index of approximately 2.4 the carrier disappears entirely. It then becomes "negative" at a higher index, meaning that its phase is reversed as compared to the phase without modulation. In fm and pm the energy that goes into the sidebands is taken from the carrier, the *total* power remaining the same regardless of the modulation index.

Since there is no change in amplitude with modulation, an fm or pm signal can be amplified without distortion by an ordinary class C amplifier. The modulation can take place in a low-level stage and the signal can then be amplified by either frequency multipliers or straight-through amplifiers.

If the modulated signal is passed through one or more frequency multipliers, the modulation index is multiplied by the same factor that the carrier frequency is multiplied. For example, if modulation is applied on 8150 kHz and the final output is on 146.7 MHz, the total frequency multiplication is 18 times, so if the frequency deviation is 500 Hz at 8150 kHz it will be 9000 Hz at 146.7 MHz. Frequency multiplication offers a means for obtaining practically any desired amount of frequency deviation, whether or not the modulator itself is capable of giving that much deviation without distortion.

Bandwidth

FCC amateur regulations (Part 97.61) limit the bandwidth of F3 (frequency or phase modulation) to that of an a-m transmission having the same audio characteristics below 29.0 MHz and in the 50.1- to 52.5-MHz frequency segment. Greater bandwidths are allowed from 29.0 to 29.7 MHz and above 52.5 MHz.

If the modulation index (with single-tone modulation) does not exceed 0.6 or 0.7, the most important extra sideband, the second, will be at least 20 dB below the unmodulated carrier level, and this should represent an effective channel width about equivalent to that of an a-m signal. In the case of speech, a somewhat higher modulation index can be used. This is because the energy distribution in a complex wave is such that the modulation index for any one frequency component is reduced as compared to the index with a sine wave having the same peak amplitude as the voice wave.

A major advantage of fm or pm, especially for vhf operators living in areas of high population density, is the elimination or great reduction of interference problems commonly associated with any form of amplitude modulation, including ssb. Also, the modulating equipment is relatively simple and inexpensive. However, assuming the same unmodulated carrier power, narrow-band fm or pm is not as effective as a-m unless a receiver designed especially for fm reception is employed.

As shown in Fig. 10-3, at an index of 0.6 the amplitude of the first sideband is about 25 percent of the unmodulated-carrier amplitude. This compares with a sideband amplitude of 50 percent in the case of an a-m signal modulated 100 percent. When copied on an a-m receiver, a narrow-band fm

or pm signal is about equivalent to a well-modulated a-m signal of one-fourth the carrier power. But with a suitable fm receiver, fm is equal to or better than a-m, watt for watt, in the kinds of voice communication for which fm is now widely used.

Three deviation amounts are now common practice: 15, 5, and 2.5 kHz, which in the current vernacular of fm users, are known as wide-band, narrow-band, and silver-band, respectively. (See box above.) The 2.5-3 kHz deviation (called nbfm by OTs) was popular for a time on the vhf bands and 10 meters after World War II. Deviation figures are given for the frequency swing in one direction. The rule-of-thumb for determination of bandwidth requirements for an fm system is:

$$2\ (\triangle F + F_{Amax})$$

where $\triangle F$ is one half of the total frequency deviation, and F_{Amax} is the maximum audio frequency (3 kHz for communications purposes). Thus, for narrow-band fm, the bandwidth equals $2\ (5 + 3)$ or 16 kHz. Wide-band systems need a 36-kHz receiver bandwidth.

It should be emphasized that "narrow-band" and "wide-band" as used here are vernacular terms. In interpreting amateur regulations, anything that does not qualify for use below 52.5 or 29.0 MHz (see box) is *wide-band* fm. Future plans for amateur use of fm for 220 MHz and higher bands could well employ bandwidths comparable to fm broadcasting (150 kHz), especially in the uhf portion of the spectrum.

Comparison of Fm and Pm

Frequency modulation cannot be applied to an amplifier stage, but phase modulation can; pm is therefore readily adaptable to transmitters employing oscillators of high stability such as the crystal-controlled type. The amount of phase shift that can be obtained with good linearity is such that the maximum practicable modulation index is about 0.5. Because the phase shift is proportional to the modulating frequency, this index can be used only at the highest frequency present in the modulating signal, assuming that all frequencies will at one time or another have equal amplitudes. Taking 3000 Hz as a suitable upper limit for voice work, and setting the modulation index at 0.5 for 3000 Hz, the frequency response of the speech-amplifier system above 3000 Hz must be sharply attenuated, to prevent excess splatter. (See Fig. 10-4.) Also, if the "tinny" quality of pm as received on an fm receiver is to be avoided, the pm must be changed to fm, in which the modulation index decreases in inverse proportion to the modulating frequency. This requires shaping the speech-amplifier frequency-response curve in such a way that the output voltage is inversely proportional to frequency over most of the voice range. When this is done the maximum modulation index can only be used to some relatively low audio frequency, perhaps 300 to 400 Hz in voice transmission, and must decrease in proportion to the increase in frequency. The result is that the maximum linear frequency deviation is only one or two hundred Hz, when pm is changed to fm. To increase the

Fig. 10-4 — Output frequency spectrum of a narrow-band fm transmitter modulated by a 1-kHz tone.

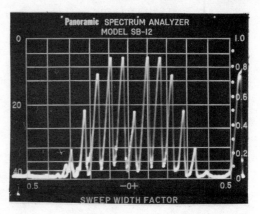

deviation for narrow-band requires a frequency multiplication of 8 times or more.

It is relatively easy to secure a fairly large frequency deviation when a self-controlled oscillator is frequency modulated directly. (True frequency modulation of a crystal-controlled oscillator results in only very small deviations and so requires a great deal of frequency multiplication.) The chief problem is to maintain a satisfactory degree of carrier stability, since the greater the inherent stability of the oscillator the more difficult it is to secure a wide frequency swing with linearity.

METHODS OF FREQUENCY MODULATION

Direct Fm

A simple and satisfactory device for producing fm in the amateur transmitter is the reactance modulator. This is a vacuum tube or transistor connected to the rf tank circuit of an oscillator in such a way as to act as a variable inductance or capacitance.

Fig. 10-5A is a representative circuit. Gate 1 of the modulator MOSFET is connected across the oscillator tank circuit, C1-L1, through resistor R1 and blocking capacitor C2. C3 represents the input capacitance of the modulator transistor. The resistance of R1 is made large compared to the reactance of C3, so the rf current through R1-C3 will be practically in phase with the rf voltage appearing at the terminals of the tank circuit. However, the voltage across C3 will lag the current by 90 degrees. The rf current in the drain circuit of the modulator will be in phase with the gate voltage, and consequently is 90 degrees behind the current through C3, or 90 degrees behind the rf tank voltage. This lagging current is drawn through the oscillator tank, giving the same effect as though an inductance were connected across the tank. The frequency increases in proportion to the amplitude of the lagging plate current of the modulator. The audio voltage, introduced through a radio-frequency choke, varies the transconductance of the transistor and thereby varies the rf drain current.

The modulated oscillator usually is operated on a relatively low frequency, so that a high order of carrier stability can be secured. Frequency multipliers are used to raise the frequency to the output frequency desired.

A reactance modulator can be connected to a crystal oscillator as well as to the self-controlled type as shown in Fig. 10-5B. However, the resulting signal can be more phase-modulated than it is frequency-modulated, for the reason that the frequency deviation that can be secured by varying the frequency of a crystal oscillator is quite small.

The sensitivity of the modulator, Fig. 10-5A, (frequency change per unit change in gate voltage) depends on the transconductance of the modulator

transistor. It increases when R1 is made smaller in comparison with C3. It also increases with an increase in LC ratio in the oscillator tank circuit. However, for highest carrier stability it is desirable to use the largest tank capacitance that will permit the desired deviation to be secured while keeping within the limits of linear operation.

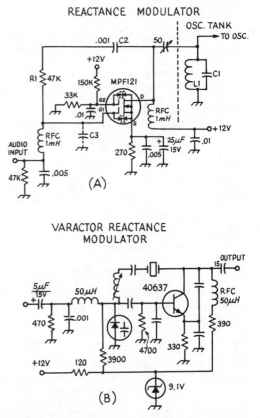

Fig. 10-5 — Reactance modulators using (A) a high-transconductance MOSFET and (B) a varactor diode.

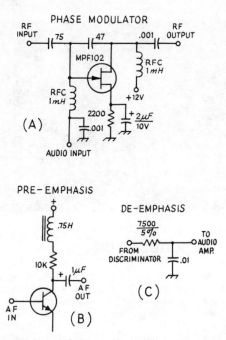

Fig. 10-6 — (A) The phase-shifter type of phase modulator. (B) Pre-emphasis and (C) de-emphasis circuits.

A change in *any* of the voltages on the modulator transistor will cause a change in rf drain current, and consequently a frequency change. Therefore it is advisable to use a regulated power supply for both modulator and oscillator.

Indirect Fm

The same type of reactance modulator circuit that is used to vary the tuning of the oscillator tank in fm can be used to vary the tuning of an amplifier tank and thus vary the phase of the tank current for pm. Hence the modulator circuit of Fig. 10-5A or 10-6A can be used for pm if the reactance transistor or tube works on an amplifier tank instead of directly on a self-controlled oscillator. If audio shaping is used in the speech amplifier, as described above, fm instead of pm will be generated by the phase modulator.

The phase shift that occurs when a circuit is detuned from resonance depends on the amount of detuning and the Q of the circuit. The higher the Q, the smaller the amount of detuning needed to secure a given number of degrees of phase shift. If the Q is at least 10, the relationship between phase shift and detuning (in kHz either side of the resonant frequency) will be substantially linear over a phase-shift range of about 25 degrees. From the standpoint of modulator sensitivity, the Q of the tuned circuit on which the modulator operates should be as high as possible. On the other hand, the effective Q of the circuit will not be very high if the amplifier is delivering power to a load since the load resistance reduces the Q. There must therefore be a compromise between modulator

sensitivity and rf power output from the modulated amplifier. An optimum figure for Q appears to be about 20; this allows reasonable loading of the modulated amplifier and the necessary tuning variation can be secured from a reactance modulator without difficulty. It is advisable to modulate at a low power level.

Reactance modulation of an amplifier stage usually results in simultaneous amplitude modulation because the modulated stage is detuned from resonance as the phase is shifted. This must be eliminated by feeding the modulated signal through an amplitude limiter or one or more "saturating" stages — that is, amplifiers that are operated class C and driven hard enough so that variations in the amplitude of the input excitation produce no appreciable variations in the output amplitude.

For the same type of reactance modulator, the speech-amplifier gain required is the same for pm as for fm. However, as pointed out earlier, the fact that the actual frequency deviation increases with the modulating audio frequency in pm makes it necessary to cut off the frequencies above about 3000 Hz before modulation takes place. If this is not done, unnecessary sidebands will be generated at frequencies considerably away from the carrier.

SPEECH PROCESSING FOR FM

The speech amplifier preceding the modulator follows ordinary design, except that no power is taken from it and the af voltage required by the modulator input usually is small — not more than 10 or 15 volts, even with large modulator tubes, and only a volt or two for transistors. Because of these modest requirements, only a few speech stages are needed; a two-stage amplifier consisting of two bipolar transistors, both resistance coupled, will more than suffice for crystal, ceramic or high-Z dynamic microphones. For more information on speech amplifiers see *The Radio Amateur's Handbook*, Chapter 13.

Several forms of speech processing produce worthwhile improvements in fm system performance. It is desirable to limit the peak amplitude of the audio signal applied to an fm or pm modulator, so that the deviation of the fm transmitter will not exceed a preset value. This peak limiting is usually accomplished with a simple audio clipper which is placed between the speech amplifier and modulator. The clipping process produces high-order harmonics which, if allowed to pass through to the modulator stage, would create unwanted sidebands. Therefore, an audio low-pass filter with a cut-off frequency between 2.5 and 3 kHz is needed at the output of the clipper. Excess clipping can cause severe distortion of the voice signal. An audio processor consisting of a compressor and a clipper, such as described in Chapter 13 of *The Radio Amateur's Handbook*, has been found to produce audio with a better sound (i.e., less distortion) than a clipper alone.

To reduce the amount of noise in some fm communications systems, an audio shaping network called pre-emphasis is added at the transmitter to proportionally attenuate the lower audio frequencies, giving an even spread to the energy in the audio band. This results in an fm signal of nearly constant energy distribution. The reverse is done at the receiver, called de-emphasis, to restore the audio to its original relative proportions. Sample circuits are shown in Fig. 10-6.

FM EXCITERS

Fm exciters and transmitters take two general forms. One, shown at Fig. 10-7A, consists of a reactance modulator which shifts the frequency of an oscillator to generate an fm signal directly. Successive multiplier stages provide output on the desired frequency, which is amplified by a PA stage. This system has a disadvantage in that, if the oscillator is free running, it is difficult to achieve sufficient stability for vhf use. If a crystal-controlled oscillator is employed, unless the amount that the crystal frequency is changed is kept small, it is difficult to achieve equal amounts of frequency swing.

The indirect method of generating fm shown in Fig. 10-7B is currently popular. Shaped audio is applied to a phase modulator to generate fm. As the amount of deviation produced is very small, then a large number of multiplier stages is needed to achieve wide-band deviation at the operating frequency. In general, the system shown at A will require a less complex circuit than that at B, but the indirect method (B) often produces superior results.

TESTING AN FM TRANSMITTER

Accurate checking of the operation of an fm or pm transmitter requires different methods than the corresponding checks on an a-m or ssb set. The common forms of measuring devices either indicate amplitude variations only (a milliammeter, for example), or their indications are most easily interpreted in terms of amplitude.

The quantities to be checked in an fm transmitter are the linearity and frequency deviation and the output frequency, if the unit uses crystal control. The methods of checking differ in detail.

Frequency Checking

The crystal-controlled, channelized operation that is now popular with amateur fm users requires that a transmitter be held close to the desired channel, at least within a few hundred hertz, even in a wide-band system. Having the transmitter on the proper frequency is particularly important when operating through a repeater. The rigors of mobile and portable operation make a frequency check of a channelized transceiver at regular intervals a recommended procedure.

Frequency meters generally fall into two categories: the heterodyne type and the digital counter. For amateur use, the vhf/uhf counterparts of the popular BC-221 frequency meter, the TS-174 and TS-175, will provide sufficient accuracy. Frequency counters that will work directly up to 500 MHz and higher are available, but their cost is high. The less expensive low-frequency counters can be employed using a scaler, a device which divides an input frequency by a preset ratio, usually 10 or 100. The Heathkit IB-102 scaler may be used up to 175 MHz, using a counter with a 2-MHz (or more) upper frequency limit. If the counting system does not have a sufficient upper frequency limit to measure the output of an fm transmitter directly, one of the frequency-multiplier stages can be sampled to provide a signal in the range of the measurement device. Alternatively, a crystal-controlled converter feeding an hf receiver which has accurate frequency readout can be employed, if a secondary standard is available to calibrate the receiving system.

Deviation and Deviation Linearity

A simple deviation meter can be assembled following the diagram of Fig. 10-8A. This circuit was designed by K6VKZ. The output of a wide-band receiver discriminator (before any de-emphasis) is fed to two amplifier transistors. The output of the amplifier section is transformer coupled to a pair of rectifier diodes to develop a dc voltage for the meter, M1. There will be an indication on the meter with no signal input because of detected noise, so the accuracy of the instrument will be poor on weak signals.

To calibrate the unit, signals of known deviation will be required. If the meter is to be set to read 0-15 kHz, then a 7.5-kHz deviation test signal should be employed. R1 is then adjusted until M1 reads half scale, 50 μA. To check the peak deviation of an incoming signal, close both S1 and S2. Then, read the meter. Opening first one switch and then the other will indicate the amount of positive and negative deviation of the signal, a check of deviation linearity.

Measurement of Deviation Using Bessel Functions

Using a math relationship known as the Bessel function it is possible to predict the points at

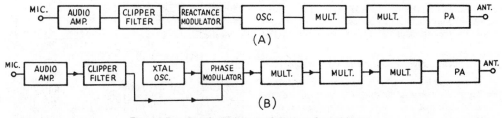

Fig. 10-7 — Block diagrams of typical fm exciters.

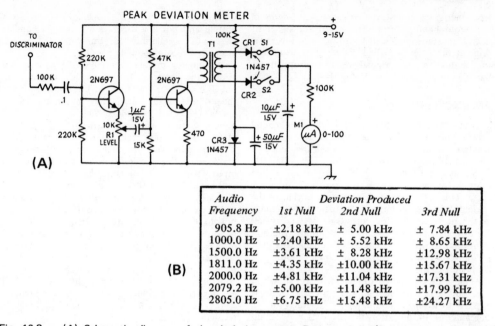

Audio	Deviation Produced		
Frequency	1st Null	2nd Null	3rd Null
905.8 Hz	±2.18 kHz	± 5.00 kHz	± 7.84 kHz
1000.0 Hz	±2.40 kHz	± 5.52 kHz	± 8.65 kHz
1500.0 Hz	±3.61 kHz	± 8.28 kHz	±12.98 kHz
1811.0 Hz	±4.35 kHz	±10.00 kHz	±15.67 kHz
2000.0 Hz	±4.81 kHz	±11.04 kHz	±17.31 kHz
2079.2 Hz	±5.00 kHz	±11.48 kHz	±17.99 kHz
2805.0 Hz	±6.75 kHz	±15.48 kHz	±24.27 kHz

Fig. 10-8 — (A) Schematic diagram of the deviation meter. Resistors are 1/2-watt composition and capacitors are ceramic, except those with polarity marked, which are electrolytic. CR1-CR3, incl., are high-speed silicon switching diodes. R1 is a linear-taper composition control, and S1, S2 are spst toggle switches. T1 is a miniature audio transformer with 10,000-ohm primary and 20,000-ohm center-tapped secondary (Triad A31X). (B) Chart of audio frequencies which will produce a carrier null when the deviation of an fm transmitter is set for the values given.

which, with certain audio-input frequencies and predetermined deviation settings, the carrier output of an fm transmitter will disappear completely. Thus, by monitoring the carrier frequency with a receiver, it will be possible by ear to identify the deviation at which the carrier is nulled. A heterodyne signal at either the input or receiver i-f is required so that the carrier will produce a beat note which can easily be identified. Other tones will be produced in the modulation process, so some concentration is required by the operator when making the test. With an audio tone selected from the chart (Fig. 10-8B), advance the deviation control slowly until the first null is heard. If a higher order null is desired, continue advancing the control further until the second, and then the third, null is heard. Using a carrier null beyond the third is generally not practical.

For example, if a 905.8-Hz tone is used, the transmitter will be set for 5-kHz deviation when the second null is reached. The second null achieved with a 2805-Hz audio input will set the transmitter deviation at 15.48 kHz. The Bessel-function approach can be used to calibrate a deviation meter, such as the unit shown in Fig. 10-8A.

Reactance-Modulator Fm Calibration

It is possible to calibrate a reactance modulator by applying an adjustable dc voltage to the modulator input and noting the change in oscillator frequency as the voltage is varied. A suitable circuit for applying the adjustable voltage is shown in Fig. 10-9A. The battery voltage is 3 to 6 volts (two or more dry cells in series). The arrows indicate clip connections so that the battery polarity can be reversed.

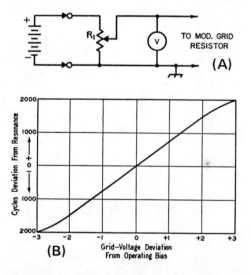

Fig. 10-9 — (A) Dc method of checking frequency deviation. R1 is 500 to 1000 ohms. (B) A typical curve of frequency deviation versus gate voltage for an fm modulator.

The oscillator frequency deviation should be measured by using a receiver in conjunction with an accurately calibrated frequency meter, or by any means that will permit accurate measurement of frequency differences of a few hundred hertz. One simple method is to tune in the oscillator on the receiver (disconnecting the receiving antenna, if necessary, to keep the signal strength well below the overload point) and then set the receiver BFO to zero beat. Then increase the dc voltage applied to the modulator input from zero in steps of about 1/2 volt and note the beat frequency at each change. Then reverse the battery terminals and repeat. The frequency of the beat note may be measured by comparison with a calibrated audio-frequency oscillator. Note that with the battery polarity positive with respect to ground the radio frequency will move in one direction when the voltage is increased, and in the other direction when the polarity is reversed. When several readings have been taken a curve may be plotted to show the relationship between input voltage and frequency deviation.

A sample curve is shown in Fig. 10-9B. The usable portion of the curve is the center part which is essentially a straight line. The bending at the ends indicates that the modulator is no longer linear; this departure from linearity will cause harmonic distortion and will broaden the channel occupied by the signal. In the example, the characteristic is linear 1.5 kHz on either side of the center or carrier frequency.

RECEPTION OF FM SIGNALS

Receivers for fm signals differ from others principally in two features: there is no need for linearity preceding detection; (in fact, it is advantageous if amplitude variations in signal and background noise can be "washed out"), and the detector must be capable of converting frequency variations in the incoming signal into amplitude variations.

Frequency-modulated signals can be received after a fashion on any ordinary receiver. The receiver is tuned to put the carrier frequency part way down on one side of the selectivity curve. When the frequency of the signal varies with modulation it swings as indicated in Fig. 10-10, resulting in an a-m output varying between X and Y. This is then rectified as an a-m signal.

With receivers having steep-sided selectivity curves, the method is not very satisfactory because the distortion is quite severe unless the frequency deviation is small, since the frequency deviation and output amplitude are linear over only a small part of the selectivity curve. Slope detection is also unsatisfactory if the receiver selectivity does not match the signal deviation closely.

The Fm Receiver

Block diagrams of an a-m/ssb and an fm receiver are shown in Fig. 10-11. Fundamentally, to achieve a sensitivity of less than one microvolt, an fm receiver requires a gain of several million —

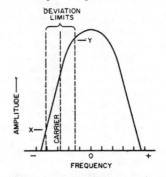

Fig. 10-10 — Fm detector characteristics. Slope detection, using the sloping side of the receiver selectivity curve to convert fm to a-m for subsequent detection.

A-M RECEIVER

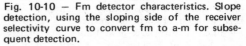

Fig. 10-11 — Block diagrams of (A) an a-m (B) an fm receiver. Dark borders outline the sections that are different in the fm set.

FM RECEIVER

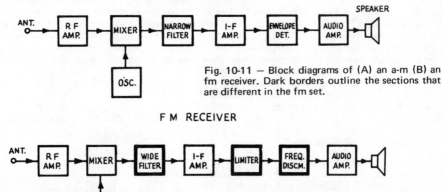

FM FILTERS

Manufacturer	Model	Center Frequency	Nonimal Bandwidth	Ultimate Rejection	Impedance (r) In	Out	Insertion Loss	Crystal Discriminator
KVG (1)	XF-9E	9.0 MHz	12 kHz	90 dB	1200	1200	3 dB	XD9-02
KVG (1)	XF-107A	10.7 MHz	12 kHz	90 dB	820	820	3.5 dB	XD107-01
KVG (1)	XF-107B	10.7 MHz	15 kHz	90 dB	910	910	3.5 dB	XD107-01
KVG (1)	XF-107C	10.7 MHz	30 kHz	90 dB	2000	2000	4.5 dB	XD107-01
Heath Dynamics (2)	–	21.5 MHz	15 kHz	90 dB	550	550	3 dB	–
Heath Dynamics (2)	–	21.5 MHz	30 kHz	90 dB	1100	1100	2 dB	–
E.S. (3)	FB-6D	10.7 MHz	15 kHz	80 dB	950	950	2 dB	AB-1C
E.S. (3)	10-MA	10.7 MHz	30 kHz	80 dB	2000	2000	4 dB	AB-1C
E.S. (3)	EL-3A	11.5 MHz	36 kHz	70 dB	50	50	4 dB	AL-1
E.S. (3)	DR-9	21.4 MHz	20 kHz	40 dB	750	750	5 dB	AR-10
Clevite (4)	TCF4-12D3CA	455 kHz	12 kHz	60 dB	40k	2200	6 dB	–
Clevite (4)	TCF4-18G45A	455 kHz	18 kHz	50 dB	40k	2200	6 dB	–
Clevite (4)	TCF6-30D55A	455 kHz	30 kHz	60 dB	20k	1000	5 dB	–

Fig. 10-12 — A list of fm-bandwidth filters that are available to amateurs. Manufacturer's addresses are as follows:

1) Spectrum International, P.O.Box 87, Topsfield, MA 01983.
2) Heath Dynamics, Inc., 6050 N. 52nd Avenue, Glendale, AZ 85301.
3) E. S. Electronic Labs, 301 Augustus, Excelsior Springs, MO 64024.
4) Semiconductor Specialists, Inc., P.O. Box 66125, O'Hare International Airport, Chicago, IL 60666. (Minimum order $5.00.)

too much total gain to be accomplished with stability on a single frequency. Thus, the use of the superheterodyne circuit has become standard practice. Three major differences will be apparent from a comparison of the two block diagrams. The fm receiver employs a wider bandwidth filter and a different detector and has a limiter stage added between the i-f amplifier and the detector. Otherwise the functions, and often the circuits, of the rf, oscillator, mixer, and audio stages will be the same in either receiver.

In operation, the noticeable difference between the two receivers is the effect of noise and interference on an incoming signal. From the time of the first spark transmitters, "rotten QRM" has been a major problem for amateurs. The limiter and discriminator stages in an fm set can eliminate a good deal of impulse noise, except that noise which manages to acquire a frequency-modulation characteristic. Accurate alignment of the receiver i-f system and phase tuning of the detector are required to achieve good noise suppression. Fm receivers perform in an unusual manner when an interfering signal is present, exhibiting a characteristic known as the *capture effect*. The loudest signal received, even if it is only two or three times stronger than other stations on the same frequency, will be the only transmission demodulated. By comparison, an S9 a-m or cw signal can suffer noticeable heterodyne interference from an S2 carrier.

Bandwidth

Most fm sets that use tubes achieve i-f selectivity by using a number of over-coupled transformers. The wide bandwidth and phase-response characteristic needed in the i-f system dictate careful design and alignment of all interstage transformers.

For the average ham, the use of a high-selectivity filter in a homemade receiver offers some simplification of the alignment task. Following the techniques used in ssb receivers, a crystal or ceramic filter should be placed in the circuit as close as possible to the front end — at the output of the first mixer, in most cases. Fig. 10-12 lists a number of suitable filters that are available to amateurs. Prices for these filters are in the range of $10 to $30. Experimenters who wish to "roll their own" can use surplus hf crystals, as outlined in ARRL's *Single Sideband for the Radio Amateur*, or ceramic resonators.

One item of concern to every amateur fm user is the choice of i-f bandwidth for his receiver, as both 15- and 5-kHz deviation are now in common use on the amateur bands. A wide-band receiver can receive narrow-band signals, suffering only some loss of audio in the detection process. However, a wideband signal will be badly distorted when received on a narrow-band receiver.

At this point it seems reasonable to assume that increasing fm activity and continued production of commercial narrow-band transceivers may gradually shift amateur operation to a 5-kHz deviation standard. But, as with the a-m operators, the

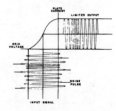

Fig. 10-13 — Representation of limiter action. Amplitude variations on the signal are removed by the diode action of the grid and plate-current saturation.

wide-band enthusiasts will be around for some time to come, lured by inexpensive surplus wide-band gear. It should be remembered that true wide-band fm has merit — on frequencies where there is room for it.

Limiters

When fm was first introduced, the main selling point used for the new mode was the noise-free reception possibilities. The circuit in the fm receiver that has the task of chopping off noise and amplitude modulation from an incoming signal is the *limiter*. Most types of fm detectors respond to both frequency and amplitude variations of the signal. Thus, the limiter stages preceding the detector are included to "cleanse" the signal so that only the desired frequency modulation will be demodulated. This action can be seen in Fig. 10-14.

Limiter stages can be designed using tubes, transistors, or ICs. For a tube to act as a limiter, the applied B voltages are chosen so that the stage will overload easily, even with a small amount of signal input. A sharp-cutoff pentode such as the 6BH6 is usually employed, with little or no bias applied. As shown in Fig. 10-13, the input signal limits when it is of sufficient amplitude so that diode action of the grid and plate-current saturation clip both sides of the input signal, producing a constant-amplitude output voltage.

Obviously, a signal of considerable strength is required at the input of the limiter to assure full clipping, typically several volts for tubes, one volt for transistors, and several hundred microvolts for ICs. Limiting action should start with an rf input of 0.2 μV or less, so a large amount of gain is required between the antenna terminal and the limiter stages. For example, the Motorola 80D has eight tubes before the limiter, and the solid-state MOTRAC receivers use nine transistor stages to get sufficient gain before the first limiter. The new ICs offer some simplification of the i-f system as they pack a lot of gain into a single package.

When sufficient signal arrives at the receiver to start limiting action, the set *quiets* — that is, the background noise disappears. The sensitivity of an fm receiver is rated in terms of the amount of input signal required to produce a given amount of quieting, usually 20 dB. Current practice using the new solid-state devices can produce receivers which achieve 20 dB quieting with 0.15 to 0.5 μV of input signal.

A single tube or transistor stage will not provide good limiting over a wide range of input signals. Two stages, with different input time constants, are a minimum requirement. The first stage is set to handle impulse noise satisfactorily while the second is designed to limit the range of signals passed on by the first. At frequencies below 1 MHz it is useful to employ untuned *RC*-coupled limiters which provide sufficient gain without a tendency toward oscillation.

Fig. 10-15A shows a two-stage limiter using sharp-cutoff tubes, and 10-15B has transistors in two stages biased for limiter service. The base bias on either transistor may be varied to provide

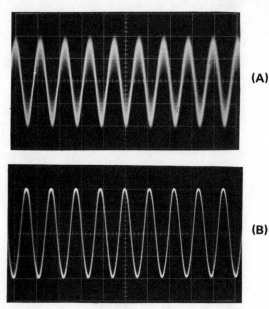

(A)

(B)

Fig. 10-14 — (A) Input wave form to a limiter stage shows a-m and noise. (B) The same signal, after passing through two limiter stages, is devoid of a-m conponents.

limiting at a desired level. The input-signal voltage required to start limiting action is called the *limiting knee*, referring to the point at which collector (or plate) current ceases to rise with increased input signal. Modern ICs have limiting knees of 100 mV for the circuit shown in Fig. 10-15C, using the CA3028A or MC1550G, or 200 μV for the Motorola MC1590G of Fig. 10-15D. Because the high-gain ICs such as the CA3076 and MC1590G contain as many as six or eight active stages which will saturate with sufficient input, one of these devices provides superior limiter performance compared to a pair of tubes or transistors.

Detectors

The first type of fm detector to gain popularity was the frequency discriminator. The characteristic of such a detector is shown in Fig. 10-16. When the fm signal has no modulation, and the carrier is at point O, the detector has no output. When audio input to the fm transmitter swings the signal higher in frequency, the rectified output increases in the positive direction. When the frequency swings lower the output amplitude increases in the negative direction. Over a range where the discriminator is linear (shown as the straight portion of the line), the conversion of fm to a-m which is taking place will be linear.

In the search for a simplified fm detector, RCA developed a circuit that has now become standard in entertainment radios which eliminated the need for a preceding limiter stage. Known as the *ratio detector*, this circuit is based on the idea of dividing a dc voltage into a ratio which is equal to the ratio of the amplitudes from either side of a

Fig. 10-15 — Typical lim-
iter circuits using (A)
tubes, (B) transistors, (C) a
differential IC, (D) a high-
gain linear IC.

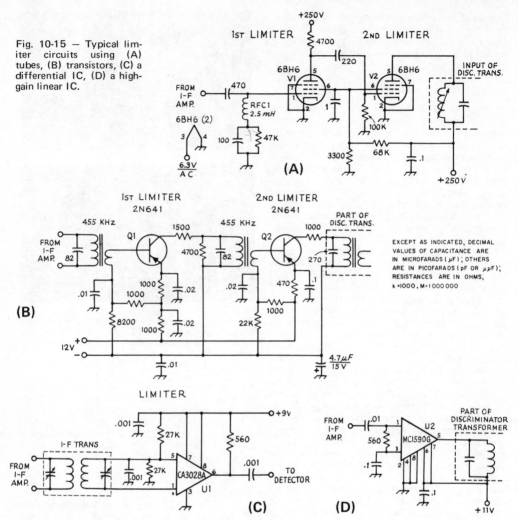

discriminator-transformer secondary. With a detector that responds only to ratios, the input signal may vary in strength over a wide range without causing a change in the level of output voltage — fm can be detected, but not a-m. In an actual ratio detector, Fig. 10-18, the dc voltage required is developed across two load resistors, shunted by an electrolytic capacitor. Other differences include the two diodes, which are wired in series aiding

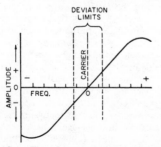

Fig. 10-16 — The characteristic of an fm discriminator.

rather than series opposing, as in the standard discriminator circuit. The recovered audio is taken from a tertiary winding which is tightly coupled to the primary of the transformer. Diode-load resistor values are selected to be lower (5000 ohms or less) than for the discriminator.

A practical discriminator circuit is shown in Fig. 10-17. The fm signal is converted to a-m by transformer T1. The voltage induced in the T1 secondary is 90 degrees out of phase with the current in the primary. The primary signal is introduced through a center tap on the secondary, coupled through a capacitor. The secondary voltages combine on each side of the center tap so that the voltage on one side leads the primary signal while the other side lags by the same amount. When rectified, these two voltages are equal and of opposite polarity, resulting in zero-voltage output. A shift in input frequency causes a shift in the phase of the voltage components that results in an increase of output amplitude on one side of the secondary, and a corresponding decrease on the other side. The differences in the two changing

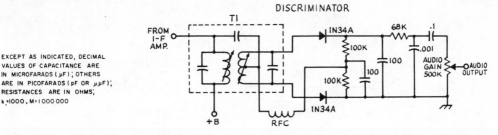

Fig. 10-17 — Typical frequency-discriminator circuit used for fm detection. T1 is a Miller 12-C45.

voltages, after rectification, constitute the audio output.

The sensitivity of the ratio detector is one half that of the discriminator. In general, however, the transformer design values for Q, primary-secondary coupling, and load will vary greatly, so the actual performance differences between these two types of fm detectors are usually not significant. Either circuit can provide excellent results. In operation, the ratio detector will not provide sufficient limiting for communications service, so this detector also is usually preceded by at least a single limiting stage.

Another popular discriminator circuit which does not require a special transformer is shown in Fig. 10-19. Often called the Travis discriminator, this arrangement uses two tuned circuits, one set above the i-f center frequency and the other set below by the same offset amount, feeding separate detectors. The outputs of the two detectors are combined by R1, which is adjusted for maximum a-m rejection. Because it can be built for any i-f, the Travis discriminator is useful as an fm detector for the Heath SB-series receivers, ARC-5s, and others with nonstandard i-fs.

New Detector Designs

The difficulties often encountered in building and aligning LC discriminators have inspired research that has resulted in a number of adjustment-

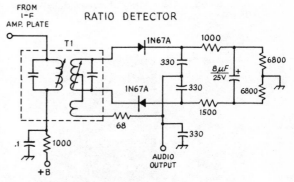

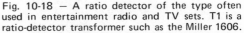

Fig. 10-18 — A ratio detector of the type often used in entertainment radio and TV sets. T1 is a ratio-detector transformer such as the Miller 1606.

free fm detector designs. The *crystal discriminator* utilizes a quartz resonator, shunted by an inductor, in place of the tuned-circuit secondary used in a discriminator transformer. A typical circuit is shown in Fig. 10-20. Some commercially made crystal discriminators have the input-circuit inductor, L1, built in (C1 must be added) while in other types both L1 and C1 must be supplied by the builder. Fig. 10-20 shows typical component values; unmarked parts are chosen to give the desired bandwidth. Sources for crystal discriminators are listed in Fig. 10-12.

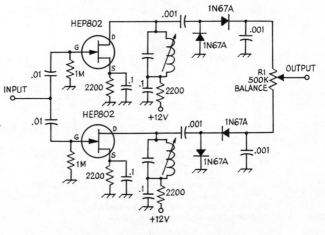

Fig. 10-19 — The Travis discriminator.

CRYSTAL DISCRIMINATOR

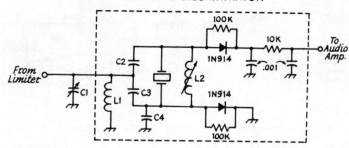

Fig. 10-20 — Crystal discriminator. C1 and L1 are resonate at the intermediate frequency. C2 is equal in value to C3. C4 corrects any circuit imbalance so that equal amounts of signal are fed to the detector diodes.

Fig. 10-21 — The digital detector.

Digital Detector

The integrated circuit, allowing complex functions to be performed in a very small package, has caused a revolution in fm receiver design. For sheer simplicity, the *pulse-counting detector*, shown in Figs. 10-21 and 10-22, has intrinsic appeal. Using inexpensive RTL logic, the detector requires 200 mV of signal from the receiver i-f system. The oscilloscope photographs of Fig. 10-23 show this digital detector at work. The first inverter, U1A, is biased to operate as a linear amplifier. The next

two stages provide "hard" limiting (Fig. 10-23B) of the i-f signal (Fig. 10-23A). The output pulse train from U3A (Fig. 10-23C) is fed to a divide-by-four circuit consisting of two flip-flops, U2A and U2B. The output of U2A (Fig. 10-23D) triggers a monostable multivibrator, which consists of R1, C1 and U1D.

The period of the multivibrator is set to be less than half of the period of the i-f signal. For an i-f of 455 kHz, the period is set at 800 nanoseconds. Output from the multivibrator consists of 800-nanosecond pulses whose repetition rate varies in direct proportion to the variation in frequency of the fm signal (Fig. 10-23E). The output of U1D is amplified by U1E and converted to an audio signal by the de-emphasis network (Fig. 10-23F). Maximum recovered audio occurs at a 50-percent duty cycle.

Advantages of the pulse-counting detector include linear detection over wide frequency ranges and inherent quieting. The self-squelching action results because the digital circuits remain inactive until the input signal reaches a threshold sufficient to trigger U2B. As the ICs are operating in the saturated mode, they provide excellent limiting, and no preceding limiter stage is required. The primary disadvantages are a low-voltage, high-current power requirement (3.6 V at 50 mA for the circuit shown in Fig. 10-22), and the very low level of recovered audio. Upper frequency limit for the RTL circuits is about 2 MHz, but other faster logic families (TTL or MECL II) can be employed for i-f systems in the 2- to 20-MHz range.

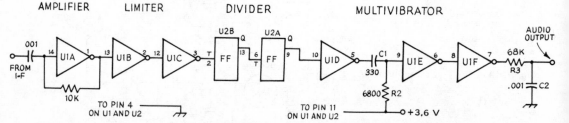

Fig. 10-22 — Diagram of the integrated-circuit detector. Resistors are 1/2-watt composition and capacitors are disk ceramic. Labeled components not listed below are marked for text reference.

U1 — Motorola MC789P hex inverter.
U2 — Motorola MC790P dual flip-flop.

Fig. 10-23 — Waveforms showing the operation of a digital detector. (A & B) Input and output of the limiter section. (C & D) Input and output of the divide-by-four circuit. (E) Output of the multivibrator. (F) Recovered audio after de-emphasis.

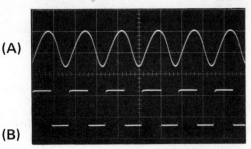

(A)

(B)

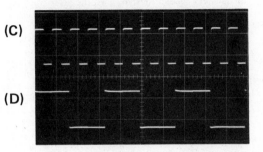

(C)

(D)

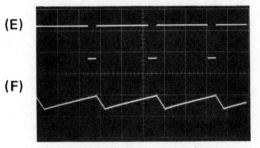

(E)

(F)

PLL   DETECTOR

The PLL

Now that the phase-locked loop (PLL) has been reduced to a single IC package, this circuit is destined to revolutionize some facets of receiver design. Introduction by Signetics of a PLL in a single flat-pack IC, followed by Motorola and Fairchild (who are making the PLL in separate building-block ICs), allows a builder to get to work with a minimum of bother.

A basic phase-locked loop (Fig. 10-24A) consists of a phase detector, a filter, a dc amplifier, and a voltage-controlled oscillator (VCO). The VCO runs at a frequency close to that of an incoming signal. The phase detector produces an error voltage if any difference in frequency exists between the VCO and the i-f signal. This error voltage is applied to the VCO. Any changes in the frequency of the incoming signal are sensed at the detector and the error voltage readjusts the VCO frequency so that it remains locked to the intermediate frequency. The bandwidth of the system is determined by a filter on the error-voltage line.

Because the error voltage is a copy of the audio variations originally used to shift the frequency of the transmitter, the PLL functions directly as an fm detector. The sensitivity achieved with the Signetics NE565 PLL is good — about 1 mV for the circuit shown in Fig. 10-24B. No transformers or tuned circuits are required. The PLL bandwidth is usually two to ten percent of the i-f for fm detection. Components R1-C1 set the VCO to near the desired frequency. C2 is the loop-filter capacitor which determines the capture range — that range of frequencies over which the loop will acquire lock with an input signal, initially starting out of lock. The NE565 has an upper frequency limit of 500 kHz; for higher frequencies, the

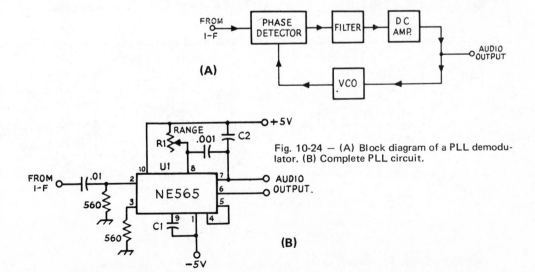

Fig. 10-24 — (A) Block diagram of a PLL demodulator. (B) Complete PLL circuit.

NE561, which is usable up to 30 MHz, can be employed.

Squelch Considerations

The high gain used in fm receivers accounts for another requisite, an audio squelch. With 140 dB or more of amplification before the detector, the noise level is high when no signal is being received. To allow monitoring for long periods without fatigue, a squelch is employed to quiet the noise until a signal is heard.

Squelch circuits are generally classified as carrier operated and noise operated. Early commercial fm squelch designs used the noise-operated circuit, while later models in tube receivers combined in the carrier- and noise-operated squelch in an effort to achieve extra sensitivity. Carrier signal levels were sensed by the voltage change produced across the grid-return resistor of the limiter stage. However, the excellent quieting sensitivities of solid-state receivers have allowed a return to the noise-operated squelch, which can be opened reliably by a $0.1\text{-}\mu V$ rf signal, when the receiver designer employs the latest techniques.

A number of squelch circuits were described by Danz in *QST* for September, 1969. All of the designs noted in this article, however, were intended for use with high-output detectors. Many of the newer detectors require a squelch circuit with high gain, such as shown in Fig. 10-25. Here, the output from the detector is split into two components by Q1, one of which is fed to the audio gate while the other is amplified by Q2. Only the noise component of the audio signal (frequencies above 5 kHz) is passed by L1-C1 to the noise rectifier. The dc output of the noise rectifier is amplified by Q3. When noise is present, Q4 and Q5 will be held on by the output from Q3. When the receiver quiets, Q4 and Q5 will shut off, opening the audio gate. Duration of the squelch "tail" — the length of time that the audio gate remains open after the input signal disappears — is determined by C1.

FM RECEIVER DESIGN

Until recently, fm receivers have followed the design shown in block-diagram form in Fig. 10-26. One or two rf amplifier stages and a double-conversion frequency scheme were used. Greater band occupancy has inspired both commercial and amateur receiver designers to work on the dynamic range and strong-signal-handling capabilities of fm receivers. As cross modulation and overload effects are primarily caused by the rf amplifier and first mixer, a good deal of research has gone into the application of various solid-state devices for use in receiver front ends. The result of this work has been a vast improvement in fm receiver signal-handling capability.

Two devices, the FET and the hot-carrier diode, are responsible for the revolution in front-end circuits. Both can be operated to provide square-law response as mixers. The sensitivity of either type is such that the rf amplifier can be eliminated in many cases. Although the hot-carrier diode has been used by the amateur fraternity, the device hasn't been popular with fm receiver designers for two reasons. To assure linear mixing, the level of oscillator injection to a diode mixer must be at least 10 dB above the strongest signal to be received. Even with a balanced bridge of hot-carrier diodes, the power required from the local oscillator is considerable. Also, the diode mixer must be followed by a low-noise i-f preamplifier for best overall receiver noise figure, introducing a new area for cross-modulation effects to appear. FET devices exhibit a slightly better noise figure (by 1 to 3 dB), and thus, are usually chosen over hot-carrier diodes.

The first field-effect transistors to gain wide acceptance were the junction types (JFET). Though still the leader in the low-noise-figure competition, the JFET also requires a rather large amount of power from the oscillator chain when used as a mixer. Early metal-oxide semiconductors (MOSFET) were easily damaged by static charges

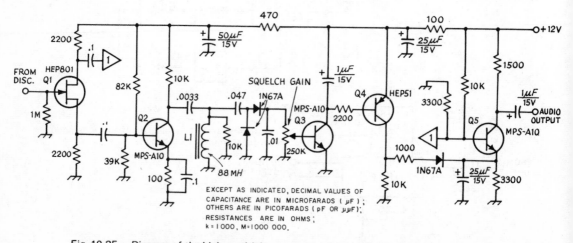

Fig. 10-25 — Diagram of the high-sensitivity squelch. L1 is an 88-mH telephone loading coil.

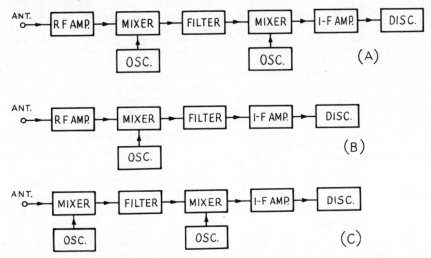

Fig. 10-26 — Block diagrams of the fm receiver designs discussed in the text.

and voltage spikes, and were considered too delicate for mobile service. However, the development of the diode-protected dual-gate models has made the MOSFET as hardy as the bipolar transistor. Only one volt of oscillator injection is required to the high-impedance gate 2 of a typical dual-gate MOSFET mixer, which eliminates the high injection level necessary for a JFET.

The designer has a choice of two basic approaches to the layout of a new fm receiver. He can use single conversion (Fig. 10-26B). But, to provide sufficient gain before the limiter, he must employ an rf amplifier, and worse, use a bipolar-transistor mixer to achieve high conversion gain. Even with an rf amplifier stage, getting sufficient i-f gain with stability can be a problem. Alternatively, a dual-conversion scheme can be employed where sufficient overall gain can be obtained in the i-f stages. With this design, Fig. 10-26C, the rf stage can be eliminated if sufficient rf selectivity can be achieved before the first mixer without seriously degrading the sensitivity of the receiver.

FM COMMUNICATIONS

Though information on fm theory and practice has been available to the amateur for many years, this mode was largely neglected until the early 1960s. Then large quantities of used commercial fm mobile equipment became available for amateur use, creating new interest. Originally designed to cover frequency ranges adjacent to amateur bands, this equipment is easily retuned for amateur use.

One feature of fm is its noise-suppression capability. For signals above the receiver threshold, wide-band fm has a signal-to-noise ratio advantage over a-m as a result of its greater "intelligence bandwidth." This same increased bandwidth, however, results in a much more abrupt signal threshold effect, causing weak signals to suddenly disappear. The generality can be made that a-m has a greater range in weak signal work but that

wide-band fm will provide greater noise suppression in local work. However, in practice, vhf fm mobiles experience greater range than previously found on a-m due to the output powers employed which are considerably higher than those common on a-m.

Operating Practices

Amateur fm practice has been to retain the fixed-frequency channelized capability of the commercial equipment. VFOs and tunable receivers tend to be unsatisfactory because of the requirement for precise frequency netting. An off-frequency signal will be received with distortion and will not have full noise rejection.

Channelized operation with squelched receivers permits continuous monitoring of the active frequencies. Long, time-consuming calls and CQs are not necessary (or appreciated) to establish communications, as all receivers on the channel "come alive" with the operator's first word. Natural, short transmissions are usually encouraged. The old monopoly switch routine, where the operator gabs to himself for 10 minutes at a time, will get him invited off a busy fm channel. Some channels are calling channels on which extended ragchewing is discouraged, whereas other channels, or the same channel in another area, may be alive with chatter. This is a matter of local determination, influenced by the amount of activity, and should be respected by the new operators and the transient mobile operator alike. Some groups have adopted the use of the "10 code" which was originated for law-enforcement communications. However, plain language in most cases is as fast and requires no clarification or explanation to anyone.

Standards

Standard channel frequencies have been agreed upon to permit orderly growth and to permit communications from one area to another. On two meters, it has been agreed that any frequency used will fall on increments of 30 kHz, beginning at 146.01 MHz. 146.94 MHz (or "nine-four") is the national calling frequency. On six meters, the national calling frequency is 52.525 MHz, with other channels having a 40-kHz spacing beginning at 52.56 MHz. Ten-meter fm activity can be found on 29.6 MHz. Usage of the 420-MHz band varies from area to area, as it is used for control channels, repeaters, and remote bases, as will be discussed later. Subdivision of the 220- and 420-MHz bands by modes and channels, on a "gentlemen's agreement" basis was under discussion at the time of publication of this book. Watch *QST* for developments.

APPENDIX

Fm Jargon

Diplexer – A device to allow two transmitters to use a single antenna.

Duplex – Simultaneous transmissions between two stations using two frequencies.

Duplexer – A device to allow simultaneous transmission and reception on a single antenna.

Simplex – Alternating transmission between two or more stations using one frequency.

Low band – 30 to 50 MHz. Also, the six-meter amateur band.

High band – 148 to 174 MHz. Also, the two-meter amateur band.

Remote base – A remotely controlled station, usually simplex.

Machine – Either a repeater or a remote base. Also called a "box."

COR – Carrier-operated relay.

CTCSS – Continuous tone-controlled squelch system. Continuous subaudible tone (250 Hz or lower) transmitted along with the audio to allow actuation of a repeater or receiver only by transmitters so equipped. More frequently referred to by various trade names such as *Private Line, Channel Guard,* and *Quiet Channel.*

Down channel – Communications circuit from the machine to the control point.

Up channel – Communications and/or control circuit from the control point to the machine.

Open repeater – A machine where transient operators are welcome.

Closed repeater – A machine where use by nonmembers is not encouraged. (When heavy expenditures are involved, freeloaders are not popular.)

Fm Bibliography

Armstrong, "A Method of Reducing Disturbances in Radio Signalling by a System of Frequency Modulation," *Proc. IRE*, May, 1936.

Crosby, "Frequency Modulation Noise Characteristics," *Proc. IRE*, April, 1937.

Noble, "Frequency Modulation Fundamentals," *QST*, August, 1939.

Grammer and Goodman, "Wide-Band FM In Amateur Communication," *QST*, January and February, 1940.

Hund, *Frequency Modulation,* McGraw-Hill Book Company, 1942.

Grammer, "Amateur FM," Technical Topics, *QST*, October, 1946. (First discussion of compatible narrow-band fm and a-m.)

Goldsmith *et al, Frequency Modulation,* in two volumes, RCA Review, RCA, 1948.

Rider and Uslan, *FM Transmission and Reception,* John F. Rider Publisher, 1948.

Lytel, *Two-Way Radio,* McGraw-Hill Book Company, 1959.

Hadlock, "Wide-Band FM Gear for 220 Mc.," *QST*, March, 1961.

Pre-Progress Line Diagrams, in two volumes, Mobile Radio Department, General Electric Company, 1968.

Wolf, *FM Schematic Digest,* Two-Way Radio Engineers, 1970.

Chapter 11

Fm Transmitters, Receivers and Accessories

The construction of equipment and accessories for the fm mode will be covered in this chapter. The reader should review the material in Chapter 10 to obtain the theoretical background of frequency-modulation techniques before attempting to build individual projects from this chapter. Chapter 10 also contains information about the adjustment of fm gear which will be needed when testing a piece of homemade equipment. Many of the projects described elsewhere in this book are applicable to fm communications as well as a-m, cw, and ssb.

Fm is now in regular use on the 28- to 420-MHz bands. Equipment for the 10-meter band is described in *The Radio Amateur's Handbook*, as are power supplies suitable for use with the projects described here. Vertical polarization is standard practice for most fm communications. Any of the popular antennas described in this book will be suitable when mounted to provide vertical radiation. References for additional information on the fm mode are listed at the end of Chapter 10.

RECEIVING FM

FM RECEIVING ADAPTERS

To put the older tube receivers such as the 75A, HRO, and Super Pro models into fm service, the receiving adapter shown in Fig. 11-2 was designed. Filament and plus B voltages are taken from the companion receiver. Obviously, the better the basic receiver, the better will be the performance of the fm receiving system. For this application sets with high-gain i-f amplifier sections and a broad-band selectivity position (such as the SP-400, SP-600, SX-73, and R-390) are excellent choices. Receivers that have only a 6-kHz or narrower bandwidth may need an extra i-f amplifier stage in the fm adapter in order to tap the receiver i-f at the output of the second mixer. Of course, a converter will also be required with the basic receiver to copy vhf fm signals.

A sample of the receiver i-f signal is passed to T1, a 455-kHz i-f transformer, which feeds amplifier/limiter V1. A low screen voltage and signal bias enhance the limiting characteristic of the tube. Further "hard" limiting action is provided by the two sections of V2, a 12AT7. A sample of the grid current of V2A is available at TP1, a test point used during alignment. A commercially made discriminator transformer converts the fm signal to a-m; the a-m is detected by CR1 and CR2. An *RC* de-emphasis network is included to match the standard pre-emphasis used on fm transmitters. Audio amplification is provided by V3 — in some receivers with high-gain audio systems this stage may not be necessary.

The adapter is constructed on an aluminum channel which is 11 inches long, 2 inches wide, and 1-3/4 inches high. A 1/4-inch lip is included on one side as a mounting foot. A Minibox or a standard chassis is also suitable as a base. The layout of the stages should be kept in a straight line so that rf feedback paths can be avoided. Point-to-point wiring is used throughout.

Alignment

"Lining up" the adapter takes time and test equipment. A VTVM or microammeter plus a signal generator are required. Good alignment cannot be accomplished by ear; if the necessary test instruments aren't available, they should be borrowed.

To start, check the alignment of the communications receiver, following the manufacturer's instructions, to be sure that the rf and i-f stages are "peaked" before the fm adapter is installed. Two simple internal modifications are required in the receiver, as shown in Fig. 11-2B and C. If the

Fig. 11-1 — The fm adapter, wired for connection to a Collins 75A2.

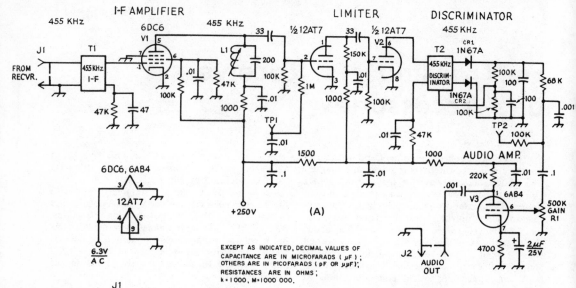

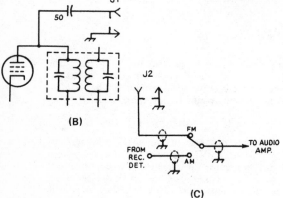

(B)

(C)

Fig. 11-2 — (A) Schematic diagram of the 455-kHz fm adapter. Resistors are 1/2-watt composition; capacitors are disk ceramic, except those with polarity marked, which are electrolytic.

J1, J2 — Phono jack, panel mount.
L1 — 430-850-μH slug-tuned variable inductor (Miller 42A684CBI).
R1 — Audio-taper composition control.
T1 — I-f transformer, 455 kHz (Miller 913-C1).
T2 — Discriminator transformer, 455 kHz (Miller 913-CD).
TP1, TP2 — Tip jack (Johnson 105-XX).

(B) Diagram of the connections to use the fm adapter with a communications receiver. The tap to the i-f stage is through a 50-pF disk-ceramic capacitor. If the receiver has a wide-band i-f system, the connection should be made to the last intermediate-frequency amplifier; for narrow i-fs, tap the first i-f stage. (C) Audio connections.

receiver has a wide i-f bandwidth, a sample of the i-f signal can be taken from the plate of the last i-f stage. Otherwise, the tap should be made at the plate of the first i-f amplifier, and an extra stage, a duplicate of V1, included in the adapter. Short lengths of shielded cable are used to carry the i-f signal to the adapter and to return audio to the receiver — see Fig. 11-2C. Some units (75A2, HRO-50) which have provision for fm adapters already have a front-panel switch wired for this purpose.

Connect the signal generator to the receiver, and set the generator to produce an S9 reading on the receiver signal-strength meter. The receiver crystal filter should be switched to its most selective position to assure that the incoming signal is being heterodyned to exactly 455 kHz. Then, with a voltmeter or microammeter connected to TP1, adjust both sections of T1 and L1 for maximum limiter current. The receiver i-f stage being "tapped" should also be realigned to compensate for the capacitance of the adapter cable.

To align the discriminator, set the receiver selectivity at the broad position, and connect the voltmeter to TP2. Voltage at this test point will swing both plus and minus, so a zero-center meter or VTVM with a lead-reversing switch should be employed. Set the secondary of the discriminator transformer for a zero-voltage indication on the meter. Then vary the signal-generator frequency plus or minus 15 kHz. Going off center frequency in one direction will produce positive voltage at TP2, while going in the other direction generates negative voltage. The primary of the transformer must be set so that, for example, if a shift down in frequency by 5 kHz produces plus 2 volts, then a change of 5 kHz in the other direction should produce minus 2 volts. Unfortunately, the two adjustments on the discriminator transformer are interlocking, so considerable experimentation is required. Also, the tuning of the preceding stages, if not centered on 455 kHz, will affect the discriminator linearity. The first time around, a half hour or more of alignment and realignment is usually required

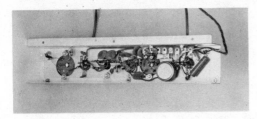

Fig. 11-3 — In this bottom view, the input transformer is to the left, followed by the i-f amplifier, limiter, and detector. On the far right are the audio-amplifier stage and gain control.

Fig. 11-4 — The solid-state fm adapter is constructed on a 6 × 2-inch etched-circuit board, mounted on a homemade chassis.

to achieve *equal* swings in output voltage for *equal* swings in frequency — a linear response.

One further check of the discriminator is required. An impulse-generating device, such as an electric shaver, should be switched on, and the receiver, set for a-m detection, tuned to point in the spectrum where the noise is strong. Then, switch to the fm adapter and adjust the discriminator transformer for best suppression of the noise pulses. If the alignment with the signal generator has been completed properly, only a

half a turn or so of the slugs will be needed to complete the phase tuning of the discriminator.

A SOLID-STATE ADAPTER

Tubes are seldom used in current designs. For those builders who prefer to be "up with the times," a solid-state version of the 455-kHz adapter was constructed. Using IC limiter/amplifier, and miniature i-f transformers, the unit requires only 25 mA at 12 V for power. See Fig. 11-5.

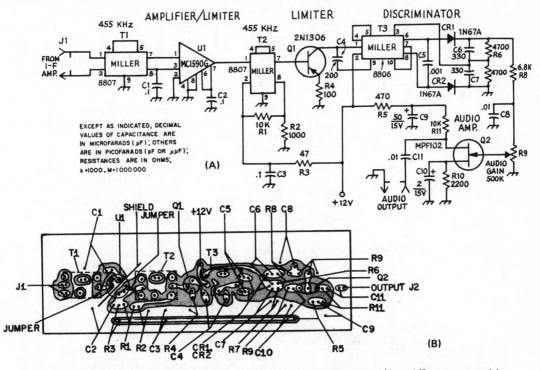

Fig. 11-5 — (A) Diagram of the 455-kHz narrow-band adapter. Resistors are 1/4- or 1/2-watt composition and capacitors are disk ceramic, except those with polarity marked, which are electrolytic. Components with reference numbers that are not listed below are noted for circuit-board location.

J1,J2 — Phono receptacle, panel mount.
R1 — Miniature 1/2-watt composition control.
T1,T2 — Miniature 455-kHz i-f transformer, 455 kHz (Miller 8807).

T3 — Miniature discriminator transformer, 455 kHz (Miller 8806).
U1 — Motorola MC1590G.

(B) Template and parts-layout diagram (not to scale).

The Motorola MC1590G provides 70 dB gain, and hard limiting action superior to that obtained with the tube version.

The unit is built on a 2 X 6-1/2-inch circuit board; a template is given in Fig. 11-5B. Because of the high gain of the IC stage, a shield is required across pins 4 and 6 to isolate the input from the output. Alignment and installation are the same as for the tube version. The bandwidth of the miniature transformers restricts this adapter to narrow-band reception. However, builders wishing a wideband version can use the J. W. Miller 8811 miniature coils combined with a 12-pF coupling capacitor to form a wide-band transformer.

A RECEIVER FOR 6-METER FM

A block diagram of the 6-meter receiver is outlined in Fig. 11-7. The front-end circuit uses 40673 dual-gate MOSFETs for the rf amplifier and mixer. Toroid coils were chosen for the signal circuits because of their self-shielding properties. A crystal-controlled JFET oscillator provides injection voltage for Q2. Trimmer C3 is included to move the oscillator frequency "on channel."

A single-conversion scheme using a high i-f was chosen for simplicity, although having 120 dB of gain at 11.5 MHz requires careful layout and good bypassing techniques to assure stability. Three Motorola MC1590s are used, although two can achieve the required gain. Three stages, each

Fig. 11-6 — Front view of the complete receiver for 6- or 2-meter fm. The unit is housed in an LMB 10 × 5 × 2-inch cabinet. Knobs are Kurz-Kasch S-748-1L.

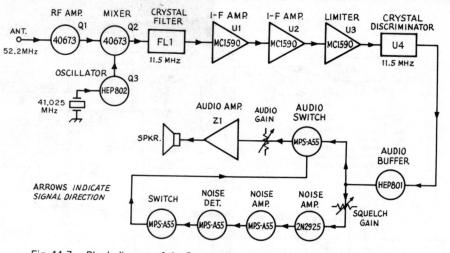

Fig. 11-7 — Block diagram of the 6-meter fm receiver using a crystal discriminator.

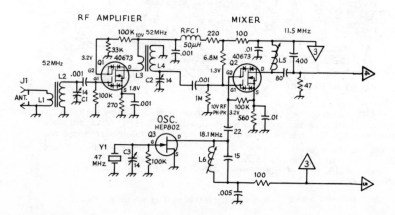

A Receiver for 6-Meter Fm

Fig. 11-9 — Schematic diagram of the fm receiver. Unless otherwise noted, resistors are 1/2-watt composition and capacitors are disk ceramic, except those with polarity marked, which are electrolytic.

C1-C6, incl. — Miniature air variable (Johnson 189-507-5).

C7 — Miniature air variable (Johnson 189-509-5).

C8-C10, incl. — Feedthrough type.

FL1 — For a wide-band 11.5-MHz i-f, ESEL MEL-3A; narrow-band 11.5-MHz i-f, ESEL-DL-11A; wide-band 10.7-MHz i-f, KVG XF-107D; narrow-band 10.7-MHz i-f, KVG XF-107B. If 10.7-MHz i-f is used, add 15-pF ceramic capacitors across L5, L7, L9, L11 and L13. (See Fig. 10-12 for a complete list of filter choices and addresses of the filter manufacturers).

J1, J2 — Phono type, panel mount.

L1 — 2 turns No. 22 enam. over L2.

L2 — 11 turns No. 22 enam. on Amidon T-50-6 toroid core (yellow code). (Amidon Associates, 12033 Otsego St., North Hollywood, CA 91607.)

L3 — 4 turns No. 22 enam. on L4.

L4 — 6 turns No. 22 enam. on Amidon T-50-6 (yellow code).

L5 — 2.96 - 3.15 - μH variable inductor (J. W. Miller 46A336CPC).

L6 — 0.37 to 0.47-μH variable inductor (J. W. Miller 46A397CPC).

L7, L9, L11 — 36 turns No. 26 enam. on Amidon T-50-2 (red code) core.

L8, L10, L12 — 16 turns No. 26 enam. over L7, L9, and L11, respectively.

L13 — 24 turns No. 22 enam. on Amidon T-50-2 (red code) core.

L14 — 88-mH surplus telephone loading coil.

Q1, Q2 — RCA dual-gate MOSFET.

Q3 — Motorola rf JFET.

Q4 — Motorola audio JFET.

Q5 — GE audio bipolar.

Q6-Q9, incl. — Motorola audio bipolar.

R1 — Linear-taper composition control.

RFC1 — 50-μH miniature choke (Millen 34300).

RFC2-RFC7, incl. — 500-μH miniature choke (J. W. Miller 70F504A1).

S1 — Spst miniature toggle.

TP1 — Vector T2.8 terminal.

U1-U3, incl. — Motorola IC.

U4 — ESEL AL-1A for 11.5-MHz i-f, KVG 107-01 for 10.7 MHz.

Y1 — International Crystal type EX.

Z1 — 2-watt audio amplifier, 1-volt sensitivity (Amperex PCA-1-14).

Fig. 11-8 — Top view of the receiver. The etched circuit board containing the front-end components is at the lower left, while the i-f amplifier/detector circuit board is bolted to the rear wall of the cabinet.

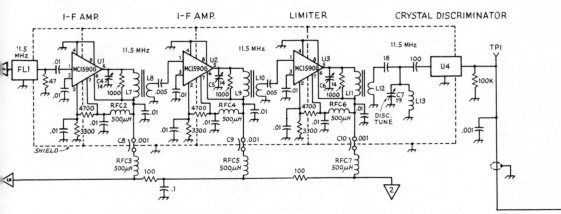

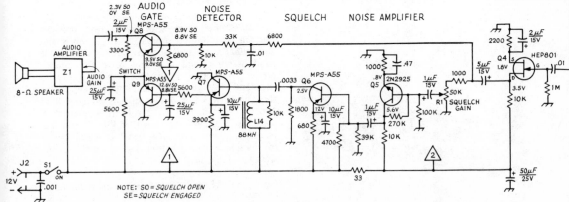

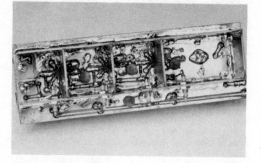

Fig. 11-10 — The bottom view of the i-f board shows the shielding and filtering used.

with resistive loading, exhibited far better stability than two '1590s running "flat out."

The i-f amplifier circuit board uses extensive shielding. The finished product looks more like a piece of vhf gear than an i-f amp., but with high gain special precautions are necessary. The front end and i-f amplifier proved to be easy to build and adjust. The squelch circuit was a bother from the beginning. The basic circuit used for the noise-operated squelch is borrowed from the Motorola MOTRAC series. Output from the crystal discriminator proved to be quite a bit lower in level than would be obtained from an equivalent *LC* discriminator. Also, Z1 (Fig. 11-9) wants to "look into" an impedance of 100,000 ohms or more. The first version of the squelch circuit had far too little gain, so a redesign was required. The final version of the circuit is shown in Fig. 11-9. The voltages noted at the audio gate, Q8, are critical; any variation from the indicated values will cause a full squelch condition where the audio gate will not open, or, no squelch operation at all.

A commercial amplifier module was chosen for the audio output section. It delivers two watts (rms) to an 8-ohm load when using a 12-volt supply. Sufficient audio output is available for comfortable copy of weak stations when operating mobile. An inexpensive imported 0.5-watt audio amplifier may be substituted if the receiver will be used only in a ham shack. Power requirements for the receiver are 12 to 13.5 volts at 70-mA drain (squelch engaged) and 200 mA (at full audio output). Since automobile electrical

systems can have voltages as high as 16, a series regulator should be included for mobile operation.

To set the receiver for the 6-meter calling frequency, 52.525 MHz, a 41.025-MHz crystal is required. When built for 52 MHz, this unit can be used for 144- or 220-MHz reception by adding a converter having 6-meter i-f output ahead of the fm receiver. Suitable designs are shown elsewhere in this manual.

Alignment

A signal generator and a VTVM are required for receiver alignment. The VTVM should be connected to terminal TP1 and set to read 0-3 V dc. The generator should be set to about 52.5 MHz, and connected to J1 on the receiver. Rotate R1 fully counter clockwise, and you should hear noise in the speaker. If no noise is heard, place your finger on the input terminal of Z1. If the audio module is working, a loud hum will be heard. No noise output indicates that the squelch may be locked up. Check the voltages given in Fig. 11-9 against those found on the audio gate.

With a cw input signal, adjust C4, C5, and C6 for a maximum reading on the VTVM. Then set C1 and C2 for maximum indicated output voltage. Set the signal to 52.510 and note the VTVM reading. Then set the generator to 52.540 MHz and adjust C7 for a VTVM reading of the same magnitude, but opposite polarity, from that obtained on the "low side" of 52.525 MHz. Repeat the procedure several times to assure a correct adjustment.

With the basic alignment completed, inject a 52.525-MHz signal. Then set C3 so that the VTVM reads zero voltage. This completes the rf and i-f alignment. Connect an antenna and advance the squelch control, R1, until the background noise disappears. The squelch should close the audio gate at one-third to one-half scale rotation of R1.

THE MK-II FM RECEIVER FOR 146 MHz

The simple receiver described here provides true fm reception. It uses a two-stage limiter and discriminator, a crystal-controlled converter for good stability, and a vernier drive for smooth tuning. Reception with the version shown is excellent. Selectivity is adequate for separating three local repeater output signals which fall at 146.79, 146.88, and 146.94 MHz. Sensitivity is such that a 0.2-μV signal with 5-kHz deviation is plainly audible. A 0.7-μV signal provides 20 dB of quieting. Limiting action is good on all but the weakest of signals.

Fig. 11-11 — Front view of the completed 2-meter fm receiver.

Fig. 11-12 — Block diagram of the assembled MK-II fm receiver. BT1 should be a large-size 9-volt battery, or 7 or 8 penlite cells connected in series.

C1 — Two-gang miniature variable, one section 40 pF and the other having 20 pF. See text. (J. W. Miller No. 1640 three-section unit used here, two gangs being connected in parallel.)

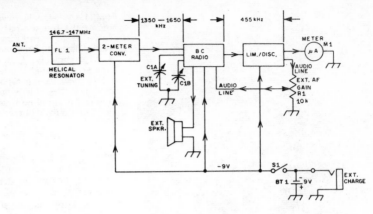

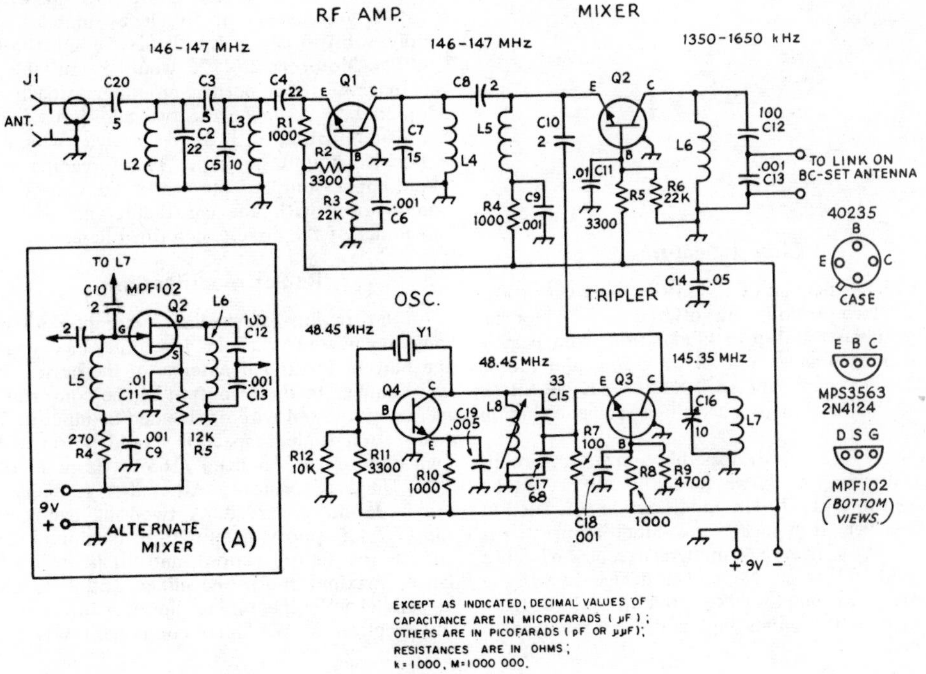

Fig. 11-13 — Circuit of the 2-meter converter. Parts not listed below are designated for pc-board layout purposes. Drawing A is discussed in the text. Fixed-value capacitors are disk ceramic. Resistors are 1/4- or 1/2-watt carbon.

C16 — 10-pF piston trimmer. Ceramic or pc-board air trimmer can be substituted.

J1 — SO-239-style chassis fitting.

L1 — Not used.

L2 — 3 turns No. 20 enam. wire, 3/16-inch ID, 1/8-inch long.

L3 — 4 turns No. 20 enam. wire, 3/16-inch ID, 5/16-inch long.

L4 — 5 turns No. 20 enam. wire, 3/16-inch ID, 5/16-inch long.

L5 — 15 turns No. 20 enam. wire, 3/16-inch ID, closewound.

L6 — 100-μH rf choke (Millen J302-100 or J. W. Miller 70F104A1 suitable). *Must be 100 μH in value.*

L7 — 5 turns No. 16 tinned copper wire, 1/4-inch ID, 3/8-inch long.

L8 — 10 turns No. 26 enam. wire, closewound on 1/4-inch dia slug-tuned form (J. W. Miller 4500-2 blank suitable). Variable inductance 0.35 to 0.6 μH required.

Q1-Q4, incl. — Npn bipolar transistor, RCA 40235 or 40637. Motorola 2N4124 or MPS3563 suitable, or any high-beta npn with f_T of 250 MHz or greater. (Q2 of inset A is Motorola MPF102, 2N5484, or HEP802.)

Y1 — 48.45-MHz 3rd-overtone crystal (International Crystal Co. type GP in FM-2 holder).

Fig. 11-14 — Inside view of the MK-II. The vacant area at the bottom has been reserved for a small transmitter and modulator. The limiter/discriminator board is mounted vertically by means of an L bracket. Four metal posts support the 2-meter converter at the upper left. The bc radio and its new tuning capacitor and gain control are housed in the shield compartment at the upper center. An aluminum cover is used to enclose the shield box during operation.

chassis ground through L6). The values of resistors R4 and R5 will have to be changed as indicated. R6 will be deleted if the JFET is used. No other changes are required. Though it was not tried, a common-gate JFET rf amplifier might work nicely at Q1, but with reduced gain over the bipolar amplifier shown.

Those wishing to use the bipolar arrangement for all four stages of the converter, but with a negative ground system (such as mobile), can simply substitute pnp transistors for Q1 through Q4. The Motorola 2N4126 would be suitable for this purpose. The positive-ground approach was adopted here to make the two additional circuit boards compatible with the bc receiver, which has a positive-ground hookup. (The foregoing technique applies only to the use of the converter in combination with the car radio, and with the remainder of the circuits described here.

Circuit Features

A block diagram of the MK-II is shown in Fig. 11-12. Two options are offered — FL1 for reducing images and cross-modulation from nearby commercial services, and M1, a zero-center tuning meter. The jack labeled EXTERNAL CHARGE should be included only if a nickel-cadmium battery is used.

Fig. 11-13 illustrates the converter circuit. Inset drawing A shows how the mixer can be changed to a JFET. The modification was tried in the receiver. It reduced cross-modulation effects caused by a nearby commercial repeater. Since the MPF102 is an N-channel device it will be necessary to employ the hookup shown (gate returned to the minus bus, and drain returned to

Bc-Set Modifications

A 6-turn link of small-diameter hookup wire must be wound over the low-impedance end of the built-in ferrite-bar antenna of the bc set. This will connect to the i-f output of the converter by means of twisted wire or shielded conductor. The two-section tuning capacitor should be set at the high end of the bc band (1650 kHz or higher), then glued in position. Alternatively, it can be removed and discarded. A two-gang bandspread capacitor of approximately 20-pF maximum capacitance (oscillator section), and 40 pF in capacitance (maximum) for the mixer section is wired in parallel with the tuning capacitor in the set. A three-section J. W. Miller component was used.

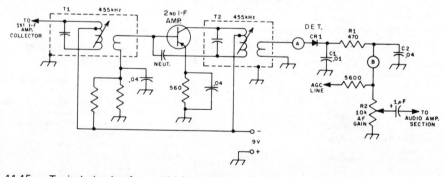

Fig. 11-15 — Typical circuit of second i-f amplifier and a-m detector of imported bc-band radios. Points marked A and B indicate where circuit is opened for addition of the limiter/discriminator. Components between points A and B are discarded. R2 is replaced by a panel-accessible gain control (see text). Values for R1, C1, and C2 are not necessarily the same in all imported sets.

Each section is 20-pF maximum capacitance, so two of the gangs are wired in parallel to provide 40 pF for the mixer tuning. A two-section broadcast variable can be used by removing the proper number of plates to secure the desired bandspread. Other styles of two-gang variables can be modified in a like manner.

Fig. 11-15 shows the typical configuration used at the second i-f amplifier and detector of most imported pocket-size bc sets. After locating the detector diode, CR1, the modifications shown can be made. Remove all components between the letters A and B. Audio gain control R2 can be replaced by a panel-mount type of the same value (with switch), or the ingenious builder can retain the original part and mount it on the front panel of the MK-II. Terminals A and B will connect to the limiter/detector board of Fig. 11-16.

The speaker from the bc radio is mounted on the front panel of the MK-II. In fact, the speaker grille from the bc set was pried off the plastic case and used between the speaker and the front panel in true miserly fashion. Some sets do not have separate grilles, so perforated metal or circuit board can be used to protect the speaker cone.

Limiter/Discriminator

The circuit of Fig. 11-16 shows that two bipolar transistors are used in an *RC*-coupled limiter strip, followed by a diode discriminator. RFC1 and RFC2 are used to prevent vhf parasitics. Two Amidon ferrite beads are used for each choke. Alternatively, a 22-ohm 1/2-watt resistor can be substituted for each choke. It can be seen that here, again, the npn transistors are connected in the circuit for a *positive* ground system. Type 2N4126 transistors can be substituted if one wishes to use this assembly with receivers that have a negative ground.

Diodes CR1 and CR2 function in a self-adjusting limiter arrangement. They can be omitted if the bc set used ahead of the limiter board is low in i-f gain. Matched diodes should be used at CR3 and CR4. Those having an assortment of germanium diodes can select two that have nearly equal dc resistance readings (when checked with an ohmmeter). Match them in resistance in both the forward (low dc resistance) and reverse (high dc resistance) directions.

Terminal E1 of Fig. 11-16 provides a test voltage (dc) for aligning the discriminator. After alignment, those wishing to can connect a zero-center microammeter between E1 and ground for use as a tuning meter. Lafayette Radio sells a low-cost miniature meter for this purpose.

Assembling the MK-II

The photographs show that the MK-II is not a miniature unit. A large portion of the cabinet has been reserved for a 2-watt fm transmitter. However, the builder can certainly shrink the 10-1/2 X 8 X 3-inch dimensions by a considerable margin if he is skilled at packing many parts into

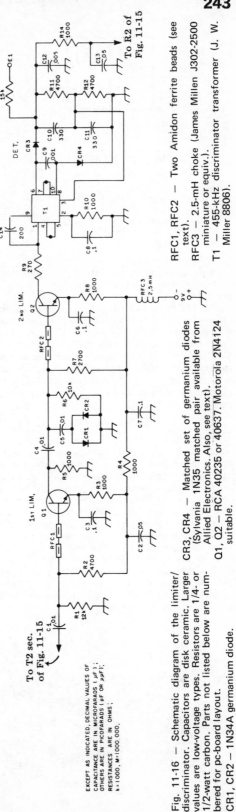

RFC1, RFC2 – Two Amidon ferrite beads (see text).
RFC3 – 2.5-mH choke (James Millen J302-2500 miniature or equiv.).
T1 – 455-kHz discriminator transformer (J. W. Miller 8806).

EXCEPT AS INDICATED, DECIMAL VALUES OF CAPACITANCE ARE IN MICROFARADS (μF) ; OTHERS ARE IN PICOFARADS (pF OR μμF); RESISTANCES ARE IN OHMS ; k =1 000, M=1 000 000.

Fig. 11-16 — Schematic diagram of the limiter/discriminator. Capacitors are disk ceramic. Larger values are low-voltage types. Resistors are 1/4- or 1/2-watt carbon. Parts not listed below are numbered for pc-board layout.

CR1, CR2 – 1N34A germanium diode.
CR3, CR4 – Matched set of germanium diodes (Sylvania 1N35 matched pair available from Allied Electronics. Also, see text).
Q1, Q2 – RCA 40235 or 40637. Motorola 2N4124 suitable.

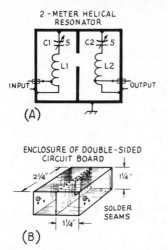

2-METER HELICAL
RESONATOR

(A)

ENCLOSURE OF DOUBLE-SIDED
CIRCUIT BOARD

(B)

Fig. 11-17 — Circuit of the helical resonator. Double-sided pc board is used for the box walls and is soldered along each seam by means of a pencil-type iron. E. F. Johnson silver-plated air-variable capacitors (No. 189-563) were used in this model, but high-dielectric piston trimmers can be substituted. Coils L1 and L2 consist of 4-1/2 turns of No. 12 copper wire, 3/4 inch long. Each coil is centered in its compartment and tapped 1/4 turn from ground to obtain a bilateral 50-ohm impedance. A 3/8 × 5/8-inch aperature is cut in the center divider, and is opposite the second and third turns of each coil. C1 and C2 are tuned for peak signal response with the resonator connected between the receiver input and the feed line. The bottom end of the assembly need not be enclosed. Ideally, the enclosure should have no soldered seams, and both it and the coils should be silver plated. This suggests the use of large-diameter copper tubing for the outer shield if maximum Q is desired.

a small space. This enclosure is fashioned from 1/16-inch-thick aluminum stock. The panel is painted dark green.

To reduce unwanted pickup of bc stations, the pocket radio is enclosed in a box made from double-sided pc board. A press-fit U-shaped aluminum lid encloses the top of the compartment. The bandspread tuning capacitor and gain control are contained in the same box. No. 6 spade bolts hold the assembly to the main chassis. Templates for the circuit boards appear in *QST* for August 1971, page 16.

Tune-Up and Use

It is suggested that the builder test the bc set independently after it is modified and mounted in its shield box. The components which were removed between points A and B of Fig. 11-15 can be clipped between those points for the test. Connect a 9-volt battery and tune in a bc station. Make certain that the new volume control and tuning capacitor are functioning as intended. Adjust the trimmers on the tuning capacitor to assure tracking of the mixer and oscillator sections of the radio. Next, connect a signal generator to the base of the mixer through a 10-pF blocking capacitor. Set the generator for 455-kHz output and align the i-f transformers for peak response at that frequency.

The next step is to connect the limiter/discriminator board to the circuit in place of the components temporarily connected between points A and B. Attach a VTVM or zero-center μA meter between E1 and ground (Fig. 11-16). If a VTVM is used, set it for the 1.5-volt scale and adjust the meter-set control so that the needle is exactly on zero. Now, apply a strong signal (several hundred μV) to the mixer input, using 1500 kHz as a test frequency. Vary the signal generator plus and minus 15 kHz while observing the meter. The signal should swing plus and minus in a linear fashion. (If a VTVM is used for the test, it will be necessary to switch the polarity back and forth with the meter reversing switch.) The meter should return to zero when no signal is present. If the foregoing conditions are not met it will be necessary to adjust T1 of Fig. 11-16 for a linear response. The alignment of T1 will be a tedious task, so plan to spend some time in the adjustment process. Alternately tweak the pink and blue cores of the transformer, a few degrees of rotation each time, then sweep across the 30-kHz range and observe the meter response. Try various settings of the cores until proper alignment is achieved. If a signal generator is not available, tune across a *strong* bc station and adjust T1 for linear response of the discriminator. After T1 is correctly adjusted, there should be no a-m detection of the bc signal when the station is tuned in to its center frequency. Readable audio will be heard, however, when tuning to either side of center frequency.

Install the bc set and the limiter/discriminator assembly in the chassis. Next, connect the 2-meter converter to the circuit. Tune in a weak 2-meter fm signal, or use the output from a vhf signal generator. Adjust L8 and C16 of Fig. 11-13

Fig. 11-18 — View of the homemade helical resonator shown in Fig. 11-17. Double-sided pc board is used for all walls but the top one in this version. Flashing copper was used for the top surface in this model, but pc board would have been suitable.

for maximum signal response at 146.8 MHz. Spread or compress the turns of L2, L3, and L4 for peak response. Use an insulated rod while making these tests. This completes the adjustments. The converter can now be bolted in place in the cabinet.

Since the MK-II represents one of the least sophisticated approaches to fm reception, some ills may become manifest. Strong signals from nearby two-way commercial services may show up in the tuning range of the receiver. Also, signals from the lower portion of the 2-meter band may appear as images. The helical-resonator filter shown in Fig. 11-17 can be built and used ahead of the receiver to reduce or eliminate unwanted responses. FL1 is easy to assemble and is very inexpensive, yet is superior in performance to most strip-line filters. Design data for these filters are given in *ITT Reference Data for Radio Engineers*, 5th Edition, Chapter 22. The filter consists of two very high-Q tuned circuits, coupled through a small aperture in the metal wall between them. Input and output taps are set for a 50-ohm impedance.

A TUNABLE 440-MHz FM RECEIVER

Though originally intended for checking signal paths between proposed uhf fm sites, this receiver also provides convenient eavesdropping on local 440-MHz fm activity, and monitoring of commercial frequencies adjacent to the high end of our 420-MHz band. It or something quite similar to it is readily put together, and can be assembled quite inexpensively. Though a duplicate can be built from the information supplied here, the reader should treat this discourse mainly as a collection of ideas. The exact units used for the receiver may not always be available, so other components may have to be adapted to the job.

In most modern TV receivers the uhf tuner is solid-state, designed to feed the 43-MHz TV i-f strip directly. The mixer output is untuned, so it is apparent that any intermediate frequency can be accommodated, depending solely on the frequency range of the tuner oscillator. One advantage of the 43-MHz i-f is the great number of low-band fm monitor receivers for this frequency range available at low cost.

It is best to avoid the narrow-band monitors that won't accept more than 5-kHz deviation. Tuning will be too sharp for the stability and tuning rate of uhf converters, and most amateur fm in the 420-MHz band is still wide-band deviation. The wide-band receiver will not be bothered seriously by any drift in the TV tuner.

The uhf TV tuner used here is a Sickles Model 228. Many tuners use the same basic electrical and mechanical layout, the only differences being in the dial-drive arrangement made for a particular TV receiver. These tuners do not have trimmer capacitors for alignment, such as were used in earlier uhf converters. Alignment is done with specialized test equipment, by precisely bending the rotor plates in the tuner. Most tuners are linear within plus or minus one TV channel, over the entire uhf TV spectrum, when they leave the factory.

Uhf Tuner Modifications

Getting this type of tuner to cover the upper 10 MHz of the amateur band is best done by adding trimmer capacitors across the tuner circuits. The sketch of the tuner as modified, Fig. 11-20, should help to make clear how this is done. Start by removing one of the two rotor

Fig. 11-19 — Panel view of the 440-MHz fm receiver. The vernier dial drives the tuning shaft of a converted uhf TV front end. At the rear is a 450-MHz Motorola fm receiver, the i-f system of which takes the output of the converted TV tuner. The meter can be connected in the limiter or discriminator circuit.

plates in the oscillator compartment. The mixer and antenna circuits will not require tuning across our small intended frequency range, so the rotor plates in the two upper sections of the tuner can all be removed.

Mount three 16-pF glass trimmers on the tuner walls, parallel to the three lines and as close as possible to them. See Fig. 11-20. Connect the trimmers to their respective lines with short pieces of heavy wire or copper strip. By bending the one oscillator rotor plate away from its stator carefully, the tuning range can be reduced to as little as 15 MHz.

Remove the 300-ohm connector and coupling loop from the antenna section by drilling out the mounting rivets in its insulating support. Enlarge the hole, and mount a phono jack or a BNC fitting for antenna connection. Run a 1/8-inch copper strip from a point on the antenna line, 1/2 inch from the wall, down to as close to the coupling port to the mixer compartment as possible, then up to the connector, as shown in Fig. 11-20. If the port is not merely an open hole in the wall separating the sections, but is a Faraday shield, as in the 228 tuner, remove the Faraday

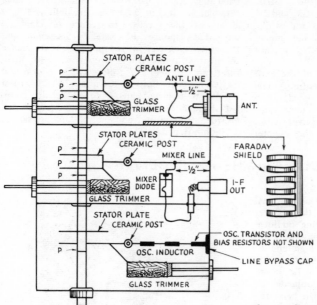

Fig. 11-20 — Bottom view of the uhf TV converter, as modified for use in the 420-MHz band. Only the oscillator circuit is tuned by the vernier dial, all rotor plates in the mixer and preselector circuits having been removed. One rotor plate is left in the oscillator section. Positions of plates to be removed are indicated by the letter P.

shield to improve interstage coupling. This shield is not visible in the tuner photo. If used, it is a comb-like insert in the port, as shown in enlarged form in Fig. 11-20.

One lead of the mixer diode in the 228 tuner runs through a small port between the oscillator and mixer sections. The other diode lead, barely visible in the tuner photo, is parallel to the mixer line and is connected to the right-hand wall of the tuner. Cut it at this point and solder the lead to the mixer line, about 1/2 inch from the wall, as shown in Fig. 11-20. In some of the better tuners the mixer diode is reverse biased, and does not go directly to ground in the mixer section. This was done for improved noise figure and should be left the way it is.

Most tuners are designed to terminate in an i-f input circuit which is at dc ground potential. If the receiver to be used does not provide a dc path, a 50-MHz rf choke should be connected from the tuner i-f output to ground to provide a dc path for the mixer crystal current. The ground end of the choke can be lifted to measure crystal current, which should be at least 100 μA.

In the receiver shown here the tuner feeds the 75-MHz i-f of a Motorola 450-MHz crystal-controlled fm receiver. The two 6AK5 frequency multipliers which provide injection to the first mixer, the front-end rf tubes and afc tube were removed to conserve power, since they are not used in this application. A National vernier dial drives the 2-plate tuning capacitor in the tuner, through a shaft extension and a flexible coupling. If there is backlash in the drive system it is not evident in the operation of the receiver. Signals tune in smoothly and easily.

A meter indicates limiter current, for signal strength observation, and as an aid in adjusting antenna systems and beam headings in fm work. The nature of fm reception makes small changes in signal level undetectable by ear. The discriminator is also metered, for ease of station tuning. Supply voltage for the tuner is dropped from the receiver B-plus line, and is regulated with a Zener diode.

Visible in the upper left portions of the photographs of the complete receiver is a grounded-base uhf preamplifier using a TIXM101 transistor. A preamp suitable for this purpose is shown later in this chapter.

The tuning range of this receiver is roughly 440 to 454 MHz. No images or other spurious responses are heard. Tuning is smooth, and sta-

Fig. 11-21 — Looking into the bottom of the tunable 440-MHz fm receiver shows the converted TV tuner below the vernier dial. A transistorized rf preamplifier, also built into a TV tuner case, is visible just to the left of the tuning shaft.

tions are easily "zeroed" on the discriminator meter.

The sensitivity is adequate for monitoring on line-of-sight paths, but not for weak-signal DX work such as is commonly done around 432 MHz. The TV tuner alone is very poor; on the order of 10 microvolts for 10-dB quieting. If one wishes to be able to hear the weak ones, a much better mixer is needed, and it should be preceded by a good low-noise rf amplifier.

TRANSMITTING FM

AN FM TRANSMITTING ADAPTER

The circuit given in Fig. 11-23 is a transmitting adapter which will provide frequency modulation for older 6- and 2-meter exciters, such as the Clegg series. Audio input from a microphone is amplified and clipped to increase speech effectiveness and to provide constant deviation. The output of the speech clipper is passed through a 6-dB-per-octave filter to shape the audio response so that the phase modulator will produce fm directly. Crystals cut for 8 MHz are employed. For transmitters such as the Clegg 22er that require a high drive level, the alternative output circuit (Fig. 11-23B) should be used.

Fig. 11-22 — The fm transmitting adapter. The unit may be constructed on an etched board, as shown, or built on a metal chassis using point-to-point wiring.

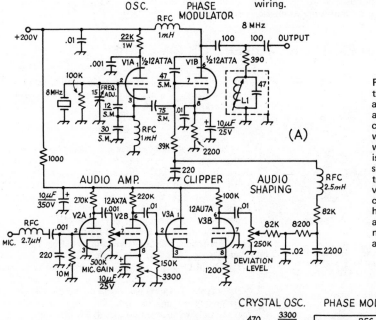

(A)

Fig. 11-23 — Diagram of the fm adapter. Resistors are 1/2-watt composition and capacitors are disk ceramic, except for those with polarity marked, which are electrolytic. L1 is a Miller 42A686CBl slug-tuned coil. For exciters which need only a volt or so of drive use the circuit at A, while for high-level drive use the alternate oscillator/ modulator section shown at B.

EXCEPT AS INDICATED, DECIMAL VALUES OF CAPACITANCE ARE IN MICROFARADS (μF) ; OTHERS ARE IN PICOFARADS (pF OR μμF); RESISTANCES ARE IN OHMS; k =1000 , M =1000 000 S.M.= SILVER MICA

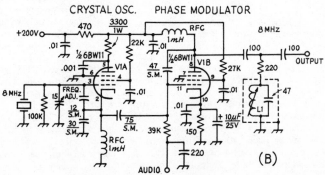

(B)

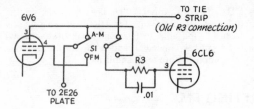

The adapter may be assembled on either a pc board or metal chassis. The crystal-frequency trimmer and deviation control should be set in accordance with the instructions outlined in Chapter 10. The microphone gain control is adjusted to provide 10 to 15 dB of speech clipping. L1, the output circuit, should be set for maximum drive to the associated transmitter.

USING A GONSET II FOR FM COMMUNICATIONS

A simple conversion of the Gonset Communicator II (or similar a-m rigs) allows fm operation with a few wiring changes that should take less than an hour. To produce narrow-band deviation, the oscillator is screen modulated with audio from the a-m modulator section. A toggle switch allows an instant return to a-m operation. No

Fig. 11-24 — Gonset fm conversion. S1 is a miniature dpdt toggle switch.

changes are needed in the receiver, as the wide bandwidth of the Gonset i-f allows slope detection of strong fm signals, such as from a local repeater.

The modifications are shown in Fig. 11-24. Drill a 1/4-inch diameter hole in the rear deck of the transmitter chassis, to the right of the microphone jack, 1/2 inch above J4. Install the miniature switch in the hole. The red wire from pin 3 of the 6V6 socket should be disconnected and run to the switch, as shown in Fig. 11-24. Then, remove the end of resistor R3 which connects to the terminal strip and connect it to S1. Add a .01-μF capacitor across R3. Set the switch for fm operation, and adjust the MIC GAIN control for approximately 1/4 rotation, which will produce approximately 5-kHz deviation. A higher setting will be needed for 15-kHz deviation. The Gonset has no speech clipping in the modulator, so the amount of deviation produced will be directly proportional to audio input. To improve the performance of the unit for both a-m and fm operation, an outboard speech clipper such as described in *The Radio Amateur's Handbook* can be added.

AN FM TRANSMITTER FOR 2 METERS

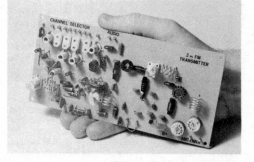

Fig. 11-25 — Top view of the rf module showing its relative size. The crystal sockets and Vector push-in terminals for connection to the crystal switch are at the upper left. The coils near the crystal sockets are for adjusting the crystals to frequency. The oscillator is at the lower left, and the PA stage is at the far right. The small loop of wire at the lower center is a B-plus-jumper.

Whether you're a would-be fm-er, or a person who has already explored the world of fm and repeaters, this little 2-watt solid-state transmitter can be the key to new operating enjoyment. No need to scoff at the QRP aspect of this project, because here we have a piece of gear that can be operated from the 12-volt automotive system, a dry-battery pack (10 size-D flashlight batteries in series, or a 12-volt lantern battery), or a simple ac-operated 12-volt dc supply. This feature makes

possible a variety of amateur applications, and noteworthy among them, emergency/portable operation.

Rf Circuit

Four low-cost bipolar transistors are used in the circuit of Fig. 11-26. Q1 is the oscillator, which uses 18-MHz fundamental crystals ground for a load capacitance of 20 pF. Output from the first stage is taken at 73 MHz, a frequency multiplication of 4. The second stage, Q2, doubles the frequency to 146 MHz. The remaining stages operate as amplifiers at 146 MHz.

Frequency modulation is effected by applying audio to a voltage-variable diode (Varicap) CR1. As the amplitude of the audio varies, the junction capacitance of CR1 changes, and this change pulls the crystal frequency above and below its preset frequency to provide fm. The amount of deviation, or swing, is determined by the audio level impressed across CR1. Normally, this will be set for 5- or 15-kHz deviation, depending upon the bandwidth in vogue for a given area. Approximately 1.5 volts of reverse bias is developed within the circuit and appears across CR1. This eliminates the need to provide back bias from the 12-volt line.

Crystals Y1 through Y4 are adjusted to the desired frequency by means of trimmer capacitors. Approximately 3 kHz of shift is possible with the value given. Regulated voltage is supplied to Q1 (and to the bias line of Q2) by

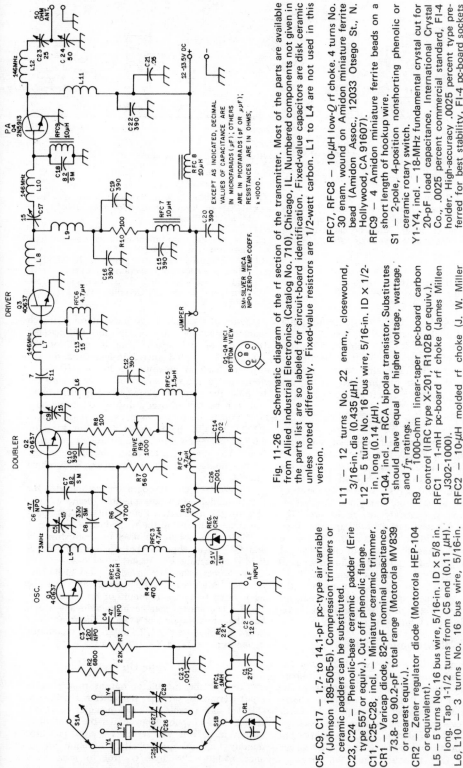

Fig. 11-26 — Schematic diagram of the rf section of the transmitter. Most of the parts are available from Allied Industrial Electronics (Catalog No. 710), Chicago, IL. Numbered components not given in the parts list are so labeled for circuit-board identification. Fixed-value capacitors are disk ceramic unless noted differently. Fixed-value resistors are 1/2-watt carbon. L1 to L4 are not used in this version.

EXCEPT AS INDICATED, DECIMAL VALUES OF CAPACITANCE ARE IN MICROFARADS (μF); OTHERS ARE IN PICOFARADS (pF or $\mu\mu$F); RESISTANCES ARE IN OHMS; k =1000.

SM=SILVER MICA
NPO=ZERO-TEMP.COEFF.

Q1-Q4 INCL.
BOTTOM VIEW.

C5, C9, C17 — 1.7- to 14.1-pF pc-type air variable (Johnson 189-505-5). Compression trimmers or ceramic padders can be substituted.

C23, C24 — Phenolic-base ceramic padder (Erie type 557 or equiv.). Cut off phenolic flange.

C11, C25-C28, incl. — Miniature ceramic trimmer.

CR1 — Varicap diode, 82-pF nominal capacitance, 73.8- to 90.2-pF total range (Motorola MV839 or nearest equiv.).

CR2 — Zener regulator diode (Motorola HEP-104 or equivalent).

L5 — 5 turns No. 16 bus wire, 5/16-in. ID × 5/8 in. long. Tap 1-1/2 turns from C5 end (0.11 μH).

L6, L10 — 3 turns No. 16 bus wire, 5/16-in. ID × 1/2 in. long (.075 μH).

L7, L8 — 6 turns No. 22 enam., closewound, 3/16-in. dia. See text.

L9 — 4 turns No. 22 enam., 3/16-in. dia, spaced to occupy 3/8 in. on form (.06 μH).

L11 — 12 turns No. 22 enam., closewound, 3/16-in. dia (0.435 μH).

L12 — 5 turns No. 16 bus wire, 5/16-in. ID × 1/2-in. long (0.14 μH).

Q1-Q4, incl. — RCA bipolar transistor. Substitutes should have equal or higher voltage, wattage, and f_T ratings.

R9 — 1000-ohm linear-taper pc-board carbon control (IRC type X-201, R102B or equiv.).

RFC1 — 1-mH pc-board rf choke (James Millen J302-1000).

RFC2 — 10-μH molded rf choke (J. W. Miller 9310-36). See text.

RFC3, RFC4, RFC6 — 4.7-μH molded rf choke (J. W. Miller 9310-28). See text.

RFC5 — 1.5-μH molded rf choke (J. W. Miller 9310-16). See text.

RFC7, RFC8 — 10-μH low-Q rf choke. 4 turns No. 30 enam. wound on Amidon miniature ferrite bead (Amidon Assoc., 12033 Otsego St., N. Hollywood, CA 91607).

RFC9 — 4 Amidon miniature ferrite beads on a short length of hookup wire.

S1 — 2-pole, 4-position nonshorting phenolic or ceramic rotary switch.

Y1-Y4, incl. — 18-MHz fundamental crystal cut for 20-pF load capacitance. International Crystal Co., .0025 percent commercial standard., FI-4 holder. High-accuracy .0025 percent type preferred for best stability. FI-4 pc-board sockets used in this transmitter. Crystals from other manufacturers may work satisfactorily if ground for 20-pF load. (International Crystal Mfg., Inc., 10 North Lee, Oklahoma City, OK 73102).

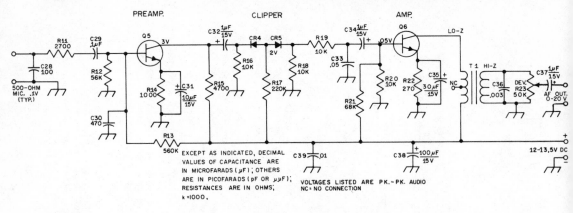

Fig. 11-27 — Schematic diagram of the clipper/modulator. Numbered components not listed below are for circuit-board identification. Capacitors are disk ceramic or paper. Polarized capacitors are electrolytic. Fixed-value resistors are 1/2-watt carbon.

CR4, CR5 — Silicon diode. 1N914 or top-hat rectifier suitable.

Q5, Q6 — Audio-type npn bipolar transistor. RCA 40231 or equiv. Also, Motorola 2N4123 or MPS-A10 suitable.

R11 — See text.

R23 — 50,000-ohm linear-taper carbon control. Pc-board type IRC X-201, R503B.

T1 — Miniature audio transformer, 10,000-ohm primary, 2000-ohm secondary, ct not used. Radio Shack/Archer 273-1378 or equiv. Connect low-*Z* winding to Q6 collector.

means of Zener diode CR2. This measure helps insure against oscillator instability.

A drive control, R9, is connected in the emitter lead of Q2 to permit the operator to reduce power to the minimum amount needed. This measure helps to prolong the life of dry batteries during portable operation.

The Modulator

Only a few peak-to-peak volts of audio are needed to provide fm. A two-stage audio channel is shown in Fig. 11-27. This circuit amplifies the microphone output to a suitable level for clipping at diodes CR3 and CR4. A small amount of forward bias is used on the diodes to permit clipping action at relatively low audio level. The 10,000-ohm resistor and .05-μF capacitor used after the clipper diodes serve as a filter to reduce the harmonics caused during clipping. Output stage Q6 amplifies the clipped audio to a maximum level of 20 volts peak to peak. The deviation control, R23, is adjusted to provide the amount of frequency swing needed. A value of approximately 3 volts pk-pk is typical for 5-kHz deviation with the circuit of Fig. 11-26.

Construction Data

If you have built a commercial kit, you can assemble this transmitter easily. Circuit-board templates for the transmitter and modulator are available from ARRL for 50 cents and a *large* self-addressed, stamped envelope. A parts-placement overlay is included in the package. Several changes included in Fig. 11-26 have not been made on the template. L1 to L4 have been replaced by C25 to C28, and C27 has been eliminated.

Some of the inductors are wound on 3/16-inch diameter phenolic rod. Any low-loss rod material (Plexiglas or polystyrene) can be used, or the coils can be wound on a 3/16-inch form, slipped off and used as air-wound inductors. If this is done, put a drop of coil dope on each inductor to hold the turns in place. The large air-wound coils can be wound over a drill bit of appropriate size. Ferrite beads are used as cores for chokes RFC7 and 8. Each choke has four turns of No. 30 enameled wire looped through its ferrite bead. The chokes, after being installed on the circuit board, are glued in place with china cement.

Glass-epoxy circuit board is recommended for the rf module. Low-cost phenolic board is suitable for the modulator. Poor-quality circuit board can cause problems in the rf module.

Heat sinks should be used on transistors Q3 and Q4. Small clip-on types are suitable. Wakefield Engineering Co. makes a wide variety of these devices. They are listed in most mail-order catalogs. Alternatively, homemade sinks can be made from 16-guage aluminum or brass stock.

The transmitter can be housed in any metal box that suits the builder's fancy. The transmitter board measures 3 X 7-1/2 inches. The modulator dimensions are 1-3/4 X 4-1/2 inches.

Tune-Up

Connect the modulator output to the audio input terminals on the transmitter board. Use shielded audio cable or small-diameter coax. Attach a No. 47 pilot lamp across the transmitter output jack. This will serve as a visual-indicator dummy load of approximately 50-ohms impedance. Adjust the drive control to nearly full resistance (low power). Plug in a crystal and

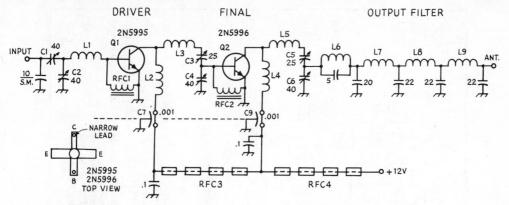

Fig. 11-28 — Schematic diagram of the 25-watt solid-state amplifier. Capacitors are disk ceramic unless otherwise noted.

C1, C2, C4, C6 — Compression trimmer.
C3, C5 — Air variable.
C7, C8 — Feedthrough type.
L1 — 1/4 X 2/3-inch copper strap.
L2, L4 — 9 turns No. 20 enam., closewound, 3/16-in. dia.
L3, L5 — 3 turns No. 14 tinned bus wire, 3/8-inch ID X 1/2-inch long.

L6 — 2 turns No. 20 enam., closewound, 1/4-inch dia.
L7-L9, incl. — 3 turns No. 20 enam., closewound, 1/4-inch dia.
Q1, Q2 — RCA power semiconductor, used with appropriate heat sink.
RFC1, RFC2 — 4 turns No. 30 enam. wound on a single ferrite bead (turns looped through the bead).
RFC3, RFC4 — Four ferrite beads on a 1/2-inch length of No. 20 wire.

apply +12 volts to the B-plus terminal of the transmitter module (negative lead to ground foil). Couple a wavemeter to L5 and adjust C5 for a maximum reading at 73 MHz.

The next step is to set the wavemeter for 146 MHz and couple it to tank coil L6. Tune C9 for maximum output indication. The same technique is used to adjust the tuned circuits of Q3 and Q4. Now, advance the drive control to obtain maximum power. The dummy load should light at this point. Retune each stage for maximum lamp brilliance. Alternately adjust the tune and load trimmers, C23 and C24, for maximum glow of the lamp. Normal operation should cause the lamp to light to full brightness or slightly more. At 13.5 volts one should be able to obtain above-normal lamp brilliance. Couple a wavemeter to the output tank and check for second-harmonic energy. Choose a setting for C23 and C24 that provides maximum rf output at 146 MHz with the lowest possible reading at the

second harmonic. The wavemeter response at 293 MHz should be very low, but some energy will be present.

Modulator Checkout

The circuit of Fig. 11-27 is designed for a low-impedance dynamic microphone (500 to 1000 ohms). If a high-impedance microphone is to be used, replace R11 with a 100,000-ohm unit. This will reduce the audio drive to Q5, thus preventing saturation of that stage. Also, the high-value resistor will give the high-impedance microphone a more suitable impedance to look into. Adjust R23 for the amount of deviation required. This can be done best by checking with another amateur who has an fm receiver of the desired bandwidth. The crystal can be rubbered to the desired frequency by adjusting its series capacitor.

A final word of caution: *Never operate this transmitter into a highly reactive load.* The SWR

Fig. 11-29 — Top view of the solid-state 1-W transmitter for 220 MHz.

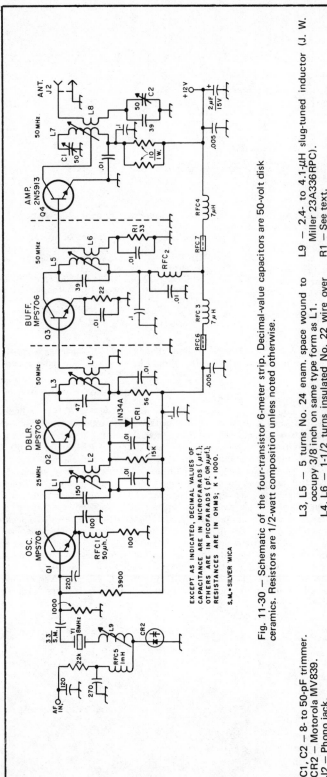

Fig. 11-30 — Schematic of the four-transistor 6-meter strip. Decimal-value capacitors are 50-volt disk ceramics. Resistors are 1/2-watt composition unless noted otherwise.

C1, C2 — 8- to 50-pF trimmer.
CR2 — Motorola MV839.
J2 — Phono jack.
L1 — 5 turns No. 24 enam. on 1/4-inch dia slug-tuned ceramic form. Space wind coil one wire diameter between each turn (Miller 4500-2 form).
L2 — 1 turn No. 22 insulated wire over B+ end of L1.

L3, L5 — 5 turns No. 24 enam. space wound to occupy 3/8 inch on same type form as L1.
L4, L6 — 1-1/2 turns insulated No. 22 wire over cold ends of L3 and L5 respectively.
L7 — 6 turns No. 20 tinned solid wire, 1/2-inch dia 1 inch long. Tap 1-1/4 turns from bottom end.
L8 — 2 turns No. 22 insulated wire, 1/2-inch dia Insert in B3 end of L7.

L9 — 2.4- to 4.1-μH slug-tuned inductor (J. W. Miller 23A336RPC).
R1 — See text.
RFC1 — 50-μH rf choke.
RFC2-RFC4, incl. — 7-μH rf choke (48 inches No. 24 enam. scramble-wound on 100,000-ohm, 1-watt resistor).
RFC5 — Subminiature rf choke.
RFC6, RFC7 — Ferrite bead.
Y1 — 8.3-MHz crystal.

should be no higher than 2:1 to prevent damage to PA stage Q4. The output circuit of Q4 is designed to work into a 50- to 75-ohm load.

Suitable substitutes for Q1, Q2, and Q3 are 2N4427 and 2N3866.

2-METER SOLID-STATE AMPLIFIER

The circuit of Fig. 11-28 was developed for use with the new RCA 2N5995 and 2N5996 npn overlay rf power transistors. Low-inductance radial-type leads are used for the base, emitter, and collector connections. The mounting stud is independent from the transistor elements. This ideal feature makes it possible to bolt the transistor to the wall of the equipment case, thus using the cabinet or chassis as a heat sink.

Both transistors are "mismatch tested" by the manufacturer. This means that an infinite load mismatch from short to open can be tolerated by the transistors during driven periods, provided the maximum junction temperature is not exceeded. The circuit shown here was tested for both short and open conditions, and no damage to the transistor resulted.

Driving power for the 2N5995 is 3/4 watt. The 2N5996 requires approximately 5 watts drive to develop its rated power output. The 2N5995 can be used as a driver for the 2N5996 to obtain approximately 20 watts output at 146 MHz. Similar circuit constants can be used for both stages.

CONVERSION OF THE 146-MHz FM TRANSMITTER TO 220 MHz

The transmitter shown in Fig. 11-26 was designed for 2-meter operation. However, by making a few changes in the circuit, it can be made to operate at 220 MHz. The oscillator, Q1, is changed from a quadrupler to a tripler. Using an 18-MHz fundamental-type crystal, the output network of Q1 is tuned to 55 MHz. The next stage, Q2, works as a doubler to 110 MHz, which in turn drives Q3. Q3 also works as a doubler, producing output at 220 MHz. There is enough drive from Q3 to provide about 1 watt output from Q4, the final stage. A 2N3866 should be used for Q3. The coil specifications given in Fig. 11-26 are the same for 220-MHz operation, except as follows:

L5 — 8 turns, tap 1-1/2 turns from C5 end.
L6 — 4 turns, 1/2-in. long.
L7 — 9 turns, closewound.
L8 — 5 turns, closewound.
L9 — 3 turns, 3/8-in. long.
L10 — 2 turns, 1/4-in. long.
L11 — 10 turns, closewound.
L12 — 5 turns, 5/8-in. long.

Also, change C19 to a 1.7- to 14.1-pF air-variable capacitor (Johnson 189-505-5). Tune-up procedure for the 220-MHz model is the same as described earlier for the 146-MHz version.

A SOLID-STATE 50-MHz FM TRANSMITTER

The four-transistor unit shown in Fig. 11-30 can be used as an exciter, or as a 1-watt transmitter. It operates from 12 volts dc, and can be modulated by the audio clipper/filter shown in Fig. 11-27.

The circuit is built on a small Minibox. Transistor sockets are used to provide for point-to-point wiring. Layout should follow the same pattern used with vhf vacuum-tube transmitters — short, direct connections.

Checkout should be done one stage at a time, starting with the oscillator. The remainder of the transistors should be removed from their sockets and a No. 49 lamp connected across L2. A faint glow should show when L1 is peaked at 25 MHz. Check each stage in the same manner, terminating the output link of each stage with the dummy lamp. A No. 47 lamp will be needed at L8 because of the higher power at the transmitter output. Full brilliance should be noted on the No. 47 lamp if all stages are working properly. Finally, tune each stage for maximum transmitter output. Power output from this transmitter is approximately 1 watt.

Once the transmitter has been adjusted for maximum output, the modulator should be connected. The check-out procedure for the modulator section is contained in the description of the 2-watt, 2-meter transmitter which appears earlier in this chapter. Once the modulator is functioning properly, adjust R23 of Fig. 11-27 for the desired deviation. The Bessel-function method or a deviation meter (both described in Chapter 10) can be used to set the amount of frequency swing.

CONVERTING SURPLUS

IMPROVING FM RECEIVER PERFORMANCE

Many older fm receivers, and some new models, do not have sufficient sensitivity or limiting capability. Also, the transceivers designed for the mobile telephone service do not have a squelch or audio power-amplifier circuit. Suitable accessory units can be constructed easily to improve the performance of a rig deficient in any of these areas.

A simple preamplifier, such as shown in Fig. 11-32 for 146 MHz and in Fig. 11-34 for 440 MHz, may be added to a receiver to increase its sensitivity and to improve limiting (as the overall gain before the limiter will be increased by 10-15 dB). The 2-meter version uses a dual-gate MOS-FET while the 440-MHz unit employs two JFETs in a grounded-gate circuit. Both amplifiers are adjusted by peaking all tuned circuits for maximum limiter current while receiving a weak signal.

Fig. 11-31 — The 2-meter preamp. may be mounted in a small Minibox or connected directly inside an fm receiver.

A receiver will have a poor limiting characteristic if the gain before the limiter circuit is insufficient, or if the limiter itself is of poor design. The circuit of Fig. 11-35 can be added to a receiver to replace an existing limiter stage. The new limiter uses an RCA CA3012 integrated circuit. Care must be used in the installation and layout of this high-gain IC to assure stability. The CA3012 will provide a "hard" limiting characteristic with about 100 mV of signal input.

If a receiver does not have a squelch or audio output circuit, the unit shown in Fig. 11-36 may be added. The circuit function is fairly simple. Noise from the discriminator is fed to the pentode section of a 7060 tube (Fig. 11-36). The gain of this noise amplifier is controlled through the action of the squelch control. Amplified noise is detected in the other half of the 7060; the dc output is amplified by half of a 7058 tube, the output of which is connected to its other half in such a way that the second half can be electric-

ally cut off. The second half is used as a switch in the audio path, turning off the audio output when the noise from the discriminator exceeds a preset level. The 7061 tube serves as an audio output stage. Insufficient bias on the 7061 will result in high tube current and low, distorted audio output. It should have a negative grid bias of approximately 10 volts. A template and parts-layout diagram for the circuit are available from the ARRL Technical Department for 50 cents and a business-size self-addressed stamped envelope.

ADDING ADDITIONAL CHANNELS

Many fm units currently available from surplus sources are single-channel models. Others provide 2-channel operation by switching between

Fig. 11-33 — The 440-MHz preamplifier is constructed in a 3 × 3-1/2 × 1-inch box made of double-sided circuit board. All abutting edges are soldered to complete the enclosure. Two 3 × 15/16-inch shields separate the tuned lines.

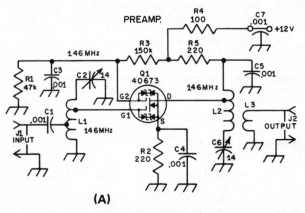

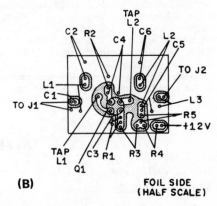

Fig. 11-32 — Circuit diagram (A) and pc-board layout (B) for the 2-meter preamplifier. Resistors are 1/4-watt composition and capacitors are disk ceramic unless otherwise noted. Components not listed below are given designators for circuit-board location purposes.

C2, C6 — Air variable (Johnson 189-506-5).

J1, J2 — Phono type, panel mount.
L1 — 5 turns No. 16, 5/16-inch dia, 1/2-inch long. Tapped at 2 turns for the antenna connection and 4 turns for G1.
L2 — 4 turns No. 16, 5/16-inch dia, 3/8-inch long. Tapped at 2 turns.
L3 — 1 turn, plastic-covered hookup wire, 5/16-inch dia, placed between two turns of L2.

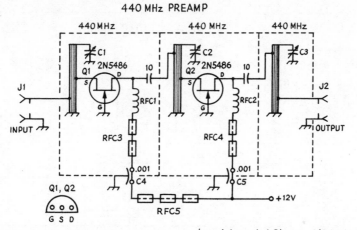

Fig. 11-34 — Schematic diagram of the uhf preamplifier. Capacitors are disk ceramic unless otherwise noted.

C1-C3, incl. — 1.4- to 9.2-pF miniature variable (Johnson 189-0563-001).

J1, J2 — BNC type, chassis mount.

L1-L3, incl. — 2-5/8 × 1/4-inch strip of brass, soldered to the enclosure on one end and to the capacitor at the other. Input and output taps (on L1 and L3) are 1/2-inch up from the ground end. Drain taps for Q1 and Q2 on L2 and L3, respectively, are made just below C2 and C3.

RFC1, RFC2 — 420-MHz choke (Miller 4584).

RFC3, RFC4 — Two ferrite beads on a short piece of No. 20 hookup wire. (Beads are available from Amidon Associates, 12033 Otsego St., N. Hollywood, CA 91607.)

Q1, Q2 — Motorola JFET.

two first-oscillator crystals with a spdt relay. In some, a dpdt relay is employed, so that the unused crystal and its netting capacitor are grounded. Most often, separate oscillators are used for each channel, selection being made by grounding the cathode of the appropriate oscillator stage.

A convenient solution to the crystal-switching problem lies in the use of diodes, changing the bias on the diode in the desired channel so that it goes from an open-circuit to a conducting condition. This is particularly convenient for remote control of the channel selection in a mobile installation, as up to four crystals can be used, and the system works quietly and with very low current drain. It is most readily applied to equipment in which one side of the crystal is grounded.

A circuit for crystal switching, for use in any equipment where one side of the crystal is grounded, is given in Fig. 11-37A. An example is the Marconi DT45. Three crystals are shown, but up to four have been used. The dc is shown here being obtained from the 12-volt ac line in the receiver, with CR4, R7, and C6 comprising the rectifier-filter circuit. The isolation capacitor, C4, should be added if one is not already in the circuit. The grid-to-ground capacitor, C5, usually about 10 pF, should be removed if there is a capacitor of this type in the circuit.

The 12 to 14 volts dc from the supply is fed through R9 and RFC4 to the anodes of CR1, CR2, and CR3. One diode, in this instance CR1, will conduct, its circuit to ground being completed through S1, R1, and RFC1. Its current, approximately 5 mA, and the resultant voltage drop across R9, brings the voltage on the diode cathodes to 8 to 9 volts positive. The full supply voltage is used to reverse-bias the diodes not selected. (There will be no voltage drop across R5-R2 and R6-R3, as the only current flow in these essentially open circuits is the minute leakage current through CR2 and CR3.) The diodes being reverse-biased, their junction capacitances are quite low. The switch does two things: it grounds R4, removing the supply voltage from the cathode of CR1, and it completes the forward-bias circuit from R9 through RFC4, CR1, RFC1, and R1 to ground.

The same power source and switching may be used for both transmitter and receiver, if it is desired to switch both simultaneously. Only separate 1000-ohm isolating resistors, R8 and R9 in Fig. 11-37A, are required.

The arrangements discussed thus far require one control wire between the operating position and the equipment for each channel to be switched. A two-channel system using but one control wire is shown in Fig. 11-37B. It requires that 12

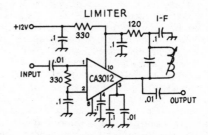

Fig. 11-35 — Diagram of a limiter which may be added between the last i-f stage and the detector of a receiver.

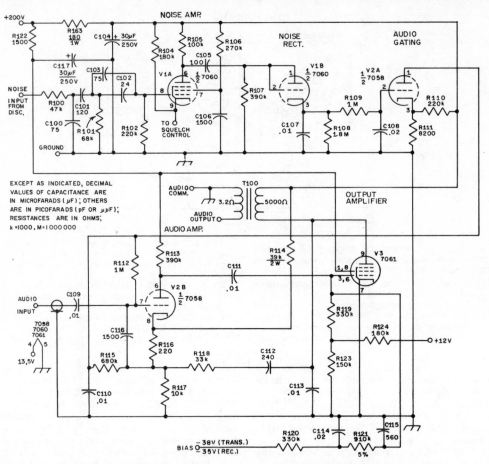

Fig. 11-36 — Schematic diagram of the audio/squelch adapter. Resistors are 1/2-watt, five-percent tolerance composition, unless otherwise noted. Capacitors may be disk ceramic or paper, except those with polarity marked, which are electrolytic.

T100 — Audio output type, 5000-ohm primary, 3.2-ohm secondary.

volts dc be available at the control position, as well as in the equipment itself. A voltage divider, R3-R4-R5 is tapped at 4 and 8 volts. The remote control switch S1 connects the switching matrix to either +12 volts or ground. In the position shown, the dc voltage is applied through RFC3 to the diodes. Note that it is applied to the cathode of CR1 and the anode of CR2. The anode of CR1 has 8 volts on it, from the voltage divider, so it is reverse-biased. The cathode of CR2 has 4 volts on it, so it is forward-biased, connecting crystal Y2 into the circuit. The situation reverses when S1 is in the other position, CR1 being forward-biased and CR2 reverse-biased.

The rf chokes, RFC1 and RFC2, affect the operation. It is easiest to get working if 2.5-mH chokes are used, but smaller ones, or TV peaking coils, may work. Oscillator output level can be checked by measuring bias developed at the first multiplier grid (or grid current) and chokes selected for best results.

This modification is easily used with Motorola or Marconi transmitters, but may be more diffi-cult with GE Progress-Line transmitters and re-ceivers. The GE units have their crystals working into a lower capacitance (10 pF) than the other two, and the modification introduces some stray capacitance, which tends to lower the frequency of oscillation. Motorola crystals, for 24-times frequency multiplication, may be used in the Progress-Line transmitters, to get around this problem. It may also be necessary to increase the value of the screen-to-cathode capacitor in these units.

Diode switching can be used in circuits where both sides of the crystal are above ground, but providing for individual frequency adjustment may be difficult. A modification for the Motorola 5V transmitter is shown in Fig. 11-37C. The tuned circuit L1-C4 is as in the original, with C3 added to tune down into the 2-meter band. The extra capacitance required is 30 to 40 pF. The netting capacitors C1 and C2 are added for individual crystal-frequency adjustment. The chokes and electrolytic capacitors, L2-C6 and L3-C7 are to be used only if necessary to remove

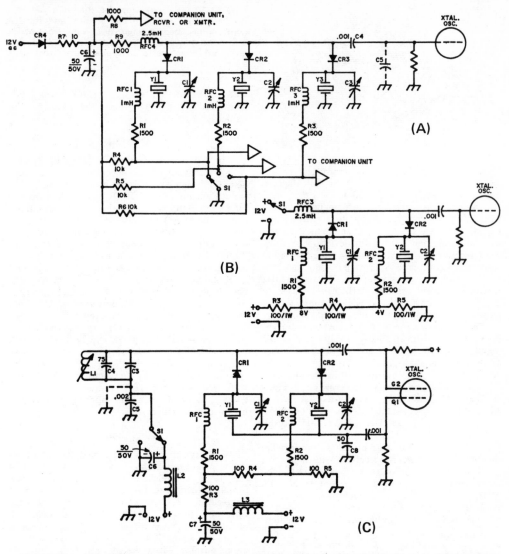

Fig. 11-37 — (A) Diode-switching of crystals having paralleled "netting" capacitors, in circuits where one side of the crystal is grounded. Three positions are shown, but up to four have been used. The dc source and the switching circuit can be used for the crystals in the companion unit of a transceiver. Power is shown here taken from the 12-volt ac line in one of the units, though an external dc source can be used. (B) Switching circuit for oscillators in which the crystal is above ground on both sides. Filtering in the 12-volt leads may be dispensed with if the voltage source is free of hum or other objectionable modulation. (C) Crystal switching of two positions with a single control wire. Values of the rf chokes RFC1 and RFC2 can be set up by experiment, though 2.5 mH is satisfactory.

hum or other modulation from the dc leads. Otherwise, the circuit is similar to that of Fig. 11-37B.

AN INEXPENSIVE VHF FM RECEIVER

For whatever amateur fm frequency you may have in mind, a 10-meter commercial fm receiver is a "best buy." A review of the advertisements and flyers from fm dealers in used equipment will show that 30- to 40-MHz crystal-controlled receiver strips are priced far below those models that are designed for 50- or 146-MHz operation.[1] The reason for the lower cost is twofold: much more 30- to 40-MHz equipment is available, and there is less demand for the older low-band gear.

[1] Dealers who offer surplus fm gear in their catalogs include:

Gregory Electronics Corp.
249 Route 46
Saddle Brook, NJ 07662

Mann Communications
P.O. Box 138
18669 Ventura Blvd.
Tarzana, CA 91356

Spectronics
1009 Garfield Ave.
Oak Park, IL 60304

Fig. 11-38 — Front view of the modified Pre-Progress GE receiver. The volume and squelch controls have been brought out to the front panel. The panel has been refinished, and a new speaker grill, cut from perforated aluminum stock, has been added.

who works for a "two-way" radio service company (such firms usually keep files on all popular models).

Crystals

The GE receiver required a 23.6-MHz "rock." A few words about the selection of crystals may help the beginner to avoid costly mistakes. The various manufacturers of fm equipment use different oscillator circuits; thus, the capacitance loading on the crystal also varies. Often a crystal that is "on channel" in one rig can be quite far off frequency in another. The crystal manufacturers can grind a crystal for any of the commercial fm rigs — if you supply the necessary information — the make, model, and serial number of your rig. Give the crystal and operating frequencies desired, and mention whether or not the crystal will be used in an oven.

For a 10-meter receiver, where the crystal frequency is not multiplied, and no oven is used, you can order a general-purpose crystal and save a few dollars — if you're a gambler. One of International Crystal's inexpensive EX crystals was tried with the 4ER7A2, and it "hit" frequency. Anyone taking this approach does so at his own risk, though.

Alignment

With crystal in hand, the next step is to get the receiver going. Though fm receiver alignment can be a complicated procedure, only a few simple adjustments are required to set up most fm receivers. Test jacks are found on most receivers, and these points can be used to check operation of the various stages. The oscillator should be adjusted for a point just below maximum output. Then the discriminator must be checked for a zero-voltage output with no signal input to the receiver. Then, injecting a signal from a crystal calibrator, the trimmer across the crystal in the hf oscillator should be adjusted so that the calibrator harmonic on 29.6 MHz also

A receiver strip that can be converted to 10-meter operation should cost $5 to $20, depending on condition, age, and model.

For monitor service, a wide-band (36-kHz-wide i-f) receiver is preferable to a narrow-band (13-kHz bandwidth) model, as amateurs currently use both wide and narrow fm deviation. A wide-band receiver can copy signals of either deviation while a narrow-band receiver is suited only for narrow-band transmissions. The 30- to 40-MHz receiver, once set on 29.6 MHz can be used to monitor that channel, or, using a converter, to receive either 6- or 2-meter fm signals.

The scheme to use a 10-meter receiver for vhf fm reception is shown in Fig. 11-39. Any of the popular converter designs may be adopted — any of the converters described in this book would be an excellent choice. Instead of using the specified conversion-oscillator crystal, however, one is chosen that will heterodyne the desired channel — 149.94 MHz for example, down to 29.6 MHz. Using a 28-MHz i-f converter, a 58.57-MHz crystal will be required.

A trial conversion was made on a somewhat dilapidated GE 4ER7A2 receiver. With a receiver in hand, the next job was to find out what crystal would be required for reception on 29.6 MHz. To obtain details on receivers made for the land mobile service, one can purchase a book of schematics,[2] or can consult with a local amateur

---

[2] Two-way Radio Engineers, Inc., 110 Tremont Street, Boston, MA 02120, has a booklet of schematic diagrams covering Motorola equipment up to the early Motrac models. Gregory Electronics (footnote 1) sells similar books of diagrams on the GE pre-Prog units.

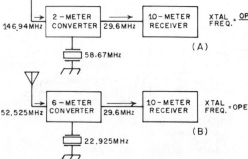

(A)

(B)

Fig. 11-39 — Frequency scheme to receive the 2- (A) and 6- (B) meter national fm calling frequencies. Often a 6- to 30-pF trimmer must be added across the converter crystal to "pull" it exactly "on channel."

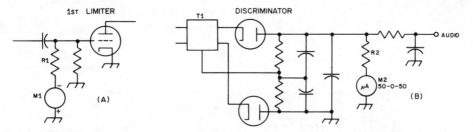

Fig. 11-40 — Connections to meter (A) limiter grid voltage and (B) discriminator output voltage. M1 may be a 0-50, 0-200, or 0-500 microammeter or 0-1 milliammeter, with R1 chosen to provide a half-scale reading with a signal input of 50 microvolts. M2 is a zero-center (50-0-50-μA) meter with an appropriate multiplier resistor (usually 0.22 to 0.47 megohms). T1 is the discriminator transformer.

produces a zero voltage reading at the discriminator output. Metering the grid voltage developed at the second limiter, any rf-stage adjustments should be peaked for maximum voltage at the limiter.

If a variable-frequency signal generator is available, it can be used to further check the discriminator. Again metering the discriminator output, check to see that a cw signal 15 kHz on either side of 29.6 MHz produces the same absolute voltage reading. (Note that the voltages read will have different polarities.) If one side or the other is off a bit, adjusting the input trimmer on the discriminator transformer will usually correct the situation.[3]

As can be seen from alignment procedure outlined above, voltages measured at the limiter and discriminator stages tell quite a bit about how a receiver is working. Constant metering of these stages will make the receiver more useful in giving reports to other stations. The first meter, Fig. 11-40, indicates the relative strength of incoming signals. One peculiarity of the fm mode is that, once a signal produces full quieting of the receiver noise, further increases in signal strength will not be detectable by ear. This limiter grid-current meter serves as an S-meter, allowing an operator to observe changes in strength of incoming signals.

A second meter, connected to the discriminator, indicates if a station being received is "on channel." Because of the temperature changes and vibration encountered in mobile operation, and because of the crystal prblems mentioned earlier, many stations can get off frequency. (On loud signals, off-frequency operation is also difficult to detect by ear.) Once the receiver is properly aligned with a crystal calibrator, the plus-or-minus voltage indication on the discriminator meter will indicate to which side, and relatively how far off, a particular station may be. Of course to remain accurate, the receiver must be checked against a frequency standard on a regular basis.

USING FM SURPLUS IN THE HOME STATION

An fm station for home use can be constructed easily and inexpensively from surplus transmitter and receiver strips. Usually, the individual strips cost less than a complete unit because they have little resale value to commercial users. Two-meter transmitter and receiver strips which have been removed from mobile rigs are now priced at about $30 each, while the 6-meter and 450-MHz models are $8 to $12. To make a home station (often called a base station by fm-ers) requires an ac-operated power supply, a control relay, and a few panel controls.

A heavy-duty homemade power supply (Fig. 11-42) provides the voltages required by the decks. The same circuit can be employed to power many types of retired mobile rigs. It has been tried with a Motorola 80D and a Motorola T44AAV, as well as the GE MTS transceiver. The large power transformer, T1, was garnered from an old TV set. T2 powers the bias circuit, while T3 supplies voltage to the tube filaments and oven heaters. R1 sets the receiver B plus at 220 V, and R2 adjusts the level of audio fed from the receiver to the transmitter when the **REPEAT** mode is selected. This feature may be omitted if operation as a repeater is not desired.

As solid-state rigs continue to replace units using tubes in mobile-service equipment, amateurs will have a chance to acquire some first-class gear. A few simple modifications are all that is required to ready a retired unit for amateur fm use.

[3] A complete alignment should only be attempted if the required test equipment is available. The manufacturer's instructions for testing and adjustment should be followed implicitly. Trial-and-error alignment will not work on most fm receivers.

Fig. 11-41 — G E Progress Line decks are used in this station. A 50-0-50-μA meter (Simpson 2123-27507) is employed to monitor various stages in the transmitter and receiver. Sampling is done at the existing test jacks on the GE decks.

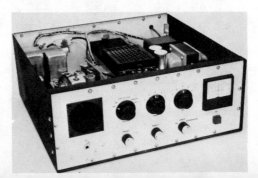

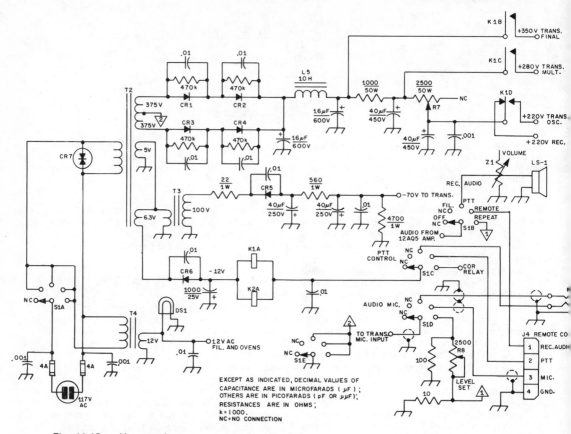

Fig. 11-42 — Homemade power supply for the G.E. transceiver, plus the audio and control switching. Unless otherwise noted, resistors are 1/2-watt composition and capacitors are disk ceramic, except those with polarity marked, which are electrolytic.

CR1-CR5, incl. — Silicon rectifier, 1000 PRV, 1A
CR6 — Silicon rectifier, 200 PRV, 1.5 A.
CR7 — Thyrector transient suppressor (G.E. 6RS20SP4B4).
DS1 — 12-volt lamp.
J3 — Microphone jack, 3 circuit, nonshorting.
J4 — 4-circuit jack, panel mount.
K1 — 3-pole, double-throw relay, 12-volt coil, 2-A contacts (Potter & Brumfield KA14AY).
K2 — Antenna relay.
L5 — Power choke, 10 H, 200 mA (Allied 6X37VG).

R7 — Wire-wound adjustable-tap power resistor.
R8 — Linear-taper composition control.
S1 — 6-pole (5 used), 5-position, 3-wafer phenolic rotary switch (Centralab PA-1020).
T2 — TV power transformer (Allied 6K91VG suitable substitute).
T3 — Filament transformer, 6.3-V, 0.6-A secondary (Allied 6K32HF).
T4 — Control transformer, 12-volt, 8-A secondary (Allied 6K80VBR).
Z1 — L pad (Calectro S2-175).

ACCESSORIES

Fig. 11-43 — The sweep generator for fm i-f alignment.

AN FM SWEEP GENERATOR

In the past a sweep generator was such an expensive piece of test equipment that it was rarely found in amateurs' workshops. Today, however, because of a new low-cost integrated-circuit function generator, anyone willing to spend an evening building a simple project can enjoy the advantages of a sweep oscillator. Such a generator is useful for aligning fm receiver i-f strips, for checking homemade i-f amplifiers and filters, and for determining the response characteristics of band-pass tuned circuits.

The heart of the sweep generator is a Signetics NE566 integrated-circuit voltage-controlled oscil-

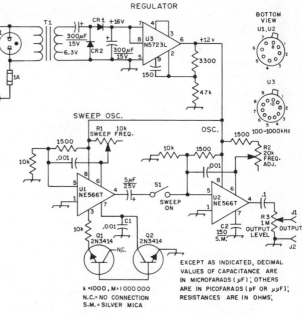

Fig. 11-44 — Circuit diagram of the sweep generator. Resistors are 1/2-watt composition and capacitors are disk ceramic (except those with polarity marked, which are electrolytic) unless otherwise noted.

C1, C2 — See Table 1.

CR1, CR2 — Silicon diode, 100 PRV, 500 mA.

DS1 — Neon indicator, panel mount, for 117 V ac.

J1, J2 — 5-way binding post.

Q1, Q2 — GE bipolar transistor, most low-power npn amplifier or switching types with medium beta should be suitable.

R1 — Linear taper, pc mount.

R2, R3 — Linear taper, panel mount.

S1, S2 — Spst toggle.

T1 — Filament type, 117-V primary, secondary 6.3 V at 300 mA.

U1-U3, incl. — Signetics integrated circuit (available from Compar, 2531 Whitney Avenue, Hamden, CT 06518; the NE566T [TO-99] costs $10.25 and the NE566V [DIP package] is $9.50; the N5723L is $2.00).

lator. The '566 produces square- and triangular-wave outputs simultaneously. The frequency of oscillation is determined by an external resistor, a capacitor, and the voltage applied to the control terminal. The device can be made to shift frequency over a ten-to-one range with exceptional linearity. The upper frequency limit of the NE566 is approximately 1 MHz.

Circuit Information

A schematic diagram of the sweep generator is shown in Fig. 11-44. Integrated circuit U2 functions as the main oscillator whose frequency can be varied from 100 kHz to 1 MHz. Control R2 provides the means of frequency adjustment. The output level from the oscillator may be varied by adjustment of R3. When S1 is closed, a sawtooth wave is applied to the control terminal of U2, sweeping the output frequency. The sweep frequency is determined by the setting of R1. The triangle-wave output from U1 is modified to a sawtooth wave using Q1 and Q2. Square-wave output from pin 3 of U1 is applied to Q2 via Q1, which is connected to function as a Zener diode. When the voltage reaches sufficient level to turn Q2 on, the timing capacitor, C1, is immediately discharged. This discharge occurs just as the triangle wave form reaches its peak voltage, preventing the down-slope side of the wave form from appearing at the output. Either the sweep timing or the frequency range of the generator may be modified by changing the value of the timing capacitor, C1 for U1 and C2 for U2.

Fig. 11-45 — Inside view of the sweep generator. Small components are mounted on Vector T2.8 terminals which have been inserted in a piece of electronic pegboard. The voltage-regulator IC is located to the far right, just above the power transformer. The small pc-mount control to the far left is used to set the sweep frequency.

Power for the generator is provided by a 6.3-volt filament transformer. A voltage doubler and an N5723 integrated-circuit regulator are employed to deliver 12 volts to the NE566s. Approximately 40 mA of current is needed.

Construction

The sweep generator is assembled on electronic pegboard. A pc board can be employed, if desired, although making a circuit board would probably double the amount of time needed to complete the project. A small $3 \times 5 \times 4$-inch cowl-type Minibox is used as an enclosure.

After checking the completed unit for wiring errors, apply line voltage and measure the dc voltage at pin 6 of U3. The reading should be approximately 12 volts. With S1 open, the output from the oscillator can be checked by monitoring the second harmonic with a bc radio. A short piece of hookup wire connected to J1 will serve as an antenna. With S1 closed, R1 should be set to produce the desired sweep frequency.

AN FM-ER'S FREQUENCY STANDARD

The fm channels now in use have been spaced at 30- or 60-kHz increments by informal agreement of those using fm repeaters. Although not all fm operation is on these channels, in most cases repeaters do operate on "standard" frequencies. The frequency standard shown in Fig. 11-47 delivers a spectrum of 30-kHz markers up to approximately 300 MHz. These markers can be used to calibrate the frequency of a 50-, 144-, or 220-MHz narrow-band receiver with an accuracy of 50 Hz or less. Of course, the standard must be first calibrated against WWV or WWVH at 15 MHz if high accuracy is to be obtained.

The frequency standard uses a high-speed TTL gate package for the oscillator, buffer, and output amplifier. A Shottky-barrier IC, the SN74S00, can be used if uhf output is desired. Two divide-by-10 ICs produce the 300- and 30-kHz markers. A National Semiconductor IC, the LM109, regulates the power supply voltage for the TTL logic. If desired, the unit can be battery operated from a 9- or 12-volt source by connecting the battery to point A of Fig. 11-47.

The frequency standard is constructed on an etched circuit board which is housed in a Ten-Tec JW-4 enclosure. Point-to-point wiring may be used, if desired. When the unit is finished and all wiring has been checked for errors, turn on the ac power and connect a voltmeter to pin 2 of the LM109. The reading obtained should be 5 volts plus or minus 0.1 volt. Then, monitoring the WWV transmission on 15 MHz, adjust C1 for zero beat with the standard-frequency transmission. The accuracy of the standard is dependent upon

Fig. 11-46 — The fm-er's frequency standard is built in a Ten-Tec JW-4 enclosure. The panel switches control the ac power and the frequency of the output markers.

the precision with which this calibration is made. Allow time for C1 to "settle down" mechanically after each adjustment. At very close to zero beat the incoming signal will vary rapidly in signal strength. The number of variations per second is the difference in frequency between the two carriers. Adjust C1 until the pulsation rate is as slow as you can make it.

A very short patch cable should be used to couple the standard to the receiver to be calibrated. With a voltmeter connected to the receiver discriminator, adjust the inductor or trimmer capacitor which calibrates the receiver crystal until a zero reading is obtained.

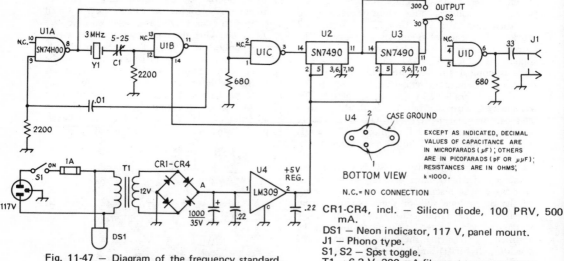

Fig. 11-47 — Diagram of the frequency standard. Resistors are 1/2-watt composition and capacitors are disk ceramic, except as noted otherwise.

A pc board is available from Spectrum Research Labs, P.O. Box 5824, Tucson, Arizona 85702, for $3.50. A template and parts layout appeared in *QST* for April, 1972.

C1 — 5- to 25-pF ceramic trimmer.

CR1-CR4, incl. — Silicon diode, 100 PRV, 500 mA.

DS1 — Neon indicator, 117 V, panel mount.

J1 — Phono type.

S1, S2 — Spst toggle.

T1 — 6.3-V, 300-mA filament type, pc mount.

U1 — TTL quad gate (Motorola, Signetics, or TI SN74H00).

U2, U3 — TTL MSI decade counter (Motorola, Signetics, or TI SN7490).

U4 — IC regulator (National Semiconductor LM109).

Y1 — 3-MHz crystal (International Crystal type EX).

Chapter 12

Repeaters – Theory and Practice

Fig. 12-1 — When selecting a repeater site, height above the surrounding area is usually an important consideration. Here, K7UDG and W7FHZ investigate a proposed repeater location near Wenatchie, Washington.

A repeater is a device which retransmits received signals in order to provide improved communications range and coverage. This communications enhancement is possible because the repeater can be located at an elevated site which has coverage superior to that of lower-lying stations. A major improvement is usually found when a repeater is used between vhf mobile stations, which normally are severely limited by their low antenna heights, especially in rough terrain.

The simplest repeater consists of a receiver with its audio output directly connected to the audio input of an associated transmitter tuned to a second frequency. In this way, everything received on the first frequency is retransmitted on the second frequency. But, certain additional features are required to produce a workable repeater. These are shown in Fig. 12-2A. The "COR" or carrier-operated relay is a device connected to the receiver squelch circuit which provides a relay-contact closure to key the transmitter when an input signal of adequate strength is present. As all amateur transmissions require a licensed operator to control the emissions, a "control" switch is provided in the keying path so that the operator may exercise his duties. This repeater, as shown, is suitable for installation where an operator is present, such as at the home of a local amateur with a superior location. It would require no special licensing under existing rules.

In the case of a repeater located where no licensed operator is available, a special license for remote-control operation must be obtained and provisions made to control the equipment over a telephone line or a radio circuit on 220 MHz or higher. The licensed operator must then be on hand at an authorized control point. Fig. 12-2B shows the simplest system of this type. The control decoder may be variously designed to respond to simple audio tones, dial pulsed tones, or even Touch-Tone signals. If a leased telephone line with dc continuity is used, control voltages may be sent directly, requiring no decoder. A 3-minute timer to disable the repeater transmitter is provided for fail-safe operation. This timer resets during pauses between transmissions and does not interfere with normal communications. The system just outlined is suitable where all operation is to be through the repeater and where the frequencies to be used have no other activity.

Remote Base Stations

The remote base, like the repeater, utilizes a superior location for transmission and reception, but is basically a simplex device. That is, it transmits and receives on a single frequency in order to communicate with other stations also operating on that frequency. The operator of the remote base listens to his hilltop receiver and keys his hilltop transmitter over his 220-MHz or higher control channels (or telephone line). Fig. 12-3A shows such a system. Control and keying features

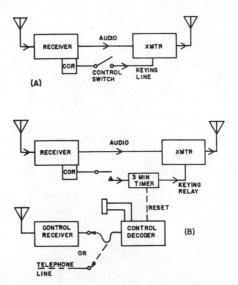

Fig. 12-2 — Simple repeaters. The system at A is for local control. Remote control is shown at B.

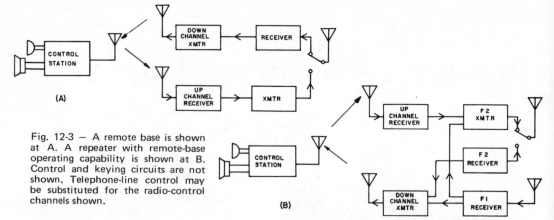

Fig. 12-3 — A remote base is shown at A. A repeater with remote-base operating capability is shown at B. Control and keying circuits are not shown. Telephone-line control may be substituted for the radio-control channels shown.

(B)

have been omitted for clarity. In some areas of high activity, repeaters have all but disappeared, in favor of remote bases, because of the interference to simplex activity caused by repeaters unable to monitor their output frequency from the transmitter location.

Complete System

Fig. 12-3B shows a repeater that combines the best features of the simple repeater and the remote base. Again, necessary control and keying features have not been shown in order to simplify the drawing and make it easier to follow. This repeater is compatible with simplex operation on the output frequency because the operator in control monitors the output frequency from a receiver at the repeater site between transmissions. The control operator may also operate the system as a remote base. This type of system is almost mandatory for operation on one of the national calling

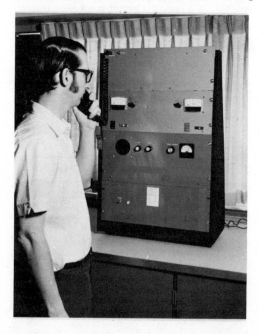

frequencies, such as 146.94 MHz, because it minimizes interference to simplex operation and permits simplex communications through the system with passing mobiles who may not have facilities for the repeater-input frequency.

The audio interface between the repeater receivers and transmitters can, with some equipment, consist of a direct connection bridging the transmitter microphone inputs across the receiver speaker outputs. This is not recommended, however, because of the degradation of the audio quality in the receiver-output stages. A cathode follower connected to each receiver's first squelch-controlled audio amplifier stage provides the best results. A repeater should maintain a flat response across its audio passband to maintain the repeater intelligibility at the same level as direct transmissions. There should be no noticeable difference between repeated and direct transmissions. The intelligibility of some repeaters suffers because of improper level settings, which cause excessive clipping and distortion. The clipper in the repeater transmitter should be set for the maximum system deviation, for example, 10 kHz. Then the receiver level driving the transmitter should be set by applying an input signal of known deviation below the maximum, such as 5 kHz, and adjusting the receiver audio gain to produce the same deviation at the repeater output. Signals will then be repeated linearly up to the maximum desired deviation. The only incoming signal that should be clipped in a properly adjusted repeater is an over-deviated signal.

The choice of repeater input and output frequencies must be made carefully. On two meters, 600-kHz spacing between the input and output frequencies is common. Closer spacing makes interference problems between the repeater transmitter and receiver more severe. Greater spacing is not recommended if the user's transmitters must be switched between the two frequencies, as happens when the output frequency is also used

Fig. 12-4 — W1FBY tries local control on a 450-MHz repeater. This "machine" uses transmitter and receiver decks from the Motorola T-44 series mobile transceivers.

for simplex operation, either for short-range communications, or to maintain communications when the repeater is not functioning. A 5-MHz spacing is recommended on 440 MHz.

Careful consideration of other activity in the area should be made to prevent interference to or from the repeater. Many "open" or general-use repeaters have been installed on one of the national calling frequencies. On two meters, a 146.94-MHz output is usually paired with a 146.34-MHz input, and many travelers have made good use of this combination where it is found. Where 146.94-MHz simplex activity has not permitted a repeater on this frequency, 146.76 MHz has been used as an alternative. On six meters, several choices of input frequencies have been paired with 52.525 MHz. The choice and usage are matters for local agreement.

In some cases where there is overlapping geographical coverage of repeaters using the same frequencies, special methods for selecting the desired repeater have been employed. One of the most common techniques requires the user to automatically transmit a 0.5-second burst of a specific audio tone at the start of each transmission. Different tones are used to select different repeaters. Standard tone frequencies are 1800, 1950, 2100, 2250, and 2400 Hz.

PRACTICAL REPEATER CIRCUITS

Choice of Equipment

Because of their proven reliability, commercially made transmitter and receiver decks are generally used in repeater installations. Units designed for repeater or duplex service are preferred because they have the extra shielding and filtering necessary to hold mutual interference to a minimum when both the receiver and transmitter are operated simultaneously. Those who wish to build their own fm transmitters and receivers will find suitable circuits in Chapter 11 of this manual and in *The Radio Amateur's Handbook*.

Wide-band noise produced by the transmitter is a major factor in the design of any repeater. The use of high-Q tuned circuits between each stage of the transmitter, plus shielding and filtering throughout the repeater installation, will hold the wide-band noise to approximately 80 dB below the output carrier. However, this is not sufficient to prevent *desensitization* – the reduction in sensitivity of the receiver caused by noise or rf overload from the nearby transmitter – if the antennas for the two units are placed physically close together.

Desensitization can be checked easily by monitoring the limiter current of the receiver with the transmitter switched off, then on. If the limiter current increases when the transmitter is turned on, then the problem is present. Only physical isolation of the antennas or the use of high-Q tuned circuits in the transmitter and receiver feeders will improve the situation.

Duplexers

The ultimate answer to the problem of receiver densensing is to locate the repeater transmitter a mile or more away from the receiver. The two can be interconnected by telephone line or uhf link. Another effective approach is to use a single antenna with a duplexer, a device that provides up to 120 dB of isolation between the transmitter and receiver. High-Q cavities in the duplexer prevent transmitted signal energy and wide-band noise from degrading the sensitivity of the receiver, even though the transmitter and receiver are operating on a single antenna simultaneously.

Duplexers fall into two general categories. The first, and simplest, consists of a number of cavities which are placed in the receiver and transmitter feeders, as shown in Fig. 12-5A. Construction details of a simple duplexer using this design are given below. The second type of duplexer uses the *hybrid ring* circuit of Fig. 12-5B. The isolation provided by a hybrid ring depends on the arrival of two signals which are of equal magnitude, but 180 degrees out of phase, at the output terminal. The signal is split into two parts at the input. One signal path is made one-half wavelength longer than the other to achieve the required 180-degree phase shift.

For duplex operation, the hybrid ring must be made to pass the desired frequency while attenuating the unwanted signal. A high-Q cavity is placed in the ring to act as a switch to take one of the signal paths out of the circuit. The cavity is resonant at the pass frequency of the hybrid ring

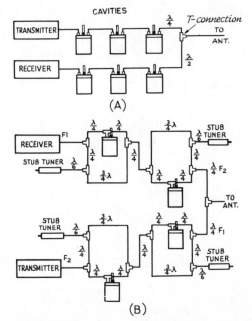

Fig. 12-5 — (A) Simple cavity and (B) hybrid-ring duplexers.

Fig. 12-6 — The 5-cavity duplexer used at the K1IGF repeater. The cavities are made to the specifications of Fig. 12-7.

construction and alignment of a hybrid-ring duplexer is beyond the scope of this text. Excellent information on this subject is contained in bulletin EMI No. 104 from Sinclair Radio Laboratories, Box 23, Tonawanda, NY 14150. The same firm manufactures a complete line of vhf duplexers.

A Homemade Duplexer

Repeater groups can easily construct a simple 146-MHz duplexer suitable for transmitters running up to 100 watts output. Insertion loss measured on a sample unit built for the K1IGF repeater was approximately 2 dB for the transmitter leg and 2.2 dB for the receiver section. The original design for this duplexer was provided by W1GAN.

All cavities are made from 4-inch dia copper drain pipe, as shown in Fig. 12-7. The cavity is tuned by means of a plunger made of 1-1/4- and 1-inch copper pipe. The top plate is machined from copper or brass sheet stock to fit tightly into the cylinder. The input and output coupling links, which enter the cavity by way of Teflon insulators, are made using No. 14 wire. A 1-1/8 × 4 × 1-1/2-inch Minibox is used to enclose the input and output connections. The transmitter cavities use 12-pF air-variable capacitors for coupling (Fig. 12-7A) while the receiver units employ inductors made from 2-1/2-inch lengths of No. 14 wire (Fig. 12-7B). Otherwise, the cavities are identical.

Rough alignment of each cavity can be accomplished using a transmitter, wattmeter and dummy load. The transmitter cavities are tuned to deliver maximum power to the 50-ohm load. The same procedure is used for the receiver cavities, but with the transmitter set on the receive frequency. Then, all cavities should be connected with short lengths of double-shielded coaxial cable (RG-9B or RG-55A), as shown in Fig. 12-5A. The cavities should be mounted in a wooden frame so that individual units do not touch each other. The only ground path should be through the feeder cables. The quarter- and half-wavelength cables that connect to the antenna should be cut carefully and checked for resonance using a dipper.

and thus will act as a short circuit at this frequency. Quarter-wavelength lines isolate the cavity from the signal so that the desired energy is not attenuated.

At the frequency to be canceled, the cavity is not resonant and therefore it acts as a high impedance in parallel with one branch of the hybrid ring. Because the cavity does contribute some phase shift, a stub tuner is included in the opposite leg as a means to adjust the ring for maximum attenuation of the unwanted signal. The

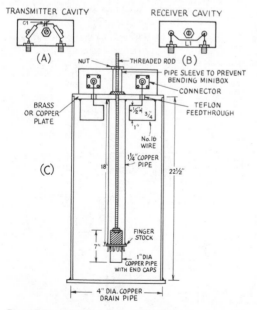

Fig. 12-7 — Details of the 146-MHz cavity filter to be used as part of a duplexer. Connections for the transmitter type are shown at A and for the receiver cavity at B. C1 is a 1.9- to 12-pF air variable (Johnson 189-505-5). L1 consists of a 2-1/2-inch piece of No. 16 silver-plated wire.

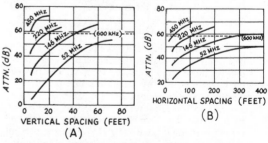

Fig. 12-8 — Charts to calculate the amount of isolation achieved by (A) vertical and (B) horizontal spacing of repeater antennas. If 600-kHz separation between the transmitted and received frequencies is used, approximately 58-dB attenuation (indicated by the dotted line) will be needed.

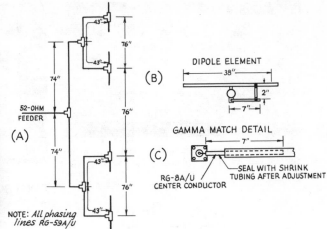

Fig. 12-10 — (A) Phasing harness, (B) dipole elements, and (C) feed-point detail of the dipole array. The gamma-match capacitor consists of a 7-inch length of the inner conductor of RG-8A/U coaxial cable over which is placed a 7-inch piece of 1/2-inch dia aluminum tubing. The gamma match of each dipole should be adjusted for minimum SWR when fed with 50-ohm cable, before the phasing harness is attached. Each phasing line should be checked with a dipper to assure it has been cut to resonance before the harness is assembled. If more than 100 watts will be fed to the antenna, the phasing lines should be made from RG-11A/U.

Fig. 12-9 — An array of dipole elements which provides approximately 6 dB of gain.

Once the duplexer has been installed, connect a signal generator to the antenna connector and recheck the alignment of the receiver cavities for minimum insertion loss. Then, remove the generator and replace it with a power meter and dummy load. Turn on the transmitter and adjust the transmitter cavities for maximum power output. When these adjustments are complete, connect the antenna. Repeak the cavities for best reception of a weak signal source, consistant with maximum power output. Several rounds of adjustments are usually needed to achieve optimum performance from the duplexer. Desensing of the receiver by the transmitter is an indication of improper duplexer adjustment or a lack of shielding of individual sections of the repeater.

ANTENNA CONSIDERATIONS

If two antennas are used at a single site, there will be a minimum spacing of the two antennas required to prevent desensing. Fig. 12-8 indicates the spacing necessary for repeaters operating in the 50-, 144-, and 420-MHz bands. An examination of 12-8 will show that vertical spacing is far more effective than is horizontal separation. The chart assumes unity-gain antennas will be used. If some type of gain antenna is employed, the pattern of the antennas will be a modifying factor.

The type of antenna chosen for a repeater may be as simple as a quarter-wave ground plane or as complex as the requirements for a particular repeater dictate. A repeater group must decide the

coverage area desired for their machine and the type of antenna pattern which is needed to provide this coverage. For directional coverage where the repeater is located at one end of the desired area, a Yagi, corner reflector, or collinear array may be suitable.

If omnidirectional coverage or a cardioid pattern is chosen, the antenna shown in Fig. 12-9 can be used. It consists of four dipoles, each fed by means of a gamma match. The dipoles may be mounted around a tower or pole to provide approximately 6 dB gain. If all of the elements are mounted on one side of the supporting mast, a cardioid pattern with approximately 9 dB gain will result. The lengths needed for the coaxial phasing harness are shown in Fig. 12-10. A commercially made version of this antenna is available from Cush-Craft, Manchester, NH 03103.

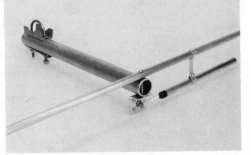

Fig. 12-11 — Close-up view of a single dipole element. A TV-type U clamp holds the assembly to a supporting mast or tower leg.

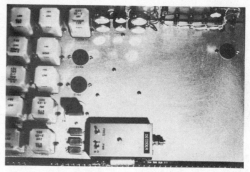

Fig. 12-12 — Front and inside (right) views of the control unit built by WA1DMX for the WA1KGQ repeater. Plug-in relays and timers are employed for easy maintenance, should a failure occur.

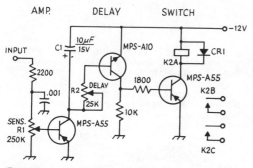

Fig. 12-13 — COR circuit for repeater use. R2 sets the length of time that K2 will stay closed after the input voltage disappears. K2 may be any relay with a 12-volt coil, although the long-life reed type is preferred. CR1 is a silicon diode.

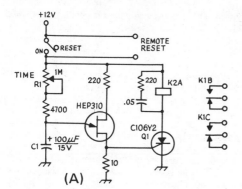

(A)

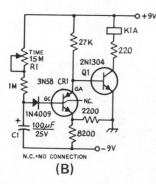

N.C.=NO CONNECTION

(B)

CONTROL

Two connections are needed between the repeater receiver and transmitter: audio and transmitter control. The audio should be fed through an impedance-matching network to assure that the receiver output circuit has a constant load while the transmitter receives the proper input impedance. Filters limiting the audio response to the 300- to 3000-Hz band are desirable, and with some gear an audio-compensation network may be required. A typical COR (carrier-operated relay) circuit is shown in Fig. 12-13. This unit may be operated by the grid current of a tube limiter or the dc output of the noise detector in a solid-state receiver.

Timers

Normally a repeater is given a "tail"; a timer holds the repeater transmitter on for a few seconds after the input signal disappears. This delay prevents the repeater from being keyed on and off by a rapidly fading signal. Other timers keep each transmission to less than three minutes duration (an FCC requirement for stations using a remote-control license), turn on identification, and control logging functions. A simple timer circuit is shown in Fig. 12-14A. A unijunction transistor sets the timing cycle while a silicon-controlled rectifier activates the control relay. If desired, an all-solid-state control system can be constructed using a flip-flop IC in place of the relay.

Two other timer circuits are shown in Fig. 12-14B and C. At B, a silicon-controlled switch,

Fig. 12-14 — Timer Circuits. (A) C1 should be a low-leakage capacitor; K1 may be any miniature relay with a 12-volt coil. Reset of the timer is accomplished by interrupting the supply voltage momentarily. (B) SCS timer. K1 may be any relay with a 6-volt coil. (C) FET timer. S1 can be a momentary-contact switch or a relay contact.

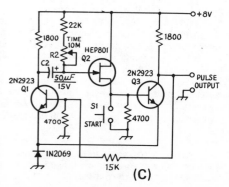

(C)

CR1, is employed in conjunction with R1 to provide up to 4 minutes of time delay. When CR1 fires, Q2 activates K1. The amount of time delay may be adjusted using R1. For circuits which require a pulse output rather than relay control, the circuit of C may be used. Q1 and Q3 are connected to form a multivibrator. The timing cycle is started by closing S1. R2 and C2 set the length of the timing cycle. Pulse output is taken from the collector of Q3.

An Audio Mixer

It is often necessary to combine audio signals at a repeater when several receivers or transmitters are to be cross connected. The mixer circuit shown at Fig. 12-15 was designed by W1ELU and W1IRH. Inputs to the mixer are activated by FET switches. When a 15-volt potential is applied to the ENABLE connection, the audio signal is passed to the adder circuit which uses an operational amplifier connected as a "summer." The sum of all of the inputs appears at the output of the op amp. More than three input sections may be used, if desired.

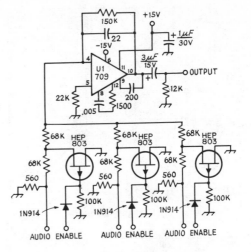

Fig. 12-15 — An audio mixer which can be controlled from a remote location. U1 is an op-amp IC (Motorola MC1709G).

LOGGING AND IDENTIFICATION

Current FCC rules require that a log be kept of repeater operations, just as with any other licensed amateur station. The most effective method of logging has proven to be a tape recorder equipped with a 10- to 20-second timer. The recorder is turned on for a short time (set by the timer) at the beginning of each series of transmissions, so that the calls of using stations may be recorded. In some systems the time must be given by the user, while on others time signals from WWV or CHU are recorded simultaneously on a second track of the tape.

Identification of the repeater itself may be done by users, but lest a forgetful operator leave the repeater unknown, some form of automatic "ID" is preferred. A tape deck with a short loop tape for voice "ID" or a digital cw generator has proven to be effective. A suitable digital unit was described in *QST* for June 1970.

THE REPEATER — A GOOD NEIGHBOR

Because a repeater is usually situated in an excellent location for vhf operation and is equip-

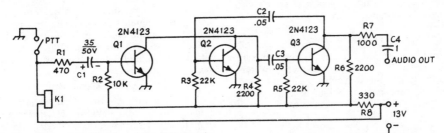

Fig. 12-17 — Schematic diagram of the "electronic whistle." The main diagram is for high-impedance output. All values of capacitance are in μF; polarity indicates electrolytic.

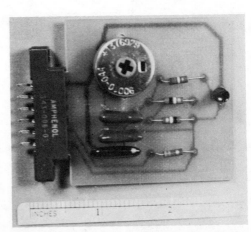

Fig. 12-18 — The single-tone encoder is constructed on an etched circuit board which fits into an Amphenol 141-006-01 edge-contact connector.

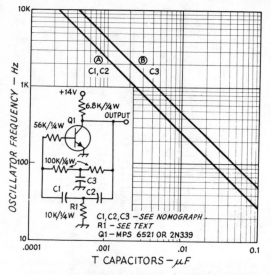

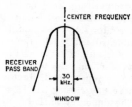

Fig. 12-21 — The "window" concept. The selectivity curve of the receiver slopes, becoming wider for strong signals. The device described effectively establishes a window 15 kHz either side of the center frequency. Any signal deviating more than 15 kHz or more than 3 kHz off the center frequency is rejected.

Fig. 12-19 — Circuit diagram of the audio oscillator (courtesy of *Electronics World* magazine). The nomogram provides the values needed for C1, C2, and C3 for any frequency from 10 Hz to 10 kilohertz.

ped with first-class gear and antenna, the potential for interference with other stations is great. Repeater owners should assure that stations on the input frequency, but not wishing to use the repeater, do not key the machine. A simple form of tone coding may be employed so that distant stations do not inadvertently turn on the repeater during band openings. Provision should also be included so that badly over-deviated or off-frequency signals will not operate the machine. Suitable devices which can be used to achieve these objectives are described below.

Tone Control

Many repeaters use a form of tone control so that a carrier on the input frequency will not inadvertently key the transmitter. The most popular form of tone control is known as tone burst, often called "whistle on," because an operator

with a good ear for frequency can use a short whistle instead of an electronically generated tone to key the repeater. A better approach, however, is a simple transistor tone generator, such as shown in Fig. 12-17.

The whistle-on device was built for use with a Motorola 30D transmitter on a 1-1/2 × 2-1/2-inch piece of Vectorbord. It is nothing more than an astable multivibrator, triggered by a one-shot. When the push-to-talk switch is closed, actuating the transmitter relay, K1, Q1 goes from saturation to cutoff, and the multivibrator, Q2-Q3, begins oscillating with a period dependent on the values of R3, R5, C2, and C3. Values given result in a "whistle" of roughly 650 Hz.

Oscillation ceases when Q1 turns on again. This is regulated by the values of R2 and C1, and is roughly 0.25 second with the values shown. The 470-ohm resistor, R1, protects the base of Q1 from current surges when the PTT switch is released.

Most of the component values are not critical, except the *RC* products which determine timing. Since the frequency is low, almost any bipolar transistors can be used. Npn types are shown, but pnp will work with opposite voltage polarity. The beta rating should be at least twice R3/R4, to assure saturation.

Tone Generator

For single-tone control, each station needs a simple, stable, audio oscillator. The design for such an audio oscillator was drawn up based on articles written by Maynard, "Twin-T Oscillator," *Electronics World*, August, 1968, and Antanaitis, "A Simple Two-Transistor A.F.S.K. Generator," *QST*, September, 1969. The criteria for the oscillator were that it should be small, and that a number of them could be interchanged quickly from a given connector. The audio oscillator was built on a circuit board designed so that it could be plugged into an Amphenol 143-006-01 circuit-board socket (see Fig. 12-18).

The circuit is shown in Fig. 12-19, and the attached nomogram is used to help choose the design frequency which depends upon the chosen values of C1, C2, and C3. Several transistors were tried and the choice of transistor did not seem critical. Of those that were tried, the 2N339 appeared to be a good substitute for the MPS6521.

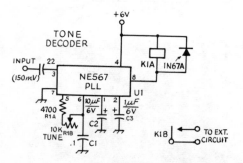

Fig. 12-20 — Tone-burst decoder. Resistors are 1/2-watt composition and capacitors are mylar. K1 is an spst reed relay with a 6-volt coil (C. P. Clare PRA-2010).

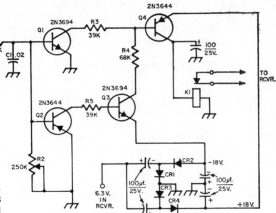

Fig. 12-22 — Circuit diagram and parts information for the 30-kHz window for vhf fm repeaters. Capacitor values are in microfarads (μF). Polarity marking indicates electrolytic. Parts not described below are marked for identification in text.

CR1-CR4, incl. — 1-A rectifier (Motorola 1N4001).
K1 — Miniature reed relay (Dunco MRR-1B-M) 12 volts dc, 576-ohm coil.
R2 — 250,000-ohm miniature trimmer-type control, linear taper (Mallory MTC-4).

Several audio units using the circuit of Fig. 12-19 have been built. The frequency of each was checked with a frequency counter. It was found that their frequencies would vary approximately 0.1 Hz around the design frequency. If R1 were replaced with a 50,000-ohm control, the oscillator would tune as much as 1500 Hz from the design frequency.

Tone Decoder

Most narrow-bandwidth tone decoders currently used in amateur repeater and remote-station applications employ several bulky *LC* circuits to achieve the required audio selectivity. The phase-locked loop (PLL) ICs, pioneered by Signetics, have simplified the design and reduced the size of tone decoders so that a complete Touch-Tone demodulator can be built on a $3 \times 5\text{-}1/2$-inch etched circuit board (about the size for a single-tone decoder using *LC* components).

A typical PLL single-tone decoder, such as might be employed for tone-burst entry control at a repeater, is shown in Fig. 12-20. One *RC* network establishes the frequency to which the PLL is tuned, according to the relationship:

$$frequency = \frac{1}{R1C1}$$

The PLL, a Signetics NE567, may be operated from 0.1 Hz to 500 kHz. C2 establishes the bandwidth of the decoder, which can be set between one and fourteen percent of the operating frequency. C3 smooths the output signal, and, when this capacitor is made a high value, provides a delay in the turn-on function when a tone is received. Up to 100 mA may be drawn by the '567 output circuit, enough to key a relay directly or to drive TTL logic. The PLL contains 62 transistors.

Off-Frequency Controller

Two common causes of unsatisfactory quality of voice transmissions through a vhf fm repeater are excessive deviation and off-frequency transmission. The simple device shown in Fig. 12-22 will cut off a repeater receiver if signals having either of these undesired characteristics are fed into it.

The reader can think of this device as a "window." Any signal outside the window no longer activates the receiver. The transmitter carrier frequency should be at the center of this

window, as seen in Fig. 12-21. As modulation is applied the carrier deviates around the center frequency in a symmetrical manner. If the deviation is too wide, distortion results. If the center frequency is not in the center of the window, the signal is also distorted. Both effects are all too familiar to operators of fm repeaters.

A repeater turns on whenever a signal is of sufficient strength to cause quieting of its receiver, thus some way of turning off the receiver is needed whenever it picks up a signal that is more than 3 kHz off the intended center frequency, or is deviating more than the bandwidth of the repeater receiver. A simple solution to this problem is shown schematically in Fig. 12-22. Its operation is based on the fact that the discriminator current in an fm receiver is zero when a signal is centered in the receiver passband, but rises if the signal is mistuned. All that is needed, then, is a dc amplifier to raise the discriminator current to a level that will operate a relay to cut off the repeater receiver.

Observations at the repeater site showed that, in a Motorola Sensicon receiver, nearly all interference came from signals that produced 10 microamperes or more of discriminator current, so the circuit was set up to respond to this value of current. With no signal, there is no discriminator current. There is still no current when a signal centered in the passband is received. When the signal is modulated, the output of the discrimina-

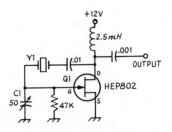

Fig. 12-23 — Circuit diagram of the oscillator which is used to provide an audible indication of off-frequency operation. Y1 is chosen for the center of the receiver i-f passband, and it may be set to the exact frequency desired by means of C1, a mica-insulated trimmer.

tor is audio, around a zero dc level, if the signal is on frequency. The filter, R1/C1, removes audio above 15 Hz from the cut-off circuit, without affecting the operation of the receiver and the system.

When an off-frequency signal is received that is within the receiver passband, current is produced in the discriminator in proportion to the amount that the signal is off-frequency. If the current is positive it turns on the first transistor, Q1. This turns on Q4, whose emitter current then actuates the normally closed relay, K1. These contacts are in series with the repeater transmitter control. When they open, the energizing signal for the transmitter is removed, and after the delay built into the transmitter is passed, the system will drop. If the transmitter was not energized to start with, the open contacts will prevent it from starting up. Thus the system prevents an off-frequency signal from starting the repeater, or will cut it off if an off-frequency signal takes over the receiver.

If the signal is off-frequency in the other direction, the discriminator current is negative, and transistor Q2 will be turned on. This turns on Q4 as before and operates the relay to shut down the system. The selection of the three resistors, R3, R4, and R5, will balance the gain so that a given distance off frequency in either direction will produce the same discriminator current. The value of R1 and the setting of R2 serve to control the drive signal to the circuit, and thus set the current

level which will energize the relay, while the gain of the circuit remains constant.

It must be realized that R1 and C1 do not make a perfect audio filter. Some audio leaks through, and the sum of off-frequency current and the attenuated audio causes unsymmetrical drive to the circuit and actuates the relay. The final factor to add in is that modulation in excess of normal (usually between 5- and 15-kHz deviation) causes the discriminator to become overloaded, and its output "kicks." This kick is added to the above factors, and further encourages operation of the relay, to prevent over deviation of the repeater transmitter.

The operation of the transistor circuitry is very fast, and the relay is a miniature reed type, with an operating time of one or two milliseconds, so circuit response is almost instantaneous. At the most, less than a second of offending signal will be heard through the repeater.

A simple gadget at the repeater will allow users to adjust their transmitters to the input frequency of the repeater. It consists of a crystal-controlled oscillator set for the center of the i-f passband of the receiver. The circuit diagram is shown in Fig. 12-23. During a "netting party," one of the repeater control stations turns on the oscillator by means of the control link. Then, by listening to the beat note transmitted by the repeater, an operator can "zero" his transmitter. Of course, no modulation should be used on the transmitter being adjusted.

AUTOPATCH AND TOUCH TONE

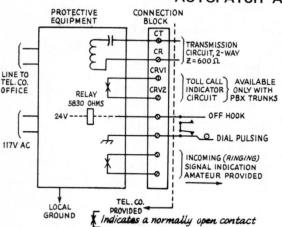

Fig. 12-24 — Typical connections for a repeater and an interface device provided by the telephone company.

Some repeater groups have provided an interconnection to the public telephone network through a device called an autopatch. Details on all phases of phone patching are contained in Chapter 15 of *The Radio Amateur's Handbook*. Typical interconnections to a telephone company interface device for an unattended repeater are shown in Fig. 12-24. Such interconnection has led to the widespread use of the telephone company's Touch-Tone system of tone signaling for repeater control

functions, as well as telephone dialing. Because all of the Touch-Tone frequencies are within the voice band, they can be transmitted by any amateur voice transmitter.

The Touch-Tone control system consists of pairs of tones (see Fig. 12-25) for each of 10 numbers and the two special functions. One tone from the high-frequency group is generated simultaneously with one tone from the low-frequency group to represent each number or function. The Touch-Tone generator pad from a standard telephone instrument is usually employed. See Fig. 12-26 for connections.

For more information on the requirements for and construction of phone patches, review the following articles in *QST*: "Phone Patching – Legitimately," March, 1969; "Legalize Your Phone Patch," May, 1969; "Phone Patching – One Year Later," November, 1970; "An Improved Phone Patch," Hints and Kinks, November, 1970; and "Phone Patching and the Telephone Network," May, 1971.

Low	High Tone		
Tone (Hz)	1209 Hz	1336 Hz	1447 Hz
697	1	2	3
770	4	5	6
852	7	8	9
941	*	0	#

Fig. 12-25 — Standard Touch-Tone frequencies for the 12-digit pad.

Fig. 12-26 — Typical connections to use a Touch-Tone pad for repeater control. Resistances are in ohms. R1 is a linear-taper composition control and J1 is a panel-mounted phono jack. Capacitors are electrolytic; color coding on the wire leads from the pad is shown in parentheses.

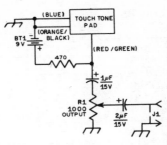

A Touch-Tone Encoder

To generate the Touch-Tone codes listed in Fig. 12-25, two special integrated-circuit function generators may be used. The ICs are Signetics NE566s, voltage-controlled oscillators that were outgrowths of phase-lock-loop technology. The circuit shown here was developed by Jim Wyland at Signetics. This design, Fig. 12-28, provides 11 number codes. If the additional frequency of the 12-button telephone pad, or the five additional frequencies of the 16-button generator are needed, one can add appropriate decoding diodes and timing resistors. The operating frequency of an NE566 is approximately:

$$Fo = \frac{2}{R1C1} \times \frac{V8-V5}{V8-V1}$$

where V8, V5, and V1 are the voltages at pins 8, 5, and 1, respectively.

In the practical circuit shown in Fig. 12-28, the value of the timing resistor (R1) is selected to generate the highest frequency desired. Additional resistors are switched in to lower the frequency of oscillation to the other Touch-Tone frequencies. Both oscillators use a .022-μF capacitor (C2) for timing. Calibration is needed only at one frequency for each oscillator since the other three tones are set by the resistor ratios used.

If a single-contact push-button switch is used, the diodes shown in Fig. 12-28 will be necessary. Close matching of the forward-voltage drops of the

Fig. 12-27 — An L-shaped piece of aluminum, bolted to the top of the utility box, provides a convenient under-the-dash mount for a mobile installation of the Touch-Tone pad.

diodes is required to prevent one of the output tones from varying slightly in frequency. A diode package such as the Signetics NE301A provides a suitable set of matched diodes. Alternatively, a keyboard with double-pole contacts or a design such as the Chromerics EF-20271, which provides the matrix necessary for Touch-Tone coding (thus eliminating the need for diodes), may be used.

A Touch-Tone Decoder

The phase-locked loop described earlier in Fig. 12-20 may be used as the basis of a Touch-Tone

Fig. 12-28 — Schematic diagram of the tone generator. All resistors are 1/2-watt composition. Capacitors are mylar.
BT1 — 9-V miniature Battery.
R1,R2 — Linear-taper, 1/2-watt composition control.
S1 — Chromerics EF-20457 keyboard (available from Chromerics, 77 Dragon Court, Woburn, MA 01801). Note: The Chromerics EF-20271 Touch-Tone encoded keyboard may also be used, eliminating the need for all 1N914 diodes.
U1,U2 — Signetics IC (available from Compar, Inc., 2537 Whitney Ave., Hamden, CT 06518).

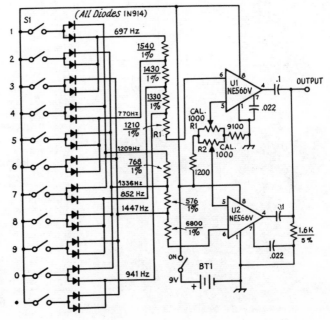

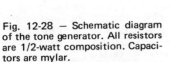

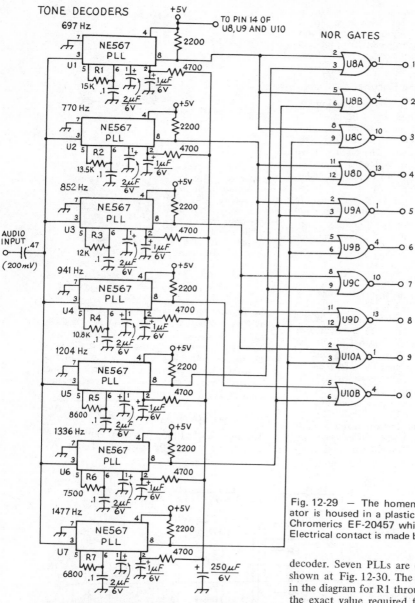

TONE DECODERS

NOR GATES

Fig. 12-30 — Touch-Tone decoder. Resistors are 1/2-watt composition and capacitors are mylar. The values indicated for R1-R7, incl., are approximate. Final adjustment of the frequency of each PLL should be made by trimming the resistor values as needed to center the phase-locked loop on the telephone-company frequency. A frequency counter facilitates the adjustment procedure. U1-U7 incl., are Signetics NE567Vs and U8-U10, incl., are Motorola MC7402Ls (2 NOR gates are not used).

Fig. 12-29 — The homemade Touch-Tone generator is housed in a plastic box. The keyboard is a Chromerics EF-20457 which has no moving parts. Electrical contact is made by chemical means.

decoder. Seven PLLs are employed in the circuit shown at Fig. 12-30. The resistor values indicated in the diagram for R1 through R7 are approximate; the exact value required for the standard Touch-Tone frequencies (Fig. 12-25) will depend on the exact value of the 0.1-μF capacitor. When a pair of tones arrives at the input of the decoder, 697 and 1207 Hz for example, after several cycles of audio have been received, PLLs U1 and U5 will activate, changing from 5 volts to about 0.4 volt at the output pins. These two "lows" will cause NOR gate U8A to change to a "high" (about 5 volts) at its output, the digit output line of the number represented by the two audio tones.

Fig. 12-31 — The Touch-Tone decoder, including a 5-volt power supply and a solid-state numerical display which is driven by the digit output lines through a diode matrix. As numbers are received and decoded, they are displayed, providing a visual check on the operation of the decoder.

Chapter 13

U H F and Microwaves

Segments of the radio spectrum have labels. From 3 to 30 MHz is "high frequency," 30 to 300 is "very high," 300 to 3000 "ultra high," and all higher "super high." But all through this book we've had trouble keeping within these semantic lines. This trouble with labels is, in a way, a capsule history of the radio art. Today's "ultra" is tomorrow's commonplace.

Webster defines ultra as "Going beyond others, or beyond due limit," yet within this writer's memory everything above 30 MHz was called "ultra high." Our *QST* column started as "On The Ultra Highs" in 1939, but it wasn't long before we began to think of frequencies up to at least 220 MHz as something rather below the "ultra" class. Today we tend to take the 420-MHz band out of this category.

Working even above 1000 MHz is today approaching a routine business, but it is well to remember that the techniques we think of as "conventional" are that way because of continuing advances, amateur and commercial. We tend now to put the frontier somewhere around 1000 MHz. Who can say where it will be tomorrow?

Any frequency "frontier" is more philosophical than technical, challenging basic concepts of amateur radio communication. Throughout our history, amateurs have cherished the element of surprise. We call CQ to see who will come back. We listen, listen — everlastingly listen — for something

new, or at least out of the ordinary. For all our emphasis on friendships made and maintained by radio, a strange voice, a new country, or even a new state stirs us. For reliable communication we tend to rely on the telephone, or the local vhf repeater. Worth for point-to-point has never done too well as a sales argument for new bands.

But much communication above 1000 MHz must, of necessity, be largely on an organized basis. Bands are incredibly wide. Beam patterns must be sharp, if communication over interesting distances is to be maintained. Cooperation in the matter of operating times, frequencies, and beam headings is the only alternative to spending fruitless hours scanning the radio horizon for signs of life. Routine "activity" as we know it on lower bands seems thus unlikely ever to develop in our microwave bands, at least until we have space well filled with communications satellites, and frequencies for them are sure to be in short supply.

We already have the know-how to transfer to the uhf and microwave bands much of the talking we do on all-too-crowded lower frequencies. Will a new generation of amateurs seize upon the opportunities that the microwaves offer? It could be that the future of our avocation hinges on a positive answer.

Equipment and methods are already well within our capabilities. What we need most, in the world above 420 MHz, is people!

UHF LINES AND CIRCUITS

The changing nature of tuned circuits as we move higher in frequency was discussed at length in Chapter 5. It may be well to review this material before going too far into uhf circuitry. Earlier we were concerned with "lumped-constant" circuits; those where inductance and capacitance exist as separate entities. In uhf work we have to think in terms of sections of transmission line.

Still higher in frequency we will abandon the line idea. Our circuits become resonant cavities, and an allied change occurs in methods used to transfer power from one circuit to another, and to an antenna. The parallel-conductor line disappears, giving way first to low-loss coax, and eventually to waveguide.

In Fig. 13-1 we have typical coaxial circuits, shorted at one end and open at the other. The line need not be cylindrical. A rectangular tube and a flat inner conductor (strip-line) work equally well. Such a line section an electrical quarter-wavelength long can replace a coil-and-capacitor circuit as the tuning element of an oscillator, amplifier, or other uhf device. Its resonant frequency can be varied in several ways. Its length can be adjusted, if two pieces of tubing are made to telescope one inside the other, as in the upper portion of circuit A. A movable disk making firm contact to both inner

and outer conductor can be moved up or down the line, as shown at the bottom of the sketch.

The line may be tuned with a variable capacitor, as in B. Adding capacitance in a tuning device, or in the form of the input or output

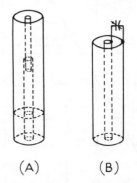

(A)   (B)

Fig. 13-1 — A coaxial tank circuit can be tuned by means of a "false bottom," as at A, or by variable capacitance across the open end, as in B. In A the effective length is adjusted by means of the shorting disk, which is movable. Good electrical contact to both inner and outer conductors is important at this point.

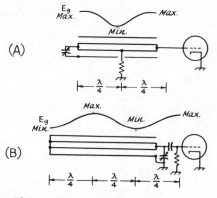

Fig. 13-2 — The useful frequency limit of a line-type tank circuit can be extended by making it a half-wave line, A, or three-quarter-wave line, B. Rf voltage distribution along the lines is shown by curved line, E_g.

capacitance of a transistor or tube, lowers the resonant frequency for a given length of line. The line must, therefore, be made physically shorter than a quarter wavelength. This loading limits the frequency over which a quarter-wave line can be used, just as in circuits discussed in Chapter 5.

The same steps can be taken to extend the frequency limit. A half-wave line is shown schematically in Fig. 13-2A. A push-pull version could have a tube at each end. Rf voltage distribution along the line is shown above it. Where a standing

wave exists along a transmission line, the rf voltage and impedance are repeated every half wavelength. If tube capacitance and lead inductance tend to make us "run out of tank circuit" with a quarter-wave line, and a half-wave line is not convenient for our purposes, we can make the line any odd number of quarter wavelengths, as for example the 3/4-wave line of B. This may have a quarter-wave resonance lower in frequency, but because of the different loading effect of tube and circuit capacitance at the two frequencies it will not be exactly one-third that of the 3/4-wave mode.

Coaxial and Strip-Line Circuits

There is no need for the conductors to be round in cross-section, or truly coaxial in nature. The strip line is often convenient for the amateur

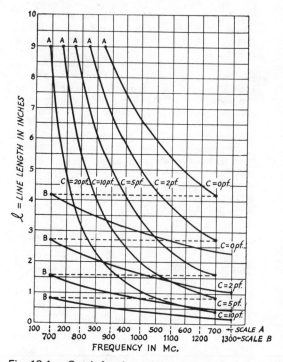

Fig. 13-4 — Graph for determining the length of a capacity-loaded quarter-wave coaxial line of 71 ohms impedance, for frequencies from 150 to 1300 MHz. The value C includes tube output and tuning capacitances.

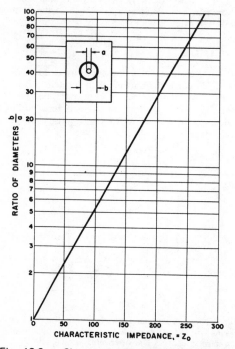

Fig. 13-3 — Characteristic impedance of coaxial lines for various conductor diameter ratios. The outside diameter of the inner conductor and the inside diameter of the outer conductor are used.

builder, and many examples appear in this book. Other shapes could be used, but coaxial or strip lines are most common.

The Q of these circuits is nearly always important, so the conductors should be of large size, and of metals having high conductivity. A coaxial line with a No. 20 wire inner conductor would be little better than a coil of the same wire size, for its ohmic resistance would be as high as the same wire wound into a coil. Electrical conductivity is particularly important at points of high rf current (lowest rf voltage), notably at the shorted end of coaxial or strip-line circuits. Insulation should be kept to a minimum, and preferably avoided entirely at or near the points of high rf voltage.

Insulation loss is introduced by a tuning capacitor, as it must be at a point of appreciable rf voltage. Movable-disk capacitors are favored, as they do not require insulating supports or metal frames that often introduce parasitic resonances.

Impedance of the line may be important in some applications. This can be obtained for coaxial lines from the formula:

$$Z_o = 138 \log \frac{b}{a}$$

where Z_o is the impedance of the line, b is the inside diameter of the outer conductor, and a is the outside diameter of the inner conductor. Knowing the dimensions of available materials, the impedance can be obtained to an accuracy sufficient for most purposes from Fig. 13-3.[1] The impedance of a strip line can be obtained from the formula:

$$Z_o = 377 \frac{S}{W}$$

where S is the spacing between the strip and the outer conductor, and W is the width of the strip. Preferably W should be several times S. This information is from Brayley.[2]

The same author gave a formula for figuring the length of coaxial tank circuits when the total circuit capacitance is known. Solution of this formula for various capacitances, at frequencies from 150 to 1300 MHz, was worked out graphically by Garrett and Manly, as shown in Fig. 13-4.[3] The top curve in each set (C equals zero pF) is for lines not capacitively loaded.

WAVEGUIDES AND CAVITY RESONATORS

Because of the loading effects of capacitance on parallel-line and coaxial circuits the useful frequency limit for any type of line circuit is somewhere around 1000 to 2500 MHz, depending on the tube or solid-state device used. At higher frequencies something different is needed, for transmission lines as well, for losses in even the best coaxial line become prohibitive. The answer lies in the use of cavity resonators and waveguides; devices in which the dimensions of conducting boxes or tubes determine the frequency at which they will operate.

Waveguide Principles

A waveguide is a metallic tube of circular or rectangular cross-section, through which electromagnetic waves can be transmitted. The walls of the waveguide are not considered as carrying current, in the sense of the conductors of a 2-wire line, but rather as a *boundary* confining the waves to the enclosed space. Energy injected at one end by capacitive or inductive coupling, or by radiation, flows through the guide to the load, by means of reflections from its inner walls.

There is an infinite number of ways in which the electric and magnetic fields can arrange themselves in a waveguide, depending on guide dimensions in wavelengths. These modes are separated into two groups: transverse magnetic (*TM*), and transverse electric (*TE*). The mode is identified by these letters, followed by subscript numerals, as $TE_{1,0}$, $TM_{1,1}$, etc. The number of possible modes increases with frequency, for a given size waveguide. The *dominant mode* (the only one for the lowest frequency the guide will pass) is generally used in practical work, as there is little point in using a larger guide than necessary for a given frequency.

Waveguide can be any cross-section, but only rectangular and circular are common. In the rectangular, Fig. 13-5, the width, x, is the critical dimension. It must be more than a half wavelength for the lowest frequency to be transmitted. Generally the height, y, is made about a half wavelength. It can be seen that waveguide has another advantage over other kinds of line, in addition to lower losses; by its very nature it can be an effective high-pass filter.

Five factors should be kept in mind in dealing with waveguide dimensions: *free-space wavelength*, λ; *guide wavelength*, λ_g, the actual length of the wave as it travels through the guide; *cut-off wavelength*, λ_c, longest *usable* wavelength, λ_u, that can be transmitted without excessive attenuation; and the *shortest* wavelength, λ_s, that can be transmitted before the next mode develops. These are obtained, for the dominant mode, as shown below:

$$\lambda, \text{ inches} = \frac{11811}{\text{Freq., MHz}}$$

$$\lambda_g, \text{ inches} = \frac{\lambda}{\sqrt{1 - \left(\frac{\lambda}{\lambda_c}\right)}} \quad (2)$$

	Rectangular	Circular
$\lambda_c =$	$2x$	$3.41r$
$\lambda_u =$	$1.6x$	$3.2r$
$\lambda_s =$	$1.1s$	$2.8r$

Typical inside dimensions of rectangular waveguide for the various amateur bands are as follows:

[1]For this and other numbered references, see bibliography at the end of this chapter.

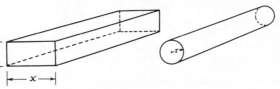

Fig. 13-5 — Waveguide cross-section can be rectangular or circular. In the rectangular, the width, X is the critical dimension. Cutoff wavelength is $2x$ or $3.41r$.

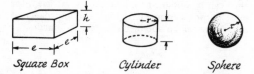

Square Box   *Cylinder*   *Sphere*

Fig. 13-6 — Forms of cavity resonators. The square and cylindrical types are merely closed-off sections of waveguide.

2300 MHz — 1.34 by 2.84 inches; 3300 MHz — same; 5650 MHz — 0.622 by 1.372 inches; 10,000 MHz — 0.375 by 0.75 inch; 21,000 MHz — 0.17 by 0.42 inch. These are standard waveguide sizes. If you were to make your own, the dimensions would not have to be this precise.

The Cavity Resonator

Now suppose that we cut off a section of waveguide, and seal off the ends. We then have what is known as a cavity resonator. The term "cavity" is frequently applied to coaxial or stripline circuits that are completely enclosed, but the name should be reserved for resonant boxes with no inner conductors, as shown in Fig. 13-6. The resonant frequency of these typical cavity shapes depends on the inside dimensions of the box and the mode of oscillation. The latter is comparable to transmission modes in waveguide. For the lowest frequency mode, the resonant wavelengths are as follows:

Square box: 1.41 *l*
Cylinder: 2.61 *r*
Sphere: 2.28 *r*

The resonant wavelength of the cylinder or box is independent of the height, when this is less than half a wavelength. In other modes of oscillation the height must be a multiple of a half-wavelength,

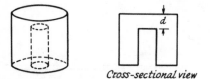

Cross-sectional view

Fig. 13-7 — Re-entrant cylindrical cavity resonator.

as measured inside the cavity. A cylindrical cavity can be tuned by means of an adjustable false bottom, when operating in such a mode. Other tuning methods include placing adjustable tuning paddles or slugs inside the cavity, so that the standing-wave pattern of the electric and magnetic fields can be altered.

Just as coaxial lines represented improvement in *Q* over coil-and-capacitor circuits near the upper limit of the useful frequency range of the latter, the resonant cavity is a means of obtaining very much better circuit efficiency at frequencies where the coaxial circuit begins to be inefficient or impractical. With care in the construction of a cavity as to silver plating and the best possible electrical conductivity where surfaces join, a circuit *Q* of several thousand is possible. A *Q* of 1000 or more is readily obtainable.

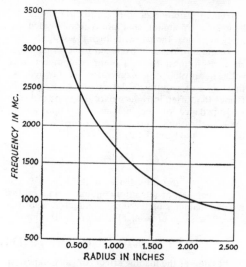

Fig. 13-8 — Radius of a cylindrical cavity for a 2C39 tube, for frequencies from 500 to 3500 MHz. From information by Ramo and Whinnery, *Fields and Waves in Modern Radio.*

A common form of cavity is the re-entrant cylinder type of Fig. 13-7. It resembles a coaxial line, with both ends closed and capacitive loading at the top, but the mode of oscillation varies considerably from that in coaxial circuits. The resonant frequency of the re-entrant cylinder cavity depends on the diameters of the two cylinders, and the distance, *d*, between the cylinder ends.

A tube commonly used in amateur work in the uhf region is the 2C39A or 7289/3CX100A5. Fig. 13-8 makes possible a quick estimate of the size of a cylindrical cavity for this tube. The graph form was supplied by Garrett and Manly.[3]

Coupling to Waveguides and Cavity Resonators

Energy may be introduced into or extracted from a waveguide or resonator by means of either the electric or the magnetic field. The energy transfer frequently is through a coaxial line, two methods for coupling to which are shown in Fig. 13-9. The probe shown at A is simply a short extension of the inner conductor of the coaxial line, so oriented that it is parallel to the electric lines of force. The loop shown at B is arranged so that it encloses some of the magnetic lines of force. The point at which maximum coupling will be secured depends upon the particular mode of propagation in the guide or cavity; the coupling

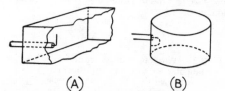

(A)   (B)

Fig. 13-9 — Coupling to waveguides and resonators.

will be maximum when the coupling device is in the most intense field.

Coupling can be varied by turning the probe or loop through a 90-degree angle. When the probe is perpendicular to the electric lines the coupling will be minimum; similarly, when the plane of the loop is parallel to the magnetic lines the coupling will have its minimum value.

TRANSISTORS AND TUBES FOR THE HIGHER FREQUENCIES

Even with the best possible circuits, the upper useful limit of frequency is determined finally by the characteristics of the devices connected to them. Capacitance between elements and inductance of leads brought out from them load down the circuit in the same way as wires and capacitors connected externally. In the tube, there is the seemingly infinitesimal time required for passage of electrons between cathode and plate. This may be only 0.001 *microsecond*, and of no importance at 1000 kHz, but it is the equivalent of a full oscillation cycle at 1000 MHz. These facts set something around 3000 MHz as the practical frequency ceiling for negative-grid tubes, and 1000 MHz for inexpensive transistors.

Only specially designed tube types will go anything like this high. At 420 MHz we have left all but a very few types behind, and at 1215 MHz no tube commonly used on lower bands is considered.

Solid-state techniques for generating power all through the uhf and microwave spectrum are available, but suitable devices are costly at present. Mass applications are lowering manufacturing costs, and power transistors and other devices for uhf and microwave communication should be more within our financial reach as markets widen.

Uhf Receiving Techniques

In receiving, where power-handling capability is not a primary consideration, the useful frequency limit is somewhat higher than in transmitting, for more-or-less conventional designs. Probably the first mass-produced uhf tube was the "acorn," a small triode with leads brought out radially through the glass envelope. In suitable circuits it will oscillate up to around 500 MHz.

More recently, the Nuvistor carried reduction of electrode size and lead length close to the practical minimum. The inexpensive 6CW4 and 6DS4 work well in our 420-MHz band. The double-ended 8058, made for grounded-grid amplifier service, does even better.

Very high-transconductance planar triodes (416B, 7768, and others) are the best rf amplifier tubes available for 420-MHz service, but they have been replaced almost entirely by moderately priced transistors, which work better and are very easy to use.

Actually there is little point in attempting to use vacuum tubes for receiving above 400 MHz, for even the best are incapable of satisfactory noise figure, compared with a well-designed transistor front end. Even at 432 MHz a good crystal mixer followed by a low-noise i-f amplifier will do just about as well as the best vacuum-tube designs. Transistor rf amplifiers are taking over the receiving job in amateur uhf circles.

Conventional Uhf Transmitting Tubes

Several glass-envelope transmitting tubes work moderately well in the 420-MHz band. The 6939 is a small dual tetrode much like the 6360, but with more compact design to extend the upper frequency limit for uhf service. It will deliver about 6 watts output. The 6524 and 6252 are dual tetrodes with plate leads brought out through the top of the envelope. They are capable of around 15 watts output in the 420-MHz band. The 5894 is a larger version of the 6252, widely used some years ago for 420-MHz work. It will give up to 40 watts output at 432 MHz. Any of these tubes operated as a tripler from 144 MHz will drive another as a straight-through amplifier, and they can be used with more-or-less conventional circuitry.

The best transmitting tubes for use at high amateur power levels in the 420-MHz band are the external-anode types beginning with the 4X150A, and continuing through later versions such as the 4CX250B and R, and the 4CX300A. These tubes are well adapted to coaxial- and strip-line circuitry. They require forced-air cooling. A conduction-cooled version, the 8072, has considerable appeal for medium-power applications where use of a blower is not convenient. Many other types of this general tube family are available, but the ones mentioned above are most often seen in amateur uhf circles. All require special sockets, which may include built-in bypassing, where desired.

Tubes generally available to amateurs for transmitting use above 1000 MHz include the "lighthouse" triode, Fig. 13-10. This old but still useful type can be picked up inexpensively on the surplus market. It comes in several styles, of which the 2C40 is the most plentiful. The "pencil triode" series of tubes, not widely used by amateurs, work up to about 2000 MHz. The 2C39 planar triode, and later versions such as the 7289/3CX100A5,

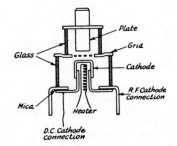

Fig. 13-10 — Sectional view of the "lighthouse" tube. Electrode spacing and lead inductance are held to near the practical minimum, making the tube useful in the uhf range.

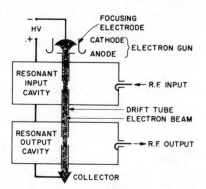

Fig. 13-11 — Essential parts of the klystron tube, shown in simplified form to illustrate the theory of "bunching."

quencies from a few hundred megahertz to many gigaherts, and for power levels from milliwatts to megawatts.

The Klystron Amplifier

Referring to Fig. 13-11, the essential parts of an amplifier klystron are the electron gun, the *drift tube*, the *resonant cavities*, and the *collector*. The cathode, anode, and focussing electrodes of the gun form an electron beam. Current flows as in a diode, when high voltage is applied to the anode. The gun electrodes focus the accelerated electrons through a hole in the center of the anode, into a cylindrical beam which flows at constant velocity through the hollow drift tube and resonant cavities, to the collector.

Rf drive applied to the input resonant cavity causes an rf voltage to exist between adjacent sections of the drift tube. (Spaces between these sections are called *interaction gaps*.) Electrons flowing past the input gap are affected by the rf voltage across it. When the voltage is positive (in the direction of electron flow) electrons in the gap are accelerated slightly. During the alternate half of the rf cycle they are retarded. Some of the electrons in the beam are thus moving faster and some are moving slower than the average rate — the beam is *velocity* modulated.

As the beam moves toward the output cavity, the fast electrons tend to catch up with the slower ones, by a process called *bunching*. When the bunches reach the output cavity gap they are well formed, and they charge the output resonant circuit as sharp pulses of rf current. The cavity acts as a resonant coupling device, and the power is fed to the transmission line, and on to the antenna. The action is not unlike that in a conventional tetrode at lower frequencies, the essential difference being that in the klystron the electron bunches are not formed by a control grid, but rather by this velocity modulation of a continuous electron beam.

There is more to a klystron amplifier than this, and some of it is suggested in the simplified schematic of the klystron dc circuits, Fig. 13-12. Most power klystrons have 3 or more cavities, because multiple-cavity designs provide higher gain and efficiency than the simple two-cavity type described. Klystrons have been built with six or more cavities, capable of power gain in excess of 90 dB. Amplifier klystrons have not been used extensively in amateur uhf communication to date, their principal employment having been in 1296-MHz moonbounce experiments,[7] where high power and extreme stability are mandatory.

The Klystron Oscillator

Most amateur work with klystrons has been with the simpler oscillator types, at power levels in the milliwatt range. Basic principles are similar to those described above, but the oscillator is of the two-cavity type. *Buncher* and *catcher* cavities are connected by a feedback loop to sustain oscillation. The catcher cavity is made resonant at the frequency of the velocity modulation of the electron beam, by changing the shape of the cavity

can be used up to around 3000 MHz in suitable circuits. The 2C39 tripler to the 1215-MHz band, described in *QST* by W6DQJ,[4] is still widely copied. WB6IOM described a 2-tube amplifier.[5] The 416B, more familiar to amateurs in receiving applications, is capable of operation up through the 3300-MHz band in suitable circuits.

Even these uhf types work poorly above our 2300-MHz band. In our 3300-MHz band and at all higher frequencies the negative-grid tube gives way to specialized types such as the klystron, travelling-wave tube, and magnetron. Costly, except as surplus, even these types are being outmoded by solid-state developments.

VELOCITY MODULATION —

THE KLYSTRON

At some point in the uhf range, just where depending on power level and application, transit-time effects render conventional tubes unusable. Electron flow from cathode to anode, in tubes we're familiar with, is in the form of short bursts, regulated by the rf charge on the grid. When transit time is an appreciable part of the rf cycle these pulses become poorly defined, and performance falls off.

Of the many devices developed to get around this problem, the power klystron[6] is probably the most interesting to the amateur. The klystron is complex and costly, and amateurs know it mainly as an occasional surplus market item, but if we are to do much with our assignments in the microwave region some understanding of its operation is almost mandatory. In one form or another, it has been used in nearly all amateur work above 3000 MHz.

The klystron uses the phenomenon of transit time to advantage, through a technique known as velocity modulation. It is capable of reasonable efficiency, high gain, good linearity, and high stability. Its chief fault from the amateur point of view, other than high cost, is that the frequency-determining circuits are usually part of the tube itself. All too often, klystrons that look like surplus bargains turn out to be built for other than amateur frequencies. They are available for fre-

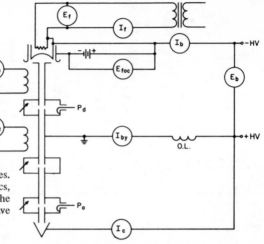

Fig. 13-12 — Basic circuit of the klystron, identifying the various voltages and currents: E_f — filament voltage; I_f — filament current; E_b — beam voltage: I_b — beam current: I_{by} — body current; I_c — collector current; O.L. — overload relay coil; I_m — magnet current; P_d — driving power; P_o — output power.

physically and by adjustment of electrode voltages. The bunched beam current is rich in harmonics, but the high Q of the catcher cavity suppresses the unwanted harmonics and keeps the output wave form pure.

Practical Microwave Communication with Klystrons

Though klystrons and other microwave devices seem strange to the uninitiated, and admittedly they are costly when purchased new, microwave communication of a practical nature can be achieved with equipment that is surprisingly simple. Thanks to the surplus market and traditional ham ingenuity, it can be relatively inexpensive as well. The techniques employed vary in detail, but the principles are basically similar — and elementary.

The method is applicable to any microwave band for which klystrons are available. Two klystron oscillators are built and mounted in parabolic antennas. Each serves the dual role of transmitting oscillator and local oscillator for receiving. A crystal mixer is built into each unit, and some of the klystron oscillator output is diverted for injection to this mixer. The two stations are identical, except for the frequency of oscillation. The two oscillators are separated in frequency by an amount equal to the intermediate frequency to be used in reception.

Let us assume that the band is to be the one at 5650 MHz. One oscillator will be on, say, 5700 MHz. We will use fm broadcast receivers for our i-f systems. This will require a mixer output frequency of about 100 MHz, so our other oscillator will be on 5800 MHz.

A klystron oscillator is very readily frequency modulated. Just a small audio voltage applied to the dc voltage on the klystron repellor element does the trick. This can be as simple a device as a microphone transformer connected in the repellor lead, with an ordinary carbon microphone the only other "speech equipment" needed. More advanced

designs will include a speech amplifier, preferably with some provision for automatic level control, to keep the modulation at a constant level.

Keeping the transmitting and receiving functions separate may be handled in several ways. Separate antennas can be used for the transmitting oscillator and the receiving mixer. This was done in some of our earlier microwave work, but more recently it has been supplanted by the simpler expedient of "polarization duplexing," first used by the San Bernardino Microwave Society, in the 1950s.[8] Here an open-ended cylindrical waveguide section has probes for transmitting and receiving, placed at angles of 90 degrees from each other. The "waveguide" may be nothing more than a beer can, as shown in Fig. 13-13. The i-f system can be an fm receiver, or even a simple superregenerative detector operating at the selected intermediate frequency.

This is inherently a duplex system, and one in which the actual operating frequencies are unimportant, so long as they are within an amateur band, and separated by the chosen intermediate frequency. There could hardly be a simpler com-

Fig. 13-13 — Looking into the open end San Bernardino Microwave Society 3300-MHz polaplexer. The klystron oscillator is mounted at a 45-degree angle, with its "antenna" in the same plane inside the beer-can waveguide section. Perpendicular to it is the receiving probe, connected to the crystal mixer, upper left. The vertical screw, upper center, is the mixer injection adjustment.

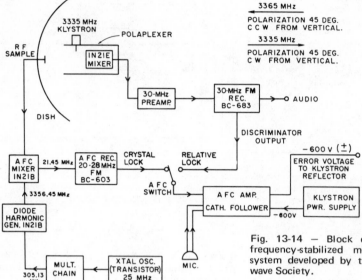

Fig. 13-14 — Block diagram of the ROCLOC frequency-stabilized microwave communications system developed by the San Bernardino Microwave Society.

munications system, yet "polaplexers" of this general type have been used in all our amateur bands above 3000 MHz, and for communication over some quite remarkable distances. Examples of this technique, too numerous for inclusion in this book, may be found in many issues of *QST*.[8]

ROCLOC — A Stabilized Klystron System

A marked improvement over the self-controlled polaplexer described above was developed by members of the San Bernardino Microwave Society, primarily the late D. L. Thompson, W6IFE, and George Tillitson, K6MBL.[9] Called ROCLOC (Relative Or Crystal Local Oscillator Control) it allows the klystron oscillator to be frequency-locked to either the incoming signal (relative) or to a harmonic of a stable crystal oscillator (crystal). Use of a tunable afc receiver allows the klystron oscillator to be moved accurately in frequency without losing frequency lock.

ROCLOC equipment has been used by SBMS members in several record-setting expeditions, including one that resulted in a 214-mile DX record for the 3300- and 5650-MHz bands.[10] A typical system is shown in block-diagram form in Fig. 13-14.

OTHER MICROWAVE DEVICES

Demand for microwave radar during World War II resulted in many devices being developed under very high priority. The klystron, the magnetron, and the travelling-wave tube had existed in principle for some time but the wartime emergency brought them into mass production and use.

The Magnetron

The magnetron and travelling-wave tube had little application to amateur communication, so they are dealt with only briefly in these pages. Essentially a magnetron is a thick-walled cylinder

of copper, with a series of identical "keyholes" in the wall around the inner diameter.[11] Each keyhole represents a transmitter circuit, the hole itself providing the inductance and the slot, or base of the keyhole, the capacitance. These keyholes ring a central emitting cylinder or cathode.

A magnetic field is applied axially, causing electrons to describe circular paths about the cathode when a high-voltage pulse is applied between anode and cathode. The critical velocity of the electron stream is reached when adjacent cavities represent positive and negative portions of the output wave. This is an oversimplified explanation, but it will suffice for our purposes, in view of the limited application of the magentron to our kinds of communication. The main uses of magnetrons are for pulsed service, where very high peak voltages are applied for very short periods, at high repetition rates. Magnetron peak power of the order of a megawatt is common, but there has been limited use of the device for continuous-wave applications.

The Travelling-Wave Tube

Gains as high as 50 dB over very wide bands in the microwave region are possible with the travelling-wave tube, shown schematically in Fig. 13-15. An electromagnetic wave travels down the helix, and an electron beam is shot through the helix

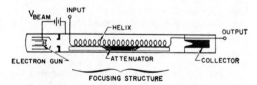

Fig. 13-15 — Basic components of the travelling-wave tube. Device is actually a complete amplifier in a vacuum envelope.

from the electron gun at the left end, in the direction of the wave propagation. When the electron velocity is about the same as the wave velocity in the absence of electrons, turning on the electron beam causes a power gain for the wave propagation in the direction of the electron motion.

The input and output ports are coaxial lines to which the ends of the helix are coupled. The beam is focussed electrically at the gun end, and magnetically along the helix, by a series of opposing-polarity magnets stacked between ferrous pole pieces.

Outstanding features of the TWT are great bandwidth and large power gain. Efficiency and power output are both rather low. The term "tube" is really a misnomer; the TWT is actually a complete broadband rf amplifier in a vacuum envelope.[12]

Solid-State Power Generation

Microwave power generation, amplification, and frequency multiplication with semiconductor devices has advanced rapidly in recent years. Manufacture of power transistors capable of operation up to at least 3000 MHz is becoming practical. The varactor-diode multiplier has been refined to the point where useful power is obtainable up to at least 35 GHz. Transferred-electron (Gunn Effect) diodes are presently available for oscillator and amplifier applications from roughly 5 to 18 GHz, at power levels competitive with or superior to familiar low-power klystrons.[13]

The Gunn Diode oscillator (up to 200 mW output) and amplifier (up to 1 watt output) appear to be particularly promising. They require only a simple 12-volt supply of good regulation, and they are well-adapted to frequency modulation. Power amplification is possible in either the linear or the locked-oscillator mode. These factors would make it appear that a solid-state version of the ROCLOC system (see Fig. 13-14) could provide a practical and effective portable microwave communications system for operation from a car battery supply. Gunn Diode oscillators are currently used for traffic-control radar systems operating just above the 10-GHz amateur band.

THE VARACTOR DIODE

Few developments have had more impact on uhf and microwave communication than the variable reactance device known as the *varactor diode*. This offshoot of the semiconductor industry made possible many improvements in receiver and transmitter design, some offering advantages never hoped for with vacuum tubes.

Notable among the varactor's contributions to uhf progress are the parametric amplifier, proposed in theory earlier but made practical by the varactor, and the solid-state frequency multiplier for transmitting applications. Diode multipliers were also known for many years, of course, but varactor multipliers work at power levels useful for transmitting. We will discuss these applications in some detail later, but first let us see how the varactor diode works. This section is mainly the work of Wayne Taft, W1WID.

Varactor Principles

Consider a small block of germanium that has been doped with impurities, so that one half is p-type material (contains free positive charges) and the other half n-type material (contains free negative charges). The result is a p-n junction diode. If a voltage of matching polarity is connected across it, free charges in the material will be repelled from the terminals and move toward the junction boundary. This nets an exchange of charge, or forward conduction.

If the applied voltage is reversed the free charges are drawn away from the junction boundary, leaving a neutral region called the *depletion layer*. No exchange of charge is possible; hence the condition of high back resistance. We are interested in the latter condition. The depletion layer is a dielectric (no free charges) and the regions outside

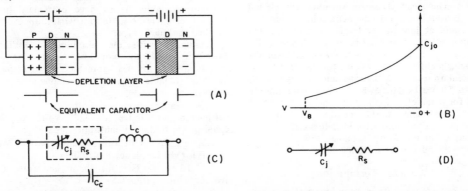

Fig. 13-16 — Characteristics of the varactor diode. Changing depletion layer with variation of applied voltage is shown at A. Capacitance decrease with increasing back-bias voltages is shown in Curve B. The complete equivalent circuit of a varactor and its mount is given in C, and the practical effect of a varactor, within its design frequency range, at D.

it are conductors (they have free charges). The two conductors thus act as the plates of a capacitor, whose plate spacing (capacitance) is dependent on the applied back-bias voltage.

In Fig. 13-16A we see the depletion layer for two conditions of back bias: low voltage, for close spacing and high capacitance; and high voltage, for wide spacing and low capacitance. A typical curve of capacitance vs. applied back bias is shown at B. This curve is good between the limits of zero bias and the reverse-breakdown voltage (V_B) of the diode. Capacitance is inversely proportional to the square root or cube root of the voltage, depending on how the semiconductor is doped. The most common type of varactor follows the square-root law, the result of an abrupt change in doping at the junction.

Practical Varactors

Up to this point we have considered the reverse-biased p-n junction as a lossless voltage-variable capacitor. Unfortunately the regions of the semiconductor containing free charges are not perfect conductors. Unavoidably they have a built-in fixed series resistance (R_s) usually between 0.1 and 10 ohms, which degrades the performance of varactor circuits from that obtainable if there were a completely lossless varactor. Further complications arise from mounting the device, as any practical package adds two important parasitic reactances. These are the internal series lead inductance and the shunt case capacitance.

The resultant varactor equivalent circuit is shown in Fig. 13-16C. The semiconductor chip itself is shown inside the broken line, with its variable capacitance, C_j, and series resistance, R_s. In series with it is the lead inductance, L_c, and in parallel with this combination is the case capacitance, C_c. The parasitic reactances limit the maximum usable frequency of the varactor. Packages are available, however, for frequencies well into the higher microwave range. By choosing varactor packaging for the frequency range of interest, package reactances can be neglected. The simple equivalent circuit of 13-16D is then sufficient to describe the varactor.

Varactor units look very much like other diodes. The small glass-case version with pig-tail leads is useful only at frequencies below about 100 MHz, and at low power levels. A stud-mounted varactor of the type used in the frequency multipliers shown in this chapter could be mistaken for a silicon rectifier diode, except for its price tag. It is useful up to 1500 MHz or so, and at power levels up to 50 watts. Microwave packages commonly used for parametric applications include the 1N21 style and a related double-ended unit. Then there are tiny "pill" varactors for strip-line circuits, and various other mountings capable of working well up into the microwave region.

Varactor Terminology

In order to specify a varactor, certain measurable "parameters" are now in use:

C_{jVB} or $C_{J\ min}$ – Junction capacitance at reverse breakdown.

$C_{j\ 0}$ – Junction capacitance at zero bias.

C_{j-6} – Junction capacitance at some specified value of reverse bias, in this instance –6 volts.

R_s – Series resistance, sometimes called "spreading" resistance.

V_B – Reverse breakdown voltage.

θ – Thermal resistance in Degrees C per watt. Useful for power dissipation calculations.

Junction capacitance is usually measured with a bridge at some low frequency, on the order of one megahertz. The value of R_s is usually determined indirectly, by Q measurements at 500 MHz or higher. In addition, two commonly used terms involve combinations of the above:

Cutoff Frequency, f_c, at a specified value of bias, and hence C_j.

$$\text{Normalization Power, } P_{norm}, = \frac{(V_B)^2}{R_s}$$

These terms equate roughly with maximum usable frequency and plate dissipation as the latter would be used with vacuum tubes. In general, for equal cutoff frequencies, varactors with higher P_{norm} will handle higher power in multiplier service. In parametric amplifiers, varactors with higher P_{norm} require more pump power.

Applications and Availability

Varactors are useful for a variety of frequency-changing and amplifying applications, including electronic tuning, phase or frequency modulators in place of a reactance modulator, parametric amplifiers, and frequency multipliers. Practical exploration was made of the first two possibilities in discussion of fm in earlier chapters of this book. We will look into the latter two below.

Once it was necessary to test various rectifier diodes in order to find one that would make a good varactor. Now many companies are producing diodes specifically for varactor purposes. These include such familiar names as Microwave Associates, Sylvania, Motorola, Amperex, and others. Most varactors now are made from silicon, rather than germanium, for better high-temperature performance. Varactors made from gallium arsenide are also available. These have extremely high cut-off frequencies, but are somewhat more expensive than the silicon types.

Familiarity with the terminology outlined above will enable the would-be user to sort out units of greatest interest from the catalog listings. Presently available varactors have characteristics as follows:

V_B – ranges from –6 volts for most parametric-amplifier diodes to –250 volts for the higher-power frequency-multiplier types.

C_{j-6} – from 0.1 pF (microwave types) to over 100 pF for vhf frequency multipliers.

f_c – 10 to 300 GHz for silicon, and up to 800 GHz for gallium arsenide.

R_s – 0.1 to 10 ohms; usually higher-capacitance units have lower R_s.

Price is roughly proportional to cutoff frequency and P_{norm}.

THE PARAMETRIC AMPLIFIER

Lowest-noise devices for uhf reception include the maser, the travelling-wave tube, and the parametric amplifier. There is little point in dwelling on the first two here. The maser must operate in a strong magnetic field. It requires certain gases, or exotic substances like rubies or garnets. Worst of all, it must be cooled to very low temperatures, requiring cryogenic techniques quite beyond the reach of the amateur worker. We have already discussed the TWT briefly in this chapter. It, too, is an expensive device; its strong point, very wideband amplification, is not required in amateur service.

This leaves the parametric amplifier, a development of some potential worth to the amateur, but one that has been little used and even less understood by most of us. Probably the best treatment of this admittedly involved subject, for the amateur reader, was a series of *QST* articles by W4AO and W4LTU[14] written at the time that early development work on paramps was just getting underway. These articles are still required reading for anyone who would understand noise problems and the potential and partial solutions. Readers without engineering background or extensive electronics experience may not find them easy to assimilate, but they are about as simple as they could be without leaving the authors open to the charge of over-simplification. What follows is, to a large extent, a condensation of their excellent work.

Bateman and Bain made a valiant effort to stamp out the almost meaningless term, "parametric," in favor of "reactance amplifier," a name more indicative of the way the amplifier works, but "paramp" seems to have won out in the years since. There is a rather large family of parametric devices, and many mechanical and electrical analogies have been used to explain their operation. We will not go into these here, but they run all the way up from the children's swing, which is probably as apt (and as confusing) as any. Many systems are "pumped" in one way or another; we'll leave the analogies at this point.

The varactor is in effect a capacitor, the value of which changes with applied voltage. It can thus be used to modulate power from an external source, in relation to a signal voltage, and therefore amplify a signal applied to it. The parametric amplifier of most interest to amateurs is physically quite simple, being mainly a diode, fed at the signal frequency, and pumped at a higher frequency simultaneously. The basic circuit, Fig. 13-17, is quite similar to a conventional crystal mixer, and it may be used for either frequency conversion or straight-through amplification.

The signal frequency, f_s, is applied to *Tank 1*. In a frequency converter, *Tank 2* is tuned to the output frequency, f_o, which may be either higher (up-converter) or lower (down-converter) than the signal frequency. The pump tank, top, has only the job of providing an efficient means for exciting the diode capacitor (varactor). The terms "pump" and "pump frequency" are, in effect, merely new names for the more familiar local oscillator and its output frequency, in this case.

In an up-converter (output frequency higher than the pump frequency) a stable power gain equal to $\dfrac{f_o}{f_s}$ could be realized with ideal diodes and lossless circuits. If the output circuit is tuned to the pump frequency *minus* the signal frequency (though still an up-converter) the gain relationship is $-\dfrac{f_o}{f_s}$. The minus sign implies that regeneration is involved and, depending on conditions, very high gains can be achieved.

As a down-converter the output frequency is always lower than the signal frequency. Where the signal is higher than the pump the relationship $\dfrac{f_o}{f_s}$ remains, but since f_o is smaller than f_s, the device is an attenuator. When the signal frequency is below the pump frequency, and $\dfrac{f_o}{f_s}$ is still less than unity, the actual gain may be very high, because of regeneration, as in the up-converter.

In the regenerative arrangements the pump frequency is always the highest in the system, and is equal to the sum of the signal and output frequencies. In the regenerative conditions the signal in the input circuit is amplified by regenerative action, and the device may be used as an rf amplifier merely by taking the output from this point, instead of from the output circuit, *Tank 2*. The difference frequency must still appear in the output circuit, however. The terms "idler" and "idler frequency" have become standard names for the output tank and the energy therein. They have no purpose in our life, but they must exist.

For practical purposes, the approximate noise figure of the amplifier of Fig. 13-17 can be obtained from the formula:

$$F = 1 + \frac{R_a}{R_1} + \frac{f_s}{f_i}$$

where F is the noise figure, R_a is the shunt resistance across the input circuit represented by the antenna, R_1 is the shunt resistance represented by the losses directly associated with the tank

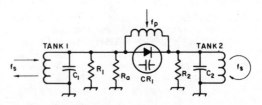

Fig. 13-17 — Basic circuit of a parametric amplifier shows its similarity to a crystal mixer.

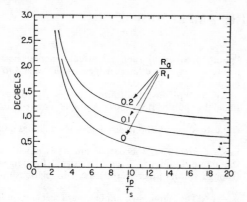

Fig. 13-18 — Noise figure of the parametric amplifier of Fig. 13-17, as a function of frequency and antenna loading.

circuit and diode, f_s is the signal frequency, and f_i the idler frequency.

The last two terms of the equation added together are a measure of the noise generated by the amplifier. Each should be kept small, so that their sum is a minimum. The second term can be kept small by coupling tightly to the antenna, so that R_a is much less than R_1. The third term may be kept small by using an idler frequency much higher than the signal frequency. This means, of course, a still higher pump frequency.

The way that the noise figure varies with pump frequency and various values of $\frac{R_a}{R_1}$ is shown in Fig. 13-18. The bottom curve, for $\frac{R_a}{R_1} = 0$, represents an idealized case in which R_1 is considered infinitely large. This curve illustrates the value of a high pump frequency. For example, if a pump frequency 5 times the signal frequency is used, the contribution from idler noise will be 0.2. The noise figure under idealized conditions would then be 1.2, or about 1 dB. In any practical circuit, however, the contribution from $\frac{R_a}{R_1}$ will add to this.

Thus, when you are straining for lowest possible noise figure it would be more practical to use a pump frequency in the range of 7 to 10 times the signal frequency. The contribution from idler noise will then be in the range of 0.11 to 0.17, leaving some room to maneuver in with respect to the contribution from $\frac{R_a}{R_1}$

From here on, analysis of the parametric amplifier is very involved, and will not be dealt with in detail in this text. Though the noise figure equation, even in the simplified form given above, gives us indications on how to keep noise figure to a minimum, it is by no means the whole story. Nothing has been said as to how much capacitance variation is required from the varactor and its pump, but it may be said that the following conditions are desirable in a practical device:

1. High idler and pump frequencies relative to signal frequency.
2. High tank-circuit Q.
3. High-Q semiconductor capacitor, or varactor, CR1.
4. High available capacitance variation, $\triangle C$, in the varactor.
5. Small values for C1 and C2.

Practical Considerations

For a given gain, the regenerative amplifier configuration (basic circuit, Fig. 13-17) is the least stable of the arrangements outlined above. Its noise performance, however, is quite good. Furthermore, it may be used directly ahead of an existing receiver or converter. Another big advantage is that instability in the pump does not affect the frequency stability of the output. Typically, 20 dB of fairly stable gain is available over a bandwidth of 100 to 200 kHz at 432 MHz. This is enough bandwidth for weak-signal communication as presently done on this band.

A practical paramp consists of a varactor properly coupled to the necessary tuned circuits and pump. In the vhf range lumped circuits are useful, but at uhf and higher, coaxial, strip-line, or cavity resonators are necessary. In the microwave region these can be constructed from waveguide. Resonators should always be high-Q, to prevent losses and poor noise figure. Mechanical stability is extremely important in a regenerative setup, as small mechanical variations can completely upset the tuning.

Varactors designed for paramp service have low breakdown voltage, usually between -5 and -10 volts. Typical zero-bias capacitances are on the order of 0.2 to 5 pF. Cutoff frequencies range from 20 GHz up, but in general the higher the cutoff frequency the better the noise figure. Typical diodes are the Microwave Associates MA-450 and 460 series, and the Sylvania D4075, D4140, and D4141 series.

Paramp Limitations

Someone may be wondering about the noise associated with the amplifier output load, and whether it is amplified along with the signal by the regenerative action of the circuit. It is, and the coupling problems involved can be solved only by the use of an esoteric device known as a *circulator*. The circulator has the unique property of permitting power to flow in one direction only, between certain pairs of terminals. By properly connecting a circulator in a receiving system using a paramp, the noise generated in the load can be made harmless by dissipating it in a resistive system.

Without a circulator, checking noise figure by means of a noise generator can lead the worker astray, in that *apparent* noise figures much lower than the actual are indicated. Another "fudge factor" in noise generator measurement with a paramp is the low *indicated* noise figure obtained when a pump frequency only twice that of the signal frequency is used. Such an arrangement is fundamentally limited to a minimum noise figure of 3 dB, but noise generator measurements may indicate a noise figure of *zero* dB. These factors were undoubtedly at the bottom of some early amateur enthusiasm for paramps.

All this is not to say that the parametric amplifier has no place in the amateur uhf picture. It certainly does have, for those amateurs sufficiently skilled in receiver work to assess what is being accomplished with the many adjustments required. The paramp as generally used in the amateur field is a very tricky item. The pump frequency and power level should both preferably be adjustable, in the interest of precise adjustment, yet both should be reasonably stable, so that they will stay put when other adjustments are made. These two attributes are not readily combined in rf power sources at several GHz!

Most paramps built by amateurs have used klystrons for pump sources. A 432-MHz paramp requires something around 4000 MHz or higher, for best results. Since the power and frequency stability of a klystron oscillator are both relatively poor, adjustment of a paramp using one becomes something approaching black magic. The pump frequency and the diode bias must be adjusted, and then the pump power increased, while fiddling with the other two items. All three react on each other. If the operator finally does get things peaked up for optimum results, a slight change in load impedance (such as may occur when the antenna is rotated and objects of differing reflecting properties appear in its pattern) will throw the adjustments off, and the work starts all over.

Measurement of the various "parameters," an over-worked word we'll use this once, since we're talking about parametric amplifiers, is all but impossible. Adjustment for optimum results is cut-and-try, to a degree probably not encountered in any other amateur electronic endeavor.

Results can be worth the trouble. Even without the circulator (and not many amateurs have access to one) it should be possible to develop noise figures around 3 dB at 432 MHz. This is better than is likely with vacuum tubes or crystal mixers, but no improvement over the better uhf transistor amplifiers. They pretty well take over the burden of low-noise reception at 432 MHz and should do the same for higher frequencies eventually.

Until such times as they do, there is considerable to be gained from use of the paramp for 1000 MHz and up. There is little practical value in a paramp for lower amateur bands, except for practice and experience. The principles are applicable at any frequency, and suitable pump sources for lower bands are readily obtained. The amateur who wants to learn more about paramp construction and adjustment can work with them at 50 or 144 MHz, where measurement of results is considerably easier than at uhf.

The Bateman-Bain series[14] describes practical paramp construction for 144 MHz. An effective paramp for 1296 MHz was described in January, 1961, *QST*.[15] A modification of this for 432 MHz appears in October of the same year.[16] A 432-MHz paramp with crystal-controlled pump, the work of K2CBA and W1WID, was described in Edition 1 of this Manual.

FREQUENCY MULTIPLICATION WITH POWER VARACTORS

We are indebted to Henry H. Cross, W1OOP, for the first practical information on use of varactors for frequency multipliers in transmitters for 432 MHz. The following is mainly from his *QST* treatment of this subject.[17]

Power varactors now available to amateurs will give up to 15 watts output on 432 MHz when driven with 30 watts on 216 MHz. They will do almost as well tripling from 144 MHz. The tripler described below will give a substantial signal on 432 when driven by nothing more than any of the popular a-m transmitters such as the Communicator. No auxilliary power or audio is required.

The dc voltage-capacitance characteristics and the output voltage as a function of time, for sine-wave current input, are shown in Fig. 13-19. Once the diode draws conduction current, the theory gets more complicated, but harmonic output does not cease, so the complications can be ignored for small currents. If the multiplier is retuned each time the drive level is changed, an

input-output curve similar to the upper curve of Fig. 13-20 is observed. For one tuning condition, the lower curve applies, and this is the case where a-m is applied to the input. The function is not perfectly linear, but in on-the-air tests the 432-MHz signal from a 2-meter phone rig and a varactor multiplier sounds quite satisfactory; better in fact than some 432-MHz plate-modulated set-

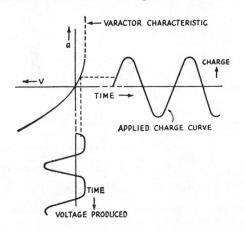

Fig. 13-19 — Dc voltage-capacitance characteristics, and output voltage as a function of time, of a varactor multiplier for sine-wave input current.

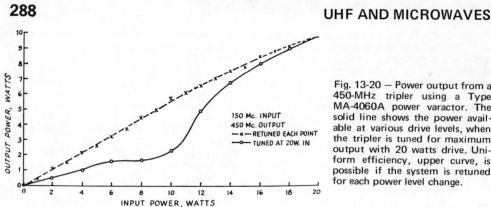

Fig. 13-20 — Power output from a 450-MHz tripler using a Type MA-4060A power varactor. The solid line shows the power available at various drive levels, when the tripler is tuned for maximum output with 20 watts drive. Uniform efficiency, upper curve, is possible if the system is retuned for each power level change.

Fig. 13-21 — Interior of a doubler stage using a power varactor. Driven with 20 watts on 216 MHz, it delivers 10 watts on 432, yet it requires no power supply or modulator.

ups. Doubling from 216 MHz to 432, with a unit like that in Fig. 13-21, the varactor does even better.

VARACTOR DOUBLER FOR 432 MHz

The circuit of the varactor doubler is given in Fig. 13-22. This works well with any 220-MHz transmitter of moderate power. To operate in the segment of the 420-MHz band usually reserved for narrow-band work, 432 to 436 MHz, the 220-MHz rig is tuned down to 216 MHz, by using a crystal at

about 8 MHz even, and retuning the various stages to the lower frequency.

The trap, L5C5, is mostly to simplify tuning; without it changing the output capacitor, C3, would also change the tuning of the 216-MHz circuit. The double-tuned input and output circuits help to establish that the measured output is on the desired frequency. The circuits are rather low-Q, however, and use of a coaxial or strip-line filter in the line to the antenna or following amplifier is recommended, to prevent radiation on the driving frequency.

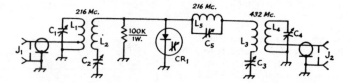

Fig. 13-22 — Schematic diagram and parts information for the varactor doubler.

C1, C2 — 8.7-pF miniature variable (Hammarlund MAC-10).

C3, C4 — 5-pF miniature variable (Hammarlund MAC-5).

C5 — 9-pF subminiature variable (Johnson 189-503-4).

CR1 — Power varactor (Microwave Associates MA-4060A).

J1, J2 — BNC coaxial fitting.

L1 — 4 turns No. 20, 3/8-inch dia, 3/8 inch long. Tap at 1 turn.

L2 — 5 turns No. 20, 3/8-inch dia, 3/8 inch long.

L3 — 2-1/2 turns No. 20, 3/8-inch dia, 1/4 inch long.

L4 — 2 turns No. 20, 3/8-inch dia, 1/4 inch long. Tap at 1 turn.

L5 — 3 turns No. 22, 1/4-inch dia, 1/4 inch long.

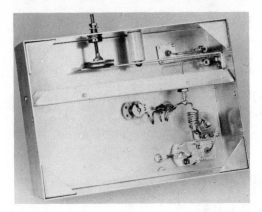

Fig. 13-23 — The 432-MHz varactor tripler. The input circuit is at the lower right and the varactor with its biasing resistor is at the center. Details of the 432-MHz strip-line tank circuit are given in Fig. 13-23A.

VARACTOR TRIPLER, 144 TO 432 MHz

A simple varactor tripler with improved efficiency and reduced unwanted-frequency output is shown in Fig. 13-23, with the circuit in Fig. 13-24. Early varactor multipliers used resonant traps to remove the driving-signal and idler frequencies from the output. This tripler, built by W1CER, omits the traps and uses a strip-line output circuit, as shown in Fig. 13-23A, to give higher selectivity at 432 MHz. Only the input circuit, L1C1, and the input matching network, C1C2, are on 144 MHz. The series circuit, L2C3, tunes to the idler frequency, in this case the second harmonic, 288 MHz. The third harmonic, 432 MHz, is taken off through coupling loops L3 and L5, and the quarter-wave strip-line, L4C5.

Overall efficiency is considerably higher than when the extra trap circuits are included, and the output is relatively free of unwanted frequency components. It is still desirable to follow any varactor multiplier with a separate coaxial or strip-line filter, to be sure that unwanted frequencies are not passed on to the antenna or following

amplifier. Up to 14 watts output at 432 MHz is possible with 20 watts drive on 144 MHz, with this tripler.

Construction

The tripler is built in a 5 × 7 × 2-inch chassis. A shield runs the length of the chassis 2 inches from one wall, forming a 2-inch square trough inside the chassis. A National TPB polystyrene feedthrough connects the varactor to L3.

Details of the strip-line circuit construction are shown in Fig. 13-23A. The line is a 5-inch brass strip 1/2 inch wide, having a 1/2-inch "foot" at the bottom for bolting the strip to the chassis. The input and output links are tuned with cylindrical ceramic trimmers. The low-potential ends of L3 and L5 are soldered directly to the tops of these. C5 is made by cutting two 1-inch disks from sheet brass. One is soldered to the end of L4, and a mount for the other made from a Miller 4400 coil form. The ceramic form itself is broken off the mount, and the slug removed from the end of the

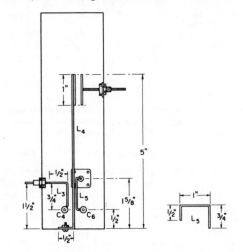

Fig. 13-23A — 432-MHz tank-circuit details for the varactor tripler. L3 and L5 are coupling loops made from No. 14 wire, and L4 is a 1/2-inch-wide brass strip.

Fig. 13-24 — Circuit diagram of the 432-MHz varactor tripler. The strip-line output circuit gives better attenuation of unwanted harmonics than is possible with lumped-constant circuits.

C1 — 15-pF variable (Hammarlund MAPC-15).
C2 — 25-pF variable (Hammarlund MAPC-25).
C3 — 15-pF variable (Johnson 160-107).
C4, C6 — 10-pF ceramic trimmer (Centralab 829-10).
C5 — See Fig. 13-23A.

CR1 — Varactor diode (Amperex H4A/1N4885).
J1, J2 — BNC coaxial receptacle, chassis mounting.
L1 — 6 turns No. 16, 3/8-inch dia, 1/2 inch long.
L2 — 3 turns No. 12, 3/8-inch dia, 3/4 inch long.
L3, L4, L5 — See Fig. 13-23A.

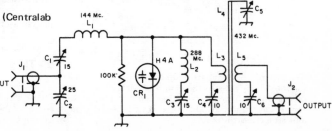

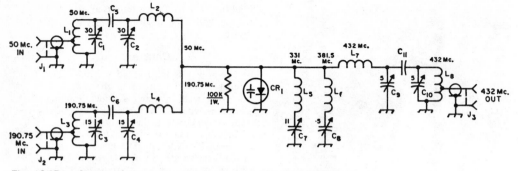

Fig. 13-25 — Circuit of the parametric converter. Resistances are in ohms (K = 1000); capacitances are in pF.

C1, C2 — 30-pF variable (Johnson 160-130).
C3, C4 — 15-pF variable (Johnson 160-107).
C7 — 11-pF variable (Johnson 189).
C8, C9, C10 — 5-pF variable (Johnson 189).
C5, C6 — Gimmick, 3 turns No. 18 solid plastic-covered hookup wire twisted together; 1/2-inch length for 190 MHz; 3/4-inch length for 50 MHz (Johnson trimmers may be used as shown in photos).
C11 — Gimmick, 2 pieces 1/8 X 7/16 copper ribbon overlapped 3/8 inch, spaced 0.020 inch.
CR1 — Varactor diode (Amperex H4A/1N4885).

J1, J2 — BNC female.
J3 — Type N female.
L1 — 10 turns No. 20, 1/2-inch dia; tap at 3 turns (B&W 3003).
L2 — 10 turns No. 20, 5/8-inch dia (B&W 3007).
L3 — 3-1/2 turns No. 18, 1/2-in. dia; tap at 1 turn (B&W 3003).
L4 — 3 turns, same as L1, without tap.
L5 — 4 turns No. 18, 1/4-inch dia, spaced wire dia.
L6 — 3 turns No. 18, 1/4-inch dia, spaced 2 times wire dia.
L7 — 2 turns No. 18, 1/4-inch dia, spaced 2 times wire dia.
L8 — 2 turns No. 18, 1/4-inch dia, spaced, tap at 1/2 turn.

threaded rod. The disk is then soldered to the end of the rod. The coil-form base is mounted on the chassis so that the two disks are opposite each other. For better mechanical stability of the tuning shaft, a 6-32 lock nut can be placed on the shaft.

Adjustment

The varactor multiplier will operate most effectively if the input circuit represents a 50-ohm load on the driver. Start tune-up with an SWR bridge connected between the 144-MHz energy source and J1. Adjust C1 and C2 for lowest reflected power at 144 MHz. It is well to use lower than full 144-MHz drive for this initial adjustment. Now

Fig. 13-26 — Parametric up-converter for transferring a 50-MHz ssb signal to 432 MHz. The large black object, a heat-dissipating cap for the varactor, taken from a 2C39A tube, is not needed if an all-metal chassis is used.

tune C3 and C5 for maximum output at 432 MHz. If the two cylindrical trimmers, C4 and C6, are set near maximum capacitance when this is done, they will require only a slight repeaking for maximum output.

The input capacitors need not be repeaked for maximum 432-MHz output. If the driver stage is set up for operation into a 50-ohm load, and the tripler input circuit is adjusted for zero reflected power at 144 MHz, optimum 432-MHz output will follow with proper adjustment of the 288- and 432-MHz circuits.

The tuning and efficiency of a varactor multiplier are related to drive level, so final adjustment should be made at the power level where maximum efficiency is desired. The curves of Fig. 13-20 illustrate this.

Operation with Modulated Drive

Adjustment of the varactor multiplier while checking the modulation linearity at the output frequency will permit the multiplier to be used somewhat in the manner of a linear amplifier. Like proper adjustment of the linear, tuning for linearity in a multiplier results in much lower output. Typically, a multiplier capable of delivering 8 watts on cw or fm will yield about 2 watts or reasonably linear a-m output. With cw or fm, the process is merely a matter of "tuning for max."

TRANSMITTING CONVERTER FOR 50 TO 432 MHz

A varactor diode can be used as a combination mixer and multiplier, to produce a 432-MHz signal from a 50-MHz source. The transmitting converter of Figs. 13-25 to 13-27 originally described by

Fig. 13-27 — Under side of the 50-to-432 converter. The 50-MHz circuits are at the lower left, 190.75-MHz circuits at the upper left, and 432-MHz output circuits with idler tanks along the right side. The varactor diode is at the top just to right of center.

W1IGJ in *QST* for March, 1966, uses 50-MHz energy from a Heathkit HX-30 (ssb exciter of about 6 watts output) and 10 to 15 watts of energy on 190.75 MHz to produce about 3 watts of ssb output on 432 MHz. With the HX-30's tuning range of 50 to 51 MHz, the resulting output frequency range is 431.5 to 432.5 MHz.

The 190.75-MHz pump energy is doubled in the varactor to 381.5 MHz. The unwanted product, 381.5 − 50.5 = 331 MHz, is also generated, and must be supported by the idler circuit, L5, C7 in Fig. 13-25. This frequency does not appear in the output. There is some 381.5-MHz energy in the output, but this is removed easily with a coaxial or strip-line filter.

Circuit Description

The input parallel-tuned circuits, L3C3 for the pump frequency, and L1C1 for the signal frequency, are lightly coupled to the varactor via pi networks. Although this appears unsatisfactory at first glance, it will be noted that the reactance of the 50-MHz pi-network inductor, L2, at the pump frequency is so high as to constitute an open circuit. Conversely, the pump inductor, L4, presents essentially no reactance at the signal frequency but the capacitor to ground, C4, does. Therefore essentially no loading of the signal frequency occurs.

The output has series-tuned idler circuits for 381.5 Mhz (pump frequency × 2) and 331 MHz (pump × 2 minus signal), and two resonant circuits for 432 MHz (pump × 2 plus signal). Output is taken from a tap on the output tuned circuit.

As may be seen in the photographs, the unit is built in an inverted 4 × 6 × 2-inch chassis. The mounting plate is 1/16-inch-thick double-sided printed-circuit board (0.040 copper may be used if desired). All components are mounted on this plate. Wiring is done with at least No. 18 wire going point-to-point. Most leads are inherent in the components. The varactor heat sink shown is not necessary if a solid metal mounting plate is used.

Adjustment and Operation

Adjustment of the converter is a little tedious since there are eight interacting controls. First apply about 10 to 15 watts of pump power through an SWR indicator, and adjust C3 and C4 for minimum SWR. A field-strength meter tuned to 381 MHz placed nearby will serve to detect the doubling operation. Tune C8 for maximum 381-MHz signal. Go back and forth a few times between C3, C4, and C8, adjusting for maximum 381-MHz signal and minimum SWR (they should coincide).

Now connect a load, preferably a wattmeter, to the output and apply about 1 watt (30-percent scale on the HX-30) to the 50-MHz input. Tune the wavemeter to 331 MHz and adjust C1, C2 and C7 for maximum as above. Now tune the wavemeter or other output indicator. Note that a high wavemeter indication at 432 MHz indicates only circulating current in L7C9 − *not output*. At this point it is well to go back and start again. Since all the adjustments interact to some extent you should go through at least three times. Do not be upset if the output indicator on the HX-30 goes up when connecting to the converter; this is normal. A 6-dB pad between the HX-30 and the converter gives better carrier suppression since you can use more audio (sideband power) while the carrier level output of the HX-30 remains essentially constant.

The unit exhibits good linearity when used to drive a 2C39 grounded-grid amplifier to about 12-15 watts output. There is some leakage of the 381.5-MHz signal into the output; this is removed by a couple of tuned amplifiers or by a simple high-*Q* filter (see Chapter 15). With no filter the 381-MHz signal is at least 20 dB down from the 432 output.

This same scheme can be used to convert from a 28-MHz ssb exciter, with appropriate changes in pump frequency and idler resonances. It is possible to triple from the pump source instead of doubling, with little change in efficiency. The overall performance is nearly the same except for slightly higher pump power requirements to make up for additional loss.

VARACTOR TRIPLER FOR 432 TO 1296 MHz

Fig. 13-28 — Varactor multiplier for 1296-MHz output with 432-MHz drive, designed and built by W1WID. Case is a 3-1/8 X 1-inch brass box. Large screws at the left are the movable elements of capacitors C4, C5, and C7.

The line circuits are cut from flashing copper 3/8 inch wide. In the model shown they are made of separate strips soldered together, but they could be cut as shown in Fig. 13-30. L3 is an "L" in shape as well as in function. The 1/8-inch hole in one end fits over the varactor post. At the other end is C4, which is merely a piece of 3/8-inch brass or copper tubing, soldered to the strip, and facing toward the top of the chassis. Running through the

Fig. 13-29 — Interior of the 1296-MHz varactor tripler. Coils and variable capacitors are the 432-MHz circuits. Inductances for 1296 MHz are copper strips. L-shaped shield of brass isolates input and output circuits.

Happily varactor multipliers work almost as well on higher frequencies as in the 432-MHz applications just described. A varactor tripler for 1296-MHz output with 432-MHz drive is shown in Fig. 13-28. It is the work of Wayne Taft, W1WID, who also contributed the basic information on varactors earlier in this chapter.

Except for the 432-MHz circuits, coils and capacitors are out of the question for this application. Strip lines are used in an ingenious and relatively simple manner. The circuit, Fig. 13-31, is almost identical to that of the 432-MHz triplers described early in this chapter, but the circuits will require explaining, to the reader accustomed to the way such things look on lower frequencies.

The varactor is mounted in the center of a brass box 3-1/8 inches square and 1 inch high. Adjacent to the BNC input fitting near one corner of the box is the 432-MHz input circuit, L1C1. A small piston-type trimmer, C2, couples energy to C3 and L2. The latter may be seen connected to the varactor at the center, though the varactor itself is out of sight under the strip-line circuits for 1296 MHz.

chassis is a No. 10 brass screw, which is the "rotor" of C4. It runs into the cup formed at the end of L3 by the brass tubing.

Construction of L4 is somewhat similar, except that coupling capacitor C6 is built into it. The capacitor C5 is merely another No. 10 screw that runs down so that its end makes a small variable capacitance to ground at the right-angle turn in L4.

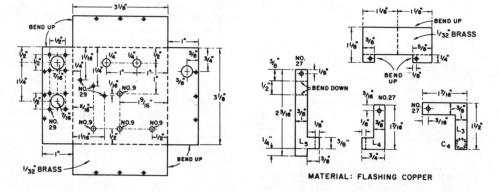

Fig. 13-30 — Details of the case and copper strip lines for the 1296-MHz tripler.

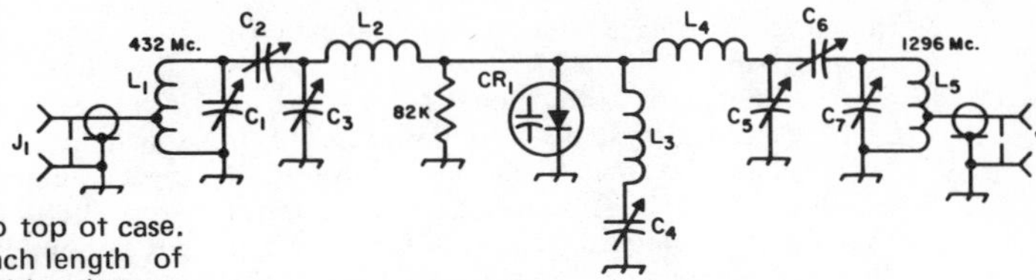

Fig. 13-31 — Schematic diagram of the 1296-MHz tripler.
C1, C3, — 5-pF, miniature trimmer (Hammarlund MAC-5).
C2 — 0.5- to 5-pF piston trimmer.
C4, C5, C7 — 10-32 brass screws, running through brass nuts soldered to top ot case. Locknuts are nylon. C4 has 1/4-inch length of 3/8-inch brass or copper tubing soldered to underside of L3, to increase maximum capacitance.
C6 — Bent-up tabs on L4 and L5, approximately 3/32 inch apart. Bend for adjustable capacitance.
CR1 — Varactor diode (Microwave Associates MA4062D).

J1, J2 — BNC fittings.
L1 — 3 turns No. 18, 1/4-inch dia, 3/8 inch long, ct.
L2 — Like L3, but 2 turns.
L3, L4, L5 — Copper strip lines. See text and Fig. 13-30.

There is no brass cup at this point, as only a very small capacitance is required. Coupling between L4 and L5 (C6 in the schematic) is made by bending up the ends of the short arms of L4 and L5. These 1/8-inch wide surfaces then face each other about 3/32 inch apart.

The output inductance, L5, is the most complex piece. It is bent into U shape at one end to support itself at the same height from the chassis as the other inductances. The output tap for the BNC connector is made at a point 13/16 inch from this end. Capacitor C7 is the third brass screw, the end of which provides cariable capacitance in the same manner as described for C5.

All this is an involved way of saying that tuned circuits really reach an elementary simplicity at frequencies this high. They are confusing only when we think of "coils" and "capacitors" in their 3-to-30-MHz connotation. The small shield visible in the photograph is the full height of the box. It isolates the 432-MHz circuits from the output, thereby keeping the level of the unwanted 432-MHz energy in the output lower than it would be with an open layout.

RECEPTION ABOVE 420 MHz

Except where fm or TV is involved, most reception in the 420-MHz band is done with converters and communications receivers. The circuitry and construction of such converters vary little from similar devices for the vhf bands, so most of our information on 420-MHz reception is in Chapters 3 and 4. Fm receivers can use quite similar front-end stages and circuits. Their special requirements in the i-f and detection stages are dealt with in Chapters 10 and 11.

In ATV work, the "i-f system" is usually a conventional home TV receiver. The uhf front end can be either a modified uhf TV tuner or a converter (crystal-controlled or tunable) built for the purpose. Because of the great bandwidth of a TV signal, stability requirements in the oscillator are not severe. A tunable converter can be made satisfactorily stable for this use. Such a converter, made from a common uhf TV tuner, is described in Chapter 11. It is shown in use with a low-band fm receiver, but it could work into a home TV receiver on any of the lower channels equally well. Choose a channel that is not in use locally.

Most conversions of surplus uhf fm gear or TV front ends leave something to be desired in the matter of sensitivity. Any of the rf amplifier circuits described in this book should take care of this deficiency adequately. A simple low-cost amplifier shown immediately following this section was developed by W6ORG for ATV use. It should serve equally well for other modes.

The Crystal Mixer

Many 420-MHz receiving systems, and nearly all receivers for higher bands, use crystal mixers. With the best crystal diodes and circuits, the mixer noise figure is almost independent of frequency, up to around 10,000 MHz. Unlike tube and transistor mixers, which usually have some conversion gain, the diode mixer has a conversion *loss*. This must be added to the noise figure of the system following the mixer, to obtain the overall noise figure of the uhf receiver having a crystal mixer.

The 1N21-series crystal diodes, frequently used in uhf and microwave mixers, have suffixes A through F, indicating progressively better mixer action and higher price. Nothing below a 1N21C is desirable, if noise figure of the mixer is important. The 1N21F (most costly) is capable of 6 dB, compared with 9.3 dB for the 1N21C. Few, if any, tubes will match the 1N21F in mixer service above about 500 MHz, especially if the diode is followed by a good low-noise i-f amplifier. Some fairly expensive uhf transistors are probably at least as good, up through the 1215-MHz band, and their use will make the quality of the following amplifier less important. No simple receiving system for frequencies above 1000 MHz is good enough so that the noise figure of the following i-f amplifier can be ignored entirely.

Choosing the Intermediate Frequency

The i-f should be as low as practical, as low noise figure is more readily obtainable below about 30 MHz than at higher frequencies. It cannot be too low, however, or image response (including noise at the image frequency) becomes an adverse factor. A desirable i-f for a 432-MHz converter may be 14, 21, or 28 MHz, since communications receivers for these ranges are universally available.

Nearly all receivers have rather poor noise figure (it is not really important in hf work) so a low-noise i-f or rf amplifier, or both, should be provided in any uhf receiving system. The low-noise i-f is particularly important at frequencies above 1000 MHz, where rf amplifier performance deteriorates rapidly with increasing frequency.

Often 50 or even 144 MHz will be used for the converter output frequency. This is useful where a good converter for the vhf band in question is already a part of the station equipment. The i-f need not be tunable in this case; a typical setup might be a 432-MHz converter working into a 50-MHz one, which then works into a tunable receiver at 14 MHz.

Two 1296-MHz converters of excellent design have appeared in *QST, The Radio Amateur's Handbook,* and previous editions of this *Manual.* One by K6AXN[18] has a selective trough-line front end, a crystal mixer, and 14-MHz output. The other, by W6GGV and K6UQH[19] features aperture coupling in the mixer system, and 144-MHz output. A 2300-MHz converter with 144-MHz output was described by W4HHK.[20]

Injection Considerations

Stability is critical if narrow-band uhf reception is undertaken. The converter crystal oscillator should run at the lowest practical input, and the crystal should be isolated from temperature variations due to component heating and cooling or air circulation. Putting the crystal inside the box is recommended. Injection should be as free of harmonic content as possible. Any injection makes mixer noise, and injection on other than the desired frequency is sure to degrade the noise figure of a crystal mixer. Finally, the injection system should be coupled loosely to the mixer, to prevent loss of signal energy through the injection circuits.

The latter two points are often neglected in amateur designs, with the result that mixers for 420 MHz and up having noise figures in excess of 15 dB are not uncommon. When a good rf amplifier is used ahead of the mixer, the amplifier establishes the noise figure of the system, but with a crystal mixer alone the above considerations must be handled with care if satisfactory reception is to be achieved.

INEXPENSIVE 440-MHz PREAMPLIFIER

The simple preamplifier of Fig. 13-32 was built from information supplied by Tom O'Hara, W6ORG, of the Southern California ATV Club. Tom makes and sells similar amplifiers for a nominal sum, primarily for use with commercial fm gear that has been converted to 440-MHz ATV reception. The amplifier shown was built and tested in the ARRL Lab, and used in 432-MHz reception. Its performance is adequate for most purposes, being probably as good as can be obtained with inexpensive transistors.

The amplifier is assembled on a 2-1/4-inch square circuit board having one copper side, etched

approximately as shown in the sketch included with the schematic diagram. Parts layout is not particularly critical, and ours is slightly different from that used by W6ORG, to permit experimenting with input and output loading adjustments.

In its simplest form the W6ORG amplifier has only one adjustment, the collector circuit capacitor, C5 in Fig. 13-33. Two others are shown in our diagram: the input loading control, C1, and C4, which serves a similar purpose in the output circuit. These are not necessary for good results, but they are helpful in adapting the preamp to various antenna and receiver situations.

Another variation from the original layout is the inclusion of a decoupling resistor, R1, and the second feedthrough bypass capacitor, C3. Without these (and with 12 volts connected to C2) there was instability resulting from rf voltage on the supply lead. If lower supply voltage is used, a lower-value resistor can be substituted for R1, as regenerative effects increase with increasing supply voltage.

Adjustment

When C1 is a fixed value (5 pF in W6ORG's units) and the lead to J2 is tapped directly onto L1, eliminating C4, regenerative effects develop under certain conditions of loading, both input and output. This is not necessarily bad, as controlled regeneration makes for higher gain than would normally be possible with a single stage. With a very poor receiver you may need all the gain you can get. If the receiver front end needs only a little help from the preamp, C1 can be set so that the

Fig. 13-32 — Simple one-transistor preamplifier for 432-MHz receivers. The variable loading capacitor, C4, was added after the picture was made.

Fig. 13-33 — Schematic diagram of the uhf preamplifier. Circuit-board etching is shown at the lower left. Coupling between L1 and J2 can be direct, or through variable capacitor C4. All numbered components are described in the text.

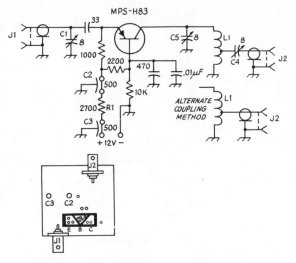

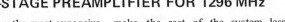

antenna loads the input heavily, resulting in stable and uncritical operation over a wide band. Similarly, using the output capacitor C4, in place of direct tapping of J2 onto L1, permits adjustment of loading for various receiver input conditions.

It is well to start adjustment with a low supply voltage, increasing to normal after the amplifier is working well. Fairly good results are possible with 6 volts or less. Tune in a weak signal with the main receiver, and peak C5 for best reception. That's all there is to it, if C1 is a fixed capacitor and the direct connection is used between L1 and J2. If a variable-voltage supply is available, it would be well to try different voltages, as gain should be greater with higher voltage, up to a maximum of about 13.

If the tuning of C5 seems extremely critical, or if there is actual oscillation in the stage, the variable capacitors should be tried. Increasing C1 should broaden the stage tuning, as it loads the amplifier more heavily. It can be used, in effect, as a bandwidth control, if amplifier bandwidth is important. The purpose of C4, if used, is to tune out any reactive effect in the circuit between L1 and the receiver. If the tuning of C5 changes appreciably with differing lengths of coax between J2 and the receiver input, you need the capacitor C4 in the circuit.

With direct coupling to L1, the circuit is merely a 1-3/4-inch piece of No. 20 wire. It is soldered to the collector tab on the circuit board, and it rises vertically about 3/8 inch. It then bends 90 degrees and runs horizontally for one inch, bending down at a 45-degree angle to solder to the circuit board surface near the BNC mounting flange. The inner conductor tip of J2 is soldered to L1 at this 45-degree bend.

To install C4, unsolder L1 from the tip of J2 and bend the wire slightly away from it. Solder the tabs of C4 to L1 and J2 as directly as possible, in such position that C4 taps on L1 at its approximate midpoint. Subminiature printed-circuit air trimmers are ideal for C1, C4, and C5.

Results

With a supply voltage of 12 to 13, and 2700 ohms for R1, current drain is about 2 mA. If the stage is stable, R1 can be reduced in value. Current drain should be 3 mA or less. Gain, with C1 adjusted for good stability, can be as much as 20 dB. More is available, at the expense of more critical tuning and narrower bandwidth. The preamp was tested ahead of a good transistor converter for 432, and also with a very poor crystal mixer often used as a trial horse in such circumstances. As much as 35 dB could be obtained with usable stability, but this much is seldom needed. It did make the poor mixer show up quite well, however. In the stable condition, the preamp gave results equal to anything we've tried, other than amplifiers with quite expensive uhf transistors.

A TWO-STAGE PREAMPLIFIER FOR 1296 MHz

At around 1000 MHz, even the most expensive uhf transistors drop off in performance very rapidly. Carefully built preamplifiers using transistors are still capable of improving the performance of the best crystal mixers, up through at least 1300 MHz. On higher bands the parametric amplifier is about the only low-noise receiving system that is within the capabilities of the amateur.

At 1296 MHz, where most weak-signal communication is done in the 1215-MHz band, a single transistor stage of optimum design will mask the noise of the better crystal-mixer receiving systems. Two stages are advisable, however, as their gain will make the rest of the system less critical. The two-stage amplifier of Fig. 13-34, built by WA2-VTR,[21] has a gain of around 19 dB, which should take care of all but the worst mixers. The best transistor should be used in the first stage. If the first stage works well, the noise figure of the

Fig. 13-34 — The two-stage preamplifier for 1296 MHz is built in separate units. The first stage is at the right. A jack for plugging in a small 9-volt transistor radio battery is shown in the foreground.

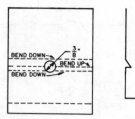

Fig. 13-35 — Details of the thin brass shield plate used to support the transistor in the first rf amplifier stage. Dimensions will depend on the case size and height of the tuning capacitors used. The emitter leads are soldered to the horizontal "shelf" made by bending the plate as seen in the end view.

second is not quite so important, so long as it builds up the total gain to an adequate level.

Construction

Transistors used in early work with 1296-MHz amplifiers had wire leads. The KMC KC5200 and K5500 used here have flat ribbon leads, making possible a mounting having substantially no lead inductance. Most transistor makers now produce types capable of working well above 1000 MHz. Usually these have small tablet-shaped cases and ribbon leads. All are fairly expensive. The "accordion-pleated" shield plate shown in Fig. 13-35 suspends the transistor on its emitter leads, with the base lead on one side and the collector lead on the other. These two leads are soldered to their respective strip lines, L1 and L2, with the minimum possible length.

The input and output coupling capacitors are no-lead disks, though conventional disk ceramics may be used if the minimum possible lead length is assured. Their value is not particularly critical. The tuning capacitors, C1 through C6, should be high-quality short piston or coaxial capacitors, 3/4 inch center to center.

In the two photographs the first stage is shown at the right side. The boxes are handmade of thin sheet brass. Standard aluminum Miniboxes could be used, though brass or copper facilitates soldering direct to the case. The shield in the first stage should extend nearly the full width and height of the box. This is not so important in the second stage, which has a tuned circuit only on the output side. The bent brass mounting plate in the second stage is primarily to insure minimum emitter lead inductance.

The interior views show the input sides at the bottom. It will be seen that the strip for the input circuit, L1, is wider than that for the output, L2. The transistor has higher input than output capacitance, requiring less inductance in the input circuit. All strip inductors are brass and are 3/4 inch long. They are soldered directly to the tops of the tuning capacitors and are pi-networks.

Adjustment

A signal source is necessary in tuning up the preamplifier. Most small two-meter transmitters put out enough energy on the 9th harmonic to be plainly audible at 1296 MHz. Transistorized "beacons" commonly used by amateur uhf experimenters are fine. Anything strong enough to be heard on the converter, without the preamplifier, will serve. Just be sure that, if you are listening to a harmonic, it is the *right* one.

Initial peaking can be done with no voltage on the preamp. If a 50-ohm antenna is used the tuned circuits will be close to optimum adjustment if peaked first in this way. The same is true if one is fortunate enough to have a 1296-MHz signal generator with 50-ohm termination.

Now apply about 5 to 6 volts, and check the current on each transistor. Adjust the bias controls, R1 and R2, for 1 to 2 mA on the 5200 and 2 to 15 mA on the 5500. Now reduce the strength of the signal and adjust the tuned circuits for maximum

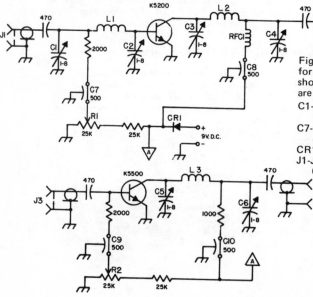

Fig. 13-36 — Circuit diagram and parts information for the preamplifier stages. The upper portion should be used for a single stage. Capacitor values are given in pF.

C1-C6, incl. — 1 to 8 pF, high-quality short piston or coaxial trimmer. (Johnson used here.)
C7-C10, incl. — 500-pF feedthrough, button mica or ceramic.
CR1 — Protective diode. 10 mA or more.
J1-J4, incl. — BNC receptacle, UG-290/U or 625/U.
L1 — Brass or copper strip, 5/8 X 3/4 inch.
L2 — Brass or copper strip, 1/4 X 3/4 inch.
L3 — Brass or copper strip, 1/2 X 3/4 inch.
R1, R2 — 25,000-ohm miniature control.

Fig. 13-37 — Interior views of the two preamplifier stages, again with the first stage at the right. The input ends are toward the bottom of the picture.

Fig. 13-37 — Interior views of the two preamplifier stages, again with the first stage at the right. The input ends are toward the bottom of the picture.

response. Readjust the bias for minimum noise on the first stage and maximum gain on the second. *Do not exceed 4 mA on 5200.*

The preamplifier as shown has a socket for plugging in a small 9-volt transistor radio battery. This may now be used, and a final peaking and bias adjustment made for best results. Bear in mind that optimum signal-to-noise ratio is the objective. This can be achieved by careful adjustment of the first stage, and it is not likely to be the same as for maximum signal level. The second stage can be used as a gain control, to some extent, though this is best done in the first i-f amplifier. The gain of the two stages is about 19 dB, when the system is adjusted for best noise figure. Not many amateurs will be able to measure noise figure accurately at this frequency, but it should be under 5 dB. A system noise figure of 3 dB is possible with these

transistors at 1000 MHz, but at 1296 MHz it may be slightly higher.

POWER TRIPLER OR AMPLIFIER FOR 432 MHz

The power required to drive a 432-MHz kilowatt amplifier to maximum output is more than is readily obtained with a varactor multiplier. Also, the cost of an amplifier capable of taking a full kilowatt input may be a bit high for many users of the 420-MHz band. Thus there is continuing interest in power triplers, and in single-ended amplifiers, using the external-anode type of tube.

The tripler of Fig. 13-38 and the amplifier of Fig. 13-40 were built by Dick Stevens, W1QWJ, to satisfy these two requirements. They are nearly identical in construction, except for the grid circuits, and even these are quite similar schematically. Details of both are given under the diagram, Fig. 13-39. Previous editions of this Manual carried descriptions of a similar design, with a cylindrical plate circuit. There is nothing sacred about coaxial construction, so W1QWJ (who was also partly responsible for the coaxial version) decided to try a sheet-aluminum housing, in the interest of simpler metal work for the average builder. Results with the two versions were practically identical, so the aluminum-box form is shown here. The coaxial model is in the 1972 ARRL *Handbook*.

Construction

The plate circuits of the tripler and amplifier are identical, for all practical purposes. Each uses a quarter-wave line, tuned at the plate end with a 1-1/2-inch brass-disk capacitor, C1, driven by 10-32 threaded brass rod. The rod passes through a panel bushing (1/8-inch shaft bushing tapped for 10-32) mounted in the front surface of the aluminum box. The plate inductor, L1, is 2-3/8 inches of 1−5/8-inch OD copper pipe, fitted with 1/2-inch finger stock at the plate end. If finger stock is not readily available, a removable wrap-around brass or copper strip, held in position with a hose clamp, will work equally well.

Fig. 13-38 — Interior of the 144-432 power tripler. The plate compartment and circuit are similar to those of the straight-through amplifier of Fig. 13-40. The main portion of the case is a single U-shaped piece of sheet aluminum. The cover plate, not shown, fastens to the end plates and divider with self-tapping screws.

The line terminates in a 3-inch-square piece of stiff brass or copper, which forms one surface of the bypass capacitor, C3. Insulation for C3 in the tripler is 10-mil Teflon. This will do for the amplifier if it operates at low plate voltages, but for use at full plate-voltage rating the Teflon thickness should be 1/32 inch. The assembly should be held in place with screws passing through ceramic or Teflon shoulder washers in the end plate of the box. The insulation requirements of the tripler are less stringent, as it probably will always be used at moderate plate voltages, and without modulation.

The output-coupling loop, L2, and its series capacitor, C2, are plainly visible in both photographs. The portion of the loop parallel to L1 is about 5/8 inch long. The spacing from L1, for optimum output, will vary slightly, depending on

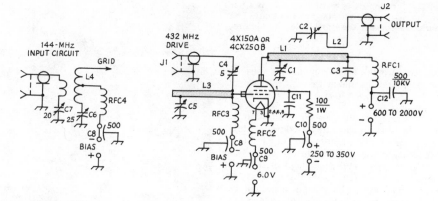

Fig. 13-39 — Schematic diagram and parts information for the 432-MHz tripler and amplifier. Principal difference between the two units is in the grid circuit.

C1, C5 — Copper or brass disk, 1-1/2-inch dia. Stationary plate fastened to L1 2-1/8 inch from C3.

C2 — 10-pF shaft-type trimmer, grounded-rotor type.

C3 — 3 X 3-inch plate soldered to end of L1. Center hole 1-1/2-inch dia. Insulated from case with 10-mil or 1/32-inch Teflon. See text.

C4 — 5-pF miniature trimmer. Solder direct between grid terminal and J1.

C6 — 25-pF trimmer, shaft type.

C7 — 20-pF miniature trimmer, shaft type.

C11 — Built into socket (not important in tripler).

C12 — 500-pF 10kV TV "doorknob."

J1 — BNC fitting.

J2 — N-type fitting.

L1 — Copper pipe, 1-1/2-inch ID, 2-3/8 inches long. 1/2-inch finger stock at anode end. C3 soldered to far end.

L2 — 1-1/2 inches No. 14, bent in L shape. Sides are 5/8 inch each after soldering to L2 and J2.

L3 — Copper pipe, 1/2-inch ID and matching pipe cap, total length 3-1/8 inches. Center of C5 7/8 inch from open end. Shaft of C5 1-1/8 inch from inside right edge of box.

L4 — 4 turns No. 20, 5/8-inch dia, 1 inch long. Tap RFC 2-1/4 turns from grid end.

L5 — 2 turns No. 22 plastic-insulated, 1/2-inch dia. Twist ends 2 turns and insert between turns of L4.

RFC1, RFC2, RFC3 — 10 turns No. 22 enam, closewound 1/4-inch dia.

RFC4 — 30 turns No. 22 enam, 1/4-inch dia, 1-1/8 inch long. Ready-made 2-meter choke usable.

the operating conditions, but will average 1/4 inch. Because it is in a low-impedance circuit, the series capacitor, C2, can be a miniature type with .017-inch spacing (Johnson 160 series).

The high voltage is brought through the end of the assembly, on one of the screws holding C3 in place. A TV-type door-knob capacitor, C12, bypasses the B+ side of the choke, RFC1. The capacitor, the choke, and the terminal for C3 should be covered by some kind of protective enclosure, to prevent accidental contact with the high-voltage line.

The sheet-aluminum cases are made from U-shaped pieces to give a 3-1/2-inch square cross-section. The amplifier is 9 inches overall, and the tripler 7-1/2 inches. The cover, not shown in the photographs, fastens to the bent-over end pieces and the divider, and has 3/8-inch bent-over flanges on the long sides. The interior length of the plate compartment is 4 inches in both units. Other

dimensions are not particularly critical, except where given in the parts list.

The socket used for the tripler is not a critical item. An inexpensive one without built-in bypassing should work satisfactorily in this stage. The latest type, having a raised screen ring, is advisable for the amplifier, though an earlier version without it is used here. The screen ring and socket in the tripler are separate units (E. F. Johnson) that are somewhat less expensive than complete single assemblies. No tube chimney is needed, as the only path for the cooling air is into the grid compartment, through the socket and anode fins, and out through the open end of L1.

Varying contact resistance to ground in tuning mechanisms using rotating-disk capacitors is often a problem, especially after protracted use. This is solved in the W1QWJ units quite simply, by means of a tension system at the panel. A piece of aluminum or brass 1/8 × 1 × 1-1/2 inches in size is drilled and tapped to pass the drive screw. Holes tapped for 6-32 or 4-40 are made either side of the center hole. The plate is threaded onto the shaft, and rubber grommets are slipped over the mounting screws, between the panel and the metal plate. The tension on these is set firm enough to maintain

Fig. 13-40 — 500-watt power amplifier for 432 MHz. Grid and plate circuits are half-wave lines, tuned with disk capacitors. Plumbing components are used for both lines.

Fig. 13-41 — This is not a view of a partly finished project. It is the interior of a strip-line kilowatt amplifier built by K2RIW. The "line," actually a 5 X 9-inch piece of circuit board stock, is tuned at the right side by a beryllium-copper spring capacitor plate, controlled by means of a fish-line drive. Small collars soldered to the cover fit into mylar chimneys attached to the tube anodes, to confine the airflow for greatest cooling effectiveness.

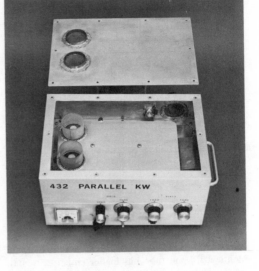

good shaft-to-ground contact, but not enough to make the threads bind or strip. Other mechanical details of the units should be apparent from the photographs.

Operation

Normally the tripler is operated well below maximum ratings for the tube used. Using it as a driver for a kilowatt amplifier calls for something around 25 watts output, so the plate voltage can be 800 volts or less. The 2-meter driver also should be capable of about 25 watts output. Operating conditions can be anything within reason, so long as the dissipation ratings of the elements concerned are not exceeded. Screen dissipation can rise to dangerous limits with high driving power and low plate voltage, so this is something to watch in setting up a tripler with this type of tube. The screen voltage circuit shown for the K2RIW amplifier, Fig. 13-45, is recommended, except that 250 volts might be safer than 300 in the tripler application.

Because relatively low input is required for the tripler, the tube can be the sort occasionally found on the surplus market. A glass-insulated tube of the early 4X150A variety should be adequate for this use.

Operation of the 4CX250B and similar tubes as amplifiers is covered in detail in Chapter 6, for both linear and Class-C conditions. This amplifier has been operated for considerable periods at 500 watts input, with little sign of the varying output and tuning drift that may occur when excessive heating of tube and components is present.

HIGH EFFICIENCY 432-MHz KILOWATT AMPLIFIER

The section on power amplifier design, Chapter 5, goes to some length in showing why "parallel operation is not practical for the higher vhf bands." How then can there be a 432-MHz amplifier in which two 4CX250B-series tubes are used in parallel? The answer lies in a qualifying statement added in this edition to accommodate developments like the 432-MHz amplifier described herewith: "It is possible to use certain vhf and uhf tubes in parallel with properly designed strip-line and cavity circuits. These require a complete break with conventional coil-and-capacitor concepts."

The amplifier of Fig. 13-41, designed and built by Dick Knadle, K2RIW,[22] not only makes parallel connection practical; it is the most effective kilowatt amplifier configuration yet described for 432-MHz operation, in literature available to the average uhf enthusiast. Parallel use of 2C39As in a 1296-MHz resonant cavity was described by WB6IOM in *QST* and the *ARRL Handbook*.[5]

The strip-line tank circuit is so simple that one gets the impression, upon lifting the cover of the K2RIW amplifier for the first time, that the builder hasn't finished the job. The basic idea is that the inductance of a strip-line can be made as low as desired, simply by making the inductor wider. Any number of tubes can be paralleled and resonated, so long as the intertube resonances — push-pull modes — are controlled. Details of the "mode-killing" are not given here, nor are several other interesting and useful ideas incorporated in this unique design. Study of the full treatments by

Fig. 13-42 — Interior of the 432-MHz amplifier, with the half-wave strip-line removed. The tuning flapper, C5, is fastened to the right sidewall. A similar string-drive capacitor plate, C4, is soldered to the power output jack on the rear wall. The plate-circuit rf choke, RFC1, is mounted on a feedthrough bypass capacitor, C7, in the upper left corner of the picture. Positions of C4 and C5 are those for maximum power output.

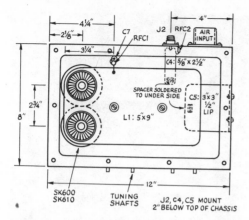

SK600
SK610

TUNING
SHAFTS

J2, C4, C5 MOUNT
2" BELOW TOP OF CHASSIS

Fig. 13-43 — Details of the plate compartment, showing placement and dimensions of all major components.

K2RIW in *QST*[22] and *Ham Radio*[23] is strongly recommended.

In this amplifier the parallel grid and plate networks force the voltages on the two tubes to be identical. If one tube has higher emission it may draw slightly higher plate current, but this is of little consequence because this happens to be the condition under which the amplifier will produce the greatest output with these two tubes. Such tube unbalance could be troublesome in a push-pull amplifier, or in a parallel one of conventional design.

Troublesome stray resonances, almost inevitable with conventional coils, tuning capacitors and coupling loops, are avoided by use of a flapper-type tuning capacitor, and a similarly constructed capacitive output probe. These are C5 and C4, respectively, in the schematic diagram, Fig. 13-44. The fish-line method of controlling these capacitors has a further advantage: it eliminates variable contact resistance to ground, a problem that often develops with rotating-disk capacitors using screw-thread drive.

Construction

The amplifier is built in two Premier 8 × 12 × 3-inch chassis, screwed together top to bottom. The top surface is cut away, leaving a 3/4-inch rim all around for mounting the top plate. The cover is 0.091-inch aluminum, though thinner would probably have been equally good. Installation of Pem-nuts, Rivnuts, or other blind fasteners on this rim is recommended. Any builder is likely to be called upon to show the "innards.. of the amplifier frequently, and holes for self-tapping screws won't stand this kind of use.

The two 1-5/8-inch air-exhaust holes directly above the tube anodes have copper screening soldered across them, on the inside. The air intake hole on the back wall is similarly screened. The surface of the box around the hole edges was tinned with Kester aluminum solder, using an iron tip on a propane torch. The screening is tinned with ordinary solder, where it is to contact the aluminum, and then tacked in place using the iron attachment and torch. Such a soldered screen gives better shielding than most compression mounting methods. The narrow collars that align with the

tube chimneys are sections of 1-5/8-inch brass tubing, 3/8 inch high, also soldered in place. The four butt-joint corners of the upper chassis have spots of solder in the centers of the cracks, on the inside, to insure good rf shielding.

Placement of holes for the sockets on the chassis and the holes in the strip-line, L1, should be done carefully. Misalignment will cause skewing of the tubes in the sockets, which may result in poor contact and make tube insertion difficult. The resonator is made of a 5 × 9-inch piece of 1/16-inch double-sided glass-epoxy circuit board. This is easy to cut and solder, and the conductor thickness is more than adequate, since rf current skin depth in copper is 0.125 mil at 432 MHz. Any rigid good conductor greater than 1-mil thickness should do equally well.

Finger stock around the tube holes is soldered to both sides of the copper-clad board. Intrinsic capacitance between the two surfaces eliminates need for any other connections. Some builders of the amplifier have made anode connectors of flashing copper, clamped to the tubes in various ways. Such connectors are satisfactory, but they hamper tube replacement. The strip-line is mounted above the groundplane on two 1-1/2-inch porcelain or Teflon spacers.

Cooling air comes into the upper chassis through a 1-1/2-inch screened hole and divides into two paths. About three-fourths goes through the tube anodes and chimneys and out through the screen top-cover holes. The rest passes through the tube sockets and out through a 3/4-inch screened hole in the side of the lower chassis. This flow pattern is beneficial in several ways. The cool air first flows around the plate-circuit components, which are suspected sources of detuning due to heating in many closed-in amplifiers. Secondly, full air pressure is available at the tube anodes, which need cooling most. The sockets create greater back pressure than the anodes, resulting in the 3:1 flow division in favor of the anodes.

The anode chimneys are 10-mil Mylar, 1-5/16 inch wide. The material is cut long enough to overlap about one-fourth turn when wrapped around the tube anode. Two tubes are placed end to end, and the Mylar wrapped around their anodes and held in place with rubber bands. The overlap is then glued with silicone rubber adhesive, with the rubber bands left on until the adhesive is dry. Be careful that the chimneys are not so long as to separate the finger stock from the tube anodes, when the cover is tightened down. Ten-mil Mylar is often used by draftsmen, so it should not be hard to obtain. If the air flow is not sufficient there may be melting of the Mylar. More air is then called for, or chimneys can be made of sheet Teflon.

The capacitor plates, C4 and C5, are made of 0.008 beryllium copper, but many other springy conductive materials are usable. The natural rest position of each is made so that it is just below L1, so they do not come dangerously close to it, in any position. This is preferable to placing any kind of insulating material on the plates to prevent electrical contact, as dielectric losses can be appreciable. The mounting end of C5 is bent 90 degrees, 1/2 inch from the end. A stiffening plate 1/16-inch thick is cut to fit this portion where it is bolted to the chassis wall. The edge of C4 is soldered directly to the center pin of J2.

Fishing string is fastened to the free end of each flapper capacitor. Each string goes through a small chassis hole and is wrapped around a Bakelite adjustment rod in the lower chassis. The rods are

drilled with small holes to take the string. Slight misalignment of the shaft bushings causes enough friction so that the capacitors hold their settings.

The power-sampling capacitor, C6, is a metal tab suspended 3/16 inch below the center pin of J2. Semirigid coax carries the rf power to the lower chassis, where the diode CR1, and associated components are located. The outer conductor is soldered to the chassis at the point where it runs through. If semirigid coax is not available, an insulated wire inside small copper tubing should do equally well, as only a very small amount of power is needed. If the inner conductor is stiff, the capacitor plate can be supported on the wire alone. Its size and position should be such that about a

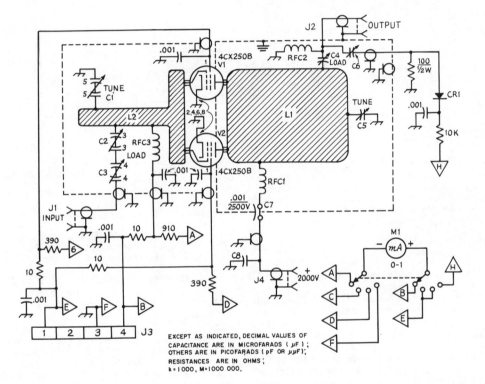

Fig. 13-44 — Schematic diagram and parts information for the 432-MHz kilowatt amplifier. In the interest of conveying mechanical information, some parts are not shown in conventional schematic form.

C1 — 5-pF per section butterfly (Johnson 160-205).
C2 — 3-pF per section butterfly (Johnson 160-203).
C3 — 4.5-pF per section printed-circuit butterfly (Johnson 189-251-5).
C4 — String-driven loading capacitor. See text and Fig. 13-43.
C5 — String-driven tuning capacitor. See text and Fig. 13-43.
C6 — Copper disk, 1/4-inch dia, 3/16 inch below J2 center conductor. See text.

C7 — .001-μF 2500-volt feedthrough (Erie CSK-711).
C8 — .001-μF 3000-volt disk ceramic.
CR1 — Hewlett-Packard HP-2301 diode.
J1, J2 — N-type coaxial fitting.
J3 — 4-pin male power connector.
J4 — High-voltage connector (MHV type).
L1 — 5 X 9-inch double-sided glass-epoxy circuit board. Round corners 5/16-inch radius. (Half-wave strip-line.)
L2 — Half-wave grid circuit, flashing copper. See Fig. 13-47.
RFC1 — 5 turns No. 18, 1/4-inch dia, 1 inch long, axis vertical.
RFC2 — Like RFC1, but 1/2 inch long.
RFC3 — 0.1-μH rf choke (Ohmite Z-460).
Meter functions: Position A-B — grid current, 100 mA; C-E — Screen current, V1, 50 mA; D-E — screen current, V2; F-H — relative power output.

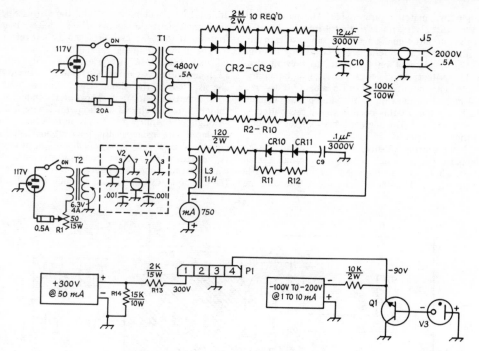

Fig. 13-45 — Details of power supplies for the 432-MHz amplifier. Capacitors with polarity shown are electrolytic. Parts not described are numbered for text reference. Only the external circuits of the screen and bias supplies are shown.

CR2-CR11, inc. — 3000-V 500-mA diode, 20-A surge rating.

I1 — 117-volt pilot lamp.

J5 — MHV connector.

L3 — 11-H 500-mA choke (UTC D3227, surplus).

P1 — 4-pin plug to match J3.

Q1 — Npn transistor, 10 watt, 100 VCE, beta at least 14 (Delco DTS-401).

R1 — 50-ohm 15-watt control. Adjust for 5.5 V at V1 and V2.

T1 — 4800 V, ct, 500 mA (UTC D3221, surplus).

T2 — 6.3V 5-A filament transformer (UTC S-55).

V3 — 5651, VR-90 or 90-V 1-watt Zener diode.

3/4-scale reading is obtained on the meter, at full power output.

The grid circuit tuning and loading capacitors, C1 and C2, are butterfly types, to avoid sliding contacts to grounded rotors. C3 is a screw-driver adjustment trimmer, used to set the range of C2. One stator of C1 is soldered to a ground lug on the chassis floor. The other stator is soldered to a lug on the lower side of L2, 4 inches from the grid end. One stator of C2 is connected similarly to L2, at a point 2-1/4 inches from the grid end. The other C2 stator and one stator of C3 are soldered to an ungrounded lug bolted to the top of a

3/8-inch threaded ceramic insulator, fastened to the chassis. The outer conductor of the RG-58 input cable is soldered to a ground lug under the insulator, and the inner conductor to the other stator of C3. Bakelite rods extending through the front are used for adjustment of C1 and C2. Proper settings will make the amplifier look like a 50-ohm load over all reasonable drive levels.

Careful shielding of all leads entering the grid compartment is required, if the drive requirement is to be kept low. There is a strong rf field in the area of the 4CX250B grid circuit, and any leads not completely shielded and grounded will couple power out. Note that no wiring of any kind is placed in the area under or near L2.

The grid compartment shield is a modified 5 × 7 × 3-inch aluminum box, held in place with sheet-metal screws. Slots are cut in the box around the tuning shafts and input cable, for easy removal.

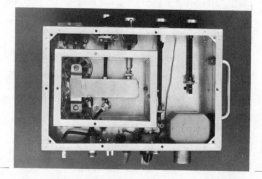

Fig. 13-46 — Bottom of the 432-MHz amplifier, showing grid-circuit details. Butterfly capacitor mounted at 45-degree angle, lower center of the grid compartment, is C3. C2 is just above C3, out of sight. C1 is near the right end of L2. Bakelite shafts, right, carry the fish-line to C5, right, and C4. Their bushing mounting plates are slightly misaligned to create tension on the shafts.

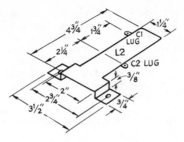

Fig. 13-47 — Details of the half-wave grid line, L2. Material is flashing copper or similar sheet brass.

Five 1/2-inch holes are drilled in the end adjacent to C1, to permit free air flow.

Power Supplies

The amplifier requires 2000 volts at 0.5 ampere, 300 volts at 50 mA, and −90 volts, with a 50-mA current sinking capacity. The choke-input solid-state supply for the high voltage (Fig. 13-45) tion, and a built-in spike arrestor consisting of CR10, CR11, and C9. The choke and meter in the negative lead contribute to safe operation and reliability. The bleeder resistor is connected so that the meter does not read the bleeder current. Use of RG59 coax and MHV connectors for running the high voltage from the supply to the amplifier is a good safety measure. (MHV connectors are similar to BNC, except for having an extended center insulator. They are rated to 5000 volts, and they automatically maintain a ground through the coaxial shield.)

The amplifier is protected from high screen voltage by R14, which drains off negative screen current that can occur during some operating conditions. With R13 in the line to the screens, dissipation cannot exceed 12 watts under any condition. Most tubes used in this amplifier deliver maximum power output with about 5 mA positive

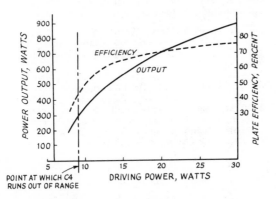

Fig. 13-48 — Output and plate efficiency of the 432-MHz amplifier, when operated Class C, with bias, screen voltage, and plate voltage fixed at −90, +300, and +2000 volts, respectively, varying the drive level from 8 to 30 watts. Input drops with decreasing drive, so operation is always at safe levels of plate dissipation. Suggestions for linear operation are given in the text.

screen current, so R13 normally drops the 300-volt supply only about 10 volts.

The grid bias supply need not deliver much current; rather it must act as a load for the 20 mA the tubes normally deliver when driven into Class-C conditions. This calls for a shunt regulator, able to tolerate 100 mA without failure, in case drive is momentarily applied without plate voltage. Without a shunt-regulated supply, bias can increase when drive is applied. This may increase the drive requirement for full power output, and cause back-bombardment of the tube cathodes.

Performance

The builder of the amplifier tested it very thoroughly using the best laboratory equipment available for this kind of work. He used a 20-watt 144-MHz source and his 144-432 tripler[23] to drive

Fig. 13-49 — Rear view of the K2RIW 432-MHz kilowatt amplifier.

the amplifier. Maximum efficiency (with fixed conditions of plate, screen, and bias voltage) was obtained with around 22 watts drive. The curves of Fig. 13-48 show the power output (solid line) and plate efficiency (broken line) for various drive levels. It will be seen that nearly 350 watts output can be obtained with only 10 watts drive. With the bias and screen supplies described, plate current drops with decreasing drive levels, so the plate dissipation remains at a safe level at any power output condition, down to one watt or less.

The operating conditions described by K2RIW are convenient for anyone who wants a simple way of transmitting cw or fm, over a wide range of power-output capability without changing supply voltages. If the amplifier is to be used as a linear, with a-m or ssb, provision for changing at least the screen and plate voltages would be desirable, to preserve linearity and efficiency at low-input conditions. Something like the operating conditions described for the 50- and 144-MHz linear amplifiers in Chapter 6 would then be in order. It should be emphasized that the series-shunt resistor network in the screen supply and the shunt-regulated bias supply systems used by K2RIW and shown in Fig. 13-45 have great merit, and could well be incorporated in any amplifier using this series of tubes. They should help materially to correct problems reported by some users, and to prolong what has been normally a record of excellent tube life, with this tube family.

The testing and measurement program conducted by K2RIW also included a thorough check for spurious outputs, using instrumentation not normally available for amateur work. His tripler, though probably more effective than most in reducing radiation at the driving frequency, does put out 28 milliwatts on 144 MHz, which is enough to be heard over a considerable area on that band. The parallel amplifier, running at 700 watts output on 432, reduces the 144MHz output by 50 dB. Referred to the 432-MHz output, the spurious outputs are down as follows: 144 MHz − 71 dB, 288 MHz − 69 dB, 864 MHz − 45 dB, and 1296 MHz − 50 dB. With the amplifier running into a tuned antenna system, the rejection of the unwanted frequencies should be even higher than the above exceptional figures. Spectrum analyzer examination showed no other significant outputs, from dc to 12.4 GHz.

PULSE COMMUNICATION ON 2300 MHz AND UP

Microwave communication with simple oscillator-type transmitters requires a very wide bandwidth, transmitting and receiving. While much good work has been done with such inherently low-efficiency systems, something better is needed if the full amateur potential of the microwave region is to be realized.

The usual alternative, use of crystal control and narrow-band receiving techniques, makes a very marked improvement but it entails considerable effort and expense. The pulse system shown in block-diagram form in Fig. 13-50 represents a desirable compromise between these two extremes. Stability requirements are no greater than with the simple oscillator approach, yet the communications range can be nearly equal to that obtained with narrow-band cw. Cost and complication are considerably lower than with narrow-band methods.

Pulse is a wide-band mode by nature, so it is permitted only in the microwave region, where amateur assignments are wide enough to accommodate it. The system shown was developed by John T. Zimmer, W2BVU, and Robert F. Guba, W1QMN, for use in the 2300-MHz band, but it is applicable to higher bands, except 10,000 MHz, where pulse is not permitted. Their full treatment in QST[24] and condensations in the 1965 and 1968 editions of this Manual describe a system well within the reach of the experienced amateur. Many versions have been built, mostly from surplus

components, and they have shown repeatedly that they are capable of providing reliable communication over distances comparable to those covered on the vhf bands.

The rf portions of the transmitter and receiver can be identical with those used for simpler systems.[25] The effectiveness of pulse is obtained through special characteristics of the modulator in the transmitter, Fig. 13-46A, and the threshold detector in the receiver, B. Both involve relatively simple circuitry.

SURPLUS GEAR FOR THE MICROWAVE BANDS

Amateur operation on the frequencies above 1000 MHz would hardly have been practical, had it not been for many items of equipment obtained on the surplus market at a fraction of their original cost. To describe in detail how all this gear can be used would take a book larger than this one. Much of the necessary information for making use of microwave surplus is in QST. Nearly all the references in the bibliography below employ surplus in one way or another.

Some surplus items that have not been treated extensively in QST are described briefly below. There are many others, and as uhf and microwave communication converts gradually from tubes to solid-state devices there will undoubtedly be more.

APR-4, with tuning head *TN-54* − Radar receiver, 2150 to 4000 MHz. LO in tuning head.

APR-5A − Radar receiver, 2150 to 5000 MHz, in one unit.

APR-9, with tuning head *TN-128* − Radar receiver, 1000 to 2600 MHz. LO in tuning head.

APG-5 or *APG-15* − Tail-gun radar, 2700 to 2900 MHz. Has 2C43 pulse oscillator and 2C40 LO, both in coaxial circuits readily convertible to 2300-MHz band. Have been used in W2BVU-W1QMN pulse system of Fig. 13-50.

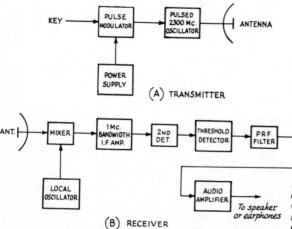

Fig. 13-50 — Block diagram of a complete pulse communications system for the 2300-MHz band. Communications range approximates that obtainable with narrow-band methods, with much simpler and less expensive equipment.

2J39 Integral-magnet magnetron, 9-kW peak-power output, 3267 to 3333 MHz.

FPN-13 – Naval radar, crystal-controlled, 8 to 9 GHz. Output stage has V-45 klystron, useful as quintupler to 10 GHz. Has cavities useful for 2300; 3 with 2C39s.

UPX-6 – Crystal-controlled transmitter and receiver (base unit for use with APX-6) 1215-1300 MHz. Power and pulse circuits useful for any microwave band.

BIBLIOGRAPHY

1 Holladay and Farwell, "Beer-Can Baluns for 144, 220 and 432 Mc.," February, 1965, QST.

2 Brayley, "Coaxial-Tank Amplifier for 220 and 420 Mc.," May, 1951, QST.

3 Garrett and Manly, "Crystal Control on 10,000 Mc.," November, 1963, QST.

4 Robertson, "Tripler for the 1215-Mc. Band," July, 1955, QST.

5 Laakmann, "Cavity Amplifier for 1296 Mc.," January, 1968, QST; ARRL Handbook, 1968-1972.

6 Badger, "An Introduction to the Klystron," August, 1961, QST.

7 Orr, Harris, "Project Moonbounce," September, 1960, QST.

"W3GKP and W4HHK Work on 2300 MHz!" World Above 50 Mc., December, 1970, QST.

8 Simple duplex phone equipment for all amateur microwave bands has been described many times in QST. The following references should be helpful to anyone interested in this approach to microwave communication.

3300 MHz.:

Baird, "Radio Club for Microwave Enthusiasts," December, 1957, QST.

Bredon, "Let's Go Microwave," June, 1958, QST.

Peterson, "Practical Gear for Amateur Microwave Communication," June, 1963, QST.

5650 MHz.:

Merchant and Harrison, "Duplex Phone on 5300 Mc.," (Temporary band, later changed to 5600 Mc.) January, 1946, QST.

Prechtel, "Experimental Transceivers for 5650 Mc.," August, 1960, QST.

10,000 MHz.:

McGregor, "Dishing Out the Milliwatts on 10 kMc.," February, 1947, QST. Basic information repeated in several ARRL Handbook editions, 1948-1954.

21,000 Mc.:

Sharbaugh and Watters, "Our DX – 800 Feet!" August, 1946, QST. Same Authors, "World Above 20,000 Mc.," May, 1959, QST., includes information on equipment for 50,000 Mc.

9 Jensby, "Stable Microwave Oscillators," July, 1966, QST.

10 Kolbly and Munn, "Microwave DX, California Style," September, 1970, QST.

11 Argento, "Centimeter Wave Magnetrons," December, 1945, QST.

12 Scott, "The Travelling-Wave Tube," July, 1963, QST.

13 "Gunn Diode Circuit Handbook," Microwave Associates, Inc., Burlington, MA 01803. Copyright 1971.

14 Bateman and Bain, "New Thresholds in V.h.f. and U.h.f. Reception," December, 1958, and January, February, and March, 1959, QST.

15 Troetschel and Heuer, "A Parametric Amplifier for 1296 Mc.," January, 1961, QST.

16 Sager, "Parametric Amplifier for 432 Mc.," Hints and Kinks, October, 1961, QST. A complete 432-MHz paramp was described in Edition 1 of this Manual.

17 Cross, "Frequency Multiplication with Power Varactors," October, 1962, QST.

18 Krivohlavek, "1296-Mc. Converter Without Complications," March, 1961, QST. Also ARRL Handbook, 1962-1968.

19 Meyer, "Crystal-Controlled 1296-Mc. Converter," September, 1962, QST; ARRL Handbook, 1970-1972; 1965 and 1968 editions of this Manual.

20 Wilson, "2.3-GHz Crystal-Controlled Converter," April, 1971, QST, p. 34; May, p. 87.

21 Vilardi, "Two-Stage Transistor Preamplifier for 1296 Mc.," December, 1968, QST.

22 Knadle, "High-Efficiency Parallel Kilowatt for 432 MHz," QST, two parts, beginning April, 1972.

23 Knadle, "Dual-Band Stripline Amplifier-Tripler for 144 and 432 MHz," Ham Radio, February, 1970.

24 Guba and Zimmer, "Pulse: A Practical Technique for Amateur Microwave Work," February through May, 1963, QST. Essential details reproduced in 1965 and 1968 editions of this Manual. Photocopy of the Manual text, 15 pages, $1.50, from ARRL.

25 Koch, "Simplified Oscillators for 2300 Mc.," February, 1948, QST. Basic information in ARRL Handbook, 1949-54, and in reference 22, above.

Other useful QST references to uhf and microwave equipment and techniques include the following, listed by bands.

420 MHz:

Poland, "Converting FM Equipment," August, 1968.

Clement, "Using Motorola TU-110 Series on 420 MHz," September, 1971.

1215 MHz:

APX-6 conversion – September, 1960; February, 1961; February, 1968, p. 82.

Fisher and Turrin, "UHF Directional Couplers," September, 1970.

Scott and Banta, "Using the Helical Antenna on 1215 Mc.," July, 1962.

Troetschel, "Quad Helix for 1215," August, 1963.

Fisher, "Interdigital Bandpass Filters," March, 1968.

Vilardi, "Easily-Constructed 1296-MHz Antennas," June, 1969.

2300 MHz:

2300-MHz Harmonic Generator, October, 1968, p. 94.

Moonbounce, July, 1969, p. 54. Pulse Record, February, 1969, p. 53. Tropo Record, September, 1970, p. 96.

Many useful publications devoted to microwave techniques and theory are available from the U.S. Government Printing Office, Washington, DC 20402. Write for list of titles and prices.

Chapter 14

Test Equipment for the V H F Station

Many vhf men tend to be experimenters at heart. Much of the pleasure and satisfaction to be derived from vhf work comes from striving for the best possible performance from our stations, whether they are lavish or modest in nature. Thus it is important that we acquire suitable test equipment, and the know-how to use it effectively. This does not necessarily mean a laboratory full of expensive gear. Much of what is needed can be provided at moderate cost, particularly if we are willing to take the time and trouble to make some of it ourselves.

All ham gear costs money, and the average amateur investment in equipment is rising every year. Regrettably, this does not always apply to the percentage of the total budget that is devoted to test equipment. Yet whether we buy our operating gear or build it ourselves, only by having adequate testing and measuring equipment, and using it regularly and well, can we be sure that we are getting maximum return from the money spent on transmitters, receivers, and antennas. Nowhere is this more true than in the vhf field.

Most amateur test equipment is essentially the same, regardless of the frequencies we intend to concentrate on. Things like volt-ohmmeters, oscilloscopes, meters in general, the audio oscillator, the grid-dip meter — these are standard items that we will not dwell on extensively in these pages. Rather, we will devote our space mostly to simple gadget-type items, tailored to the vhf man's needs. We'll start with the simplest of them all.

LAMPS — POOR MAN'S METERS

Good meters are a very worthwhile investment. Every ham should have a few, but they do not have to be built into everything. Knowing what to test and measure, and being able to make a meaningful interpretation of what the meters tell us, is more important than having shelves full of expensive test equipment. An experienced and knowing ham can do good work with a meter or two, a few pilot lamps, neon bulbs, and some simple wavemeters. There is no substitute for experience in this department, and the way to get the experience and knowhow is to start right in, building simple equipment and making it work.

Current and Power Indicators

More can be done with pilot lamps as current and power indicators than most hams realize. The information of Table 14-I can be put to use in a

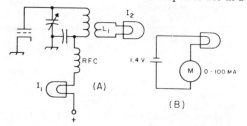

Fig. 14-1 — Pilot lamps can be used as current and power output indicators. Lamp I1 can substitute for a plate-current meter, where only a rough indication is needed. I2, inductively coupled to the plate circuit, provides an indication of rf power output. Lamps can be calibrated roughly for brilliance, as shown at B. Here a 2-volt 60-mA pilot lamp is connected in series with a single flashlight cell and a 100-mA meter, for calibration purposes.

number of ways. Most of the lamps listed are available in radio or even hardware stores. The rating in amperes, right column, tells us that these lamps draw 0.06, 0.1, 0.12, 0.15, 0.17, 0.2, 0.25, 0.4, and 0.5 amperes, at normal brilliance. These figures (60 to 500 milliamperes) are close to ranges of milliammeters we would buy if we had an unlimited budget. Obviously, lamps can replace meters in many uncritical circuits where we need merely an approximate indication of current being drawn. Lamps are fuses of a sort, too; they'll burn out if current goes very high for any reason.

Lamps serving as current and power-output indicators are shown in Fig. 14-1A. Lamp I1 is a plate-current "meter." Connected in the line from the plate circuit, it gives an indication of plate current being drawn. If the stage is supposed to draw 30 to 60 mA, a 2-volt 60-mA pilot lamp (No. 48 or 49) will do. It can be mounted in a socket, to make it easy to replace if burned out. You can burn out a lot of them for the price of one good meter.

Lamp I2 is a dummy load and power-output indicator. The coil L1 is a single turn of insulated hookup wire about one inch in diameter. With the loop coupled to an rf circuit carrying power, the lamp will light due to power absorbed. With a very low-power circuit the loop can be hung over the coil in the plate circuit, or inserted between its turns. For looser coupling, needed where the power output is much over 1/10 watt, the lamp can be taped to an insulating rod to be used as a handle to hold the loop at the desired distance from the tank circuit.

We can tell several things from these two lamps. They can be calibrated roughly for both current and power from known dc sources. At a current of

50 mA, which it will draw from a 1.4-volt cell connected as in 14-1B, a No. 48 or 49 bulb gives off considerably less light than at its rated 60 mA, but still enough to be clearly visible. From its normal rating, we know that full brilliance indicates 120 milliwatts of power. We thus have four useful references with which to work: 50 mA and 60 mA of current, and 70 and 120 milliwatts of power. Similar references can be set up easily for other lamps in the table. These are rough indications, of course, but there are plenty of places where they are good enough.

Using Neon Lamps

Neon lamps of various sizes are handy as indicators of rf fields, as they will ignite when merely held near a hot circuit, if the field is strong enough. Held close to a transmitter tank circuit, or to the end of an antenna carrying rf power, they will glow with a brilliance and color that conveys several bits of information. The brilliance is a relative rf power indicator, and the color is somewhat of an indication of frequency. At the low end of the rf range the glow is a bright orange, changing gradually to purple with increasing radio frequency. In the vhf range the neon glow is markedly more toward the purple than the orange. Glow color can thus be an indication of the frequency range of a parasitic oscillation, as an example.

A neon lamp or pilot lamp connected at the center of a half-wave dipole gives an indication of relative power at some distance from a transmitting antenna. The pilot lamp is the better for this purpose, for the neon must be subjected to a fairly high rf voltage to ignite the gas, whereas the filament of a lamp glows at once from the heat being dissipated.

Any of the lamps mentioned can be an aid to making a rough check on frequency, when absorption wavemeters or Lecher wires are used. We'll cover these applications later in this section.

Neons or pilot lamps can be used to give a rough indication of standing-wave ratio on open-wire or other balanced transmission line. A lamp with a coupling loop attached, or a neon bulb held close to the line, will brighten or dim in proportion to the rf voltage along the line. Two lamps, one at the minimum and another at the maximum point of rf voltage, thus provide a direct indication of SWR that can be roughly calibrated against brilliance indications from a similar lamp in a metered dc circuit.

The Twin-Lamp SWR Indicator

A fine example of the use of lamps to do a much-needed job is the Twin-Lamp SWR indicator originally described by vhf enthusiast W4HVV

TABLE 14-I – PILOT-LAMP DATA

Lamp No.	Bead Color	Base (Miniature)	Bulb Type	RATING	
				Volts	Amp.
40	Brown	Screw	T-3¼	6-8	0.15
40A[1]	Brown	Bayonet	T-3¼	6-8	0.15
41	White	Screw	T-3¼	2.5	0.5
42	Green	Screw	T-3¼	3.2	**
43	White	Bayonet	T-3¼	2.5	0.5
44	Blue	Bayonet	T-3¼	6-8	0.25
45	*	Bayonet	T-3¼	3.2	**
46[2]	Blue	Screw	T-3¼	6-8	0.25
47[1]	Brown	Bayonet	T-3¼	6-9	0.15
48	Pink	Screw	T-3¼	2.0	0.06
49[3]	Pink	Bayonet	T-3¼	2.0	0.06
49A[3]	White	Bayonet	T-3¼	2.1	0.12
50	White	Screw	G-3½	6-8	0.2
51[2]	White	Bayonet	G-3½	6-8	0.2
53	––	Bayonet	G-3½	14.4	0.12
55	White	Bayonet	G-4½	6-8	0.4
292[5]	White	Screw	T-3¼	2.9	0.17
292A[5]	White	Bayonet	T-3¼	2.9	0.17
1455	Brown	Screw	G-5	18.0	0.25
1455A	Brown	Bayonet	G-5	18.0	0.25
1487	––	Screw	T-3¼	12-16	0.20
1488	––	Bayonet	T-3¼	14	0.15
1813	––	Bayonet	T-3¼	14.4	0.10
1815	––	Bayonet	T-3¼	12-16	0.20

[1] 40A and 47 are interchangeable.
[2] Frosted bulb.
[3] 49 and 49A are interchangeable.
[5] Use in 2.5-volt sets where regular bulb burns out too frequently.
* White in G.E. and Sylvania; green in National Union, Raytheon, and Tung-Sol.
** 0.35 in G.E. and Sylvania; 0.5 in National Union, Raytheon, and Tung-Sol.

years ago in *QST*.[1] It works on the principle of separating the outgoing from the reflected power on a transmission line, by a combination of inductive and capacitive coupling. The Twin-Lamp is merely two 60-mA pilot lamps connected to two coupling loops, and to one side of the transmission line, as shown in Fig. 14-2. The schematic circuit is given in A, and the mechanical details in B.

The Twin-Lamp can be made up permanently attached to a short section of Twin-Lead, which can be inserted in the transmission line as needed, or left permanently connected. A similar arrangement can be made for open-wire lines. Length of the loops, L1 and L2, depends on the frequency and power level. Two to four inches in length

[1] For this and other numbered references, see bibliography at the end of this chapter.

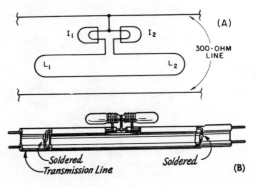

(A)

300-OHM LINE

(B)

Fig. 14-2 – The Twin-Lamp is a simple standing-wave indicator for use with balanced line. Lamps I1 and I2, in the schematic diagram, A, are 2-volt 60-mA pilot lamps, with their tips soldered together and connected to one side of the 300-ohm line. Loops L1 and L2 can be made from short pieces of Twin-Lead, as shown at B.

should be suitable for vhf work at average power levels.

The lamp nearest the transmitter end will light when power is fed to the line. If the SWR is low, the lamp at the other end will remain dark. At moderate ratios the lamp on the antenna side will glow, and with a bad mismatch the two will be about the same brilliance. The device should not be thought of in terms of *measurement* of SWR, but it does give a usable indication of adjustment, and it tells whether the SWR is high or low, which is all that is really important in most instances.

ABSORPTION WAVEMETERS

One of the most useful items of test equipment in a vhf station is the absorption wavemeter. Fortunately, it is also simple and inexpensive. Anyone who does much work with vhf equipment should have a few of them. Three that take care of basic vhf requirements are shown in Figs. 14-3 to 6.

A wavemeter can be a sophisticated device, but in its simplest form it is merely a tuned circuit whose resonant frequency for various capacitor settings has been calibrated. When the wavemeter is coupled to a circuit carrying rf power it will absorb some of the power when tuned through the frequency of the source. Indication that this is happening can be obtained in several ways.

If the stage to be checked is an oscillator, tuning the wavemeter through its frequency may cause a shift in frequency. This can be heard on a receiver tuned to the oscillator frequency. Any current drawn by an oscillator or amplifier stage will nearly always show some change, and the power output will dip, so any of these indications, or a combination of them, can be employed. The frequency of an oscillating detector can be checked with the wavemeter in a similar manner. The hiss level of a superregenerative receiver will dip when the wavemeter tunes through its receiving frequency. The regenerative detector may go out of oscillation, or the frequency of the beat note will change, due to wavemeter absorption.

The approximate frequency of any unwanted oscillation in a transmitter or receiver can be learned with the wavemeter in much the same way. Check the current drawn by the oscillating stage, and watch for a quick change as the wavemeter is tuned. In a receiver, listen to the effects of the oscillation, and note when they change abruptly in any way as the wavemeter is adjusted.

Wavemeters can be made to cover side ranges of frequency with rough calibration, or narrower ranges with more accurate calibration. We show both types here. With the wide-range type, frequencies go by so rapidly as the tuning capacitor is rotated that the frequency indication is necessarily only approximate, but it is a very useful tool. Two of our wavemeters are this kind. The first tunes from 45 to 155 MHz, giving coverage of the 50-MHz band, the 144-MHz band, and other highly useful spots such as 48, 72, 96, and 100 Mhz, as well. The other spans 113 to 255 MHz, passing through the 144- and 220-MHz bands along the way. The third is the bandspread type, having a fixed capacitor in parallel with the variable one. Covering 120 to 160 MHz, it spreads the 144-MHz band enough so that a fairly good indication of actual frequency is possible, if the wavemeter is made, calibrated, and used with care.

Construction

The wavemeter should be solidly built, to retain its calibration in normal handling and use. Ready-made coil stock provides the required rigidity, if connected with the absolute minimum of lead length. Some kind of indicating knob and scale arrangement is desirable, so that a permanent calibration can be made. Construction should be such that the instrument can be held in the hands without affecting the calibration, and used with reasonable safety around live circuits.

Many arrangements are possible; those shown are merely one approach to the problem. Each is mounted on two pieces of aluminum, a handle and a panel area. The handle is about 1 × 6 inches and the panel is roughly 2-1/2 inches in diameter. One of the screws holding these pieces together has a soldering lug attached, with a clip lead soldered to it for grounding the wavemeter frame, in the interest of safety. The variable capacitors are the type in which the rotor is grounded directly by the mounting shaft and nut, these being less subject to hand-capacitance effects than variables with ungrounded mounting studs. One type of coil stock (B&W Miniductor No. 3002, having No. 20 tinned

Fig. 14-3 — Three simple wavemeters for vhf use. The two at the left have wide-range circuits, while the third is a band-spread version. Each has a clip lead connected to the handle, for grounding to the chassis of the equipment being tested, in the interest of safety.

wire, 1/2 inch in diameter, 8 turns per inch) is used in all three.

The wavemeter for 50 and 144 MHz has a 50-pF variable (Hammarlund HF-50) and 4-3/4 turns of coil stock. The bottom of the coil is soldered to the right stator post (as we look at the back of the wavemeter) with less than 1/8 inch of exposed lead. The wire end of the top of the coil is 7/8 inch long, its last 1/4 inch being soldered to the rotor lug. The position of the coil is such that it is coaxial with the rotor shaft. Knobs are Johnson 116-222-5, though any indicating pointer or dial-type knob will do.

The unit for 144 and 220 MHz has a 15-pF variable (Hammarlund HF-15) and roughly 2-1/2 turns of coil stock. The top edge of the coil lines up with the center fo the rotor shaft in this model. The top lead is about 3/4 inch long, and the bottom one substantially nil.

The band-spread model uses a double-spaced capacitor, originally 15 pF (Hammarlund HF-15X) with all but the back two rotor plates removed. The stator is left intact. The coil is practically identical to that in the second unit, except that the top lead is 1-1/8 inches long. The coil is connected between the left stator post and the rotor lug. Laid tightly against the ceramic end plate of C1, and connected with the shortest possible leads between the stator post and rotor lug is a 5-pF ceramic fixed capacitor, C2. It is out of sight behind the variable capacitor in Fig. 14-4.

Calibration

Pieces of white card cut to 2-1/4-inch diameter disks are mounted under the nuts holding the capacitors to the frames. With the capacitor full out or full-in, the knob is set on the shaft so that its indicator points straight up when the wavemeter is held in the left hand. A mark is made on the white card to indicate that this is one end of the tuning range. Swinging the capacitor around 180 degrees, another mark is made to indicate the other end.

A calibration accurate enough for most purposes can be made with a calibrated grid-dip meter.

Known frequencies of transmitter or receiver stages may also be used. Calibration points throughout the range can be marked on one half of the capacitor range, giving calibration points at 48, 50, 72, 90, 100, 120, and 140 MHz on Unit 1. The other half of the full circle of rotation can be marked for 50 to 54 and 144 to 148 MHz, the two amateur bands we're interested in.

The second unit was calibrated at 115, 125, 150, 175, 200, 220, and 250 MHz on one half of the scale, and the 144- and 220-MHz bands on the other. The bandspread version has nicely spread points at 120, 125, 130, 140, 150, and 160 MHz on one side and 144 to 148 on the other.

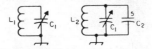

Fig. 14-5 — An absorption-type wavemeter can be the simplest form of tuned circuit, as in L1-C1, at A. Circuit B has less capacitance in C1, a fixed capacitor, C2, in parallel, and a smaller value of inductance in L2, for a band-spread effect.

If care is used in duplicating the originals, you can copy the dial scales reproduced here, Fig. 14-6, and you'll be close enough for ordinary work. Direct calibration with a reliable frequency source is much better, of course. You very likely can borrow a grid-dip meter for this purpose, if you do not own one.

Using the Wavemeters

We have already described some of the uses for the instruments, but here are practical examples. Suppose you have a 50-MHz crystal oscillator. You know it is oscillating, but you're not sure whether it is on the right overtone. Or perhaps you want to check a frequency multiplier to see if it is operating on the right harmonic. Connect a meter in the plate circuit, or in the grid circuit of the following stage, if any. Lacking a meter, use a lamp load or a neon indication, as in Fig. 14-1. Now, connect the wave-meter clip lead to a ground point

Fig. 14-6 — These wavemeter scales may be copied, if construction is exactly like the original units. White cards are 2-1/4 inches in diameter. Calibration should be regarded as rough only, until checked against a source of known frequency accuracy.

in the equipment, and hold the wavemeter so that it couples to the tuned circuit in question. Rotate the wavemeter dial slowly, watching the meter or output indication. There will be a quick dip downward as the wavemeter tunes through the frequency at which the stage is operating. Hold the wavemeter as far as possible from the circuit being checked, and still get the dip indication. This will show the frequency of the rf power with the best accuracy.

Watch out for live circuits. Remember that even low voltages can be lethal. Large amounts of rf power absorbed by the wavemeter may cause rf burns on sensitive skin. Always be on the alert to keep hands and other parts of the body away from any circuits carrying ac or dc voltages. The wavemeter circuits can be enclosed in transparent plastic, if desired, but constant attention to the ever-present danger of high voltage is the only real protection.

SIMPLE FIELD-STRENGTH INDICATOR AND WAVEMETER

Fig. 14-7 — A field-strength indicator and wave-meter for 50 and 144 MHz. The coil size is set so that the tuning range is approximately 47 to 175 MHz.

be copied with accuracy sufficient for most pur-poses, if the parts and layout of the original are duplicated. With values given the range is roughly 47 to 175 MHz, covering the 50- and 144-MHz bands with some leeway on both ends of the scale. The various frequencies from 48 MHz up, com-monly encountered in vhf transmitters, are also marked on the white scale, making the meter handy in checking oscillator and multiplier stages. Our brethren on lower bands may find this gadget useful for checking the frequency and source of vhf parasitic oscillations or harmonics in their equipment for the "dc bands."

A small plastic meter box with a sloping front panel is used for a case. If a metal box is used, the instrument will have less hand-capacity effect than with a case of insulating material, but it will interfere with its use as a simple wavemeter. The ground connection shown in broken lines in Fig. 14-8 is for a metal-box version, and represents the grounding of the rotor of C1. Parts may be arranged to suit the maker, so long as rf leads are kept short. Note the copper-strap short across the meter terminals. This should be kept in place whenever the plastic-box instrument is not in use, to prevent damage to the meter in strong rf fields.

Uses

A rough idea of the gain, pattern, and front-to-back ratio of a vhf beam can be obtained by setting the field-strength meter up at a distance out in

Some sort of field-strength indicator is a must for vhf antenna work, and it can be useful in other ways. The instrument of Fig. 14-7 doubles as a wavemeter. In this role it is more sensitive and versatile than tuned-circuit absorption wavemeters just described. The diode CR1 rectifies rf current, and the meter reads the resultant direct current. You can get visual indications of rf field strength and frequency without metering the circuits under examination.

With a pickup antenna connected to J1, the meter will indicate relative power being radiated by a vhf antenna, for use in evaluation or adjustment. Sensitivity depends on size of the pickup antenna, closeness of coupling between L1 and L2, type and condition of the diode, and range of the indicating meter. The lower the meter range the better. With a 100-μA meter the instrument will give full-scale deflection at 100 feet or more from a vhf beam, if a half-wave pickup antenna is used. With a 1-mA meter the separation is considerably less, for a given transmitter power and antenna gain.

The tuning range of C1-L2 can be calibrated with a grid-dip meter or any other source of rf power of known frequency, or the scale shown can

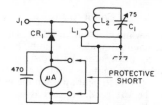

Fig. 14-8 — Schematic diagram of the field-strength meter. Ground connection shown in broken lines is for metal-case construction.

C1 — 75-pF miniature variable (Hammarlund APC-75B).

CR1 — 1N34 or other vhf diode.

J1 — Insulated tip jack.

L1 — 1 turn insulated hookup wire, 1/2-inch diameter, spaced 1 turn from L2.

L2 — 3 turns insulated hookup wire, 1/2-inch diameter, 1/4 inch long. Adjust turn spacing for desired tuning range on C1.

Meter is 100 microamperes, though up to 1 mA is usable, with reduced sensitivity.

Fig. 14-9 — Rear view of the field-strength meter. Note copper strap across meter terminals. This should be kept in place when the instrument is not in use, to protect the meter.

front of the antenna under test and then performing substitutions or adjustments. No diode is linear, so changes in meter reading are only indications, not accurate measurements. A favored method of evaluation, with a device of this kind, is to measure the power input to the antenna that will give a constant reading as conditions are changed. If power in the line can be read accurately the power ratios thus obtained give a fair indication of the results of the antenna adjustments or changes. More on this in the chapter on antennas.

In using the instrument as a wavemeter a pickup antenna may or may not be required. Usually an rf indication can be obtained by holding the wavemeter near the circuit to be checked. Tune the capacitor slowly until a meter indication begins to show, then move the instrument away to keep the meter from going off scale. If the diode is in a strong enough rf field there will be rectified current regardless of the setting of C1. In such circumstances it is advisable to use a pickup antenna a few inches long or more and move the instrument farther away, in order to prevent direct pickup by the diode. Varying the coupling between L1 and L2 is helpful in eliminating this blocking effect. Be sure to take all due precautions against high-voltage shock and rf burns in using this and other items of rf test equipment.

A sensitive microammeter is costly and fragile. Especially when working around high power, it is easy to run the 100-μA meter off scale without realizing it. To prevent damage to the meter it is advisable to keep it shorted at all times when the instrument is not in use. A strip of copper about 1/4 inch wide is kept wrapped around the meter terminals for this purpose, and is removed only when work is to be done.

REMOTE-INDICATING FIELD-STRENGTH METER

A limitation on the usefulness of a simple field-strength meter of the type shown in Fig. 14-7 is that when it is in a good position for doing its job the instrument may be far from the man who wants to observe its fluctuations as he makes adjustments. The ideal spot for a field-strength pickup device is as far out in front of the antenna being worked on as possible, and preferably in about the same plane. At this distance and height it must be observed by a separate worker, or the man making adjustments will have to use field glasses to read it, if he can see it at all.

The logical remedy is to make the pickup portion of a field-strength indicating device a separating unit, put it up where it will do the job required, and then run a line down to a meter at or near the adjusting position. The field-strength meter of Fig. 14-10 can be used with the meter box and pickup unit plugged together, as shown, or connected by means of a cable of any desired

length. The meter box itself is made usable for other measuring jobs by building a switch and appropriate multiplier circuits into the case. As a general-purpose test meter it can read 0 to 50 or 0

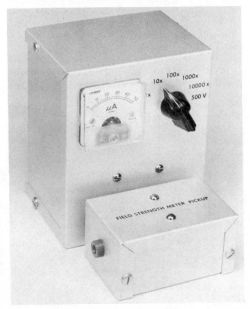

Fig. 14-10 — A vhf field-strength indicator and general-purpose test instrument for dc measurement. The small pickup unit can be plugged into the indicator as shown, or connected to it by a 2-wire cable of any desired length. Antenna rods or wires plug into jacks at each end of the small box. The meter can be used with test leads for measuring direct current and voltage. Ranges are 0 to 50 and 500 microamperes, 5, 50, and 500 milliamperes, and 0 to 500 volts dc.

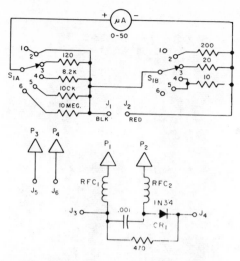

Fig. 14-11 — Schematic diagram of the remote-indicating field-strength meter. Resistors in the indicatorunit should be 5 percent or better for good meter accuracy.

CR1 — Any small rf diode, 1N34 or equivalent.

J1, J2 — Insulated tip jack (Johnson 105-601 to 611, depending on color).

J3, J4 — Insulated "banana jack" (Johnson 108-901 to 907).

J5, J6 — Insulated tip jack and sleeve (Johnson 105-701 to 711).

P1, P2 — Insulated tip plug, male (Johnson 105-601 to 611, with 5/8 inch No. 12 wire soldered in jack).

P3, P4 — Insulated tip plug (Johnson 105-301 to 311).

RFC1, RFC2 — 1-watt resistor wound full length with No. 30 enamel.

S1 — 2-section 6-position switch.

to 500 microamperes, or 5, 50, or 500 milli-amperes, and 0 to 500 volts, dc. The multiplier circuit also allows different levels of sensitivity in the field-strength indicating role.

As may be seen from the lower portion of Fig. 14-11, the pickup unit, a 1-5/8 × 2-1/8 × 3-1/4-inch Minibox, contains only a diode, a resistor to complete the dc circuit, a bypass capacitor, two rf chokes, and two "banana jacks," one at each end of the box. These take plug-in wires or rods, which make up a half-wave dipole. Something shorter is usable, if maximum sensitivity is not important. There are no tuned circuits, so the system will work on any frequency. The only selectivity is the very slight amount introduced by the length of the pickup dipole.

On the back of the small case are two pin plugs. These take matching pin jacks on the end of the remote cable, or they can plug directly into the pin jacks on the 3 × 4 × 5-inch Minibox used for the meter case. The two-conductor connecting cable can be any available wire. Ordinary zip cord for home-appliance wiring is convenient. Coax or Twin-Lead that may have seen better days is also suitable.

Layout of parts in both units is generally uncritical, and obvious from the pictures. The lower the meter range used, the more sensitive the instrument becomes. A fairly inexpensive imported 50-microampere meter (AMD MRA-38) is shown. With this meter it is possible to get a usable indication of rf at up to several hundred feet away from a good beam, if a half-wave pickup antenna is plugged into J3 and J4. It is used with a 100-foot cord by the author.

There is really only one important rule in using the instrument: Be *sure* that you have the multiplier switch, S1, set in such a position that the meter movement will not be banged off-scale. When there is the slightest doubt about the magnitude of the reading to be expected, start on the highest current range and work down. This applies whether you are reading plate current in a transmitter or using the instrument as a field-strength meter. A 50-microampere meter can be burned out in a tiny fraction of a second. Play safe!

The meter ranges other than 0-50 μA are obtained by introducing various resistances in the meter circuit, as shown in Fig. 14-11. This means that shunts in circuits being checked may affect the accuracy of current readings. For more on field-strength-meter techniques see the previous item, and Chapter 8.

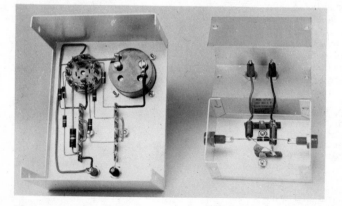

Fig. 14-12 — Interiors of the field-strength meter pick-up unit, right, and meter box, left.

A TRANSMATCH FOR 50 AND 144 MHz WITH SWR INDICATOR

The antenna coupler (Transmatch) shown in Fig. 14-13 will permit unbalanced transmitter output lines (50-75 ohms) to be matched to balanced feeders in the 300- to 450-ohm impedance range. Also, coax-to-coax matching is possible with this circuit, permitting 50-ohm lines to be matched to 75-ohm lines, or vice versa. In situations where a high SWR condition exists, this coupler will enable the transmitter to look into a matched load.

The built-in Monimatch-type SWR indicator enables the operator to tune the Transmatch for minimum reflected power, assuring a good match between the transmitter and the feed line. Remember that the use of devices of this kind will not correct for any mismatch that exists at the antenna end of the line. Although it assures a good match between the transmitter and the line, it can only disguise the fact that a mismatch exists at the antenna.

The Circuit

Balanced circuits are used for both bands. Butterfly capacitors are employed for good circuit symmetry. The links of tuned circuits L2 and L3 in Fig. 14-14 are series-tuned to tune out reactance in the line. Switch S1 transfers the SWR bridge element from one tuned circuit to the other, providing visual indication of the matching adjustments. Section S1B shorts out the unused tuned circuit to prevent interaction. Switch S2 selects either the forward- or reflected-power sampling circuits from the bridge and supplies their rectified dc voltages to R1, the meter sensitivity control which is adjusted for full-scale meter reading when S2 is set to read forward power.

Construction

A homemade 12 × 5 × 5-inch aluminum cabinet is used. (See September, 1966, *QST*, p. 17 for construction details.) If a similar layout is followed keeping all leads as short as practical, the complete unit can be housed in a commercially available chassis or cabinet. The rf tuning controls are mounted in a straight line across the front of the cabinet. The SWR bridge element is bolted to the bottom of the case (inside) between the input jack, J7, and the band-change switch, S1. Shielded audio cable is used to connect the output of the bridge to the lugs on S2. Short lengths of RG-58/U coax cable connect L2 and L3 to S1A. The shield braids of both cables should be grounded to the chassis at each end.

A 2-lug terminal strip is bolted to the chassis directly under the center of L1. Similarly, a second terminal strip with two lugs is mounted under the midpoint of L4. These strips serve as mounting points for links L2 and L3. No. 12 wire connects the rotors of all four tuning capacitors in to one another. The ground bus is also connected to the main chassis at one point. This procedure assures a better ground return for the capacitors than might

Fig. 14-13 — Antenna couplers for 50 and 144 MHz combined with an SWR and relative-power indicator, in one package.

be possible by relying upon the physical contact provided by the shaft bushings.

Make coil taps by bending No. 6 solder lugs around the coil wire at the proper spots, then soldering the lugs in place. No. 20 wire is used to connect the taps of L1 to jacks J1 and J2. A short piece of 300-ohm twin line connects the taps of L4 to J4 and J5. A No. 6 solder lug is bolted to the outside (back) of the cabinet as near to J1 as possible. Another such lug is placed adjacent to J4. When operating coax-to-coax style, a short jumper wire connects J1 to its ground lug, or J4 to its ground lug, depending on the band being operated. The jumper must be removed for balanced-feeder operation.

The Bridge Element

The SWR element is of the Monimatch variety. The circuit is given in Fig. 14-14A, with its physical layout shown in B. The inner line, L6, is a 4-inch length of 1/4-inch OD copper tubing. One end of L6 is soldered directly to the center lug of J7, the remaining end supported by a small standoff insulator. The line is mounted in plastic blocks for additional support, making sure that it is centered within the walls of L8, the aluminum outer channel. J7 should be mounted on the back wall of the box so as to be centered on the axis of L6 when it is in position. The pickup lines, L5 and L7, are made from No. 16 wire, each 3 inches in length, and are spaced 1/8 inch away from L6, being supported by the plastic blocks. Once they are in place, a drop of Duco cement should be added at each point where they pass through the plastic blocks.

The 150-ohm terminating resistors (1/2-watt units) are mounted inside the channel, L8, and are soldered to ground lugs. Diodes CR1 and CR2 attach to the remaining ends of wires and are routed out through small holes in the walls of L8. It is important that the physical placement of the diodes, the resistors, and the pickup wires be symmetrical. The better the symmetry, the better will be the balance of the bridge, electrically. The diodes and their related 0.001-μF bypass capacitors are attached to small terminal strips that are mounted near the holes in L8. If matched resistors

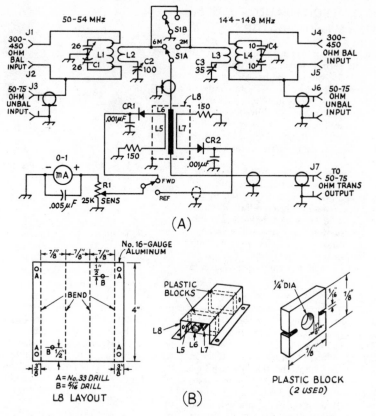

Fig. 14-14 — At A, the schematic diagram of the vhf Transmatch. Capacitance is in pF unless otherwise noted. Resistance is in ohms, K = 1000. At B, physical layout of the bridge element and the plastic insulating blocks.

C1 — 26-pF per section butterfly (E. F. Johnson 167-22).
C2 — 100-pF miniature variable (Millen 20100).
C3 — 35-pF miniature variable (Millen 20035).
C4 — 10-pF per section butterfly (E. F. Johnson 167-21).
CR1, CR2 — Germanium diode, 1N34A or equiv.
J1-J4, incl. — Insulated binding post.
J5-J7, incl. — SO-239-style chassis connector.
L1 — 7 turns No. 10 copper wire, 1-1/2-inch dia, spaced one wire thickness between turns. Tap 2-1/2 turns from each end.
L2 — 2 turns No. 14 enam. or spaghetti-covered bare wire, 1/2-inch dia, over center of L1.

L3 — 2 turns No. 14 enam. or spaghetti-covered bare wire, 1-1/2-inch dia, over center of L4.
L4 — 5 turns No. 10 copper wire, 1-inch dia, spaced one wire thickness between turns. Tap 1-1/2 turns from each end.
L5 — 3-inch length of No. 16 solid wire.
L6 — 4-inch length of 1/4-inch dia copper tubing.
L7 — Same as L5.
L8 — See drawing.
R1 — 25,000-ohm control, linear taper.
S1 — 2-pole 2-position rotary, single section, phenolic switch (Centralab 1462).
S2 — Spst rotary, single section, phenolic switch (Centralab 1460).

and matched diodes are used in the bridge circuit, electrical balance will be even better than is possible with random-selected components. Since the bridge is a relative-reading instrument, the latter condition is not vital.

Operation

Attach the vhf transmitter to J7 with a short length of coax cable. Connect a balanced feeder to J1 and J2 (for 50-MHz operation), or to J4 and J5 (for 144-MHz operation). Set S1 to the desired band position and switch S2 to read forward power. Initially, R1 should be set for minimum

meter sensitivity. Apply power from the transmitter — low power until initial tuning is completed — and adjust R1 for full-scale meter reading. For 144-MHz operation, tune C3 and C4 in the same manner. Repeat the tuning until no further reduction in reflected power is possible. The meter should fall to zero, indicating a 1:1 match. Switch S2 back to the forward position and set R1 for a full-scale meter reading. No further adjustments will be needed unless the transmitter frequency is changed appreciably. The tuning procedure is identical for matching coax to coax. In doing so, however, the antenna feed line (coax) is connected to either J3 or J6 and the shorting strap (discussed

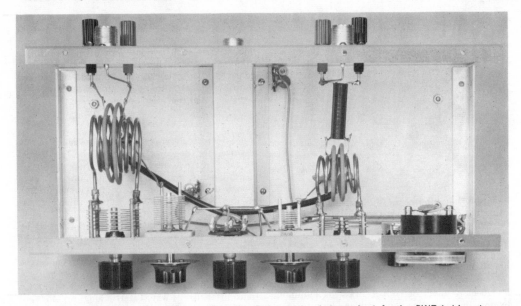

Fig. 14-15 — Inside view of the Transmatch. The 6-meter circuit is at the left, the SWR bridge element is at the center, and the 2-meter circuit is to the right of the bridge element. The meter, S2, and R1 are at the far right.

earlier) must be connected to J1 or J4. In some situations, it may be possible to get a better match by leaving the shorting strap off.

After the coupler is tuned up, the transmitter power can be increased to its normal level. This unit will handle power levels up to 500 watts (transmitter output power) provided the coupler is tuned for a matched condition at all times.

Reduced power (less than 50 watts) should be used during initial tuneup, thus preventing parts from being damaged by heating or arcing. The coupler should never be operated without a load connected to its output terminals. Such operation will usually destroy the 150-ohm resistors and the diodes, CR1 and CR2, in addition to causing arcs in the Transmatch.

A VHF IMPEDANCE BRIDGE

It is often helpful to be able to measure impedances of input and output circuits of vhf converters, transmitters, cavity filters, dummy loads, and antennas. Most impedance-matching devices described in amateur literature are ineffective above about 30 MHz, because of inaccuracies resulting from excessive internal capacitance and inductance. The bridge of Figs. 14-16 through 18 was tailored to the needs of the vhf operator. Minimum lead inductance and components chosen for vhf qualities permit reasonable accuracy in the vhf range.

An SWR bridge can be used to secure a proper match between circuits, or between a circuit and its load, but this does not allow measurement of the terminal impedance when a mismatch is present. This impedance bridge will enable the user to make direct readings of impedance in the 10-to-500-ohm range, thus permitting the solution of a variety of matching problems.

Construction

It is suggested that the builder duplicate, as nearly as possible, the physical layout. Flashing copper 1/4 inch wide is used for leads in the bridge portion of the circuit, to keep down lead in-

Fig. 14-16 — Simple vhf impedance bridge. Settings of the variable control, marked on the front of the case, represent values of impedance corresponding to nulls in meter indication.

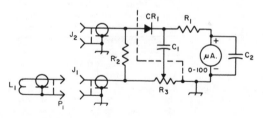

Fig. 14-17 — Interior of the impedance bridge. Inside the shield, right, are the coaxial terminals, the variable control, R3, and the load resistor, R2. Feedthrough insulators may be improvised from 1/4-inch Teflon rod. Leads thereto are 1/4-inch-wide copper strips. Load resistor R2 is connected directly between the terminals of J1 and J2.

ductance. A shield of copper, brass, or aluminum divides the metering and bridge circuits. The potentiometer R3 is a 2-watt carbon control, with linear taper, so that the resistance scale will not be cramped at one end. It is mounted on an insulating plate, rather than on the metal box, to reduce capacitance between the chassis and the metal shield on the control. The insulated mounting plate is then fastened to the minibox, with the control bushing centered in a 5/8-inch hole.

The bridge resistor R1 is a 5-percent 1-watt carbon. It is made of two 1000-ohm 1/2-watt resistors in parallel, in the example shown. R2 should be 50 ohms, a value not readily obtainable. This is within the possible range of 47-ohm 10-percent tolerance resistors, so a stock of these can be checked for the nearest to the desired 50 ohms. The value of a resistor can also be raised by filing into the carbon element. Be sure that the ohmmeter used for checking the resistance value is reliable, if accuracy is desired.

The jacks J1 and J2 are mounted as closely together as their flanges permit. The meter is a 100-microampere type, for maximum sensitivity when using the bridge with rf sources of low power output. It is an inexpensive 1-3/4-inch square imported model (Calrad).

Checking and Calibration

A pointer knob on R3 and a paper dial scale pasted to the end of the Minibox provide for calibration. Select a number of 1-watt carbon resistors of values between 10 and 500 ohms, to be used as calibration loads for the bridge. Attach the link L1 to the input jack J1. Couple a grid-dip meter or some other low-power source of rf power to the link. Use a frequency around 145 MHz if best accuracy is wanted in the 2-meter band.

Attach a low-value resistor to J2 with the shortest possible leads. Adjust the coupling between the rf source and L1 for full-scale reading on the bridge meter, or as high a reading as possible if less than full-scale. Next, adjust R3 for a null in the

bridge meter reading, making certain that the null is as deep as possible. Mark the dial scale, and jot down the value of the load resistor used. Repeat this process with various resistor values unitl a complete set of calibration points has been obtained. A new scale can now be made and marked permanently with India ink, indicating the resistance values at the check points.

Uses

The more nearly a load is to being purely resistive, the deeper the null will be. As a load becomes reactive, as frequently happens in rf measurements, the null is less pronounced. Even though the null is poor, the readings remain useful, as they approximate the actual value of the impedance under measurement.

Vhf matching networks may be checked by presetting the bridge to the desired value of resistance, and then making adjustments to the matching network until the null is obtained on the bridge meter. Adjust carefully for best null. A Gamma-match system can be adjusted without a transmitter in this way. Insert a length of coax, of the impedance of the line to be used, between the antenna and the bridge. This line should be a multiple of a half wavelength long electrically, so that the antenna impedance will be repeated at the output terminal. This cable permits the operator to take readings without being in the immediate field of the antenna. A 2-wavelength section should be about right for work in the 144-MHz band. If the coax is solid-dielectric (not foam) RG-8 or similar, a test cable of 107 inches will do.

Other devices such as the coaxial-line filters of Chapter 15 may be checked for input and output impedance by using line sections that are multiples of a half wavelength, and a dummy load of the correct impedance. The filter input or output circuit can then be adjusted for a null at the desired impedance. Transmitter or converter input or output circuits can be adjusted in a similar manner. Unknown values of impedance can be

Fig. 14-18 — Schematic diagram of the vhf impedance bridge.
C1 — 0.002-μF disk ceramic.
C2 — 0.001-μF disk ceramic.
CR1 — 1N82A diode. 1N34 also usable.
J1, J2 — Coaxial connector, SO-239.
L1 — 1 turn No. 12 enamel, 1-inch diameter.
P1 — Coaxial plug, PL-259.
R1 — 500-ohm carbon, 1 watt.
R2 — 50-ohm carbon, 1 watt.
R3 — 500-ohm 2-watt control, linear taper (Allen Bradley). Case is 2-1/4 × 2-1/4 × 4-inch Minibox.

determined by attaching the bridge to the circuit being tested, and then sweeping across the bridge range for a null.

Though a grid-dip meter is mentioned as a power source, a low-powered transmitter can, of course, be used in these various applications. The frequency stability of the transmitter is an advantage, but be sure that it has output only in the desired frequency range. Use of a coaxial filter in the transmitter output may be desirable, in order to prevent harmonics and subharmonics from reaching the bridge.

AN INEXPENSIVE DIRECTIONAL COUPLER

Precision in-line metering devices that are capable of reading forward and reflected power over a wide range of frequencies are very useful in amateur vhf and uhf work, but their rather high cost puts them out of the reach of many vhf enthusiasts. This device by Tom McMullen, W1SL, is an inexpensive adaptation of their basic principles. You can make it yourself for the cost of a meter, a few small parts, and bits of copper pipe and fittings that can be found in the plumbing stocks at many hardware stores. It can be as accurate as you want to make it.

Such an instrument is known by several names: directional coupler, in-line wattmeter, SWR indicator, and so on. W1SL calls his a "line sampler."[2] It can be left in the antenna line at all times, without consuming appreciable power or affecting reception. Commercially available units are also simple. It is their precision workmanship and reliable calibration over wide frequency ranges that make them costly to buy, though a joy to own.

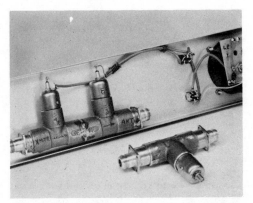

Fig. 14-19 — Two versions of the line sampler. The single unit described in detail herewith is in the foreground. Two sections in a single assembly, made by W1NTH, provide for monitoring forward and reflected power without probe reversal.

Construction

The sampler consists of a short section of hand-made coaxial line, in this instance of 50 ohms impedance, with a reversible probe coupled to it. A small pickup loop built into the probe is terminated with a resistor at one end and a diode at the other. The resistor matches the impedance of the loop, not the impedance of the line section. Energy picked up by the loop is rectified by the diode, and the resultant current is fed to a meter equipped with a calibration control.

The principal metal parts of the device are a brass plumbing T, a pipe cap, short pieces of 3/4-inch ID and 5/16-inch OD copper pipe, and two coaxial fittings. Other available tubing combinations for 50-ohm line may be usable. The ratio of outer-conductor ID to inner-conductor OD should be 2.4/1. For a sampler to be used with other impedances of transmission line, see Fig. 8-28 for suitable ratios of conductor sizes. The photographs and Figs. 14-19 and 20 just about tell the rest of the story.

Soldering of the large parts can be done with a 300-watt iron or a small torch. A neat job can be done if the inside of the T and the outside of the pipe are tinned before assembling. When the pieces are reheated and pushed together, a good mechan-

ical and electrical bond will result. If a torch is used, go easy with the heat, as an over-heated and discolored fitting will not accept solder well.

The inside of the line section must be smooth and without gaps or burrs. Any protrusions into the line must be removed with a file or reamer. If a tubing cutter is used, apply minimum pressure, or large burrs will be formed and will be hard to remove.

Coaxial connectors with Teflon or other heat-resistant insulation are recommended. Type N, with split-ring retainers for the center conductors, are preferred. Pry the split-ring washers out with a knife point or small screwdriver. Don't lose them, as they'll be needed in the final assembly.

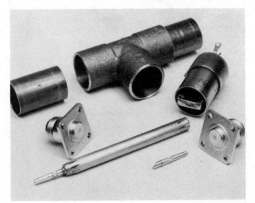

Fig. 14-20 — Major components of the line sampler. The brass T and two end sections are at the back of the picture. A completed probe assembly is at the right. The N connectors have their center pins removed. The pins are shown with one inserted in the left end of the inner conductor and the other lying in the right foreground.

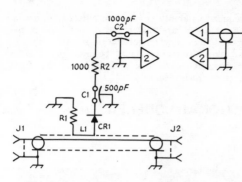

The inner conductor is prepared by making eight radial cuts in one end, using a coping saw with a fine-toothed blade, to a depth of 1/2 inch. The fingers so made are then bent together, forming a tapered end, as seen in Fig. 14-22. Solder the center pin of a coaxial fitting into this, again being careful not to overheat the work.

In preparation for soldering the body of the coax connector to the copper pipe, it is convenient to use a similar fitting clamped into a vise as a holding fixture, with the T assembly resting on top, held in place by its own weight. Use the partially prepared center conductor to insure that the coax connector is concentric with the outer conductor. After being sure that the ends of the pipe are cut exactly perpendicular to the axis, apply heat to the coax fitting, using just enough so that a smooth fillet of solder can be formed where the flange and pipe meet.

Before completing the center conductor, check its length. It should clear the inner surface of the connector by the thickness of the split ring on the center pin. File to length, if necessary, slot as with the other end, and solder the center pin in place. The fitting can now be soldered onto the pipe, to complete the 50-ohm line section.

The probe assembly is made from a 1-1/2-inch length of the copper pipe, with a pipe cap on the top to support the upper feedthrough capacitor, C2. The coupling loop is mounted by means of small Teflon standoffs on a copper disk, cut to fit

Fig. 14-21 — Circuit diagram for the line sampler.
C1 — 500-pF feedthrough capacitor, solder-in type.
C2 — 1000-pF feedthrough capacitor, threaded type.
CR1 — Germanium diode 1N34, 1N60, 1N270, 1N295, or similar.
J1, J2 — Coaxial connector, type N (UG-58 A/U).
L1 — Pickup loop, copper strap 1 inch long × 3/16 inch wide. Bend into "C" shape with flat portion 5/8-inch long.
M1 — 0-100μA meter.
R1 — Composition resistor, 82 to 100 ohms. See text.
R3 — 50,000-ohm composition control, linear taper.

inside the pipe. The disk has four small tabs around the edge for soldering inside the pipe. The diode, CR1, is connected between one end of the loop and a 500-pF feedthrough capacitor, C1, soldered into the disk. The terminating resistor, R1, is connected between the other end of the loop and ground, as directly as possible.

When the disk assembly is completed, insert it into the pipe, apply heat to the outside, and solder the tabs in place by melting solder into the assembly at the tabs. The position of the loop with respect to the end of the pipe will determine the sensitivity of a given probe. For power levels up to 200 watts the loop should extend beyond the face of the pipe about 5/32 inch. For use at higher power levels the loop should protrude only 3/32 inch. For operation with very low power levels the probe position can be determined by experiment.

The decoupling resistor, R2, and feedthrough capacitor, C2, can be connected, and the pipe cap put in place. The threaded portion of the capacitor extends through the cap. Put a solder lug over it before tightening its nut in place. Fasten the cap with two small screws that go into threaded holes in the pipe.

Calibration

The sampler is very useful for many jobs, even if it is not accurately calibrated, though it is desirable to calibrate it against a wattmeter of known accuracy. A good 50-ohm dummy load is a must. (More on loads elsewhere in this chapter.)

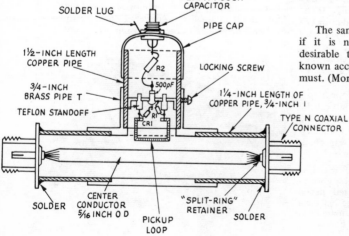

Fig. 14-22 — Cross-section view of the line sampler. The pickup loop is supported by two Teflon standoff insulators. The probe body is secured in place with one or more locking screws through holes in the brass T.

The first step is to adjust the inductance of the loop or the value of the terminating resistor, for lowest reflected-power reading. The loop is the easier to change. Filing it to reduce its width will increase its impedance. Increasing the cross-section of the loop will lower it, and this can be done by coating it with solder. When the reflected-power reading is reduced as far as possible, reverse the probe and calibrate for forward power, by increasing the transmitter power output in steps and making a graph of the meter readings obtained. Use the calibration control, R3, to set the maximum reading.

Variations

Rather than use one sampler for monitoring both forward and reflected power by repeatedly reversing the probe, it is better to make two assemblies by mounting two T fittings end-to-end, using one for forward and one for reflected power. The meter can be switched between the probes, or two meters can be used.

The sampler described was calibrated at 146 MHz, as it was intended for 2-meter repeater use.

On higher bands the meter reading will be higher for a given power level, and it will be lower for lower-frequency bands. Calibration for two or three adjacent bands can be achieved by making the probe depth adjustable, with stops or marks to aid in resetting for a given band. And, of course, more probes can be made, with each calibrated for a given band, as is done in some of the commercially available units.

Other sizes of pipe and fittings can be used, by making use of information given in Chapter 8 to select conductor sizes required for the desired impedances. (Since it is occasionally possible to pick up good bargains in 72-ohm line, you might like to make up a sampler for this impedance.)

Type N fittings were used because of their constant impedance, and their ease of assembly. Most have the split-ring retainer, which is simple to use in this application. Some have a crimping method, as do apparently all BNC connectors. If a fitting must be used that cannot be taken apart, drill a hole large enough to clear a soldering iron tip in the copper-pipe outer conductor. A hole of up to 3/8-inch diameter will have very little effect on the operation of the sampler.

SILICON DIODE NOISE GENERATOR

One of the most useful tools in adjusting vhf receivers is a noise generator.[3] In its simplest form a noise generator is a diode drawing current, and therefore making noise. This noise extends all across the rf spectrum, up to a frequency determined mainly by the circuitry and the diode used.

Such a crystal-diode noise generator is shown in Figs. 14-23 through 25. Noise figure cannot be "measured" with a device of this kind, but it is handy as a noise source for adjusting a vhf receiver for best noise figure. The lower the diode current for a given margin of diode noise over receiver noise, the better the receiver is working.

Construction

The noise generator is built in an aluminum Minibox 3-1/4 × 2-1/8 × 1-5/8 inches in size (Bud CU-3001-A). Only the load resistor, R1, the diode, CR1, and the bypass capacitor, C1, are critical as to mounting position. These should be connected with absolutely minimum leads, if the generator is to be useful above 100 MHz or so. R1 is inside the adapter sleeve of P1. C1 should be a button-mica or other capacitor having good uhf characteristics.

Ordinary disk ceramics are not suitable above 50 MHz.

The coaxial plug should match the connectors on the receiving equipment with which the generator is to be most often used. The PL-259 plug with UG-176/U adapter was used here. The flange on the adapter is only very slightly larger in diameter than the threaded portion, so using it as a means of clamping the assembly to the generator case is not very satisfactory. To give more binding surface, washers of flashing copper were made for both sides of the mounting hole. One is shown in Fig. 14-25. Cut with shears from one edge to the washer hole, and bend the washer at the break slightly, so that it can be threaded onto the adapter sleeve. Use one of these washers on each side of the box, which must be drilled for a 3/8-inch hole to pass the threaded portion of the adapter. One washer can be soldered to the adapter flange and the other to the end of the plug sleeve, to make the whole assembly less likely to work loose in using the noise generator.

The battery is the 9-volt type commonly used in small transistor radios. A mercury battery is

Fig. 14-23 — Silicon-diode noise generator for vhf receiver testing, with its audio detector, left, for smoothing out noise readings. Tip jacks in the noise generator permit taking diode current readings.

Fig. 14-24 — Interior of the diode noise generator. The diode, load resistor and bypass capacitor should be connected with the shortest possible leads.

worth the difference in price as its voltage will remain practically constant throughout its useful life. This makes possible a reasonably accurate calibration of the generator's noise output in terms of the setting of the series control, R2.

Connection to the battery is made by means of a terminal block removed from the top of a dead battery. The fiber insulating plate on which the terminals are mounted is fastened to the front wall of the box. The smaller of its terminals is grounded to the case, and the other is backed up by two layers of plastic insulating tape. The assembly thus acts as both connector and mounting plate for the battery.

The large end of the diode is held in a plate clip of the type used for metal tubes. The smaller end contact was removed from an old octal wafer socket. Many different diodes are usable if the upper limit of frequency is not important. Silicon rectifier diodes of the kind used in power-supply work can be used at 50 or 144 MHz, but they draw considerable current, and do not work well at higher frequencies. Uhf mixer diodes of the 1N21 series are recommended. Also used with good results: 1N25 and 1N32. Germanium diodes such as the 1N34 are not satisfactory. A good diode will give plenty of noise with no more than about 2 mA diode current. You may want to put a fixed resistor in series with R2 to keep the current below this point, if all your work is going to be with receiver front ends known to be in quite good working order.

The tip jacks, J1 and J2, are for measuring current through the diode. This will run about 10 mA maximum with the 1N21 series diodes, but may be higher with other types. The setting of R2 is not meaningful when batteries other than the

Fig. 14-24 — Interior of the diode noise generator. The diode, load resistor and bypass capacitor should be connected with the shortest possible leads.

mercury type are used, but the diode current is directly related to noise output, and can be calibrated roughly in noise figure.

The load resistor, R1, should be a value equal to the line impedance of the antenna system to be used. If a 51-ohm resistor is not available, 47 ohms is close enough for ordinary purposes in work with 52-ohm antenna systems. Use a 75-ohm resistor if the line is 72 ohms. A 68-ohm load may be used if both 52- and 72-ohm lines are to be encountered. The value is not particularly critical, as the noise generator is not a precise test instrument.

Using the Generator

In receiver work the generator is best connected directly to the receiver or converter antenna jack. Run the receiver with its avc off, if possible. Turn up the rf and audio gain controls until receiver noise is heard. Keep the rf gain control as low as possible, in order to prevent overload, except where the gain of the first stage in the receiving system is affected by the gain control setting. This is rare in vhf receiving setups, but it may be found in lower band gear. Note the level of the receiver noise, by ear or by connecting an ac voltmeter, dB meter, or the audio detector described later, across the speaker or earphone terminals. Now turn on the noise generator, starting with R2 at its maximum resistance setting. If no increase in noise is heard, reduce the resistance slowly until noise begins to rise.

Use a noise increase that you can remember or measure. The lower the crystal current required to give this noise increase, the better the receiver. This gives a rough comparison of one vhf converter to another, provided that they are for the same band. Preferably, the converters so compared should be used with the same receiver. Adjustment of antenna coupling, oscillator injection, tests on various tubes or transistors, or checking any other factor affecting receiver performance, can be done with a noise generator of this type. Line loss in a length of coaxial line can also be measured, by connecting the line between the noise generator and the converter, noting the difference in noise through the line, and with direct connection of the generator.

In receivers having no provision for removing avc, some other method of measuring noise output must be made. The receiver S meter can be used, if it responds to the receiver's noise level with the generator turned off. If it doesn't, it may be necessary to run the noise-generator output higher than normally would be the case, in order to get a meter rise indication on generator noise.

Any receiver adjustment that makes it possible to obtain a given noise increase with a lower diode current, or a greater S-meter reading increase with the same level of diode current, is an improvement.

As shown, the noise generator produces in excess of 20 dB of noise at 50 and 144 MHz, and enough to be usable with any fairly good receiver

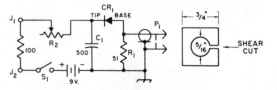

Fig. 14-25 — Schematic diagram of the noise generator. Two washers, right, are used to mount the coaxial plug to the case.

C1 — 500-pF button mica.
CR1 — Silicon mixer diode, 1N21, etc.
J1, J2 — Insulated tip jack.
P1 — Coaxial plug, PL-259, with UG-176 adapter.
S1 — Toggle or pushbutton switch.
R1 — 51-ohm 1/2-watt carbon, mounted inside adapter sleeve of P1.
R2 — 50,000-ohm control.

at 220 and 420 MHz. The amount of noise and the upper useful frequency limit depend on the diode used, and on its condition. Avoid subjecting the diode to strong rf fields, or to excessive current. If you buy a good diode, it will probably come encased in metal foil, or otherwise shielded. Keep it that way until it is installed in the noise generator, and then use the lowest diode current that will give satisfactory noise output.

A refinement some users like is to substitute a pushbutton switch for the toggle type for S1. If this is the microswitch type it can be closed with light finger pressure, making it easy to take readings without the likelihood of disturbing the setting of the diode-current control, R2.

Audio Detector for Noise-Generator Work

In using a vacuum-tube voltmeter or other ac output meter in noise-generator work the erratic nature of the meter indication is often a problem. Noise is random in nature, and unless the meter is highly damped, the needle will fluctuate constantly, making it difficult to establish a reference. The device shown with the silicon-diode noise generator in Fig. 14-23 is a simple audio detector to smooth out such meter readings.

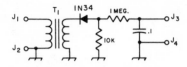

Fig. 14-26 — Schematic diagram of the average-type audio detector shown in Fig. 14-23. Parts arrangement is uncritical.

J1, J2, J3, J4 — Tip jack.
T1 — Small audio output transformer. Low-impedance winding connects to J1, J2.

Originally described by KØDJP in *QST*,[4] it is merely connected to the speaker or earphone terminals of the receiver, and the meter is then connected to its output terminals. The detector is shown schematically in Fig. 14-26. Use is the same as if the meter were connected to the receiver directly. The above reference is well worth reading by anyone interested in improving receiver performance.

Though the audio detector is shown with the crystal-diode noise generator, it is helpful with other types of noise generators, wherever the flickering of the meter indication may be troublesome.

LOW-POWER DUMMY LOADS

In order to test a transmitter legally, an amateur must use a dummy load. Most of us put our rigs on the air for test purposes for brief periods, but the considerable running of a transmitter that is usually required during construction and trouble-shooting should not be done with the transmitter feeding an antenna. When an antenna test is unavoidable, the operator should be sure that the frequency to be occupied is not being used for communication at the time. If an appreciable transmitter-on time is contemplated, a non-radiating load is the only considerate (and legal) approach to testing.

Once it was the usual thing to hook a lamp of suitable wattage across the output terminals. This may still suffice, but it leaves much to be desired in most instances. Few lamps or combinations thereof come anywhere near to being 50-ohm loads, in the vhf range, and consequently they may be all but useless for any meaningful testing. Exceptions are some small pilot lamps (within their limited power-handling capabilities), and incandescent lamps of around 100-watt rating. Several blue-bead pilot lamps in parallel may make a fair vhf load, and some 100-watt lamps singly or in parallel are usable at frequencies in the vhf range.

Lamps in between these power levels are highly reactive, and the impedances they represent vary greatly with the power being dissipated. Low-wattage incandescent lamps, 15 to 40 watts, are particularly poor. Lamps larger than the 100-watt size nearly always develop "hot spots" in a portion of their filaments, making them unreliable as power indicators. They also tend to go gassy and burn out before reaching their normal power level. Lamps of intermediate wattage can be improved somewhat as rf loads by connecting a variable capacitor in series to tune out the reactance they and their leads represent. See Fig. 14-27A.

Put this combination on the output of your SWR bridge, and feed in some rf power. Tune the capacitor for lowest reflected power, not maximum lamp brilliance. Readjust transmitter output coupling for maximum output, after the load is matched as well as you can get it. A maximum value of 100 pF should serve for 50 or 144-MHz loads. Use 50 pF if nothing lower than 144 MHz is to be used, and 25 pF is enough for higher bands, if the combination will work at all.

The resistive load, B, is much better, within its power capabilities. Two such dummy loads using paralleled resistors are shown in Fig. 14-28. Three

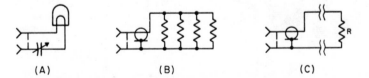

(A)   (B)   (C)

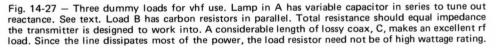

Fig. 14-27 — Three dummy loads for vhf use. Lamp in A has variable capacitor in series to tune out reactance. See text. Load B has carbon resistors in parallel. Total resistance should equal impedance the transmitter is designed to work into. A considerable length of lossy coax, C, makes an excellent rf load. Since the line dissipates most of the power, the load resistor need not be of high wattage rating.

Fig. 14-28 — Two vhf dummy loads of the type shown schematically in Fig. 14-27B. Copper fins on unit at right aid in dissipating heat, and disks provide low-inductance parallel connectors.

considerations are important here: the resistors must be the composition (carbon) type, the inductance of the leads must be kept to an absolute minimum, and the power to be dissipated should be kept below the rated total wattage of the resistors used, except for brief tests.

Any number of resistors can be connected in parallel, so long as they are all the same wattage and the same resistance. Six 330-ohm 1-watt carbon resistors are paralleled by soldering their ends to straps of flashing copper in the unit at the left. One strap solders to the coaxial fitting sleeve, and the other is narrowed down to fit inside the sleeve and make contact to the pin. The portion inside the fitting is covered with insulating spaghetti or plastic tape, to prevent shorts.

A somewhat better load, where higher dissipation is wanted, is seen at the right. Here disks of

flashing copper are used, and the resistors mounted in a circle, to keep inductance down. Nine 470-ohm resistors are used in the unit pictured, but thirteen 680-ohm or nineteen 1000-ohm resistors would probably do equally well.

These are not perfect loads, but they are much better than lamps. They show no greater than 1.2:1 SWR at 50, 144, or 220 MHz, with the best match (close to 1:1) at 50 MHz. Don't take the wattage ratings of the resistors too literally. They get warm at a dissipation of 1 watt each, and when they get more than just warm to the touch, the resistance value may begin to change. This is not too much of a problem ordinarily, as the power is usually on for only a fraction of a minute at a time, just long enough to take a reading or make a quick adjustment. The cooling fins on the unit at the right help to keep the heat flowing out of the resistors, and it will dissipate more than 10 watts safely for brief periods; no more than a few seconds at a time.

The load at C is the best of all. In fact, the principle is used in some of the best rf wattmeters and dummy loads made. If you've got 100 feet of coax that is too lossy for use on an antenna, don't throw it away; it is an ideal dummy load. Looking back to Table 8-III, we see that 100 feet of RG-58/U (even in new condition!) has a loss of 6 dB per 100 feet at 144 MHz. This means that you can put the circular load of Fig. 14-28 on the end of it, feed 40 watts into the other end, and the resistors will just reach their rated dissipation. At 420 MHz you could run 60 watts into the line and it wouldn't hurt the load. You can even short the end of the line, or leave it open, and it will make hardly any difference in the SWR reading at 432 MHz.

A load of this kind is a good match at any frequency where the loss is 6 dB or more, and its power-handling capability is considerable, for short test periods. If the coax can be coiled loosely and subjected to a cooling air blast, it can be made to take just about any amateur power for short periods.

Improved Resistive Load for 432 MHz

The resistor-bank load of Fig. 14-29 has a detachable tuned circuit, which can be connected to improve its performance in the 420-MHz range. Six 330-ohm 1-watt resistors are soldered between the center-conductor tip and the edges of the flange of an SO-239 coaxial fitting. Without tuning the load is close to a pure resistance at 50 MHz, but it becomes more reactive at progressively higher frequencies. At 144 MHz the indicated SWR is 1.3:1. It rises to about 1.5:1 at 220 MHz, and to 1.9:1 at 432. None of these figures is too bad for most purposes, but it is possible to make a near-perfect load out of the resistor bank, by adding the tuned circuit shown.

Fig. 14-29 — 5-watt dummy load, with detachable circuit for tuning out the reactance of the load at 432 MHz. The trimmer is disconnected from the resistor junction when the load is used on bands below 420 MHz.

The loop of wire and trimmer capacitor provide means for cancelling out the reactance of the resistors and their leads at 432 MHz. The *LC* circuit can work on only one band conveniently, and it is really needed only at 432, so a connection between the trimmer and the resistor junction is made when an accurate match is needed for 420-MHz band work. The loop is 2-1/4 inches of No. 16 wire, bent into C shape, and soldered to one corner of the flange. The top end is soldered to the movable plate of the trimmer. The stationary plate is soldered to the center pin, or not, as needed. When using the load with the circuit

connected, tune the trimmer for minimum reflected-power indication.

Similar tuning can be used for lower frequencies, but turns of wire, rather than a small loop, may be needed. Or tuned loads can be made for each band, for accurate work.

It is well to check a batch of resistors with an ohmmeter before selecting those to be used in such a load. Six resistors actually 330 ohms each would give a load of 55 ohms. About 20 330-ohm resistors were measured with an ohmmeter and the lowest 6 of them were used. The resulting total resistance of the load is 53 ohms, very close to the figure needed.

FREQUENCY MEASUREMENT WITH LECHER WIRES

Here is a measuring instrument that is almost as old as radio communication, but it is still a handy item for the vhf or uhf experimenter. The length of an electromagnetic wave can be measured directly on a transmission line, by observing the distance between points of maximum or minimum rf voltage. Lecher Wires are a means of doing this reliably and accurately. If you are accustomed to using metric scales you can read wavelength directly, the distance between the voltage peaks or nodes being a half wavelength at the frequency being measured. (A meter is 39.37 inches, which as every vhf man knows is a half wavelength at 150 MHz.)

Construction

The wires in the portion of the instrument to be used for measurement must be without insulating material in direct contact. Provision must be made for holding the wires taut, and in uniform spacing. The shorting device must make firm contact, and the distance between peaks (or nulls) must be measured precisely, if accurate measuring is to be undertaken. These objectives can be met

easily and inexpensively in numerous ways, one of which is shown in our practical example, Figs. 14-30 and 31.

The construction requires little explanation, and dimensions are not critical. The base of the assembly is made from two straight pieces of 1 × 2-inch pine, fastened together in a T-shaped cross-section, and supported on two blocks of wood. The anchors for the measuring line are of similar material. The wires are held tight with turnbuckles at the left end, and are supported on insulators at the right end.

How long you make the line depends on the lowest frequency you want to measure. The model shown is 7 feet long, which will take care of measurement from the 144-MHz band up well into the microwave region. If you want to start at the 220-MHz band an overall length of about four feet will suffice.

A rough Lecher-Wire measurement of wavelength can be made by running a knife or screwdriver blade along any bare-wire transmission line, but if you want to measure accurately something like the shorting blade and carrier shown here must be incorporated, to give repeatable results. The

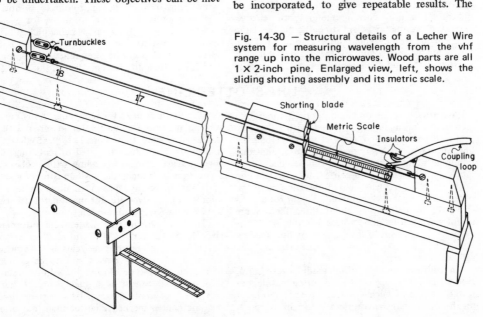

Fig. 14-30 — Structural details of a Lecher Wire system for measuring wavelength from the vhf range up into the microwaves. Wood parts are all 1 × 2-inch pine. Enlarged view, left, shows the sliding shorting assembly and its metric scale.

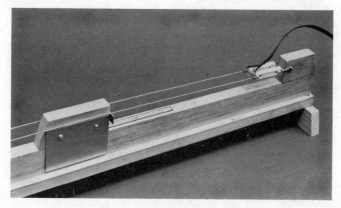

Fig. 14-31 — Close-up view of the coupling end of the Lecher Wire assembly. Overall length depends on how low the user wishes to be able to go in frequency.

block rides on the base strip, with two metal side plates keeping it in alignment. These plates need not be metal, but it is convenient that way. At the right end of the travelling block is a notched metal short. The wires are kept tight enough so that a good electrical contact is made by this plate.

The base is marked off in tenths of a meter, beginning at a point directly under the coupling end of the line. The travelling short has a transparent metric scale (most stationery stores have them) fastened to its underside, so that readings can be taken directly in metric units of length. (Inches and feet don't enter into this at all.)

Now we have to couple to the rf source in some way. The propagation factor of the coupling line is of no importance, so it can be Twin-Lead or anything in the way of a balanced line that may be handy. From here on the operation is much like that with an absorption-type wavemeter, except that the Lecher Wires are much more accurate if made and used properly.

Measuring Wavelength and Frequency

The energy source can have any of several indicators: a grid current meter, plate current meter, rf voltmeter, field-strength meter, lamp load, or whatever. The coupling loop of Twin-Lead, at the right end of the Lecher Wires, is shorted at the end. This loop is placed near the rf circuit so as to couple some energy from it. The loosest coupling that will work is the best.

Now, run the sliding short along the Lecher Wires, watching for a change in the indicator, whatever it may be. When the change occurs, note the reading on the base and block scale. Let's say it's 0.255 meter. Now move the carrier along until a second dip is found, and note the scale reading. Suppose it is 0.937. Subtract the first reading from the second, the answer in our example being 0.682 meter. This is a half wavelength at the frequency being measured. To convert this to frequency in megahertz, divide 150 by the wavelength just measured. Our answer shows that we have just missed the 220-MHz band, and we're on 219.9 MHz.

Making use of the Lecher-Wire principle does not always require a system specially built for this purpose. Any two parallel wires or rods with one end coupled to an rf power source can be pressed into service, so long as there is little or no solid insulation between them, in the area used for measurement. Just running a screwdriver along the wires, and noting the approximate position of peaks or nulls, will serve to show, for example, whether the right harmonic is being picked off in a multiplier system. The assembly described is capable of quite accurate frequency measurement, which is quite a different matter.

UHF SLOTTED LINE

A slotted line, as its name implies, is merely a section of transmission line, fitted with a movable probe to permit sampling the rf voltage along the line, through at least one maximum and one minimum point. If more peaks can be checked, so much the better, but you can get by with just one "max and min." At least two of one and one of the other is better, and the minimum length for a good 420-MHz slotted line is about three feet. Some useful work can be done with a 3-footer on 220 or even 144, however, if the length of line feeding into it is adjusted so that at least one peak and one valley can be observed.

In addition to measuring standing-wave ratio, the slotted line is useful for measuring wavelength in the manner of Lecher wires. The scale mounted on the front of the instrument is for this purpose.

If a diode is used for rectifying the rf current, varying readings on the meter in series with the diode show only that there is *some* SWR on the line. When you adjust the load or matching device for the least change in reading with probe movement, you have made the best adjustment you can, with the matching system or load in use. The numbers themselves are not meaningful otherwise, until the device is calibrated in some way.

The line shown was made from information given by Pitt Arnold, WØIPE, in a talk at a Central States Vhf Conference some years ago. Admittedly this is a "make-do" device, not to be compared with laboratory-type slotted lines in accuracy of measurement, but it is a highly useful and instructive tool in many ways. Its sensitivity in SWR measurement is markedly better than that of even

Fig. 14-32 — Input end of the slotted line. Peaks or nulls of diode current, indicated on the meter as the probe is moved along the line, show half-wave intervals. Scale measures half-wave-lengths in inches, or in centimeters if a suitable scale is available. Three dummy loads are shown in the foreground: a sealed resistor load in a BNC fitting, left; a tuned frequency-sensitive load, center; and a No. 47 pilot lamp and fitting, right.

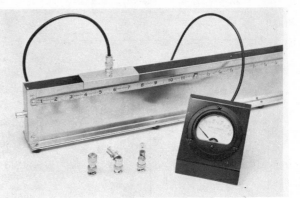

quite expensive equipment of the calibrated-wattmeter type.

Construction

The inner conductor is half-inch OD aluminum tubing, centered between two plates about four inches high. The space between the inner surfaces of the plates is 0.9 inch. We used two L-shaped side plates, bolted to a base plate. All are 3/32-inch sheet aluminum. A better arrangement might be to use thicker side plates, with tapped holes in their bottom edges. The principal item of importance is that the assembly be sturdy enough so that the spacing between the side plates will remain constant when the instrument is used.

If solid rod is available for the inner conductor, the ends can be drilled and the center pins of the coaxial fittings inserted therein. BNC or N-type fittings can be connected to the line in this way. Do not use the so-called uhf fitting, SO-239. BNC fittings are convenient for use of the instrument in demonstrations. Solid rod of the right size was not at hand, so half-inch aluminum tubing was used. Thin strips of brass about 3/8 inch wide were bolted vertically to both sides of each end of the tubing, bent toward each other, and soldered to the center conductor of the coaxial fitting. That it was not possible to eliminate rise and fall of rf current completely shows that this makeshift is not perfect, but in spite of this the instrument is more sensitive to SWR variations than other uhf test equipment available to the average amateur.

The end plates and the mounting for the probe are made of 1/32-inch sheet aluminum, bent in U shape, with BNC sockets (UG-290/U) mounted with their diagonals perpendicular to the long axis of the plate, and centered in the large surface. The tip-to-tip dimension of this fitting's flange is just over 0.9 inch, so the corners should be filed down to make the assembly a smooth fit over the top or end surface of the line. Occasional light applications of silicone-base lubricant will permit the probe assembly to slide easily along the top of the line. The end plates are made in a similar manner, and are fastened to the front and back surfaces of the line with self-tapping screws. The dimensions of these parts are given in Fig. 14-33. Mounting holes need be drilled only in the end plates, not in the probe assembly.

Rubber feet with 8-32 screws are used to fasten the base plate to the side plates. The holes in the flanges of the latter are tapped for 8-32 thread.

A 36-inch scale mounted along the front surface of the line measures the distance between voltage peaks or valleys. A millimeter scale simplifies the mathematics involved in frequency measurement. The scale shown in a replacement unit for use in a pocket tape, and was originally 6 feet long. It is mounted on standoff washers, so that the edge of the probe mount will slide just inside its top edge.

The size of the coupling loop on the probe and its position with respect to the inner conductor of the line will depend on the power input to the line, and on the sensitivity of the meter used. If a self-controlled oscillator is used as an energy source it is desirable to couple as loosely between the source and the line as possible. Loose coupling between the probe and the line is also desirable, as too much coupling will broaden out the peak and valley indications and make frequency measurements inaccurate. Make the loop on the probe of such size and shape that it can be used for close coupling, and then bend it up to operate with the loosest coupling that will give a satisfactory meter indication. See Fig. 14-35.

If a self-controlled energy source such as a uhf dipper is used with the line, it can be coupled to a small loop of insulated wire, mounted in a BNC fitting and plugged into the input end of the line. With a transmitter having 50-ohm output, a coaxial cable is used between the transmitter and the line input. When the transmitter has one watt or more output the coupling between the line and probe can be quite loose. As the instrument is actually used you will find it possible to work out optimum coupling for various purposes. For the time being, a loop of the type shown and described will be adequate for most uses. For greatest versatility, make up several probes.

Uses

A good way to become familiar with the slotted line is to check dummy loads at 432 MHz. The first requirement for this is that the energy fed into the line be free of harmonics. Use a coaxial or strip-line filter between the rf source and the line. Filtering is especially important if the energy source is a

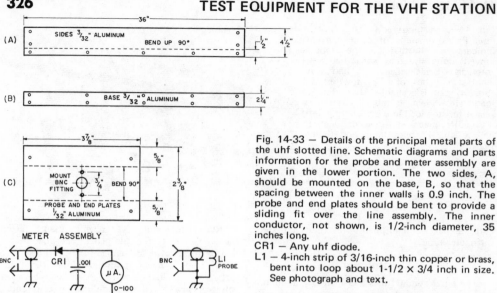

Fig. 14-33 — Details of the principal metal parts of the uhf slotted line. Schematic diagrams and parts information for the probe and meter assembly are given in the lower portion. The two sides, A, should be mounted on the base, B, so that the spacing between the inner walls is 0.9 inch. The probe and end plates should be bent to provide a sliding fit over the line assembly. The inner conductor, not shown, is 1/2-inch diameter, 35 inches long.

CR1 — Any uhf diode.

L1 — 4-inch strip of 3/16-inch thin copper or brass, bent into loop about 1-1/2 × 3/4 inch in size. See photograph and text.

varactor multiplier. A simple varactor system is almost certain to have enough power at unwanted frequencies to foul up the slotted line indications.

Start with a load that will represent some mismatch. A No. 47 pilot light soldered into a BNC fitting will do, and it has the advantage of giving some visible indication of relative power. Put such a load on the output end of the slotted line, and connect the input to the energy source capable of about one watt output at 432 MHz. A 2-meter transmitter of 2 to 5 watts output, a varactor multiplier and a strip-line filter (such as described in this Manual) will make a fine beginner's demonstration setup.

Adjust the input to the line so that the lamp shows some glow. Now insert the probe and watch the meter indication carefully. It may be found that with the coupling loop as shown in the photograph the meter will go off scale before the probe is resting in its normal operating position. If so, bend the loop back until a satisfactory reading is obtained. Now slide the probe slowly along the line, and record the maximum and minimum current readings. You'll probably find that the meter will go to zero at the minimum rf voltage points, when the coupling is adjusted for about a 3/4-scale reading at the peaks. Obviously, a No. 47 lamp is not a very good load at 432 MHz!

A much better one-watt load can be made by soldering a 51-ohm 1-watt composition resistor inside a BNC fitting. Cut a copper or brass disk the size of the end of the fitting, and drill a hole that will just pass the resistor lead, at the center of the disk. Solder the resistor lead to the disk, and then solder the disk to the end of the fitting. With this load in place you'll probably find not much more than 10 percent variation in probe current along the line, at 432 MHz, and perhaps less at 220 or 144 MHz. This is a pretty fair load, but remember that its dissipation capability is limited. Do not run it at one-watt input or more for any longer than necessary to get readings. Continued heating of the resistor is likely to cause it to change value and destroy the usefulness of the load.

A good load, but one that is frequency sensitive, can be made by mounting the resistor in the fitting, with a variable capacitor in series. Select the resistor, if possible, so that its dc resistance will be between 50 and 52 ohms. Adjust the capacitor with an insulated screwdriver until a setting is found that shows the smallest variation in current as the probe is moved along the line. The best observed with this arrangement is a variation of about 2 microamperes in a reading of about 50 μA. Use readings that are available at some distance in from the ends of the line for this adjustment, as coupling to the line changes appreciably in the last few inches at each end.

Wavelength measurements should now be tried. The distance between two nulls or two peaks of probe current is a half-wavelength. Be careful not to overcouple with the probe for this work, or the indication will be excessively broad, or even double-humped. If a self-controlled energy source is used, tight coupling will pull the frequency enough to render measurements highly inaccurate.

Fig. 14-34 — Interior of one end of the slotted line. Strips of thin brass, barely visible here, are bolted to the center conductor and soldered to the BNC fitting centered on the end plate of the line.

A uhf oscillator, set at an unknown frequency, can be coupled to the input end of the line by means of a 1-inch diameter loop of wire soldered into a BNC fitting. Operate the slotted line without a load, or with a load having an impedance other than 50 ohms, so that an appreciable SWR will be seen with the probe. Measure the distance between nulls. Bend the probe until zero reading is obtained. Now move slowly each way until one microampere is seen on the meter. Observe these two 1-μA points, and take the midpoint between them. Now move along the line to the next null, and find its exact location in the same manner. We find the points to be 12-5/8 inches apart, let's say. The frequency of oscillation is then found from the formula:

$$F = \frac{5905}{S}$$

where F is the frequency in MHz and S is the spacing of the nulls in inches. So

$$F = \frac{5905}{12.625} = 468 \text{ MHz}$$

If you have a millimeter scale the numbers are simpler, for

$$F = \frac{300,000}{2S}$$

where S is the spacing of the nulls in meters. A millimeter scale would show these same nulls to be 32 millimeters apart, which is a *half* wavelength.

$$F = \frac{300,000}{2 \times 32} = 468 \text{ MHz}$$

If coupling is held sufficiently loose that nulls can be read accurately, frequencies in the vicinity of the 420-MHz band should be well within one percent when measured in this way.

Calibration

Because of the characteristics of the diode, the relative currents indicated on the meter are not directly translatable into SWR. The meter reads rectified current, whereas the SWR is the ratio of I_{max} to I_{min} in rf current. If we have a wattmeter capable of reading rf power output with a fair degree of accuracy we can make a calibration of the dc meter readings in terms of rf power. This was done using a Bird Thruline Wattmeter, Model 43, with a 10-E (400 to 1000 MHz) plug-in unit.

With this instrument, and one plug-in unit, the highest forward-reflector power ratio that can be read with appreciable accuracy is 100 to 1 (10 watts forward, 0.1 reflected) corresponding to an SWR of 1.22:1. A dummy load was deliberately mismatched to give this 1-percent reflected-power condition, using the wattmeter. The load was then checked with the slotted line probe adjusted to give a maximum current indication of 100 μA. The minimum was measured at 65 μA, showing that the slotted-line was capable of indicating SWR values far lower than could be measured by other means available.

Fig. 14-35 — Underside of the slotted-line probe. Position of the coupling loop with respect to the center conductor should be adjusted for the minimum coupling usable at the power level of the energy fed into the line, if maximum accuracy is to be achieved. A light coating of silicone-base lubricant on the inner edges will assure smooth operation and good electrical contact.

With a 100-μA meter and a single probe position with respect to the inner conductor of the line the highest SWR that could be measured was just over 3:1. At this point the max-and-min readings were 100 and zero. The best SWR sensitivity that could be indicated reliably was represented by meter readings of 100 and 95. Making a rough graph of the range where reflected-power wattmeter readings and slotted-line meter readings could be compared indicates that reasonable SWR-reading accuracy down to at least 1.07 to 1 is not difficult, with this addmittedly imperfect instrument.

How important is it to be able to read SWR under 1.2:1? Not very, if all you are interested in is getting an antenna to work as well as it is practical to make it. But being able to *see* low values *is* important, if you are attempting to measure antenna performance. Forward-power readings needed to achieve certain reference readings on a field-strength meter can be translated into gain measurements in experimental work with antennas, *if* the reflected power is down very close to zero. Unless it is, all such readings are suspect. The slotted line will let you measure closer to zero-reflected than any conventional in-line meter system.

BIBLIOGRAPHY

1 Wright, "The Twin-Lamp," *QST,* October, 1947, p. 22.

2 McMullen, "The Line Sampler," *QST,* April, 1972.

3 Tilton, "Noise Generators—Their Uses and Limitations," *QST,* July, 1953, p. 10. Detailed information on vacuum-tube noise generators is also in the *ARRL Handbook,* 41st edition and later.

Noise generator information was brought up to date and equipment for 420 MHz and higher frequencies was described in a three-part symposium, *QST,* February, 1964, pp. 23-35.

4 Frye, "Adjustment Procedures for V.H.F. Converters," *QST,* October, 1958, p. 24.

Chapter 15

Interference Causes and Cures

In one respect amateur radio is vastly different from most other hobby-type activities: from its earliest days it has existed in competition with other services. Because we occupy frequencies that are under constant pressure from other users of radio, amicable and successful solution of our interference problems is vital to our very existence.

With occupancy of the radio spectrum rising daily, electronic devices of infinite variety in almost every home, and population density increasing almost everywhere, interference problems inevitably tend to multiply. Interference is a two-way affair. We both cause it and suffer from it, but the first is our major concern in these pages. Fortunately some of the steps we take to cure our neighbor troubles are beneficial in our vhf receiving situations as well.

In handling TVI and related interference problems two cardinal points should be kept in mind:

Interference is primarily a public-relations problem, not a technical one. Every form of it can be cured; it is getting the job done amicably that is difficult.

Being able to demonstrate that the transmitter is not at fault is important, but it is not enough. The amateur *must* understand the factors involved, and be able to take or recommend corrective measures. Nobody is going to do this for us.

THE NATURE OF TVI

With these facts of community life established, let's look at the causes and cures of TVI, the vhf man's major interference problem. The principal forms of TVI from vhf transmitters are listed below, in the approximate order of their importance:

1) *Blocking* Every user of the 50-MHz band in a Channel 2 area knows about this. It may run all the way from a light cross-hatching of the picture to complete blackout. Nearly always the visual effects change with transmitter modulation. Usually there is audio interference along with the picture trouble. The vhf man's worst interference problem, it has been responsible for a high percentage of all complaints reaching FCC in recent years. It is much worse in Channel 2 than on higher channels, but it is possible on all channels, 2 through 6, in receivers near to a 50-MHz station. Blocking of Channel 13 by 220-MHz energy is similar, but by no means so severe.

2) *Audio Troubles* Rf pickup by the detector or audio circuits of a receiver (TV or radio) results in your voice riding through almost regardless of the tuning of the receiver or even the setting of the audio gain control. Picture reception may be clear. This problem is not confined to TV receivers; it is common in all devices having audio amplifiers: hearing aids, hi-fi and public-address systems, record and tape players, musical instrument amplifiers, and so on.

3) *Image Response* This basic weakness of all superheterodyne receivers is explained in Chapter 3. As most commonly encountered in amateur vhf circles it is responsible for reception of 2-meter signals in Channel 2, in TV receivers having the currently used high intermediate frequency. If an old TV set with a 21-MHz i-f does not show interference from your 144-MHz transmitter, and a newer one does, this is likely to be the cause. Along with it there will probably be some audio trouble (2), if you are using amplitude-modulated phone.

4) *Harmonics of Oscillator or Exciter Frequencies* Usually this shows up as a crosshatch pattern, independent of modulation, changing or disappearing when the transmitter frequency is shifted. Usually trouble develops only when the harmonic falls in a sensitive part of the TV channel. See Fig. 15-1 and 2. Examples of common combinations are the 9th harmonic of 6-MHz stages and the 7th harmonic of 8-MHz ones, falling in Channel 2; the 10th harmonic of 8 MHz in Channel 6; 7th harmonic of 25 MHz in Channel 7; 4th harmonic of 48 MHz in Channel 9 or 10, depending on the operating frequency. There are others, but these are the most common sources of trouble. Exciter frequencies may also get directly into the receiver's i-f system, in some instances.

5) *Final-Stage Harmonics* The 4th harmonic of 50 MHz falls in Channels 11 to 13, depending on the operating frequency. Various harmonics of 50, 144, and 220 MHz fall in the uhf TV band, though usually they are not strong enough to cause much trouble. The 2nd harmonic of 50 MHz falls in the fm broadcast band, and while this did not give us much trouble in the past, increasing use of fm is changing this picture.

There are many other possible sources of TVI from the operation of amateur vhf transmitters, but it is safe to say that at least 95 percent of our problems are covered by the above list. Items 1 and 2 are by far the most troublesome. We will look into each in some detail, but first go back over the list and be sure that you understand each one. Then remember, despite all you may have heard, these interference problems *can* be solved.

The frequencies assigned to television and fm broadcasting in the vhf range are shown in Fig. 15-1, together with the harmonics of the 50-MHz band that fall in this range. Prevention of radiation in these assignments, Items 4 and 5, is the amateur's responsibility. Items 1, 2, and 3 are receiver defects, which must be corrected at the receiver.

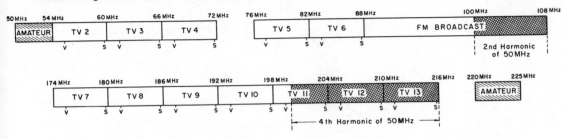

Fig. 15-1 — Frequencies assigned to vhf television and fm broadcasting in the United States. The approximate positions of the video and sound carriers are indicated on each TV channel. Crosshatched areas show second and fourth harmonics of the 50-MHz band. Positions of the amateur 50- and 220-MHz bands with respect to the TV channels are also indicated.

It is of utmost importance that the amateur know how to recognize the nature of the interference, so that he can correct the trouble if it lies in his transmitter, or recommend the corrective measures to be taken at the receiver. The earlier the amateur gets into the matter the better, for friendly relations between him and the set owner are vital, if a solution is to be reached.

CORRECTING TV RECEIVER DEFICIENCIES

Fundamental blocking (1) is a receiver problem. The rf circuits of a TV set are broad in frequency response. If they were not, picture quality would suffer, since the television picture and its sound occupy a channel 6 MHz wide. It is not easy to build a receiver that will pass 54 to 60 MHz and reject rf from a nearby amateur station operating on 50 to 54 MHz. It is unlikely that TV manufacturers will ever mass-produce receivers that do it effectively.

Though blocking troubles are much more severe in Channel 2, if the 50-MHz signal is strong enough it may block the receiver on all low-band channels, 2 through 6. Clearing any channel above 2 is usually done quite readily. The simple stub to be described later will nearly always handle it. Why clearing Channel 2 of 50-MHz interference is more difficult is obvious from Fig. 15-2, which shows the locations of the sound and picture carriers in a TV channel, as well as the interference potential of any signal falling in the channel. In Channel 2 the picture carrier is at 55.25 MHz, which is just too close to the 50-MHz amateur signals to make it a simple matter to keep the latter below the overloading level.

There is a related problem in connection with 50-MHz interference to the TV sound in Channel 2, in receivers of the intercarrier sound type, which nearly all TV sets are. With such receivers a signal 4.5 MHz below the picture carrier can cause severe sound interference, the severity depending on the selectivity and alignment of the TV receiver's i-f system. 55.25 MHz − 4.5 MHz = 50.75 MHz. This makes 50.75 MHz the worst possible spot on which to operate in the 50-MHz band with a-m phone, from the standpoint of sound interference. Proper alignment of the TV set makes a big difference with this trouble, but a practical fact of life in a Channel 2 area is that staying well away from 50.75 MHz is very desirable. Any operating frequency above 50.4 MHz makes interference very much more likely.

The approximate range over which 50-MHz signals are likely to overload TV receivers in Channel 2 was shown graphically in *QST* by 50-MHz pioneer W2IDZ. Fig. 15-3 is from his now-classic treatment of the 50-MHz TVI problem which paved the way for today's thousands of 50-MHz enthusiasts who now manage to live with Channel 2.[1] This is a matter of effective radiated power. If your transmitter puts out 100 watts, and your antenna has a gain of 10 dB (10 times) your ERP is 1000 watts. If the antenna's main lobe fires into the TV antennas your sphere of evil influence will be roughly 400 feet in radius.

[1]For this and other numbered references, see bibliography at the end of this chapter.

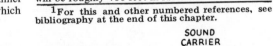
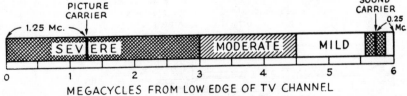

Fig. 15-2 — Locations of the video and sound carriers in a black-and-white TV signal, showing relative severity of interference caused by harmonics falling in various parts of the channel. This information can be put to good use by vhf amateurs in instances where mild harmonic interference is encountered. The trouble may be corrected, or at least alleviated considerably, by shifting the operating frequency so that the offending harmonic is moved out of a sensitive frequency range.

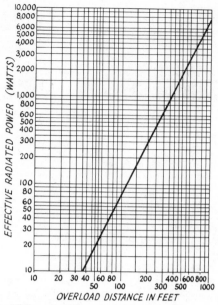

OVERLOAD DISTANCE IN FEET

Fig. 15-3 — Average overload distance for a TV receiver on Channel 2 and an amateur station between 50 and 51 MHz. The effective radiated power is the transmitter output multiplied by the antenna gain (*not* in decibels). The supersensitivity of misaligned inter-carrier-type receivers to 50.75-MHz signals is not included.

You can cut your interference potential in several ways without touching a TV installation. Raising the 50-MHz antenna to the point where its main lobe of radiation is well above the TV receivers and antennas can knock the ERP at the receiver down by 20 dB or more. This would be the same as using 10 watts instead of 1000 at the left side of Fig. 15-3. The net effect of a 20-dB reduction in signal level at the TV antenna is a reduction in interference radius by roughly a factor of 10 in distance; a very large difference in a built-up residential area. Blocking interference has a sort of threshold; raising the antenna may put you on the safe side of it.

Where the receivers and antennas are close to the transmitter the latter should be well shielded and the transmission line nonradiating, if the high amateur antenna is to pay off to the greatest extent. This is particularly important in the multi-family dwelling. The indoor dipole (often the timid soul's last resort) may be the worst possible approach in such circumstances.

Getting the radiated power well above the TV sets also helps the effectiveness of any corrective

measures used on the receivers. A high-pass filter installed on the receiver may be relatively ineffective if there is a strong rf field around the receiver itself. Complete shielding of the receiver, a difficult and seldom-taken step, may then be the only interference cure.

Finally, it is important to remember that interference range is directly related to the transmitter power. *Nobody* has to run high power all the time. On the vhf bands a high percentage of all communication can be carried out just as well with 10 watts as with 1000. Dropping power that much, when we don't need all we *can* run, means the difference between a 40-foot and a 400-foot interference radius. Even 0.1 watt is effective for local chats, and it will cure practically every interference problem.

Though what has been said thus far is mainly concerned with 50-MHz blocking-type interference, the principles apply equally to image and audio problems, regardless of the amateur transmitting frequency.

Using Stubs and Traps

If the fundamental interference is mild and the TV signals are strong, a simple quarter-wave stub of Twin-Lead cut to the transmitter frequency and connected to the TV receiver antenna terminals will take care of it. The stub is a good first step in any case, as it costs almost nothing, is easy to try, and ordinarily has little or no effect on TV reception. Such a stub is an electrical quarter-wavelength at the transmitter frequency, open at the far end. If it is fitted with open-end lugs at the other end it can be slipped under the receiver antenna terminals readily.

Start with a piece a bit more than $0.82\frac{\lambda}{4}$ in length, about 50 inches for 50 MHz or 17-1/2 for 144. Connect the stub at the antenna terminals, and trim it for length while watching the interference. When the interference level drops trim in small increments until interference disappears. The stub should have a negligible effect on the TV reception where a reasonably strong TV signal is available, and it will be effective for any but the worst cases of interference.

Another type of stub, this one tunable and requiring no electrical connection to the TV set, is shown in Fig. 15-4. It is a double stub, used sandwich-fashion on both sides of the line to the TV receiver, and tuned for resonance at the transmitting frequency. It is thus a tuned trap, coupled to the line of the receiver. It is somewhat more effective than the self-resonant stub just described, and it may have less effect on the TV

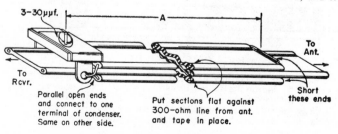

3-30 μμf.

To Ant.

To Rcvr.

Parallel open ends and connect to one terminal of condenser. Same on other side.

Put sections flat against 300-ohm line from ant. and tape in place.

Short these ends

Fig. 15-4 — Sandwich-type trap for installation in the 300-ohm line to the TV receiver. Approximate lengths (dimension A) are 40 inches for 50 MHz and 11 for 144. Two traps are in parallel, one on each side of the TV line.

reception. It is convenient to make one up on a section of line that can be connected between the receiver antenna terminal board and the line to the TV antenna. The setup can be pretuned to the transmitter frequency, and thus be ready for a quick test.

The stub is shorter than the self-resonant type, to allow for the capacitive loading. About 38 to 40 inches is suitable for 50 MHz, and 10 to 11 inches for 144. A worthwhile refinement for a stub that will be used for test purposes is substitution of a split-stator variable capacitor for the mica trimmer shown. This allows adjustment for stub resonance without introducing hand-capacity effects, and interference can be nulled out much more effectively. Once it is determined that this type of stub does the job, an inexpensive trimmer like that shown can be put on. It will work just as well, but is harder to tune accurately.

Traps tuned to the transmitter frequency can be inserted in the receiver line. Often a single trap in one side of the line will do the trick, or one can be connected in each leg. These can be resonated with the aid of a grid-dip meter to the transmitting frequency. For highest selectivity use the smallest amount of inductance that will tune to the transmitting frequency, with the capacitor available. Typical tuned circuits in vhf equipment in this Manual can serve as models.

In this discussion the accent has been on 50-MHz applications but the principles apply to any vhf problem where the interference is coming in on the antenna or transmission line to the receiver. Direct pickup of rf by the receiver, or by its ac line, will not be affected by stubs, traps, or filters at the antenna terminals. All these devices are more effective if connected right where the antenna line enters the receiver chassis, rather than at the terminal board on the back of the cabinet, if there is an unshielded run of Twin-Lead from the terminal board to the tuner input of any appreciable length.

It is well to have any treatment ready for quick application, and to have the actual work done by the owner's serviceman, or by the local TVI Committee representative. Even when the neighbor is friendly he may be a little nervous about your working on the receiver. The quicker and more effectively the job is done, the better.

If you have a functioning TVI Committee, they probably already have a demonstration filter for this purpose. If none is available, you are not required to supply it. The set owner should be encouraged to take up the matter with the dealer from whom the set was purchased, as many manufacturers make provision for supplying filters where needed.

PICKUP BY AUDIO CIRCUITS

Next to TVI of a visual nature, the most common interference problem for vhf operators using amplitude modulation is rf pickup and demodulation by audio amplifiers and other electronic devices using similar circuits. Much of this is audio-only interference to reception of TV and radio programs, but it occurs in every kind of electronic device using high-gain amplifiers. It is increasingly troublesome with high-fidelity record and tape systems, as these rarely have any interference-prevention measures built-in.

Where the amateur is using conventional amplitude modulation the interference is usually all-too-clear reproduction of the operator's voice, often at very high levels, unaffected by the amplifier gain control. With a sideband signal, the interference may sound like ssb as received on an a-m detector. Sideband is a form of amplitude modulation and allows the offending amateur only a slight breathing spell.

Because only amplitude changes at an audio rate are involved, there is an obvious cure: going over to fm or cw. So long as there is no blocking of the program material by the rf power from the

transmitter, these modes cause no trouble. Using them has been a way of living in harmony with one's neighbors in many densely populated areas, where a-m would have set off immediate neighborhood strife.

Stub and trap remedies discussed above are rarely useful with audio interference, as the energy gets into the detector or amplifier stages directly, rather than by way of the antenna. Long unshielded leads to speakers, remote gain controls, phono pickups, tape heads, and the like are always suspect. Converting them to shielded wire, or to better shielding than they may have had originally, is recommended. Usually circuits connected to the first amplifier are the trouble spots, but any long lead may pick up rf energy and conduct it into the amplifier. Later stages give less trouble. Though they may have rf pickup potential, the gain from there on is far lower than when the first stage is included.

Once the source of the troublesome rf pickup is traced down, remedies are simple, though often subject to some cut-and-try. Recommendations shown for vacuum tube amplifiers, Fig. 15-5,

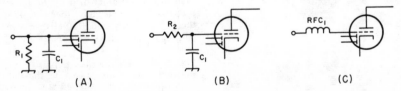

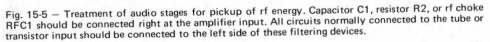

Fig. 15-5 — Treatment of audio stages for pickup of rf energy. Capacitor C1, resistor R2, or rf choke RFC1 should be connected right at the amplifier input. All circuits normally connected to the tube or transistor input should be connected to the left side of these filtering devices.

should be applicable to transistor stages. Rf chokes used should be for the band in question, though a single choke may work for both 6 and 2 meters. Where bypassing is called for, use values that will not affect the audio quality. Fortunately, effective vhf bypass values (.001 μF and lower) are in this category. Series-resonant bypassing (see Chapter 16) may be the best and simplest treatment of all, for one-band problems. Whatever corrective measure is finally used, it should be applied as close to the offending tube or transistor input element as possible. Remove all normal connections, insert the rf choke or resistor, and reconnect the circuits at the left end of the choke or resistor.

Decoupling of the heater circuits of the audio stages may be necessary, though this is unlikely. Series-resonant bypassing or ferrite-bead chokes are fine for heater decoupling, if needed.

Clearing up audio problems is simple in principle, but the set-owner may not take kindly to the amateur's digging into his equipment. If there is any doubt, the wise approach is to give the owner's serviceman the necessary information, and have him do the job. Servicemen who are not amateurs may have little knowledge of the problem, so you may have to use diplomacy in two directions. Thus it is doubly important that you know precisely what you are talking about, in recommending corrective measures.

Pickup by the receiver's ac line may be a factor, though not too often in vhf work. Rf filtering of the ac line where it enters the receiver is the answer here. Heavy-wire chokes (No. 18 or so) and good rf bypassing are the treatments. Filters on the plug end of the ac cord, where it plugs into a wall outlet are almost never of any value.

KEEPING HARMONICS AT HOME

So far we've been concerned mainly with troubles that arise as a result of receiver deficiencies. With vhf TVI, at least, they are in the vast majority. The possibility that the transmitter may be at fault should not be overlooked, however, and every possible check should be made on this before operating extensively in an area where there are TV sets nearby. The importance of doing this before the TVI complaints begin to roll in cannot be over-emphasized. If you have demonstrated to your own complete satisfaction that your transmitter is "clean," you can face your neighbors with confidence and good humor. These personal attributes are of inestimable value, for this TVI business, remember, is a public-relations problem.

CHECKING FOR HARMONICS

The first order of business is to be sure that all available channels can be received clearly on your own TV receiver. If there is interference from your transmitter in any of them, don't wait for the angry phone calls. Find the trouble, and fix it – right now! If the various treatments

already outlined do not clear up the interference, find out why, at once. Just because you have a 500-dollar superwhatsis transmitter does not guarantee that it is free of the troubles described in Items 4 and 5. Running it indiscriminately on the air can only bring down the righteous anger of the neighborhood around you. By then you may have lost the war, but the fighting will drag on and on.

If your own TV receiver does not respond to treatment for fundamental-frequency and audio-rectification ills, Items 1, 2, and 3, you've got harmonic problems. The first step is to find out where the offending harmonic energy is coming from. Put a non-radiating dummy load on the transmitter, and check again. Use a good load (see Chapter 14), preferably shielded. There are some good ones available ready made and in kit form, if you don't want to make one from scratch. Do not use a lamp load; it can radiate plenty of energy to cause interference.

If there is no interference with the dummy load on, the harmonic radiation is from the antenna, and your problems are well on the way to solution. There are several simple and practical corrective measures. One of the best is a tuned antenna coupler, particularly if your antenna is fed with balanced line of any kind. Details in Chapter 8. Also very worthwhile is a high-Q coaxial or strip-line filter. More on these later in this chapter, and in *QST*.[2]

A low-pass filter connected in your antenna line is good harmonic radiation insurance, but such filters are rather difficult to make and adjust properly. You can buy them ready made, and there have been good 50-MHz designs in every edition of the ARRL *Handbook* for many years.

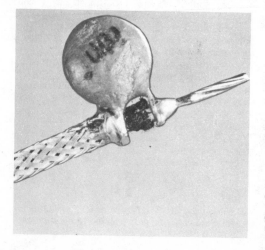

Fig. 15-6 — Method for bypassing the end of a shielded power lead. Leads to the 0.001-μF disk capacitor should be soldered as close as possible to the capacitor body. Shield over the wire should be grounded to the chassis at frequent intervals. This method is suitable for harmonics only up to about 100 MHz.

There is little point in repeating such information here, when it is so widely available already.[3]

Both the antenna coupler and the high-Q filter have an important advantage over the low-pass filter: they protect the receiver more effectively, preventing overloading from strong signals below the amateur band in use, as well as above it. They might be quite helpful if you have a near neighbor who runs high power on the lower frequency ham bands, or on some higher one.

Harmonic Sniffing

Harmonics that get out by way of the antenna disappear when the dummy load test is made. If the interference persists you have work to be done on the transmitter or its power circuits. Some kind of harmonic "sniffer" is now required. The simple field-strength indicator of Fig. 14-7 may be enough. It will cover TV Channels 2 through 6 as it stands. A smaller coil for L2 will permit it to tune up through Channel 13, if need be. Plug a stiff wire or rod into J1 for a pickup antenna.

With the transmitter running into a dummy load, place the pickup antenna close to the ac leads, power cable, any unshielded tubes or circuits, exposed meters, variable capacitor shafts, or any other part of the transmitter that could be radiating harmonic energy. If you find some you have a shielding or filtering job ahead; perhaps both.

Another effective harmonic radiation detector is the TV set itself. Cut a piece of Twin-Lead long enough to reach from the TV set to any part of the transmitter you want to check. Connect one end to the receiver antenna terminals. Short the other end to make a coupling loop. Tape bare wires so that there will be no shorting of high voltage into the TV set. Now use the Twin-Lead as a probe, coupling it to any suspected part, wire, or circuit. If there is harmonic energy present the interference level will increase markedly as the probe is placed near the guilty component.

We used to build in complete harmonic protection into every transmitter. Experience has shown that so much TVI is the result of receiver deficiencies that we no longer do this. The chances are that any reasonably well-designed vhf transmitter will be practically TVI-free, and that the receivers will be the culprits — but you cannot rely on it. If your own TV set shows evidence of harmonic interference, particularly with the transmitter on a dummy load, the chances are good that some of your neighbors will see the same evidence, unless it is visible in your own receiver only when in very close proximity to the transmitter.

Harmonic Suppression

Curing TVI is not a black-magic operation, whether it is the fault of the receivers or your transmitter. All transmitters generate harmonics. Yours is a veritable Pandora's Box full of them; you just have to keep the lid down — tight. Shielding is relatively easy. Most transmitters al-

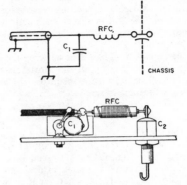

Fig. 15-7 — Most effective filtering for harmonics up through the high TV channels is accomplished by use of the method shown in Fig. 15-6, plus an rf choke and feedthrough capacitor, RFC and C2, for bringing power leads out of the chassis of a vhf transmitter.
C1 — 0.001-μF ceramic disk (see Fig. 15-6).
C2 — 500-pF or 0.001-μF feedthrough capacitor.
RFC — 14 inches No. 26 enam., closewound on high-value 1-watt resistor or 3/16-inch form.

ready have it, but adding it is no great chore. Just be sure that the shielding completely encloses every part of the rf portion of the rig. Then, if the harmonics still come out, you can find the leaks and stop them. Here are the common leaky spots:

Power Cabling Even with complete shielding, leads coming out of the rf portion of a transmitter are likely to have harmonic rf on them. Getting rid of it is no great problem. Shielded wiring in the transmitter is good insurance. Where the lead comes out of the transmitter housing it should be filtered. The simple device of Fig. 15-6 will take care of harmonics and other spurious radiations in all the low TV channels, 2 through 6. Ground the shield on the wire at intervals inside the rig, and at the point where it leaves the enclosure.

If exciter or final-stage harmonics, such as 4 × 48 or 4 × 50, are radiated by power leads, the 15-6 method may not work, since disk ceramics are ineffective above about 100 MHz. Bringing out leads on feedthrough capacitors is much better. See Fig. 15-7.

Chassis Leaks Harmonics, especially those in the upper vhf and uhf TV bands, can leak out of strange places. One exciter for 50 and 144 MHz built by the author showed harmonic interference in Channels 10 through 13. This got no worse when the exciter drove a kilowatt amplifier. Some harmonic energy was found on the power leads. Decoupling as shown in Fig. 15-7 helped, but there was a faint pattern left.

Using a TV set for the visual indicator, it was found that the metal rings on the exciter tuning knobs were hot with harmonic energy. The receiver blacked out when the Twin-Lead probe was brought near to them. The variable capacitors tuning the exciter stages were the type having small rectangular studs for mounting, providing no way of grounding the rotors directly to the panel. Substituting variable capacitors having threaded bushings on the rotor shafts, permitting direct grounding to the panel or chassis cleared this trouble completely.

Long cracks in a chassis, or between the chassis and its cover plate, can act like slot radiators for harmonics. This is why transmitter shielding is fastened with so many screws.

Harmonic Generators

A transmitter with perfectly clean output can still have harmonic troubles, for harmonics can be generated in strong rf fields. Crystal diodes and many other rectifiers, intended or accidental, can do it. Look out for them, wherever they may be. Check for corroded connections in the antenna system, in your own array, or in the TV antenna. Watch for poor metal-to-metal contacts not directly connected to either your antenna system or that on the TV set being interfered with. This condition is found fairly often on apartment house roofs, where the litter from years of erection and decay of TV antennas may be strewn, and metal oxides are turned into harmonic generators by the impact of appreciable amounts of transmitter rf power. Try for shipshape installation of the amateur antenna, and for antenna height that puts the main lobe of radiation completely above the TV antennas and rooftops.

Designing Around Harmonic Problems

Where radiation of harmonics of oscillator or exciter frequencies is causing trouble in the high vhf TV channels, as in the 4th harmonic of tripler stages working from 48 to 144 MHz, it is often possible to use a different frequency multiplying sequence and avoid the problem. This is not an ideal cure, since radiation on anything but the wanted frequency should be held to the practical minimum, but it can be an easy solution to a local problem. There is nothing sacred about common frequency multiplying practices, and many 2-meter men in Channel 10 areas have found relief by changing the order of frequency multiplication from 8-24-48-144 to 8-24-72-144. There can still be energy in Channel 10 (8th harmonic of 24 MHz), but it is almost certain to be far lower than when the 48-144 sequence is used.

Another example of taking the easy way out is the elimination of the 10th harmonic of 8.4 MHz in Channel 6 in 50-MHz transmitters by going to 6.3 MHz or 12.6 MHz in the oscillator stage. Again, this is not the best solution, but it may be a practical one in some circumstances. The right way to do the job is to fix the installation, so that the offending harmonics are not allowed to get through to the transmitting antenna, or to the TV receiver.

A sure cure for most of these troubles is a high starting frequency in the exciter. With a 72-MHz oscillator in a 2-meter rig there is no chance of a harmonic in Channel 10. (A 48-MHz oscillator would be no help.) In a 50-MHz transmitter many of the troubles can be cleared by starting with a 50-MHz oscillator. It should be emphasized that this does nothing for the fundamental-overload problem in the low TV channels, however, and most 50-MHz TVI is of this nature. The 50-MHz oscillator also does not prevent radiation of a 4th harmonic in Channel 11, 12, or 13. This must be suppressed by techniques discussed a few paragraphs back.

Antenna-Mounted TV Boosters

Antenna-mounted broad-band boosters using bipolar transistors, currently popular in TV fringe areas, overload very readily, adding greatly to the vhf man's interference problems. This is especially troublesome, as it results from the viewer's having purchased an expensive antenna system, usually when a color TV receiver is installed. Conversion to field-effect transistors, raising the amateur vhf antenna, and installation of a stub on the booster input are known cures. This problem, currently one of the most difficult encountered by vhf men, is likely to be with us for some time.

COAXIAL AND STRIP-LINE FILTERS

If harmonics or other spurious frequencies appear in the output of an amateur vhf transmitter they can be kept out of the antenna by a high-Q tuned circuit inserted in the line between the transmitter and the antenna. Such a "filter" will pass only a very narrow band of frequencies, offering a substantially impassible barrier to most others. The tuned filter can be helpful in receiving as well, since it will reject energy on frequencies other than the desired ones, and thus prevent overloading from out-of-band signals.

Antenna couplers described in Chapters 8 and 14 perform this function, but higher rejection of unwanted frequencies is possible with the tuned-line filters of Fig. 15-8. Examples are shown for each band from 50 through 450 MHz. Construction is relatively simple, and the cost is low. Standard boxes are used, for ease of duplication. Coaxial-line filters, also using low-cost components, may be found in *QST* for October, 1964.[2]

Quality of the filter elements is important for best results. Use large conductors and the best possible connections, particularly in high-current areas. Copper or brass, preferably silver-plated, is fine. Aluminum is satisfactory, and even fruit juice cans can be used, if all metal-to-metal contacts are clean and solid. Insulation should be kept to a minimum, especially at or near the high-impedance end of the line. A movable-disk capacitor, requiring no supporting frame or insulating material, is good for line tuning. If conventional variable capacitors are unavoidable, use types with high-quality insulation, and preferably no metal frame other than the minimum needed to support the plates. The type with threaded shaft bearing, permitting direct grounding of the rotor, is preferable.

The filter is not a magical device. To get high selectivity and rejection of unwanted frequencies it should not be loaded too heavily. A properly adjusted filter has some insertion loss, and its tuning is critical. If the rejection need not be

Fig. 15-8 — High-Q strip-line filters for 50 MHz (top), 220, 144, and 420 MHz. Those for the two highest bands have half-wave line circuits. All use standard chassis.

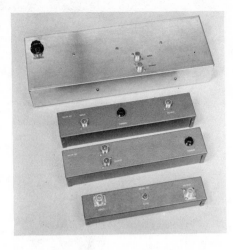

extremely high the coupling into and out of the filter can be adjusted to broaden response and reduce insertion loss. Two filters can be used in series, for very high rejection of unwanted frequencies. What you want to do with a filter determines how you adjust and operate it.

A typical use for a coaxial or strip-line filter is to prevent radiation of unwanted harmonics of the exciter frequencies in a 50-MHz transmitter. The filter of Fig. 15-10 is selective enough to pass 50-MHz energy and attenuate the 7th harmonic of an 8-MHz oscillator, that falls in TV Channel 2. With an insertion loss at 50 MHz of about 1 dB, it can provide up to 40 dB of attenuation to energy at 57 MHz in the same line. This should be more than enough to take care of the worst situations, provided that the radiation is by way of the transmitter output coax only. The filter will not eliminate interfering energy that gets out from power cables, the ac line, or from the transmitter circuits themselves. It also will do nothing for TVI that results from deficiencies in the TV receiver, such as the various problems we have already discussed.

Building the Filters

When information on the strip-line filters shown here was first published, considerable mail was received from prospective users, who did not understand just how they are made. This was true particularly of the 50-MHz model, mechanical details of which are not immediately apparent from the photograph, Fig. 15-10. In an attempt to answer these questions, an equivalent circuit is shown for the two general types.

Though they look very different mechanically, the 50- and 144-MHz filters are similar electrically, as seen in Fig. 15-9A. The 144-MHz model, Fig. 15-11, is readily understandable as a conventional quarter-wave line, grounded at one end and tuned at the other. The 50-MHz filter, Fig. 15-10, is also a quarter-wave line, but it is folded back on itself, to conserve space and permit use of a standard chassis. Its L1 is a strip of aluminum, with a mounting lip at the lower right end bolted to that end surface of the chassis. The two coaxial fittings are above and below the strip, the upper one being out of sight in the picture. What appears to be a fitting on the bottom surface is actually a reflection. The ends of the two coupling loops and the end of L1 all ground to the chassis in the lower right corner of the picture. The partition down through the middle is grounded to the main chassis surface, and to the right end. The line element is isolated from the chassis, except at the ground point, lower right. The tuning capacitor is in the upper right corner.

The 220- and 432-MHz filters are half-wave lines, in which L1 is grounded to the case at both ends, and tuned by a variable capacitor, C, at the middle. The output and input loops, L2 and L3, are at opposite ends of the line, for balance. All filters shown are bilateral. The coaxial fittings are

marked "input" and "output" but the decals could be exchanged.

The 50-MHz filter case is a $6 \times 17 \times 3$-inch chassis (Bud AC-433) with a cover plate that fastens in place with self-tapping screws. An aluminum partition down the middle of the assembly is 14 inches long, and the full height of the chassis, 3 inches. Construction should be clear from the photograph.

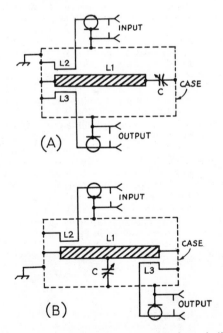

Fig. 15-9 — Equivalent circuits for the strip-line filters. At A, the circuit for the 6- and 2-meter filters is shown. L2 and L3 are the input and output links. At B, the representative circuit for the 220- and 432-MHz filters. All four filters are bilateral, permitting interchanging of the input and output terminals.

Fig. 15-10 — Interior of the 50-MHz strip-line filter. Inner conductor of aluminum strip is bent into U shape, to fit inside a standard 17-inch chassis. Coupling is by L-shaped loops about 1/4 inch above and below the tuned line, lower right.

Fig. 15-11 — The 144-MHz filter has an inner conductor of 1/2-inch copper tubing, grounded to the left end of the case and supported at the right end by the tuning capacitor.

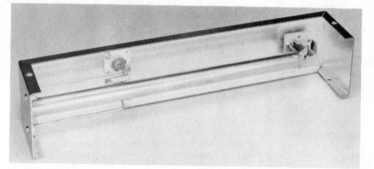

The inner conductor of the line is 32 inches long and 13/16 inch wide, of 1/16-inch brass, copper, or aluminum. In the model shown this was made from two pieces of aluminum spliced together to provide the 32-inch length. Splicing (visible at the left end of the U-shaped inner conductor) seemed to have no ill effect on the circuit *Q*. The sides of the "U" are 2-7/8 inches apart with the partition at the center. The line is supported on ceramic standoffs. As may be seen from Fig. 15-10, these were shimmed up with sections of hard wood or bakelite rod, to give the required 1-1/2-inch height.

The tuning capacitor is a double-spaced variable (Hammarlund HF-30-X) mounted 1-1/2 inches from the right end of the chassis. Input and output coupling loops, visible on each side of the line, lower right of Fig. 15-10, are of No. 10 or 12 wire, 10 inches long. Spacing away from the line is adjusted to about 1/4 inch. This may be increased for higher rejection, but this will result in increased insertion loss. The position of the input and output coaxial connectors is shown in Fig. 15-8.

The 144-MHz model, second from the bottom in Fig. 15-8, is housed in a 2-1/4 × 2-1/2 × 12-inch Minibox (Bud CU-2114-A). The inner conductor (see Fig. 15-11) is 1/2-inch copper tubing 10 inches long. One end is slotted 1/4 inch deep with a hacksaw. This slot takes a brass angle bracket 1-1/2 inches wide, 1/4 inch high, with a 1/2-inch mounting lip. The 1/4-inch lip is soldered into the tubing slot, and the bracket is then bolted to the end of the box, so as to be centered on the end plate.

The tuning capacitor (Hammarlund HF-15-X) is mounted 1-1/4 inches from the other end of the box, in such a position that the inner conductor can be soldered to the two stator bars, as seen in Fig. 15-11.

The two coaxial fittings (SO-239) are 11/16 inch in from each side of the box, 3-1/2 inches from the left end. The coupling loops are No. 12 wire, bent so that each is parallel to the center line of the inner conductor, and about 1/8 inch from its surface. Their cold ends are soldered to the brass mounting bracket.

Fig. 15-12 — A half-wave strip line is used in the 220-MHz filter. It is grounded at both ends and tuned at the center.

Fig. 15-13 — Construction of the 420-MHz filter is similar to the 220-MHz one, except that it is shorter, and a disk-type tuning capacitor is used.

The 220-MHz filter uses the same size box as the 144-MHz model just described, but the circuit is a half-wave line, grounded to each end of the box and tuned at the center. The inner conductor is 1/16-inch brass or copper, 5/8 inch wide, just long enough to fold over at each end for bolting to the box. It is positioned so that there will be 1/8 inch clearance between it and the rotor plates of the tuning capacitor. The latter is a Hammarlund HF-15-X, mounted slightly off-center in the box, so that its stator plates connect to the exact midpoint of the line. The 5/16-inch mounting hole in the case is 5-1/2 inches from one end. Two small holes drilled in the inner conductor allow it to slip over the stator posts, for soldering in place.

The links for input and output coupling are at opposite ends of the box, as seen in Fig. 15-12. The SO-239 coaxial fittings are 1 inch in from opposite sides of the box, 2 inches from the ends. Their coupling links are No. 14 wire, 1/8 inch from the inner conductor of the line.

The 420-MHz filter is similar in design, using a 1-5/8 × 2 × 10-inch Minibox (Bud CU-2113-A). A half-wave line is used, with disk tuning at the center. The disks are 1/16-inch brass, 1-1/4-inch diameter. The fixed one is centered on the inner conductor, the other mounted on a No. 6 brass lead-screw. This passes through a threaded bushing, which can be taken from the end of a discarded slug-tuned form. An advantage of these is that some kind of tension device is usually included. If there is none, a lock nut can be used.

Type N coaxial connectors were used on the 420-MHz model. They are 5/8 inch in from each side of the box, and 1-3/8 inches in from the ends. Their coupling links of No. 14 wire 1/16 inch from the inner conductor are visible in Fig. 15-13.

Adjustment and Use

If you want the filter to work on both transmitting and receiving, connect up your system as shown in Fig. 15-14. With this arrangement you need merely adjust the filter for minimum reflected power reading on the SWR bridge. This should be zero, or close to it, if the antenna is well matched. The bridge should be used, as there is no way to adjust the filter properly without it. If you try, adjust for best reception of signals on frequencies close to the ones you expect to transmit on. This works reasonably well only if the antenna is well matched.

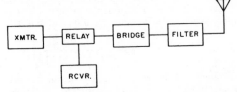

Fig. 15-14 — Preferred method of connecting a tuned filter in the antenna line of a vhf station makes the selectivity of the filter available for both transmitting and receiving.

When the filter is properly adjusted (with the SWR bridge) you may find that reception can be improved by retuning the filter. Don't do it, if you want the filter to work best on the job it was intended to do: the rejection of unwanted energy, transmitting or receiving. If you want to improve reception with the filter in the circuit, work on the receiver input circuit. To get maximum power out of the transmitter and into the line, adjust the transmitter output coupling, not the filter. If the effect of the filter on reception bothers you, connect it in the line to the transmitter only.

Don't expect the filter, or any other device you can connect onto your station, to be a TVI cure-all. There is no such magic box available, at any price. Curing TVI calls for some understanding of what goes on in transmitters, antennas, and TV receivers. There is no easy way out, but by the same token, there is no completely hopeless situation. Every form of interference *can* be cured.

BIBLIOGRAPHY

[1]Ladd, "50-Mc. TVI — Causes and Cures, " June and July, 1954, *QST*.

[2]Tilton, "Coaxial-Tank V.H.F. Filters," October, 1964, *QST*.

[3]ARRL *Handbook*, Interference Chapter, all modern editions. Also Tilton, "TVI Hints for the V.H.F. Man," April, 1953, *QST*.

Other references of interest to the vhf worker include the following *QST* items:

U.H.F. Strip TVI—Proofing the ARC-5 V.H.F. Transmitter," Johnson, November, 1950, *QST*.

Techniques for dealing with various forms of TVI were included in scores of *QST* articles of the early 1950s. They are of historical as well as technical interest, since they tell the month-by-month story of the TVI battle that was eventually won by the amateur.

Chapter 16

Bits and Pieces

Many vhf enthusiasts are experimenters at heart. Their first projects, when they are bitten by the vhf bug may be kits or duplicates of *QST* or *Handbook* items, but soon the urge develops to custom design and build vhf gear. This can take the form of studying published constructional articles for ideas, and then adapting them to one's own needs. We like to think that much of the material in this book will be used in this way. Eventually, with accumulated knowledge and experience, most vhf men get to the point of designing for their own requirements, rather than merely duplicating to the last nut and bolt what someone else has already worked out.

This last section of our book is for these amateurs. It will be something of a hodge-podge of ideas and techniques that might have been worked into other chapters, but which more logically fall into the "Hints and Kinks" category. The *QST* section under that title has been a most-read feature for generations. We hope that our version of it will find equal acceptance. Our thanks go to the scores of vhf men who supplied the items you will find here and elsewhere in this manual.

IMPARTING THE "COMMERCIAL LOOK"

Well-built ham gear of good design usually works at least as well as equipment purchased ready made, but it seldom looks the part. Even the simplest equipment can be given a quality look, if the builder will devote a little time and thought to appearance of the final product of his building efforts. Expensive cabinets are not necessary; even simple chassis-mounted units having no front panel or cabinet, in the usual sense, can be made neat and attractive in appearance with the use of a little paint, decals, and care in layout.

Painting

Every hardware store today carries aerosol-spray enamels, in a wide variety of colors. Black, grey, and white are favored for ham gear, but other colors have their uses. Matching or contrasting colors can give many nice effects. If this book were printed in color the reader could better appreciate the value of judicious use of paints, in other than the conventional grey and black. This trend to color in homemade ham gear should be credited to Doug DeMaw, W1CER, who pioneered use of color freely in ARRL construction projects. He contributed the following suggestions.

The best paint job is usually possible if the metal parts are drilled, ready for assembly, but the equipment is not actually put together. This is practical on all but the most experimental items, and even these can usually be rebuilt in finished form, once the bugs are taken care of. Clean the metal with fine steel wool, to remove rough spots and dirt. With new aluminum this treatment is desirable to remove the high gloss, making a better base for paint. For exceptional durability, spray a first coat of zinc chromate, an undercoating finish also available in spray cans.

After the rub-down, clean with a grease solvent. Avoid touching the metal with the bare hands, as skin oils and acids can cause blemishes in the finished work. Prop the work up with a large area of newspaper or other protective covering under it. Spray paints dry quickly so dust is no problem, but select a place that is well ventilated and clean.

If you've not used aerosol sprays before it may be well to practice a bit with some metal scraps. Read the directions; don't assume that you know how to handle these sprays. The manufacturer probably knows more than you do, and he wants your results to be good.

Shake the can thoroughly. Keeping the nozzle at least 12 inches from the work, spray with a sweeping motion, using just enough to cover. More will surely cause runs of paint, destroying the appearance. Allow several minutes for complete drying, and spray again, evenly and lightly. Now put the work aside for at least 24 hours. This allows the paint to age, and greatly lessens the chance of damage in handling.

Two-tone finishes can be made neatly by masking off any area that is to be painted a different color, or, in the case of aluminum, left its natural finish. Wherever metal is to be natural in color, a coating of clear lacquer will keep it looking its best much longer than if it is left uncoated. Large areas can be masked off with newspaper, with masking tape only at the edges. Press the tape firmly along the paint boundary desired, to prevent seepage under the edge of the tape. Keep the tape on until the paint has dried thoroughly.

After using spray paint, turn the can upside down and press the nozzle for a few seconds to clean out the spray jet. This simple precaution, often ignored though it is included in the directions, will make the next job much simpler than if it is omitted.

When using two different colors on a surface be sure that they are compatible. Test them in advance; some different paint bases may react on one another.

Old transformers and chokes can be made to look like new by painting. Clean them thoroughly of rust, loose paint, grease, etc. before spray painting. Sanding or scrubbing with steel wool may be needed.

Highlighting can be applied to cabinets and panels by painting with a base color such as grey or black, and then spraying over lightly with gold, silver, or copper. For an effect of depth, use clear spray over the finished product. Take plenty of drying time between these operations.

Applying Decals

Neat labelling provides the final touch, and it is of practical value when other amateurs may want to use your equipment. Typewritten or hand-inked labels pasted onto equipment make it look like the work of a rank beginner, regardless of how skillfully the electrical and mechanical work has been done. Decals are easy to apply. A book of them with enough to last through many projects costs less than $2.00. They are available in black, white, and gold.

The label desired is cut from the sheet and then soaked in water to separate it from the paper backing. Slide the decal onto the metal surface and move it into the desired position. If you get it slightly awry, dampen it and move it with a small brush. When it is lined up properly blot the moisture with absorbent cloth or paper towel. The label can be moved again by moistening, until it is permanently dissolved with Tekni-Solv or lacquer thinner. This should be applied with a small brush, using just enough to moisten the label area.

The solvent should be tested on a paint sample, as some solvent-paint combinations cause wrinkling and peeling. Paint should be allowed to dry for at least 48 hours before applying the solvent.

Other Appearance Factors

Choice of knobs can make or break the appearance of homebuilt gear. Occasionally an amateur will devote a lot of time and effort to building a neat outfit, and then spoil the whole effect with a random collection of knobs. Parts arrangement is important, too. Controls don't have to be perfectly balanced in their distribution over a panel area, but pleasing arrangements nearly always can be made without resorting to string drives, remote controls, and various other mechanical devices.

Speaker grills offer an opportunity for appearance highlights. A grill of perforated aluminum painted black, mounted against a grey panel, will give a pleasing effect. With some thought and advance planning, and the expenditure of a little extra time, the final product of your handiwork can be something you'll be proud to show off to your friends.

SILVER PLATING — WHAT IT DOES, HOW TO DO IT

Silver is one of the best conductors known. Where very high conductivity is important, silver plating will improve almost any other metal. In addition, silver has a special attribute: it remains a good conductor when oxidized, whereas few other metals do. For these reasons many items of military uhf gear are silver plated throughout, and copious silver plating has come to be almost synonymous with quality in the minds of vhf and uhf workers.

But silver is expensive, so it is not so widely used in amateur applications. Just how much does it do for us, and is it worth the cost? There is no single answer, except that silver plating probably never did any harm, and it may be helpful. It makes soldering much easier, and it certainly improves metal-to-metal contacts, especially sliding ones. It is well worthwhile in the portions of circuits where rf current is high, as in the shorted end of a coaxial or parallel-line rf circuit.

Silver plating makes a measurable improvement in the Q of a vhf circuit; 5 to 10 percent increase in 200-MHz coils wound of copper ribbon resulted from before-and-after measurements in the ARRL Lab. It is probable that copper and brass tank circuits of the type used in the 144- and 432-MHz amplifiers described in this book would be slightly better after plating. Tests on typical items have shown no measurable improvement in transmitter efficiencies through plating, but these have not been made on enough circuits to be sure that no benefit is obtainable. Certainly the long-term conductivity of silver-plated items, as compared with copper or brass counterparts that oxidize quickly with handling and use, should have some bearing on the value of plating to the amateur.

Plating can be done in several ways. First, you can take your parts to a plating shop. This costs money, but assures a good job. There are at least three do-it-yourself methods now available, including a home version of the process the plating shops use.

For this you need a silver anode and a quart of concentrated plating solution. Both are available from distributors of plating materials. They cost $6.00 each from Hoover & Strong Co., Tupper Bldg., Buffalo, NY. Other items required before you set up in the plating business are a voltage source, 1 to 3 volts dc; a 2-quart plastic dish, a 5-quart rinsing bucket, degreasing solvent, a pair of clip leads, and some fine steel wool. The plating solution will enable you to plate with other metals as well as silver. The plastic containers can be obtained from any hardware store.

Preparing the Work

Copper, brass, and bronze are most suitable for silver plating. Steel can be plated, if it is first plated with copper. Whatever the metal it should be cleaned and polished before immersion in the plating bath. Rub it down with fine steel wool, and clean in a degreasing solution. Chemical houses supply degreasers, or you can boil the work in a mild solution of laundry detergent. Rinse thoroughly in clean hot water. Handle only with rubber gloves; finger oils and acids will prevent the metal from plating properly.

Plating

Use distilled water to dilute the plating solution, usually 3 quarts of water to 1 of solution. This must be at room temperature. Too warm a bath will cause discoloration, and too cold will make for spotty plating. Connect the metal to be plated to the negative side of a 1-1/2-volt cell, and slide it into one end of the plating tank. Connect the silver anode to the positive terminal, and submerge it at the opposite end. Maintain a spacing of at least 6 inches between anode and work. Too close spacing causes excessive current flow and discoloration. Agitate the work frequently to prevent bubble formation on it.

Immersion time is usually 5 to 10 minutes. Longer will give heavier coating, and it is best to err on this side, as far as the rf quality of the plating is concerned. The higher the voltage the rougher the finish. Something between 0.5 and 1-1/2 volts is best.

After plating is completed rinse immediately in fresh clean water, preferably lukewarm. Do not touch with the bare hands if you want a clean surface. To preserve the finish, spray with clear lacquer after the work is thoroughly dry. A lacquer spray does not affect the ability of the surface to take solder. If incomplete plating is found near solder areas it is probably due to the presence of flux. Such areas can be scrubbed with a stiff brush and xylol or alcohol. Replating can be done as needed, in the manner already outlined.

Caution: Silver plating solutions contain cyanide. Avoid breathing the vapors from the bath. In mixing, pour the plating solution into the water, *not* vice-versa. Wash hands thoroughly after any contact with the fluid. Do the plating in a well-ventilated room. Store the chemicals in clearly marked containers, out of the reach of children.

Other Methods

Plating kits are available in several forms. An inexpensive one is made by Miniplating, Box 161, Middleboro, MA. This consists of a plastic cylinder for holding two penlite cells, an electrode that fits in the end of the cylinder, clip leads, and a jar of plating solution in jelly form. The electrode is covered with a spongelike plastic. The silver kit is inexpensive; extra jars of plating concentrate are available separately.

To use the kit the electrode is dipped in the jelly, the clip lead connected to the work, and then the surface to be plated is rubbed with the coated electrode until silver is deposited.

Another method, very simple to use, involves a plating powder. It is applied with a damp cloth dipped in the powder, and then rubbed onto the surface to be plated. Because some rubbing is required, the resulting surface comes out very nice and smooth. The material, called COOL-AMP, is made by a company of that name, 8603 S.W. 17th Ave., Portland, OR. The powder is sold only in jars, minimum order 1 pound, but a little goes a long way. Several would-be platers could do quite a bit of work each with one pound, which covers about 6000 square inches!

Both the above methods are best used with rubber gloves. The plating materials are a little rough on the skin otherwise, and neater work is possible if the fingers are kept from direct contact with the work or the plating substances. Several of the items described in this book were plated using the kit or the powder.

VARIABLE-FREQUENCY CRYSTAL HOLDER

The frequency at which a crystal oscillates is affected by the capacitance of metal pressure plates either side of the crystal in the holder, in mounts such as the FT-243, shown in its original form at A in Fig. 16-1. In B, a flexible top electrode is substituted, and provision is made for varying the pressure this exerts on the crystal, thus varying the capacitance.

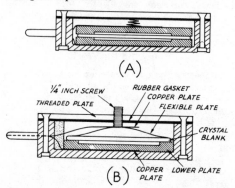

(A)

(B)

COPPER LOWER PLATE
PLATE

¼" INCH SCREW   RUBBER GASKET
THREADED PLATE   COPPER PLATE
                 FLEXIBLE PLATE
                         CRYSTAL
                         BLANK

Fig. 16-1 — Cutaway views of the FT-243 crystal holder, in its original form, A, and modified, B, for variable frequency control. In the latter a spring with adjustable pressure is substituted for the upper electrode. Spring tension is adjusted by means of a small screw in the cover plate.

Fig. 16-2 — An FT-243 surplus crystal, modified for variable frequency control.

In this system by W4RMU for swinging the crystal oscillator frequency, a spring electrode of 0.004-inch brass or 0.003-inch steel shim stock is used as the top plate, in place of the usual top electrode of the holder. The top cover of the crystal holder is drilled and tapped to take a 1/4-inch screw (fine thread preferred, but 1/4-20 is usable) which provides the pressure adjustment. The copper plate that made contact with the original electrode in the holder serves the same purpose in the revised one. The spring plate is bent around a 5/8-inch rod to give the curvature needed.

It is important that the corners of the pressure plate be completely free of roughness or burrs. Polish them carefully with an emery stone or very fine file. The range of frequency shift will be from the point where the spring plate touches the crystal at its center (low end of the range) to the point where the pressure no longer holds the crystal firmly in place.

A modified FT-243 crystal is shown in Fig. 16-2. The amount of frequency shift will vary from one crystal to another, with the types that are convex-ground giving the greatest usable swing. Activity varies somewhat over the frequency swing, dropping off quickly at each end. A typical surplus crystal on 6006.667 kHz, which originally gave a 2-meter frequency of 144.16′ MHz now gives coverage from that frequency to 144.25 MHz, with substantially no change in final grid drive. This is in a conventional 6CX8 tetrode oscillator.

CAPACITOR ROTORS — TO GROUND OR NOT TO GROUND?

The question of grounding the rotor of a tuning capacitor, whether to do it, and if so, how, bothers many builders of vhf gear. In single-ended circuits, Fig. 16-3A and B, grounding of the rotor, as in A, is usually the preferred method. The bypass capacitor, C1, may be far from perfect, with the result that the rotor will have some rf voltage on it, and it may radiate harmonics, or make the tuning sensitive to hand capacity.

Choice of the tuning capacitor, C2, may be important, too. Some variables have metal studs embedded in the ceramic end plate for mounting. With these a connection, usually to a rotor spider, must be made for grounding. The resultant lead inductance may be enough to leave the rotor above ground for rf voltage, at frequencies above 100 MHz or so. The capacitor having a threaded rotor bushing, for direct grounding to the panel or chassis, is much better for grounded-rotor circuits.

In the push-pull circuit, C, or any other where a split-stator capacitor is used, grounding the rotor or not depends on several factors. If the center-tap of the plate coil is bypassed to ground there is no need to ground the rotor, and it may not be necessary in other circuits. Especially in the upper vhf and into the uhf range, grounding the rotor of C3 may unbalance the circuit severely, though this depends to some extent on the capacitor construction. With small butterfly types, as in a 6360 amplifier stage, it is almost impossible to avoid rotor grounding. In these circuits, with their well-balanced miniature capacitors, there is no reason for doing otherwise, but the coil center-tap should not be bypassed if the rotor is grounded. In split-stator capacitors with two sections in line on a single rotor shaft, some unbalance almost always results from rotor grounding. In one 432-MHz tripler-amplifier formerly in the ARRL *Handbook*, running the tuning capacitor rotors above ground was a necessity. So great was the unbalance with the rotors grounded that neither tripler nor amplifier stage would operate at all in that condition.

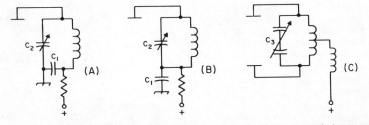

Fig. 16-3 — Because the bypass, C1, may not be completely effective, the grounded-rotor circuit, A, is preferred to that in B, which bypasses both the rotor and the low end of the plate coil. In the push-pull circuit, C, the rotor is best left ungrounded, unless the design of C3 is such that good balance to ground is assured.

SERIES-RESONANT BYPASSING

It is well known that the inexpensive disk-ceramic and "dog-bone" types of capacitors are relatively ineffective for bypassing above about 100 MHz or so. This is due mainly to their considerable lead inductance, even when they are connected as close to the elements to be bypassed as possible. Actually this lead inductance can be used to advantage, by selecting lead lengths that make the capacitor series-resonant at the frequency to be bypassed.

This approach is recommended by WA2KYF, who supplied the information in Table 16-I, showing capacitor and lead-length combinations for effective bypassing of rf energy at frequencies

TABLE 16-I

Values of capacitance in pF required for resonance at frequencies commonly encountered in amateur-band vhf work, for leads of 1/4, 1/2, and 1 inch in length.

Frequency MHz	1/4-Inch Leads	1/2-Inch Leads	1-Inch Leads
48-50	800	400	200
72	390	180	91
96	220	100	56
144	100	47	25
220	39	20	10

commonly encountered in vhf work. The values are not particularly critical, as a series-resonant circuit is broad by nature. The impedance of a series-resonant by-pass is very close to zero ohms at the frequency of resonance, and it will be lower than most conventional capacitors for a considerable range of frequency.

A high-capacitance short-lead combination is preferable to a lower value with longer leads,

because the former will be less likely to allow unwanted coupling to other circuits. For example, a 100-pF capacitor with 1/4-inch leads is a better bet than a 25-pF with 1-inch leads, for bypassing at 144 MHz. The series-resonant bypass is worth a try in any circuit where instability is troublesome, and conventional bypassing has been shown to be ineffective. Screen, heater, and cathode circuits are usually good candidates.

HINTS ON PARABOLIC ANTENNA DESIGN AND CONSTRUCTION

Effective work above 1000 MHz almost requires a parabolic antenna. The usual solution is a trip to a surplus depot or military junkyard, but parabolas of moderate size are not too difficult to make. A 5-footer (23 dB gain at 2300 MHz) built for the first amateur work on 2300 MHz ever, and still a good design, is shown in Fig. 16-4. This picture is from a description by Koch and Floyd of their pioneering 2300-MHz work, in *QST* for July, 1946. How the reflector was made is fairly obvious from the photograph, and Fig. 16-5. The dimensions need not be in inches; the proportions can be used for any size dish.

Much interesting information on practical parabolas was given by WA9HUV in "The World Above 50 Mc," June, 1971, *QST*. His homemade 12-footer for 432 and 1296 MHz is shown in Fig. 16-6. The following is from the *QST* report. A 10-page photocopy of the full WA9HUV construction and design information is available from ARRL Headquarters for $1.00.

Illumination and Element Spacing

It will be seen that spacing between reflector elements is appreciable, and that not all the reflector area is "filled" with tubing. Would-be dish builders may not realize that though the contour must be kept close to the ideal, the density of the reflector need not be high. Reduction of the

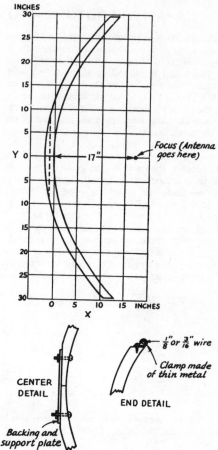

Fig. 16-4 — A homemade parabolic reflector for 2300 MHz. The model shown is 5 feet in diameter, using proportions shown in Fig. 16-5.

Fig. 16-5 — The frame for a parabolic reflector can be cut from plywood or pine shelving, using the dimensions or proportions given above. The shape of the curve can be computed from the formula $Y^2 = 4AX$, where A is the distance from the center to the focal point, in this case 17 inches.

density in the four areas around the outer portion of the dish has a negligible effect on the overall efficiency of the system.

The limit for spacing of reflector components has been shown by theoretical analysis and leakage-loss measurement to be greater than many might expect.[1] The 3-inch spacing used in this array is closer than is needed for optimum results

[1]*Microwave Theory and Design,* Vol. 12, MIT Radiation Laboratory Series, BTF Edition, p. 449.

at 1296 MHz. Theory indicates that the dish will work at 2300 MHz with a loss of only 3 dB, compared to a solid reflector. If it were to be used for 432 only, the spacing could be as much as 12 inches without appreciable loss.

Placement of the feed is determined mainly by the beamwidth of the feed antenna and the size and shape of the parabola. The pattern of the feed should be wide enough to cover the entire parabola, yet not so wide that appreciable power spills over the edges of the dish. Remembering the shape of the pattern of a dipole and reflector, and the way the power drops off beyond the 3-dB points, it can be seen having the 3-dB points just inside the edges is a fairly good approximation. It happens that the patterns of the dipole-and-reflector at 432 and the cylindrical horn at 1296 are quite similar, so one position is satisfactory for both. The feed assemblies are about 60 inches out from the dish center.

The curvature of the parabola is then determined by the optical requirement for beamforming (collimation) that the distance from the source to any point on the reflector, and back out to an imaginary plane in front of the dish, be the same. All energy from the source must arrive at the imaginary plane simultaneously, producing what is known as a *plane phase front*, and the narrowest possible beam. The 60-inch focal length of this design is critical to about plus or minus one inch.

Bending the Metal

Reflector components of the WA9HUV dish were bent to the desired shape with the aid of a very simple "jig." Once the desired curve was determined, large nails were driven into the studding in a garage wall, and the dish elements bent so that they just touched each nail. This is done quite readily with the smaller sizes, and it is not too difficult with the larger sizes, if done a small amount at a time, and with great care. The garage studs in this instance are 16 inches apart center to center. This called for fixture nails at 1.07, 4.25,

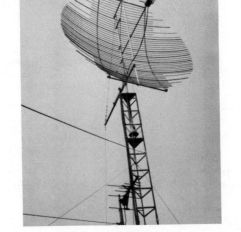

Fig. 16-6 — The WA9HUV 12-foot dish for 432 and 1296 MHz atop its 50-foot tower.

9.6, 17, and 26.7 inches lower, progressively, for each nail out from the center point of the curve.

The curve should be smooth, and the final result should just touch each nail as the element rests on the jig. The shape of the dish can be controlled to some extent during assembly. Final positioning can be adjusted to match the curve of a test gauge at all points.

Results

By early 1972 the WA9HUV 12-foot dish had been in service more than two years, on 432 and 1296 MHz, with excellent results on both bands. Beamwidths are 14 degrees on 432 and 6 degrees on 1296 MHz. These result in gains of 21 dBi and 29 dBi, respectively, assuming 2-dB illumination loss.

MAKING AND USING RF CHOKES

General-purpose rf chokes can be bought almost as cheaply as they can be made, but winding your own has its points. If choke efficiency is important, you can probably make a better one than you can buy, and for random applications a few turns of wire on a resistor, or self-supported, may suffice.

Applications

A choke is used to keep rf out of a circuit, or in another. For vhf applications something between a quarter and a half wavelength of wire wound up into a coil will do. It should preferably be of small diameter (usually 1/4 inch or less) and 3 to 6 times as long as it is wide. In some circuits a carbon resistor will work just as well; maybe better, if there is not a heating problem. Fig. 16-7 shows resistors used for decoupling the plate-power leads of familiar rf amplifier circuits. R1 and R2 can be anything from a few hundred to several thousand

ohms. They can be used for voltage-dropping as well, as in the case of Nuvistor stages that must run at around 70 volts, with a power source that may be as high as 200 or 250 volts.

For decoupling the heater circuits chokes must be used. RFC1 and RFC2 can be wound on small resistors, preferably of 10,000 ohms or more. RFC3 and RFC4 prevent signal loss to ground, when low-value cathode resistors are used. This is not a critical application; almost any choke will do.

The shunt-feed plate choke in a transmitter amplifier, RFC6 in Fig. 16-8, is a more critical matter. This choke has the whole rf power of the amplifier across it, at high impedance, and it had better be a good one. On the other hand, the output choke, RFC7, never sees much over 50 ohms impedance, so long as the transmitter is working into a well-matched load. Its quality is not a matter for great concern, and it is mainly a protective device, to prevent dc voltage from

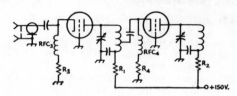

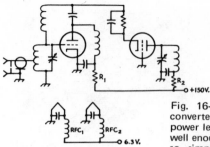

Fig. 16-7 — Typical rf amplifier circuits for vhf receivers or converters. Resistors R1 and R2 are used for decoupling of the power leads. Rf chokes could replace them, but resistors do the job well enough. In the heater circuit the current is too high for resistors so simple rf chokes, RFC1 and RFC2, must be used. In the grounded-grid amplifier, right, chokes RFC3 and RFC4 are inserted in the cathode leads, to prevent signal loss to ground. Heater circuit chokes are the same as for the cascode circuit at the left. The quality of the chokes is not particularly critical in either application.

appearing on the antenna line, should C1 break down. The grid choke, RFC5, is not particularly critical.

Placement of an rf choke may have considerable bearing on its performance. Fig. 16-9

TABLE 16-II

Rf Chokes for 50-, 144-, and 220-MHz Service		
Frequency	*Inductance*	*Description*
50 MHz	7.8 to 9.5 μH	B&W Miniductor No. 3004, 1-3/8 to 1-9/16 inch long.*
50 MHz	8.3 μH	No. 28 dsc, spacewound on 1/2-inch Teflon rod. Winding 1-3/4 inch long. See text
50 MHz	7.2 μH	No. 28 dsc, closewound on 1/4-inch Teflon rod. Winding 1-7/16 inch long.
144 MHz	2.15 μH	No. 22 Nyclad, closewound 1-3/16 inch on 1/4-inch Teflon rod.
144 MHz	1.42 μH	31 turns No. 28 dsc, spacewound on 1/4-inch dia self-supporting.
(Above 144-MHz chokes work well on 220 MHz.)		
220 MHz	0.6 μH	13 turns No. 22 Nyclad on 1/4-inch Teflon rod.
220 MHz	0.75 μH	17 turns No. 28 dsc spacewound on 1/4-inch Teflon rod. Winding 5/8 inch long.
220 MHz	0.52 μH	22 turns No. 22 Nyclad closewound on No. 24 drill, self-supporting.

*Excellent for use except where high temperatures are involved.

shows right and wrong positions for the rf choke on a 2-meter plate line. The pipe-line amplifier of Chapter 6 was built originally as shown at the left of Fig. 16-9. When power was applied the rf choke went up in smoke. Moved to a position outside the "U" of the plate line its replacement has run coolly ever since.

There is no "good" place to put a choke used in the manner of RFC6 in Fig. 16-8. It has to be close to the tube, so it is subjected to considerable heat, as well as to high rf voltage and heavy dc flow. Consequently this rf choke must have large built-in safety factors in all categories.

Designing for the Job

To handle the dc load without overheating, No. 28 wire is about as small as is safe to go in an rf choke for heavy-duty transmitting applications. Larger is better, if there is room. Space-winding the turns increases the heat-dissipating qualities, making it possible to use smaller wire than when the turns are closewound. Most heat trouble in rf chokes develops from their being used in hot places, and being subjected to high rf voltages, rather than to excessive dc flow alone.

Wire size is important in heater chokes, especially where the current to several tubes runs through a single choke. No. 22 or 24 wire is about as small as should be used in heater leads, ordinarily. These or larger sizes can be used for self-supporting chokes for the higher bands.

Distributed capacitance limits the range over which an rf choke will work. This makes the

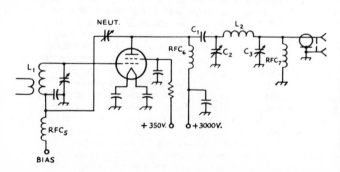

Fig. 16-8 — Transmitter applications for rf chokes vary markedly in regard to the quality of choke needed. In the grid circuit, RFC5 has no very difficult job to do, and any choke suitable for low-power use is suitable. The shunt-feed choke, RFC6, must meet severe requirements, especially in high-powered amplifiers. It is effectively across the transmitter tank circuit, and is subjected to high temperature, current, and voltage. The output choke, RFC7, is mainly a safety device and it operates under much less stringent circumstances.

Fig. 16-9 — How a choke is positioned with respect to other circuits may be important. The choke at the left is coupled to the plate line of the transmitter tuned circuit. Outside the loop, as at the right, makes the choke far less subject to rf breakdown.

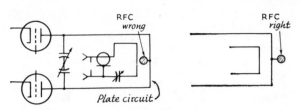

space-wound choke superior to the close-wound one. A minimum of cement on the windings is also desirable. The space-wound 50-MHz choke in Table 16-II, shown in the upper right of Fig. 16-10 is as good as you can make for that band, and better than most chokes you could buy. It is good at 144 MHz as well, and even serviceable at 220 MHz. A closewound choke of fine wire, heavily doped with lacquer, might be usable on only one vhf band, and very likely it would not be too good, even there.

Making Your Own

To set up in the rf choke business we need some wire: No. 22 enamel (Nyclad or Formvar preferred); No. 28 enamel, silk or cotton covered; and No. 30 or 32, of any similar insulation. Silk- or cotton-covered wires take cement nicely, but enamel is OK otherwise, and it is usually most readily available.

High-value 1/2- or 1-watt resistors make good winding forms for use at 144 MHz and higher. A 2-watt resistor is big enough for a 50-MHz choke, but Teflon or Nylon rod stock is better. Do not use polystyrene or lucite, if any heat is to be involved. These materals will melt in the heat of an average transmitter enclosure. Teflon rod can be found in plastics supply houses, in 1/4- and 1/2-inch diameter. It drills and taps nicely, it won't melt, and its insulating quality is excellent. Bakelite rod or even wood dowelling is good enough for the less-critical choke applications. The smallest-diameter prepared coil stock is usable for 50-MHz chokes, but it won't stand much heat.

Space-winding rf chokes is easy. First drill through the rod at spacings indicated under *winding length* in Table 16-II. Now measure off slightly more than a *half* wavelength of wire. Double it back on itself and feed the end through one of the holes in the rod. Now wind the coil as if it were to be bifilar. If you clamp the other end of the double wire in a vise, or tie it down firmly otherwise, this can be done easily. Keep the wires under tension, and be sure that they are not twisted at any point. Wind tightly and then feed the end through the other rod hole.

Now remove one of the wires by unwinding carefully, keeping it under tension throughout. The remaining wire will be space-wound as neatly as if done by machine. Apply a thin coating of polystyrene cement, using a bit more around the lead holes, and your choke is done. It will be dry and ready for use in a few minutes. If having all those wire scraps left over runs against your Scotch instincts, make chokes for the lower end of the

range first. The pieces unwound will be useful for higher frequency production later.

Self-supporting chokes of excellent quality can be made by winding No. 22 or 24 wire tightly on various drill sizes, and then slipping the drill or other winding form out. If wound under tension the coil will hold its shape when slipped off the form. Turns can be spaced by running a thin knife blade between them. You can't make a better choke than this.

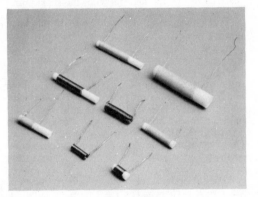

Fig. 16-10 — Typical handmade vhf chokes. At the rear are closewound and spacewound chokes for 50 MHz wound on 1/4-inch and 1/2-inch Teflon rod, drilled and tapped for end-mounting. Three 144-MHz chokes are seen in the center row, the two at the left being excellent for high-current applications. Similar types to these, but for the 220-MHz band, are in front.

You can tell a good choke from an inferior one easily enough. Connect it across your driver-stage tuned circuit, and see what it does to your final-stage grid current. Also note how much you have to retune the driver circuit to restore resonance. A perfect choke would have no harmful effects, and it would not heat up. You won't find one that good, but a well-designed choke will come close. If the choke is not a good one, don't run the test too long at any appreciable power level, or you won't have to *look* for indications — you'll smell them!

A recent development in the rf choke field is the ferrite bead. These are small beads of ferrous materials that can be slipped over wires wherever the effect of an rf choke is needed. They are particularly effective for heater decoupling purposes, as they can be placed directly on the heater lead, adding no dc resistance to the circuit.

"JUST LIKE QST, EXCEPT . . ."*

These words are voiced or written almost daily in telling the owner's sad story of instability in a transmitter or receiver he has built. Investigation nearly always shows that the builder made his own troubles, as a result of common misconceptions about bypassing and grounding. Every new project is to some extent a design problem, and a certain amount of debugging is almost inevitable, but there are right and wrong ways to do the basic jobs encountered in amateur equipment construction.

Take the matter of sockets and bypassing. Fig. 16-11 shows wrong and right methods. The wrong, upper, has Pins 4 and 9 supposedly grounded by a small wire running through the socket center ring (which is supposed to be a shield) to a lug under the mounting screw at the left. Pin 3 is bypassed to "ground" by running the low side of a disk ceramic capacitor to the center ring. What happens here? The only place that is really at ground potential is the portion of the lug that is under the mounting nut. The rest of the lug, the wire, the socket pins, and the bypass lead could all be above ground for rf. The path to ground from Pin 3 is a long one, and the other pins are common to it. This is an invitation to feedback, due to common-lead coupling.

Now look at the lower. The same pins are grounded by bending the socket lugs against the center ring and soldering them there. The lug under the mounting nut is also bent over to the center ring. This puts Pins 4 and 9 very much closer to ground potential than the wire method at the left. The capacitor from Pin 8 is in a horizontal position, and is grounded to the lug, close to the mounting nut. If the disk ceramic is capable of being an effective bypass, this wiring arrangement will give it a chance. There is almost no common path to ground between Pin 8 and the other circuits, and the center ring is much nearer to being a shield than before.

Another demon for the vhf man is the socket shown at the left of Fig. 16-12. The manufacturer very kindly provided an elevated mounting ring on this gem. Fine for use on lower frequencies, or in a hi-fi amplifier, perhaps, but it caused all manner of trouble in a 6146 amplifier for 50 MHz built by the author of this book.

This socket makes reliable contact to the chassis only at the mounting ears. If you accept the

Fig. 16-11 — Right and wrong treatments of 9-pin sockets. Instability is likely in the long wire-lead version, upper, providing common coupling through use of the center ring for the bypass capacitor perched above Pin 3. In the lower, the lug provides low-inductance path to ground for the ring and Pins 4 and 9. The bypass, Pin 8, is horizontal, and connected to the lug as close to the chassis as possible.

maker's invitation to use those ring extensions for the cold (you hope!) end of your bypass capacitors, you can very easily build in common coupling through the ring's inductance. The socket at the right, with no such conveniences, forces the user to bypass to ground, at the mounting nut, which is the right way to do it.

The best amplifiers, transmitting and receiving, have very high gain and power sensitivity. Only a little bit of feedback can make them take off. If this feedback is within the device itself, or if it is due to coupling between tuned circuits, you can neutralize or shield it out. If the coupling is built in through common ground leads and ineffective bypassing, as illustrated in these typical examples, it can grow you a lot of grey hairs.

* From a longer article, under the same title, in March, 1959, QST

Fig. 16-12 — Socket at the left with its built-in "grounding" ring is an invitation to trouble in vhf circuits. The one at the right necessitates use of grounding lugs at the mounting holes and encourages good bypassing and grounding practice.

MORE VERSATILITY WITH THE HEATH SIXER AND TWOER

The well-known "Benton Harbor Lunchbox" is a mainstay of a-m activity on 6 or 2 meters in many localities. Here are several modifications of these popular little rigs that will add to their versatility. They are the work of Lew McCoy, W1ICP.

Adding A2 for Code Communication

The 50- and 144-MHz bands are ideal for code communication — for practice or for improved signal readability when the going is rough. Unfortunately very few readymade a-m transceivers now available provide for code work of any kind, so much interesting potential of the vhf bands is lost to owners of such equipment. The superregenerative receivers in the Sixer and Twoer make it impractical to copy keyed cw, but they are fine for reception of tone modulation.

The simple transistor tone oscillator of Fig. 16-13 can be built into either unit easily. By connecting the output of the oscillator to the arm of the volume control the keyed tone will modulate the transmitter, and when the transceiver is switched to the receive position the oscillator can be used for code practice. Also, in the transmit position a slight amount of the audio tone is fed to the speaker, permitting the operator to monitor his own "fist."

The tone oscillator is mounted on a 2 × 2-1/4-inch piece of perforated unclad circuit board. This is 1/16 inch thick and is perforated with 1/16-inch diameter holes spaced approximately 1/4 inch apart. Push-in clips are available for making connections, but in the units shown the connections were made by soldering the component leads together.

The emitter of Q1, and one side each of C101, R101, and R102 (and C102 in the 2-meter unit)

are connected together and a lead run from this connection to the chassis of the transceiver. This provides a common ground for the oscillator. The key jack, J101, must be insulated from the panel, and either insulating washers or electricians' plastic tape can be used for this purpose. The jack is mounted on the panel between the microphone connector and the volume control. The oscillator assembly is supported by its own leads. When installing the board, be careful that none of the connections on the bottom touch any leads in the transceiver.

In order to monitor your own sending, a 330-ohm, 1/2-watt resistor should be connected between terminal 4 of the transmit-receive switch and the chassis, as shown in Fig. 16-13C. This feeds a very small amount of audio from the transmitter to the speaker. When transmitting A2 turn the volume control full on; otherwise, the audio oscillator output will be short-circuited to ground. For receiving or using the oscillator for code practice, the volume control should be set at a comfortable listening level. A switching circuit could be used so that the volume control setting wouldn't have to be changed, but this would have complicated the conversion and didn't seem worth the expense or crowding of components.

Metering Transmitter Output

One problem with the Twoer and Sixer is that external meters are required for tune-up, and there is no constant metering of the output. A low-cost milliammeter connected as a relative output indicator can be installed in each unit, for constant monitoring of the power going to the antenna.

The meters in Fig. 16-15 are edgewise miniature S meters. There is adequate space on the panel for both the meter and control R103 just below the

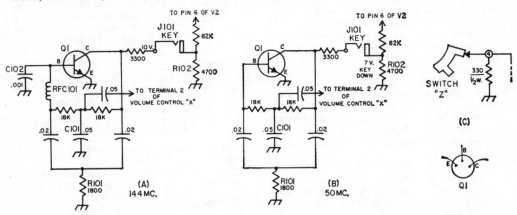

Fig. 16-13 — Circuit diagram of the code oscillator. A is the 144-MHz unit and B is for 50 MHz. Fixed resistors are 1/2 watt; resistances are in ohms (K = 1000) and capacitances are in μF. Capacitors are paper or Mylar, working voltage 25 or more. Component numbers under 100 refer to the original Heath circuit; those over 100 are the added components. C is the circuit for monitoring one's own sending.

C101 — 0.05 μF dsk ceramic, paper, or Mylar.
C102 — 0.001 μF disk ceramic
J101 — Single-circuit phone jack or phono jack.

Q1 — Npn, RCA type 40314 or similar.
R101 — 1800 ohms, 1/2 watt.
RFC101 — 2.7 μH (Millen 34300-2.7 or similar.)

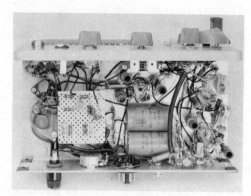

Fig. 16-14 — Interior of the "Lunchbox" with the code oscillator installed.

nameplate. The ungrounded end of R103 is connected to the meter-jack side of R13 (a 3300-ohm, 1/2-watt resistor) by an insulated wire fed under the chassis through a grommet below the meter.

Amplifier Tank Circuit Modification

Another worthwhile improvement can be made by changing the output tank circuit from capacitive to inductive coupling to the antenna. This reduces the possibility that undesired frequencies generated in the multiplier stages will reach the antenna.

Remove the coupling capacitor that goes from the tank coil (L3 in the Sixer and L4 in the Twoer) to terminal 11 of the transmit-receive switch. In the 2-meter unit, insert one side of a 3-30 compression trimmer capacitor under the nut that holds the tube socket for V4, at the chassis-edge side. The new coupling loop, L101 in Fig. 16-17, is made of insulated No. 14 or 16 solid wire. The loop for the Twoer is one turn the same diameter as the tank coil, inserted between the first and second turns, at the feedthrough capacitor end. One end of the loop is connected to terminal 11 of the transmit-receive switch and the other end to the ungrounded side of the 3-30 compression trimmer. Keep these lead lengths as short as possible.

Using the lamp dummy load that comes with the kit, tune the tank capacitor and the compression trimmer for maximum lamp brilliance. The output meter will read maximum when the lamp is the brightest. It may be necessary to reduce the sensitivity by means of R103 to keep the meter from going off scale.

Try moving the loop in relation to the tank coil, for maximum brilliance of the lamp load. Be sure to turn off the power to the transceiver when making this adjustment because the B-plus voltage

is present on the tank coil and you could get a dangerous shock.

The 6-meter installation is slightly different. The trimmer capacitor is mounted on a 3-lug terminal strip with the center terminal grounded. The strip is mounted between the crystal socket and the socket for V4, using the unused coil mounting hole as the mounting point. A 2-turn link, with the turns just slightly smaller in diameter than the tank coil, is made from insulated No. 16

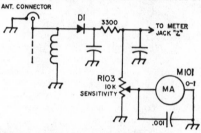

Fig. 16-16 — Addition of the metering circuit.
M101 — 0-1 milliammeter (Radio Shack 22-004, World Radio Labs 99M194).
R103 — 10,000 ohms, 1/4-watt control.

or 18 solid wire. This is positioned just inside the tank coil at the feedthrough capacitor end. The adjustment procedure is the same as with the 2-meter unit.

Remove the wire from terminal 12 of the transmit-receive switch and the antenna output terminal. A length of RG-58/U is substituted for this lead, grounding the outer conductor at both ends.

External Crystal Socket

A crystal socket on the front panel makes frequency changing much easier. This mounts on the front panel alongside the meter, and a short length of Twin-Lead, fitted with a crystal socket plug (Millen type 37412), is used to connect it to the chassis-mounted crystal socket. If you have a defunct crystal, it can be removed from its holder and the Twin-Lead soldered to the holder pins, to make a plug.

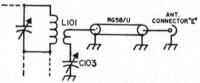

Fig. 16-17 — Tuned output circuit for the Twoer and Sixer.
C103 — For 144 MHz, 3-30-pF compression trimmer; for 50 MHz, 8-50-pF trimmer (Centralab type 822-AN or similar).
L101 — See text.

Fig. 16-15 — The Twoer and Sixer, complete with code oscillator, relative power meter, and front-panel crystal socket.